Paths of Science

Explorations
for Science Students
and Educators

Jack R. Holt
Susquehanna University

Whi
Publica

Published by Whittier Publications, Inc.
Island Park, NY 11558

ISBN 1-57604-251-0

Printed in the United States of America

10 9 8 7 6 5 4 3 2 1 0

PATHS OF SCIENCE – SECOND EDITION

PREFACE

I have designed the essays to illustrate science from a variety of perspectives. Many times, I take a historical approach. I do not do that in order to teach history; but rather I use the history to describe the science. In particular, I wish to describe science as a human activity (history) with particular rules (its philosophy and methods) and purpose (to explain nature). This enterprise is difficult because, as Leonard Krishtalka put it, "One of the differences between nature and her interpreters is that nature is not simple." Science has been successful in its ability to explain only because of very strict adherence to its rules. Although the history of science has its share of those who parade themselves in the guise of seekers of the truth of nature, the rules serve to expose them for what they are, charlatans and frauds. By far, most of those who work in the sciences do so with intellectual honesty and integrity. They contribute to advances in the sciences through their own histories and social contexts. Sometimes they are right; sometimes they are wrong. Nevertheless, the continual elimination of wrong explanations brings us closer to a vision of nature as it is. So, to paraphrase Isaac Newton, advances are made by standing on the shoulders of giants. Thus, I try to present the material in such a way that I highlight the lives and contributions of the main players. Also, I try to connect that to an ordinary life (my own).

I have designed this book around five thematic chapters, plus an introductory chapter. The themes roughly correspond to the philosophy of science, science and technology, the physical sciences, the environmental and geological sciences, and the biological sciences. The essays included in them, however, stand alone and all draw on aspects of the history and philosophy of science.

These essays have been written as part of a project called Saturday Science, which has been funded by Pennsylvania Space Grant since 1993. During that time, I have had the privilege of working with many colleagues, future teachers, and future scientists. Chief among them was Patricia Nelson, with whom I began this project and published the first edition of Paths of Science. I cannot than her enough for her help and encouragement. I am especially indebted to Mike Freeman of the NASA NOVA Project and Geraldine Russell, Richard Devon, Lisa Brown and Sylvia Stein from the Pennsylvania Space Grant Consortium for their continued support. In addition, Susquehanna University has been a willing partner in this project from the beginning. I have received administrative support especially from Donald Housley and Terry Winegar among others. Furthermore, I would like to thank the other members of the Biology Department who have been somewhat longsuffering during this project. University colleagues who have worked with me include Patricia Nelson, Benjamin Hayes, Peggy Holdren, and Jennifer Elick. Members of the clerical staff, chiefly Audrey Eroh and Crystal Reed, also has been willing to go above and beyond in support of this project. I would also like to thank our many university and middle school student assistants who have worked with us over the years to make our program a success. I am particularly indebted to Brenda Clewell, Heather Vorhauer, Michael Lescene, Cherie Ainsley, Josh Affrime, Gretchen Hoffman, Tina Parks, Denelle Lahr, Sarah Kiemle, Kelly Davis, Grier Wilt, Parry Holt, Maggie Holt, and Matt Cox. Finally, I offer my thanks to my wife, Natasha Holt, without whose support this could not have happened. I gratefully dedicate this collection to her.

Jack R. Holt
June 15, 2006

CHAPTER 1: WALKING THE PATH

My road calls me, lures me
West, east, south, and north;
Most roads lead men homewards,
My road leads me forth.
John Maesfield *Roadways.*

I walked this path in 1994 in the village of Downe on the outskirts of London. The path, worn by years of footsteps, was Charles Darwin's thinking path on the edge of his estate, Down House. As he walked the path, he contemplated complex problems, many of which scientists pursue to this day.

I chose the metaphor of a path to illustrate the nature of the scientific process. Like roads or paths in the universe of our experiences, the paths of scientific discovery course through a variety of landscapes formed by the philosophical, social, and historical contexts within which they travel. The paths intersect many other roads in their routes. At times, the roads are little more than trails, and in some lines of inquiry, they have grown to superhighways. Like most metaphors, this one fails because unlike a path that we might walk, science is a product of history and its paths are one way. Still we can try to go back down paths of inquiry by reading what scientists have written. *On a Performance of Durufle* serves as an introduction to science as a creative human enterprise.

ON A PERFORMANCE OF DURUFLE

DURUFLE'S REQUIEM

So near is man to the creative pageant, so much a part is he of the endless and incredible experiment, that any glimpse he may have will be but the revelation of a moment, a solitary note heard in a symphony thundering through debatable existences of time... -Henry Beston

I have been a member of community choruses for many years. Although limitations on my time have forced me drop out of such long-term commitments, I still occasionally join the chorus of my university for particular occasions like Baccalaureate ceremonies. The most memorable performances through the years happen to be those of any number of Requiem masses, from the stately beauty of Bach's B minor mass and moving Requiem by Mozart to the bombast of Hector Berlioz. A Requiem Mass is a choral version of the Catholic mass or service for the dead. Thus, a Requiem follows a prescribed form and order, though many of the later 20th Century Requiems deviate from the liturgical Latin text.

In the spring of 1997, I sang Maurice Durufle's Requiem in a program that featured most of his other published works. Performances like that always amazed me. Aside from the beauty of the music and the pleasure of singing in a chorus, I was struck by how so many people could come together and coordinate what they were doing.

Generally, things work because we have agreed on a number of conventions such as how the range of sounds will be divided (that is, the scale) and then how those sounds will be written. The language of Western music is written with five-lined staffs and sounds are determined by the relative placement of a note on the staff.

FIGURE 1-1. This bar of music is from an Irving Berlin tune called *Play a Simple Melody* (1914).

Consider Figure 1-1. Anyone who can play a piano can recreate what Irving Berlin had in mind when he wrote that line 83 years ago. That is possible only because we have agreed on what all of these dots and lines mean. Aside from arbitrary conventions such as notation, we are also faced with physical, biological limits that are arbitrary by nature's design. For example, the human voice can make sounds that are between 85 to 1100 hertz (or vibrations). An average person would hear the 85 hertz as an extremely low note and the 1100 hertz as a very high note. Still, we can hear well beyond that range. We can hear sounds as low as 20 and as high as 20,000 hertz. For perspective, a porpoise can make sounds between 7,000 to 120,000 hertz and can hear in the range of 150 to 150,000 hertz. Imagine what a porpoise symphony would sound like. We would not be able to hear most of it. Still, given our limitations, remarkable variety in sound production and appreciation is possible.

The acoustics (or the way in which sound bounces around) are so beautiful in the vaulted ceiling of the Zion Lutheran Church. Our unaccompanied voices and the range of sound in four part harmony resonated through the hall. Maurice Durufle (1902-1986) had been an organist and taught organ at the Paris

Conservatoire. He was also interested in plain or Gregorian chant, and much of his music reflected his interests in organ and chant.

HONK OF THE DUCKBILL

Is it possible to examine aspects of function and behavior of animals known to us only from the fossil record? The answer appears to be yes; we can reconstruct with some certainty we can reconstruct with some certainty the range over which lambeosaurines vocalized and the evolutionary relationship of low frequency honking to social behavior and ecology
.   David B. Weishampel

After a set of motets by Durufle, we left the stage and sat in the wings to listen to an organ solo. After all, Durufle was an organist, but I began to listen to the great pipes and to admire them as resonating structures. Recall that resonance is an increase in oscillation that occurs when a force is applied to an object at its natural frequency or vibration. You can see this phenomenon most easily when you push a swing. The force applied when you push is most effective at the natural rhythm of the swing. (Remember that resonance was, in part, responsible for the destruction of the Tacoma Narrows Bridge).

In the same way, a pipe of a particular length and diameter has a natural frequency at which the vibrations of air occur (see Figure 1-2). In particular, the sound is loudest when the vibration at the opening of the pipe is a big as it can get. That happens to be the diameter of the pipe. The wavelength(s) at which the peak vibration occurs depends upon the length of the pipe. Thus, long pipes have a long wavelength

(low frequency), and we hear them as low notes. Shorter pipes resonate at higher frequencies (higher notes). That is why a pipe organ has to have so many pipes to produce the range of sounds (10-8,000 hertz).

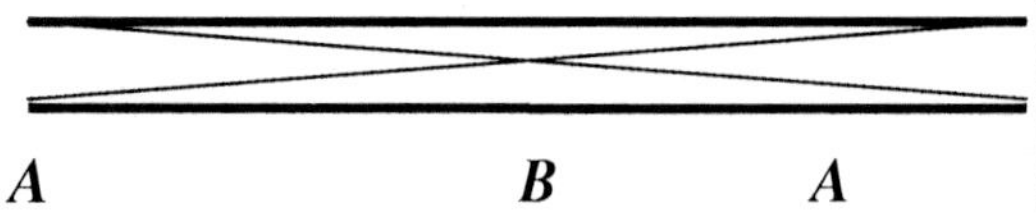

FIGURE 1-2. This is a simple figure of a pipe with a wave of air inside. At the node (*B*), there is minimal displacement of air while the greatest displacement occurs at the openings (*A*). This would be a resonating frequency.

The question of resonance had been on my mind since I had read an article by David Weishampel about the duckbilled dinosaur (a group called the labedosaurines) named *Parasaurolophus*. These animals were large (10 meters long) and able to stand upright, though they could have dropped to a four-legged stance. The tail was held stiffly out behind as a counterbalance. Perhaps, the most striking feature was a long horn-like crest that ran more than a meter back of the head (see Figure 1-3).

The fossils tell us much about these animals beyond how they stood. We have fossils of their skin. We have tracks, eggs and a range of ages for many labedosaurids. We now believe that they walked on land and moved in great herds. They could have run at a respectable speed and used their horn duck-like bill to crop vegetation that they chewed with a dental battery of 2,000 teeth. In many ways, they resembled large herd animals like bison or cows.

3

That leaves us with the question of the crest. What was its purpose? Well, it was hollow and tube-like with one end opening to the nostrils and the other end opening to the trachea. There are two current guesses. One is that the crest increased the area for olfactory (sense of smell) receptors. For an animal with an olfactory chamber more than 3 meters long, that would be a very sensitive sense of smell.

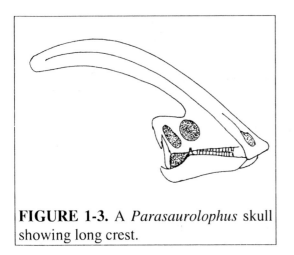

FIGURE 1-3. A *Parasaurolophus* skull showing long crest.

It seems to me, though, that the best explanation for their crests (and similar structures found on many of the related duckbills) is sound production. David Weishampel (1995 and 1997) gives evidence for their use as resonating chambers, much like the pipes of an organ. He calculated that the resonating frequencies for a tube of these dimensions and a diameter of about 5 centimeters ranged from 50 to 350 hertz. That is approximately G two octaves below middle C to F# above middle C. Younger animals with smaller crests would have made sounds at higher frequencies.

It is remarkable that we can know anything about animals that have been extinct for more than 65 million years, much less the detail that can be inferred from the fossil evidence. Still, structure only indicates what is impossible and hints at what is possible. We have fossils of skin but we cannot guess how they were colored or patterned. Likewise, we can estimate the range of vocal frequencies that they used, but we cannot know what their songs were like.

METEORITE ALH 84001
Extraordinary claims require extraordinary evidence. Carl Sagan

After a brief intermission, the chorus returned to sing the Requiem by Durufle. This time we sang with an orchestra and organ. The resonance of 100 voices melded with the resonating frequencies of tubes (brass, woodwinds and organ), strings, and drums. It was an ethereal experience, especially the Sanctus, which is, in my opinion, one of the most beautiful pieces of music ever written.

A Requiem is a mass for the dead, derived from the Latin word for rest. In this case, we were not singing for anyone who had died (except perhaps for Maurice Durufle who had died in 1986 after being bed-ridden for 11 years following an automobile accident). That brings me to a particularly sticky question. What does dead mean? Well, it means that something or someone is no longer alive. Then, what does alive mean? For a biologist that should be an easy question but I often stumble on it. I mean that I should be able to give a simple definition, but I cannot.

It is easy to determine that *Parasaurolophus* had been a living animal. Too much of it looks like most vertebrates, and therefore, it is safe to assume that it was like a vertebrate with muscles, skin, a digestive tract, respiratory systems, etc. The real questions are about the details. Did they run? Did they sing? Were they warm blooded? Did they migrate?

Raven and Johnson (1995), authors of a popular general biology text, explore this question in a particular way. That is, if astronauts were to explore another planet and look for the presence of life, how would they know that they had found it? What criteria would have to be applied? Raven and Johnson cite four attributes that are necessary for life:

1. All living things are made of one or more cells which are groups of molecules within membranes.
2. All living things take in energy and use it to grow and maintain their complexity.
3. All living things reproduce.
4. All living things have a hereditary history in which their code for construction is passed on to their progeny.

The question of what is life was on the minds of researchers headed by David McKay at the Johnson Space Center. There, he and his team are studying a very enigmatic rock, a meteorite that weighs about four pounds. The meteorite is designated ALH 84001 (It means that it was the first meteorite found during 1984 at the Allen Hills in the Antarctic).

Although Roberta Score, one of a team of seven meteorite hunters, had found this meteorite in the Antarctic in 1984, it was misidentified and laid in a drawer until 1993 when David Mittlefehldt examined it and noticed that the iron and sulfur compounds in the rock looked just like those of the 11 meteorites that had been designated from Mars. As a check he examined the ratio of isotopes of oxygen. The results were identical to those of the Martian meteorites and very different from the isotopic ratios of oxygen on Earth. Thus, Mittlefehldt determined that ALH 84001 was a rock from Mars.

Other isotopic evidence indicated that the igneous rock had been formed on the surface of Mars about 4.5 billion years ago (that makes ALH 84001 older than any rocks on the surface of the Earth and, indeed, older than any rocks retrieved from the moon). It was expelled from the surface of Mars by a meteorite that slammed into the planet about 15 million years ago. It then fell to Earth about 13 thousand years ago.

Mittlefehldt, Chris Romanek, and Everett Gibson were struck by the presence of carbonates inside the meteorite. In fact a full 1% of the rock was carbonate. That may seem like a small amount, but it was very large, particularly since the stone was igneous because carbonates are not found in igneous rock. Therefore, the carbonates must have formed later. In fact, the chemistry of the formation of carbonates requires liquid water and temperatures between 0 and 80C. Romanek, Mittlefehldt, and Gibson wrote up their observations and interpretations and published them in the prestigious British science journal *Nature*. The conclusions were astonishing. Liquid water existed on the surface of Mars 4.5 billion years ago.

This drew the attention of David McKay and others at the Johnson Space Center who began to look more closely at the carbonate globules, which they examined with light and electron microscopy. On the edges of the carbonate areas, McKay found structures that looked very much like bacteria (see Figure 1-4).

Richard Zare and Simon Clement on examination of the carbonate globules found relatively complex organic molecules called polycyclic aromatic hydrocarbons (PAHs). These often form in the residue when living cells die. This evidence together with the close occurrence of compounds that would not normally be found together unless the immediate environment was being altered in a very small space led David McKay and a host of authors to publish their results and conclusions in the journal *Science* on August 16, 1996[1].

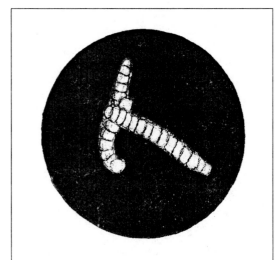

FIGURE 1-4. Sketch of the fossil-like carbonate nodules in ALH-84001. The circle indicates the average size of a bacterium on Earth.

The authors were very cautious in their presentation; after all, scientists are skeptics. They (we) are especially cautious about claims whose conclusions indicate that there was (and might still be) life elsewhere. In cases such as these, we must invoke Carl Sagan's adage, "Extraordinary claims require extraordinary evidence." Although the evidence of ALH 84001 is compelling and consistent with the existence of life, it is far from extraordinary. The results of this research are far more tentative than the conclusions that we drew about the biology and behavior of *Parasaurolophus*.

---

[1] See Red Planets and Microbes for a further exploration of this topic.

Still, the August 16 paper in *Science* is one of the most astonishing bits of research that I have ever read. The implication might be that life appears rather easily on planets that have liquid water. It also gives us added incentive to return to Mars and prospect for fossils in areas that almost certainly had liquid water. Furthermore, if life once existed, it might persist in liquid water areas under the polar ice or deep underground.

A curious conjecture and a great speculative leap is that if life appeared on Mars 4.5 billion years ago, bacteria-like spores deep within a rock like ALH 84001 could have survived the time in space (many bacteria survive desiccation, and vacuum). Also, the stone might have provided some protection from the flight through the early atmosphere and subsequent impact. This theory is called panspermia and suggests that we descended from a Martian lineage.

SCIENCE AND CREATIVITY
A Keates and a Newton, listening to each other, might hear the galaxies sing.
-Richard Dawkins

Once I stood at the door of Charles Darwin's study, the *sanctum sanctorum* for Biologists. It had been recreated to appear as it did around the time of the writing of the *Origin of Species*. The room looked as I had expected a mid-19th century gentleman's study to appear. I strained to look at his library, but I saw a few books surrounded by papers tied with string. The curator of the Down House Museum explained that Darwin was a very practical man who, with limited shelf space and time, cut the useful pages from his books and discarded the rest. I will not deny that I, a bibliophile, was disappointed. I then finished the tour with a walk through his garden and his thinking path, called it the Sand Walk, along the back of his property. While walking the path, I realized that Darwin's library was a perfect metaphor for the epistemology, or generation of knowledge, in the sciences. Like Darwin, the community of scientists considers theories and keeps all or parts of theories that are useful in explaining nature. Ideas are proposed like those of Weishampel and MacKay. The ideas are tested by various methods of science, and the larger scientific community evaluates the results. Those ideas that survive then serve to regenerate more ideas. Thus, science moves to finer and subtler understanding of the nature that we are a part of. The process of generate, test, regenerate has marked science throughout its modern period (from the time of Isaac Newton) to the present. That process is also Darwinian evolution in a nutshell.[2]

The creativity of science is manifest in the generation of theories and the design of methods to test them. Thus, the creativity and discipline of mind required to do good science is as inspired as any great art. It is as finely crafted as the musical works of Maurice Durufle; however, scientists must work in a medium that is defined by the natural universe and cannot violate the laws of nature in their explanations. Sometimes like David Weishampel they work alone, but more often than not, they tend to work in teams as in the case of David MacKay's group.

Culture, which includes the arts, also operates in the same evolutionary way. You can see that in the development of painting, sculpture, music, etc. through the ages. As in science, the present builds upon the past. Maurice Durufle and his music illustrated that quite well. He used the sound and form of medieval plainchant in music that sits squarely in the 20th Century. Certainly, the sciences and the arts are separate cultures with very different goals, but because science and art are human activities, some may find themselves as active participants in both.

The ideas of Weishampel and Mackay are still being tested and evaluated. We will never know the song of the *Parasaurolophus,* but with appropriate exploration, we might know if Mars had (has) life. So, while we can sing a Requiem for Maurice Durufle and *Parasaurolophus,* we should not sing for Mars just yet.

-1997, revised 2005

References:

Dawkins, Richard. 1998. *Unweaving the Rainbow, Science, Delusion and the Appetite for Wonder.* Houghton-Mifflin Co. New York.

Goldsmith, Donald. 1997. *The Hunt for Life on Mars.* Penguin Books. New York.

McKay, David S., Everett K. Gibson, Kathie L. Thomas-Kerpta, Hojatollah Vali, Christopher S. Romanek, Simon J. Clemett, Xavier D.F. Chillier, Claude R. Maechling, & Richard N. Zaire. 1996. *Search for Past Life on Mars: Possible Relic Biogenic Activity in Martian Meteorite ALH84001.* Science. 273(5277):924.

Plotkin, Henry. 1997. *Darwin Machines and the Nature of Knowledge.* Harvard University Press. Cambridge, Mass.

Raven, Peter H. and George B. Johnson. 1995. *Biology.* Third edition. Wm. C. Brown Publishers. Dubuque, Iowa.

Snow, C.P. 1959. *The Two Cultures.* Cambridge University Press. New York.

Weishampel, David B. 1995. *Fossils, Function, and Phylogeny.* In: J. Thomason, ed. *Functional Morphology*

---

[2] For an expansion on Darwin and Darwinism, please go to *Parasites and Darwin's Intellectual Triumph*, and *The Mentor and the Heretic*.

in Vertebrate Paleontology. Cambridge University Press. New York. pp. 34-54.

Weishampel, David B. 1997. *Dinosaurian Cacophony, Inferring Function in Extinct Organisms.* BioScience 47(3):150-159.

Questions to Think About

1. Who was Maurice Durufle?

   20th century Composer - Requiem

2. How is the pipe of an organ like the crest of a *Parasaurolophus*?

   Pipe length determines frequency, thus pitch

3. What is resonance?

   increase in the oscillation that occurs when a force is applied to an object at its natural frequency of vibration

4. What can we know and not know about the song of *Parasaurolophus*?

   Know the range, not what it sang

5. What is ALH 84001? Where did it come from?

   meteorite from mars, 4.5 billion years old, found in antarctica, contains carbonate in igneous rock

6. What can we know and not know about ALH 84001?

   - Age, what's left, how it got here
   - What was Mars like

7. Why is a strict definition of life difficult to formulate?

   - Intangible

8. How are art and science similar? How are they different?

   · need creativity and discipline
   · science cannot break laws of nature

9. What does generate-test-regenerate mean? How did Darwin's library reflect that?

   Important parts - build off successes to push into future

10. What did I mean when I wrote that we should not sing a Requiem for Mars?

    Still more exploration to be done

CHAPTER 2 – THINKING SCIENCE

The aim of science is to seek the simplest explanation of complex facts. We are apt to fall into the error of thinking that the facts are simple because simplicity is the goal of our quest. The guiding motto of every natural philosopher should be, "Seek Simplicity and distrust it."
-Alfred North Whitehead Concept of Nature , p.163.

     Jack Holt and his colleague Benjamin Hayes on a path over a lava flow on the side of Arenal Volcano in Costa Rica. The volcano was active and throwing chunks of lava down its side while we were there. The sign and rope barrier served as a warning to would-be thrill-seekers about the danger of getting much closer.

     The essays in this chapter focus on the philosophical underpinnings and boundaries of science. *Descartes' Dream*, and *Unimpeachable Logic* examine the use of deductive and inductive thinking in science. *A Rock, a Razor, and a Dinosaur* introduces the concept of Occam's Razor and its application to scientific explanation. The following eight essays show how scientists generate explanations. Abuse of the principles on which science is based will indeed make the researcher's idea "In Danger of Dead" as it goes beyond the boundaries of science or does not heed Whitehead's warning.

DESCARTES' DREAM

A USED BOOK STORE

The reading of all good books is indeed like a conversation with the noblest men of past centuries who were the authors of them, nay a carefully studied conversation, in which they reveal to us none but the best of their thoughts.   -Rene Descartes

I love to browse through used bookstores. Not surprisingly, some of the best ones happen to be in university towns. That is one of the perks of going to meetings of scientific societies because they are almost always held on large university campuses. About 10 years ago, a collection of ecological and organismal societies met on the campus of the University of Toronto. Certainly, Toronto is much more than a university town, but the city is made of many neighborhoods, each with its distinctive character. That is true, too, of the area around the university.

Between talks and meetings I wandered the university neighborhood and went into a large used bookstore. The store was average in size, but its holdings were amazing. I recall that I missed a whole session of talks because I spent so much time browsing and talking to the store owner.

Although there were several glass cases with books that appeared to be important, there was one case with some interesting and very old books. One book was covered with white velum and occupied a place of some importance. I asked if I could see the book, but the proprietor, with whom I had been talking about various old science books, just smiled and handed me a pair of white cotton gloves. He unlocked the case and urged me to open it up and read the title. I caught my breath as I read *Discours de la Methode* (*Discourse on the Method*). The

book was from the mid seventeenth century and was written by Rene Descartes.

AN ETERNAL STUDENT

There is need of a method for finding out the truth.   –Rene Descartes

Rene Descartes was born on March 31, 1596 to an aristocratic family in France. His father was a counselor of the Parliament of Brittany. On his mother's side he appeared to have been descended from a long line of physicians. His parents sent him to the Jesuit school of La Fleche in 1606. until he left in 1614. He was supposed to have been sickly as a child and even the Jesuits allowed him to sleep until noon while there, a habit that he retained through his life. After La Flesche, Descartes spent the next two years in Paris studying mathematics. He then left Paris in 1617 to study law in Poitiers. Some authorities say that he received a law degree from Poitiers; however, that appears unlikely because he left within a year and never claimed to have a degree in law. Furthermore, because he was an aristocrat, and had enough money to support himself, he did not have to worry about how to make a living. Consequently, he had no need of a degree or a profession.

Descartes became a volunteer without pay in the Dutch army of the Prince of Orange in whose service he wandered over much of Europe. He finally settled in the Netherlands in 1628. While there, he attended universities at Franeker (1629) and Leyden (1630). Again, he seemed to have been attracted to universities for the sake of learning, not to obtain a degree. Descartes was not an extravagant man, but he lived comfortably by a pension that he received from his father. Later, he inherited money from his mother's and father's estates, which allowed him the freedom to live as he chose.

How is it, then, that a man who was without ambition became a household name in Europe? In 1628, Descartes met with Cardinal Berulle who implored the young aristocrat to use his talents. In fact he stressed that God would hold Descartes accountable for how he employed his abilities.

Berulle's admonition seemed to light a fire in Descartes, who showed a burst of productive work that lasted from 1629 to 1649. During that time he lived in Holland, but although he remained in the same country, he did not like to live in the same place and moved about twenty times during that twenty-year period. Always he required that he live in the neighborhood of a university and a Catholic Church, both of which were sources of inspiration.

Much earlier, Descartes claimed to have had a series of dreams in which the method for discovering fundamental laws governing nature were revealed by "the Spirit of Truth". He "experimented with this method and the application of mathematics to questions in physics.

LAWS AND EXPLANATION

...To divide up each of the difficulties which I examined into as many parts as possible, as seemed requisite in order that it might be resolved in the best manner possible. –Rene Descartes

Descartes' method included several steps. The first of which was to reject everything so that the observer would be objective and without prejudice. The second step was to divide up the problem into as many parts as possible. In this way,

the problem could be reduced to simpler and simpler components. This reduction or simplification of the problem is really an attempt to explain the problem.

Descartes and his contemporaries were concerned with large problems like why do the planets stay where they do. That is, why do they seem to move around the sun (he agreed with Galileo on this) and not fall to the sun or fly away out of orbit. Later, Isaac Newton formulated a mathematical statement, which he called the law of gravity that described the movement of the planets. In this law, Newton said that it made no difference whether the object was a planet or an apple, two bodies attract each other according to the product of their masses and the inverse square of their distance from each other. This law describes the behavior of orbiting planets, falling apples, and any objects of mass. Nevertheless, Newton's law of gravity does not define gravity itself.

The other laws of chemistry and physics behave the same way. For example, Boyle's Law describes the relationships between the pressure, temperature, and volume of a gas. It does not explain what pressure and temperature are, but describes their relationships with mathematical precision.

Chemistry and physics are generally referred to as the physical sciences. Laws within these sciences are universal and ultimately, all phenomena in nature must reduce to one or more of the physical laws. Some claim that this is the way in which phenomena are explained, by reducing them to natural laws. In essence, this is the second step of Descartes' method. That is, the phenomenon should be reduced to descriptive laws and, thereby, be explained.

AN INVERTED PYRAMID

...To separate out what is quite simple from what is complex. –Rene Descartes

The science of Descartes was mainly that of optics and mechanics. His book *Discourse* was written around the birth of Newton (and the death of Galileo), and Descartes, himself, died before the publication of Newton's *Principia*. Nevertheless, he recognized that the physical sciences were necessarily the simpler or less complex of the sciences.

Other sciences like Biology and Geology are more complex than Chemistry and Physics. The more complex sciences are more defined by complex interactions of their constituent parts. For the sake of explanation, the landforms around my home in Freeburg, PA can be reduced to the actions of erosion, sedimentation, plate tectonics, geochemistry, climate, and hydrology. Those can be reduced to aspects of chemistry and physics. Although they are reducible to the laws of chemistry and physics, those laws do not indicate the particular interrelationships that gave rise to Pleasant Valley. That would have to be given in a narrative style more like that of a historian than a physicist although the story must not violate physical law.

Thus, I view the sciences as an inverted pyramid (see Figure 2-1) with the less complex and more abstract disciplines at the bottom. Above chemistry and physics rise geology and biology. These are crowned by the most complex of the sciences, namely Environmental Science and Psychology.

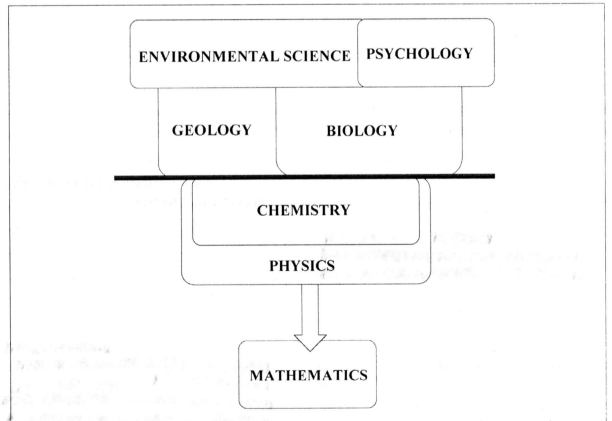

FIGURE 2-1. The hierarchy of explanation in the sciences. Sciences at the top are the more complex. Ultimately, all sciences reduce to the laws of the physical sciences (divided from the complex sciences by the horizontal bar). Physics is described by mathematics.

The simpler the science, the more easily it lends itself to the experimental method. Experimentation requires, above all, that the system in question be simple or simplified. Suppose, for example, that you are interested in the nutritional requirements of the common yeast (*Saccharomyces cerevisiae*). In particular, does it grow best on a simple sugar like glucose or a more complex sugar like sucrose (also known as table sugar, sucrose is a disaccharide made of glucose and fructose). Immediately, I imagine an experiment in which equal concentrations of yeast are measured into flasks. Half of the flasks are given sucrose and the other half are given glucose in equal concentrations. Growth response could be measured by the rate at which yeast cells divide by determining the change in cell concentration over hours or days. However, an easier way would be to measure the volume of carbon dioxide given off by the culture over time. Everything but the form of sugar must be constant in order to make this comparison. A more complex question would be to explore dietary requirements in humans. Researchers cannot put their human subjects into flasks or restrict diets sufficiently to look for deficiencies in vitamin C and incipient scurvy.

Ernst Mayr, evolutionary biologist and philosopher of biology, said that questions asked by biologists tend to fall into "What?", "How", and "Why" categories. Answers to what questions tend to be descriptive and provide a factual basis for the discipline. Unfortunately, to say that a discipline is descriptive is almost pejorative in biology. Certainly, description is the first step of any discipline. It should not be surprising, then, that much of molecular biology has been descriptive. The studies of taxonomy and biological diversity remain descriptive.

"How?" questions according to Mayr are most frequently asked in functional biology from molecular biology through physiology and development. Answers to "How?" questions tend to be answers to experiment and, therefore, are quite powerful in their ability to explain. Not surprisingly, "How?" questions are the most frequently asked questions in the physical sciences.

"Why?" questions are asked in relation to evolutionary connections between organisms or between organisms and their environment. Mayr points out that Charles Darwin made "Why?" questions legitimate in biology after publication of the *Origin of Species* in 1859. Theodosius Dobzhonsky went even farther and said "nothing in biology makes sense except in light of evolution." That is, because all living things share a common descent, life on earth bears certain fundamental similarities. These are now being explored at all levels in biology.

HISTORICAL SCIENCE
...To carry on my reflections in due order, commencing with objects that were the most simple and easy to understand, in order to rise little by little, or by degrees, to knowledge of the most complex, assuming an order, even if a fictitious one among those which do not follow a natural sequence relatively to one another.

–Rene Descartes

Descartes' third step was to reconstruct the parts of the phenomenon. That is, to take the simpler components and build more complex scenarios. This is known as prediction and is the second important function of science. Prediction begins with theories and natural laws and attempts to define particular outcomes. Experiments are special cases in which hypotheses (predictions) are tested by

14

holding most variables constant. In this way predictions can be pronounced false or confirmed.

Experiments are not the only methods to be employed in predicting nature. As the scientist explores questions of greater and greater complexity, it becomes more and more difficult to hold variables constant. By and large, ecologists face this difficulty. Interactions in a grassland or flowing stream are almost infinitely more complex than interactions within a flask of yeast.

In general, ecology occurs as two different types of subdisciplines: ecology of the species and ecology of communities. Ecology of the species is called autecology and usually is practiced by zoologists (animal biologists). A group of individuals in the same species that occupies the same area is called a population and most autecology deals with populations. Particular questions would deal with competition (either within a population or between populations), densities (reproduction and population size), predator-prey relationships, food chains, and life cycles.

Botanists (those who study the myriad of organisms that are not animals) tend to study communities or synecology. A community is the collection of populations and their interrelationships in a particular area. Questions asked by synecology includes succession (changes in communities), climax (stable communities), ecosystems (the movement of materials and energy through a community), and biodiversity.

I have explored questions that are both autecological and synecological in nature. In all cases, I tried to discover the dominant influences over populations or communities because it was impossible to discover all of the controlling factors.

Indeed, the interactions generally are the objects of study.

Aspects of history also play a large part in ecology. That is, a community exists in time as well as in space. The conditions that affect a community were influenced by the conditions that preceded them. My stream studies are strongly affected by time of year, storm events, farming practices, as well as by the biota that occurred there the preceding week or day. My students get tired of hearing me say that ecology is historical. If I failed to collect samples correctly on September 3, 1998, I would not be able to go back in time to collect them. In that sense, all ecological data are unique and ecologists are more like historians in their reconstructions except that nature does not leave records that are easily read.

FALSE PATTERNS

It must always be recollected, however, that possibly, I deceive myself and what I take to be gold and diamonds is perhaps no more than copper and glass.

—Rene Descartes

Because explanations and predictions in ecology are the products of the history of a particular population or community, patterns may appear when they do not exist. Take a very simple case. Last spring I conducted a "random walk" test in which I tossed a nickel 200 times. Prior to the "experiment", I decided that heads would have the value of +1 and tails the value of −1. The first toss was tails (-1), the second toss was heads (+1). These were independent events, each with a 50% chance of happening. However, I made them dependent such that the value of toss two equaled the sum of heads and tails (-1+1=0). Toss 200 was equal to the sum of all heads and tails. I plotted the number of the coin toss against the sum value (By the way, the graph with its X-Y coordinates was an invention of Descartes' to allow algebra to be visualized. That is why this system is called Cartesian coordinates.).

Figure 2-2 clearly shows the rise and fall that could be a pattern. It is not. This is the consequence of each point being dependent on those that preceded it. To put it another way, each point is a product of its history and subject to the contingencies of that history. For example, tosses 85 to 91 were all tails. That caused the line to plunge. However, each toss had a 50-50 chance of being heads or tails. I was concerned that the graph represented an unequal distribution of heads and counted the number of heads and tails. To my surprise, I had 98 tails and 102 heads in a random pattern.

I keep that graph on my wall in the office as a warning, a warning that was so eloquently stated by Simon and Garfunkel when they sang, "A man hears what he wants to hear and disregards the rest." If pseudopatterns can be created by the history of a coin toss, imagine the problems facing ecologists.

PLEISTOCENE PARK

And I thought that it was easy for me to select certain matters which would not be the occasion for many controversies.

–Rene Descartes

Aside from my own research, which holds the most interesting problems for me, ecology is filled fascinating problems, both large and small. One of the most interesting problems in ecology is discussed in the October 2, 1998 issue of Science. A Russian scientist, Sergei Zimov, is convinced that he can recreate a Mammoth Steppe, a cold grassland that occurred at the leading edge of the glaciers during the last ice age. The problem is greater than just making a parkland. He believes that he can regenerate a whole ecosystem.

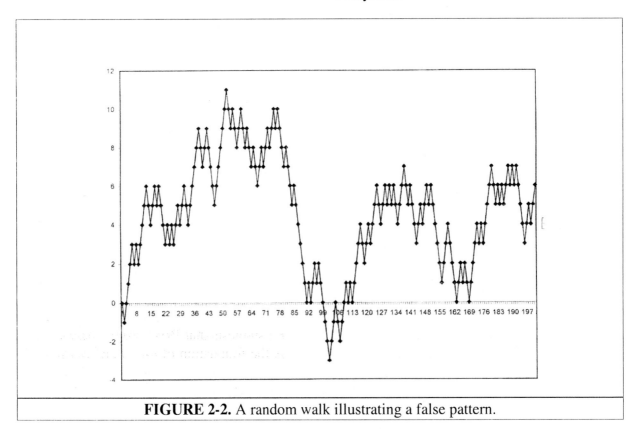

FIGURE 2-2. A random walk illustrating a false pattern.

16

Zimov and teams of scientists from Canada and Alaska think that the Mammoth Steppe grasslands were shaped by the actions of mammoths, bison and other large herbivores, themselves. That is, the constant disturbance provided by the animals destroyed the mosses and favored the growth of grasses.

Zimov plans to change an area in northern Siberia (above the Arctic Circle) that is dominated by mosses by reintroducing bison, horses, and musk oxen. His computer models suggest that the disturbance provided by the animals will destroy the mosses that grow there and allow for the revival of a cold grassland. He is even considering the introduction of Indian Elephants (What he will do with them during the long, Arctic winters I don't know).

Zimov's idea has not been met by universal enthusiasm by the scientific community. Some object that the mosses occur in Northern Siberia because the climate is much wetter now than it was during the Pleistocene. Also, there is that particularly difficult problem of a Mammoth Steppe without a mammoth. Zimov counters that the climate now probably is as moist as it was 11,000 years ago. Although there is evidence that Pleistocene-age soil was much drier than now, grasses, were much better at pulling water from the ground than were mosses. If he is successful in his attempt to establish large numbers of herbivores, he will have to add carnivores to make it a stable ecosystem. To that end, he has plans to add wolves and Siberian tigers.

Suppose that Zimov is successful. Suppose that he can establish large herds of horses (there now), the wood bison (coming from Canada) and other herbivores and carnivores. Suppose that the populations become stable, tear up the moss-dominated landscape, and grasses begin to take over. Would this prove that mammoths created the Mammoth Steppe? No, it would not. However, it would confirm that such control is possible.

This project is particularly interesting to me because it explores typical synecological problems. However, the project also attempts to reconstruct the autoecology of the extinct Woolly Mammoth. The project will last many years with a great likelihood of uncertain results. This is the predicament of complex science.

A PLEA FOR CONSILIENCE

...Long chains of reasoning..., simple and easy as they are,... had caused me to imagine that all those things which fall under the cognizance of man might very likely be mutually related in the same fashion. –Rene Descartes

Still, as difficult as it is to glean knowledge from nature, we have been quite successful. Science has advanced our understanding of the natural universe from the Renaissance to the present. E. O. Wilson attributes most of the success of the sciences to the vertical relationship in explanation from the simple to the complex sciences. The vertical association of the disciplines in sciences means that they have a common foundation of natural law.

Wilson suggests in his book *Consilience* (a word that means jumping together) that the other disciplines could be brought into a similar vertical relationship with science at their base. He suggests that Psychology could serve as the foundation of the Social Sciences. Thus, the Social Sciences would have to be consistent with the "laws of psychology". Similarly, the Social Sciences would serve as the basis for the Humanities which would serve as the basis for the Arts.

Descartes, himself, was interested in many areas of knowledge. He was the founder of modern philosophy, a physicist, and mathematician. He wrote on topics that ranged from embryology and medicine to music. He indicated that his methods were meant for a consilience-type of understanding.

In 1633 Descartes was nearing the completion of a monumental work called a *Treatise on the World*. This was a major work that attempted to integrate all knowledge. He abandoned its publication when he saw the treatment of Galileo by the Catholic Church. His next work was *Discourse on the Method*. Still, Descartes and his philosophy were controversial. Even in liberal Holland his works were viewed with suspicion by the church and civil authorities and he was protected by influential people like Princess Elizabeth, daughter of Frederick V who was in exile in Holland.

One lasting effect that he had on science was an insistence that there was a fundamental difference between mind and body. In many ways, this has been one of the greatest barriers to the consilience of Psychology with the rest of the sciences.

In 1649 Descartes was enticed to go to Sweden in the service of Queen Christina. He was to teach philosophy to her and set up an academy of science. Unfortunately, within a year, Descartes contracted pneumonia and died on February 11, 1650.

THE FOURTH ADMONITION
...I have since that time found other reasons which caused me to change my opinion. –Rene Descartes

In the end, I decided not to buy the copy of *Discourse on the Method*. Although I was sorely tempted, the book cost about as much as I could muster at the time. I still had to get home and eat for the rest of the month. The experience did cause me to seek out a copy of *Discourse* when I returned home. I read the somewhat stilted translation and was impressed by how clearly he described the practice of science.

The fourth step of Descartes' method was to repeat steps one through three to confirm the results. It is possible to repeat those steps in the simple sciences by description (answers to "What?" questions) and experiment (answers to "How?" questions). However, like Descartes' life, Zimov's Pleistocene Park, and my studies in aquatic ecology, it is impossible to repeat the steps in a historical science.

-1998

References:

Bowler. Peter J. 1992. *The Fontana History of the Environmental Sciences.* Fontana Press. London.

Carnap, Rudolph. 1966. *The Value of Laws: Explanation and Prediction.* In: Martin Curd and J.A. Cover, eds. 1998. *Philosophy of Science, The Central Issues.* W.W. Norton and Co. New York.

Descartes, Rene. 1629. *Rules for the Direction of the Mind.* Trans. Elizabeth Haldane and G.R.T. Ross. In: Robert M. Hutchins, ed. 1952. The Great Books of the Western World. Vol 31. Encyclopaedia Britannica, Inc. Chicago.

Descartes, Rene. 1637. *Discourse on the Method.* Trans. Elizabeth Haldane and G.R.T. Ross. In: Robert M. Hutchins, ed. 1952. The Great Books of the Western World. Vol 31. Encyclopaedia Britannica, Inc. Chicago.

Hempel, Carl G. 1962. *Two Basic Types of Scientific Explanation.* In: Martin Curd and J.A. Cover, eds. 1998. *Philosophy of Science, The Central Issues.* W.W. Norton and Co. New York.

Hull, David L. 1988. *Science as a Process.* University of Chicago Press. Chicago.

Mayr, Ernst. 1982. *The Growth of Biological Thought: Diversity, Evolution, and Inheritance.* The Belknap Press of the Harvard University Press. Cambridge, Mass.

Mayr, Ernst. 1997. *This is Biology, The Science of the Living World.* The Belknap Press of the Harvard University Press. Cambridge, Mass.

Nagel, Ernest. 1961. *The Structure of Science, Problems in the Logic of Scientific Explanation.* Harcourt, Brace and World, Inc. New York.

Nagel, Ernest. 1974. *Issues in the Logic of Reductive Explanations.* In: Martin Curd and J.A. Cover, eds. 1998. *Philosophy of Science, The Central Issues.* W.W. Norton and Co. New York.

Rosenberg, Alexander. 1986. *The Structure of Biological Science.* Cambridge University Press. New York.

Stone, Richard. 1998. *A bold plan to re-create a long-lost Siberian ecosystem: an international team of scientists will test whether bison, horses, and other large grazers can bring back the mammoth steppe.* Science. 282(5386): 31-33.

Wilson, Edward O. 1998. *Consilience, The Unity of Knowledge.* Alfred A. Knopf. New York.

Questions to Think About

1. What event likely pushed Rene Descartes to be productive in mathematics, science, and philosophy?

    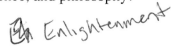 Enlightenment

2. What is the nature or characteristic of natural law?

3. What is Descartes' method?
    1) reject everything - objectivity
    2) Divide up the problem - simplify
    3) Reconstruct / Predict
    4) Repeat

4. What do I mean by the simple sciences and the complex sciences?
    Simple - Math/Physics/Chem
    Complex - Bio, psych, EV Sci
    -> More interaction based
       Questions asked

5. How does the inverted pyramid (Figure 2-1) illustrate the hierarchy of explanation in the sciences?

6. What are the three kinds of questions asked in the sciences?
    what?
    How?
    why?

7. How does a historical science differ from an experimental science?
    Experimental - easily controlled
    Historical - only study history - can't go back

8. Why did I refer to Figure 2-2 as illustrating a false pattern?

    Very misleading

9. What is the goal of Sergei Zimov?
    Create Mammoth steppe

10. What does consilience mean?
    jumping together

20

UNIMPEACHABLE LOGIC

AN IMPEACHMENT

Prosperity doth best discover vice; but adversity doth best discover virtue.

-Francis Bacon

He lay in bed barely able to believe what had happened. He had been one of the world's most powerful men. How could this happen to him? He was so ill (both physically and spiritually) that he could not rise to his own defense. Indeed, even if he had been able to do so, he was unaware of the particular charges against him.

Francis Bacon (1561-1626) knew that he had slighted the Lower House of Parliament by addressing his comments only to the House of Lords. Even more, he had earned the enmity and hatred of Edward Coke, one of the most powerful and persuasive men in England. Bacon had been instrumental in seeing that Coke was removed from office under James I. Now Coke was poised to return the favor. The parliament had made up its mind about Bacon before he was allowed to see the specifications of the charges. James I could have come to the aid of Bacon, but the king needed the money that parliament controlled.

Bacon was charged with receiving bribes while he served as a judge. As the more than 20 charges were read, he offered a weak challenge only to a few of them. After all, he had accepted "gifts" in the presence of his servants and others. It made no difference that the gifts had not prevented him from ruling against those who had given him bribes. In fact, that was why they pressed the suit so vigorously. In 1621 Francis Bacon, Lord Verulam, Viscount St. Albans, and Keeper of the Seal was expelled from office and forbidden from serving in public office again. Edward Coke had his revenge; James I had his money. Bacon was held in the Tower of London "at the King's pleasure" for a brief time and then was set free. Before he died, almost the entire sentence was commuted.

HIS EARLY LIFE

Men of sharp wits, shut up in their cells of a few authors, chiefly Aristotle, their Dictator.   -Francis Bacon

Francis Bacon was born the third son of the Lord Keeper of the Seal in the reign of Elizabeth I. Still, he was a precocious child and seemed to delight the court with his intelligence. At 12 young Francis entered Trinity College at Cambridge. He went to school but was dissatisfied with the scholastic tradition that was taught there.

The science curriculum was based on the philosophy of Aristotle (384-322 B.C.), a Greek philosopher whose theory of nature and the cosmos had been incorporated into current Christian theology. In essence, Aristotle's philosophy taught that there was a dichotomy between the heavens and the earth, the center of the cosmos. According to Aristotle, items on the earth were composed of varying amounts of each of the fundamental elemental substances: earth, water, air and fire. In turn, an item's particular composition determined its natural motion. That is, an object made mostly of earth would fall down and through an object made of water. Similarly, smoke rose in air because it was a mixture of air and fire, the lightest element. Motion in a direction other than a natural direction is called violent motion and requires a mover to accomplish it. For example, a child throwing a ball into the air, imparts impetus to the ball which continues in violent motion as long as the impetus lasts. Then, natural motion takes over and the ball falls to the ground.

There is a fundamental difference between living and non-living things in the philosophy of Aristotle. For example, all living things grow while rocks do not (except for the occasional stalactite and stalagmite). A similar dichotomy exists between the heavens and the earth. Heavenly objects such as planets and stars are made of a fifth substance, the quintessence, which is uniformly bright, unblemished and incorruptible. Like their simple compositions, heavenly bodies moved in simple circular motions. So, except to predict their future positions, an Aristotelian had no interest in looking at particular heavenly objects.

Scholastics of the European Renaissance observed nature only in order to explain natural phenomena within the philosophy of Aristotle. Again consider the example of a child tossing a ball. Aristotle said that no object can have both natural and violent motions at the same time. Thus, a ball will travel in a straight line in violent motion until the impetus gives out, then it will fall straight down. An observer who thought that he saw something else was simply mistaken. In Renaissance England it was dangerous to make such a mistake.

In 1579 Francis' father, Sir Nicolas Bacon, died unexpectedly. He had not prepared a proper will so Francis, then 18, found himself both fatherless and penniless. In order to support himself, Francis began to practice law. During the next 20 years Francis lived in near obscurity. He petitioned Elizabeth and his uncle, Lord Burghley for government offices, but was met with cold responses and empty promises again and again. Francis always lived beyond his means and was never out of debt. Then his luck seemed to change. In 1591 Bacon became the personal confidant of Robert Devereux, Earl of Essex, a powerful but erratic man. Essex covered several of Bacon's debts with a generous stipend and sought government positions for him. Then in 1601 Essex, against the advice and counsel of Bacon, entered into open rebellion against Elizabeth. Upon the capture of Essex, the queen charged Francis Bacon with pressing the prosecution against him. Bacon was successful and Essex, his former patron, was executed. Two years later James I succeeded to the throne. Then, the fortunes of Francis began a meteoric rise. In quick succession, he became Solicitor (1607), Attorney General (1613), Lord Keeper of the Seal (the same position that his father had held, 1617), Lord Chancellor and the title of Baron Verulam (1618), and made Viscount St. Albans (1621).

A CALL FOR CHANGE

Though the whole earth were nothing but academies of learned men, yet without such an experimental history as I am going to describe, no progress worthy of the human race...could be made. -Francis Bacon

During this time Bacon dreamed of establishing institutions for the discovery of nature. These would operate according to methods of observation, and, as knowledge increased, theories would emerge. He called this the inductive method, and his call for a change came in his book called *Novum Organum* (a reference to the book by

Aristotle called *Organon)*, published in 1620. This was the second in a series of intended books through which he sought to infuse natural philosophy (science) with a new vigor in what he called the great instauration. *Novum Organum* was not easy to understand. James I commented that Bacon's book was like the peace of God, in that it passeth all understanding. Edward Coke was more cruel and wrote:

> *It deserveth not to be read in Schooles*
> *But to be freighted in the ship of Fooles.*

This was an obvious reference to the illustration on the title page (see Figure 2-3). Induction is the method by which particular observations give rise to general theories. Robert Pirsig in Zen and the Art of Motorcycle Maintenance gives a simple example of inductive inference. In this scenario a motorcyclist rides down the road and hits a bump; immediately the engine backfires. He hits another bump and the engine backfires again. He then sees another bump coming and anticipates that the motorcycle will backfire. In this case, the motorcyclist constructs the "theory" that bumps cause the motorcycle to backfire.

The difficulties with inductive logic have been the topics of discussion for numerous philosophers of science. David Hume (1711-1776) argued that we create our ideas or theories about the world based upon impressions or experiences provided by our senses. Thus, if our senses cannot give us an accurate or complete picture of the phenomenon, we are left with an incomplete or incorrect theory. A bump alone could not cause the motorcycle to backfire (I know that much about gasoline engines).

Knowledge of a gasoline engine and how it works is like a theory, too, but I don't construct it. It is given to me in a book, much like Aristotle's philosophy. From that "theory" I eliminate the possibilities until I am left with the right answer. This is called deduction, and it works well if the theory is correct or complete. However, suppose that I pull out a book on steam engines to troubleshoot the motorcycle problem? I'd be far better off with induction.

An experiment is a particular method of observation in which some aspect of nature undergoes manipulation. This allows for an interpretation of nature rather than an Aristotelean anticipation of nature. So, both the Aristotelean and Experimental methods begin with observation, but then they take very different paths.

Sir Karl Popper (1902-1994) said that the experimental method could work only if observation leads to a simple statement or hypothesis that can be disproven. If I return to the motorcycle example, an appropriate hypothesis would be, "Bumps cause motorcycles to backfire." An examination of another motorcycle hitting a bump would quickly disprove that statement.

Bacon said that his inductive or experimental method required four steps:

1. List all known cases in which a phenomenon occurs. (My motorcycle backfired each time it hit a bump today.)
2. List all cases in which the phenomenon does not occur. (Your motorcycle did not backfire when it hit the same bumps).
3. List all cases in which the phenomenon occurs in differing degrees. (My motorcycle backfires today but it did not backfire yesterday).
4. Examine the three lists.

With step 2 Bacon acknowledged the importance of negative results. That is (again according to Popper) we learn by disproving or attempting to disprove a hypothesis.

DOCTRINE OF THE IDOLS

The formation of notions and axioms on the foundation of true induction is the only fitting remedy by which we can ward off and expel these idols.

-Francis Bacon

Bacon suggests that his method is necessary to understand nature because we can fool ourselves into believing falsehoods. These false impressions come from aspects of human nature, individual imperfections (such as pride, etc.), inadequacy of language, and prejudice. He called these Idols of the Tribe, Idols of the Den, Idols of the Marketplace, and Idols of the Theatre, respectively.

Idols of the Tribe

As human beings we tend to seek patterns, especially if those patterns affirm our beliefs. Suppose that I have a cold and take heavy doses of vitamin C to recover. I take the vitamin and then I recover. Doesn't that confirm that vitamin C cures colds? Proof based on a single incident like this is called anecdotal evidence. It might be that the vitamin C helped in my recovery, but there is no way to know. We would have to run a test with many participants (the more, the better). Some would be given vitamin C while others would be given sugar tablets. In this case, the sugar tablet is called a placebo and serves as a control. If there is a measurable difference in recovery, then the claim about vitamin C would be upheld.

Idols of the Den

Usually, these might be referred to as personal flaws such as pride. Bacon said, "Anyone who studies nature should be suspicious of whatever allures and captivates his understanding." That is, those who study nature need to be careful about becoming too enamored of a pet theory. Such flaws can do serious harm to science. Perhaps the most memorable example was that of Trofim D. Lysenko (1898-1976) of the Soviet Union. He promoted a plant breeding program that rejected Darwinian theory. His theory was politically correct in that it was closer to a Marxist philosophy and was enthusiastically accepted by Stalin. Scientific dissenters suffered exile or oblivion and the state of agricultural science in the former Soviet Union is only now recovering.

Idols of the Marketplace

Simply put, this is a problem related to communication. How can natural phenomena be described such that there is no ambiguity? To combat this, the disciplines of science have developed formidable batteries of jargon. These terms, though precise, are known and used by a select few making many disciplines of science inaccessible to all but the most specialized. Even so, the person reading the jargon must be moderately fluent in the language and have some experience with the concept. For example, a teacher of English in Puerto Rico was compelled to write her own English text because the standard texts from the U.S. have stories with allusions to things like snow, something that is entirely foreign to children learning English in Puerto Rico.

Idols of the Theatre

By this, Bacon meant false theories. Particularly, he referred mostly to Aristotle in this context, but any false theory or superstition would apply equally here. The best examples include U.F.O. conspiracy theories, paranormal claims, and theories that inject religion into science.

THE EARTH IS A MAGNET

Books must follow sciences, and not sciences books. -Francis Bacon

William Gilbert (1544-1603) was a court physician to Elizabeth I, a prolific experimentalist, and a contemporary of Bacon. In 1600 he published *De Magnete (On the Magnet)*, a book based on experimental work regarding the phenomena of magnetism and static electricity. Also, he considered the magnetic nature of lodestones (natural magnets), the earth, and how the magnetic attraction works. Gilbert described hundreds of experiments and dispelled many myths such as: garlic held near a magnet causes it lose its magnetism, or there are some lodestones that repel iron just as there are others that attract iron.

He describes his experiments with such care that they could be repeated today easily. For example in Book 1, chapter 12, he states the hypothesis: "A long piece of iron, even not magnetized assumes a north and south direction." His experimental method involved suspending the needle by a silk so that it is balanced (that is, parallel to the ground). Similarly, the statement, "garlic held near a compass needle causes it to lose its magnetism", is a hypothesis. A test of that hypothesis is fairly simple.

Even though *On Magnetism* was a perfect example of a work that used the inductive method and served to attack the Idols of the Tribe and of the Theatre regarding magnetism, Bacon barely acknowledged Gilbert as an experimentalist. On the other hand, Gilbert described Bacon as someone who writes philosophy like a Lord Chancellor. Considering that Gilbert died in 1603 and had a chance to read only the earliest of Bacon's essays, I have to agree.

A CHILD'S EXPERIMENT

The root of all superstition is that men observe when a thing hits but not when it misses. -Francis Bacon

One of the most interesting experiments that I have heard of in the past year was designed and executed by Emily Rosa, a nine-year old from Loveland, Colorado. Her object was to test the claims of those who use a particular practice in nursing called Therapeutic Touch for her fourth grade Science fair project.

The theory behind therapeutic touch is that living things emit an energy field and trained practitioners can detect aberrations in the field to locate health problems or to interact with the field to promote healing. Emily Rosa designed an experimental apparatus that was simply a box with two arm holes cut in to it. She could stand behind the box and extend one or the other arm through the holes into a space that was covered by a taught cloth. The practitioner of therapeutic touch could not see Emily or her arms. Subjects then had to use therapeutic touch to determine whether Emily had extended her right or left arm under the cloth.

Scientists say that such simple experiments are elegant. It is still an experiment even though there is no clear control. Indeed, many kinds of valid experiments are performed without the use of controls. Because neither the subject nor the data recorder could see Emily, the possibility of cheating was reduced to a minimum. Even if cheating were not an issue, unconscious bias (an Idol of the Tribe) would destroy the validity of the experiment. Twenty-one trained practitioners of therapeutic touch agreed to participate in the test. Out of 280 trials the subjects identified the correct hand only 123 times. That is, they were right 44% of the time.

So, what did Emily's experiment demonstrate? At a very simple level, her experiment showed that, in all, twenty-one practitioners of therapeutic touch were able to detect the energy field given off by Emily Rosa about as well as would be expected by chance (50%). More significantly, only one person performed at a level of 80% correct responses and then scored only 40% on a second trial. Thus, Emily's experiment did not check to see if practitioners could find aberrations or unhealthy places. Also, the experiment did not test whether practitioners interact with an unhealthy energy field and affect healing. Her experiment demonstrated that practitioners (with a high level of significance) were unable to detect an energy field, a fundamental tenet of the theory of therapeutic touch. The simplest answer in light of Emily's results is that the theory of Therapeutic Touch is false (an Idol of the Theatre).

A NEW ATLANTIS

Our purpose is not to stir up men's hopes but to guide their travels. -Francis Bacon

Men and women as well as children now perform such elegant experiments every day. Such was not the case in the time of Francis Bacon. Even then it was difficult to communicate the results. Bacon looked ahead to a time when institutions of learning would encourage such methods and inquiry and communication.

After his impeachment, Bacon's world collapsed. He went deeply in debt and had very few friends. What he did have was time. Bacon threw himself into starting his great instauration. He began experiments and published observations about a variety of things in nature through books such as *Natural History, History of the Winds, Of Dense and Rare, Of Hot and Cold,* and *Of the Ebb and Flow of the Sea.* It was not Bacon's intention to find final theories to these questions otherwise he would just be replacing Aristotle as intellectual dictator. Rather, Bacon sought to start the questions that would lead to fruitful lines of inquiry.

Francis Bacon looked forward to a day when the results of science would inform technology to provide practical benefit to people across the planet. An unfinished novel, *The New Atlantis,* is a story about such a time and place. In the story, the narrator is shipwrecked on an island in the Pacific with a few others. The society on the island conforms to Bacon's ideal. It is peaceful with advanced levels of science and technology, all the fruits of the inductive method. Bacon never lived to see such a thing although it seems commonplace and normal to us today.

Bacon died five years after his impeachment. Events in England were tumultuous during that time. James I died and was succeeded by Charles I who carried the disdain of Parliament to a new level. Parliament rebelled, Charles was defeated and beheaded. Cromwell became Lord Protector for a time and the monarchy returned after his death. The political revolution and restoration seemed to anticipate events in science. On November 28, 1660 a small group of scientists including Christopher Wren and Robert Boyle petitioned Charles II for a charter as a scientific society. The charter was granted and the Royal Society is the oldest continuously existing scientific society with the longest running scientific journal to communicate results in science. Significantly, the first seal of the Royal Society bore a portrait of Francis Bacon.

A LAST EXPERIMENT

Nature, to be commanded, must be obeyed. -Francis Bacon

On a cold March day in 1626, Francis Bacon was riding in his carriage when an idea for an experiment came to him. He stopped at a farm house and bought a chicken. He wondered if cold would slow down the putrefaction or decay of the flesh of the chicken. He killed the bird, gutted it and stuffed it with snow. In the process he felt himself coming down with a cold and asked to be taken to a friend's house nearby to recover. It did not help, and his cold turned into pneumonia. Francis Bacon "obeyed nature" and died on April 9, 1626 as a consequence of his last experiment.

The immediate legacy of Francis Bacon was the Royal Society. Even more, his view of science has become our view to such an extent that we generally refer to the inductive or experimental method as the scientific method. There may be philosophical problems with the inductive method, but it works. It has given us a civilization that is very dependent on the working and relationship between science and technology. We live in Bacon's *New Atlantis.*   -1999

References:

Bacon, Francis. 1597. *Essays.* 1st ed. In: Henry Morley, ed. 1883. *Bacon's Essays.* A.L. Burt Co., Publishers.

Bacon, Francis. 1605. *Advancement of Learning.* In: Mortimer Adler, et al. eds. 1952. *Great Books of the Western World.* Vol 30. The University of Chicago and Encyclopaedia Britannica, Inc. Chicago.

Bacon, Francis. 1620. *Novum Organum.* In: Mortimer Adler, et al. eds. 1952. *Great Books of the Western World.* Vol 30. The University of Chicago and Encyclopaedia Britannica, Inc. Chicago.

Bacon, Francis. 1625. *Essays.* Last edition. In: Henry Morley, ed. 1883. *Bacon's Essays.* A.L. Burt Co., Publishers.

Bacon, Francis. unfinished. *The New Atlantis.* In: Mortimer Adler, et al. eds. 1952. *Great Books of the Western World.* Vol 30. The University of Chicago and Encyclopaedia Britannica, Inc. Chicago.

Bowen, Catherine Drinker. 1963. *Francis Bacon, The Temper of a Man.* Atlantic Monthly Press; Little, Brown & Co. Boston.

Eisley, Loren. 1973. *The Man Who Saw Through Time.* Charles Scribner's Sons. New York.

Gilbert, William. 1600. *De Magnete.* In: Mortimer Adler, et al. eds. 1952. *Great Books of the Western World.* Vol 28. The University of Chicago and Encyclopaedia Britannica, Inc. Chicago.

Hampshire, Stuart, ed. 1956. *The Age of Reason, the 17th Century Philosophers.* A Mentor Book, Houghton Mifflin Co. New York.

Hume, David. 1748. *An Enquiry Concerning Human Understanding.* In: Mortimer Adler, et al. eds. 1952. *Great Books of the Western World.* Vol 35. The University of Chicago and Encyclopaedia Britannica, Inc. Chicago.

Pirsig, Robert. 1974. *Zen and the Art of Motorcycle Maintenance.* Bantam Books. New York.

Rosa, Linda, Emily Rosa, Larry Sarner, and Stephen Barrett. 1998. *A close look at therapeutic touch.* Journal of the American Medical Association 279:1005-1010.

Questions to Think About

1. Why was Francis Bacon impeached?

   Took bribes as a judge

2. Why did Bacon refer to Aristotle as a dictator?

   Just said how things are → didn't open up for ? is

3. What is the inductive method?

   Observations give rise to theory

4. What is Pirsig's "motorcycle experiment"?

   bike → ? → ?

5. What is the problem with induction?

   Failure of our senses

6. What is the Doctrine of the Idols?

   The fact we can fool ourselves into believing falsehoods.

7. Who was William Gilbert? What did he study? Although a prolific experimentalist, Gilbert did not interact with Bacon. Why?

   4 mechanical, cont physician, Magnetism → Tenjourg

8. Who was Emily Rosa? What was her experiment?

   4 year old - Therapeutic Touch

9. What was a first fruit of the *New Atlantis*?

   peaceful, high science

10. What was Bacon's last experiment?

    chicken on ice

A ROCK, A RAZOR, AND A DINOSAUR: MODELS AND THE APPEARANCE OF DESIGN IN NATURE.

A DESIGNED STONE?

The most beautiful thing we can experience is the mysterious. It is the source of all true art and science. He to whom this emotion is a stranger, who can no longer pause to wonder and stand rapt in awe, is as good as dead: his eyes are closed.

-Albert Einstein (1930)

Once I was shown a very interesting stone that had been retrieved from the Susquehanna River (Figure 2-4). The rock had a surface pattern that was like a lattice of 1cm wide ribbon-like pieces. I was immediately struck by the regular pattern, but it did not have the fine detail that I expected to see from a fossil. What was it? I borrowed the stone and studied it with a dissecting microscope, but I could see no fine detail (not atypical with many fossils). Still, the larger pattern was intriguing. Parallel ribbon-like bands crossed each other at right angles. The space between the ribbons was just irregular stone.

The more I studied the stone, the more confused I got. I sought the interpretations of biologists and geologists whose answers were equally confused. I was advised (with varying degrees of confidence) that it was a "pattern formed by the infiltration of water into a fracture, it was a fossil plant, a fossil turtle, a fossil fish, a pattern left by vibrations created by the railroad or heavy object that sat on the stone. But almost everyone turned away from it with an "I don't know" or a "Very interesting".

FIGURE 2-4. A most interesting stone.

We tend to seek patterns in objects and connect those perceived patterns to other familiar objects. In that way we build our metaphorical scaffold of the reality around us. Thus, we seek regularities or patterns and try to explain them. Sometimes, the patterns are purely accidental, and we make connections that do not exist. For example, one time I went through Penns Cave in central Pennsylvania. As the guide took us through the cavern in a boat, he pointed out formations that looked like a variety of familiar objects. There were stalagmites that resembled a castle, a knight, and the Statue of Liberty. There were others that were a bigger stretches of the imagination like a stalagmite prairie dog that really looked like an owl. Frankly, I was not so much interested in what they might accidentally resemble as much as I was interested in the patterns of their formation and the streaks of minerals associated with them.

That stalagmites resembled more familiar objects occurred only because I took the suggestion made by the guide and fit it into my mental pattern of that object. This is the same thing that happens when we see familiar objects in the patterns created by clouds. The point is that clouds have to have shape. Some of those just accidentally resemble the familiar.

A BRIEF HISTORY OF HELMETS

Artifacts are experiments. They are experiments first with what is possible and then (perhaps) with what is preferable.

-Clifford A. Hooker (1987).

Some things, indeed most familiar things that we come into contact with, are engineered or designed by other humans to perform particular tasks or functions. Such human-created objects or artifacts are manifestations of beliefs and values of their creators. They also bear their own design histories.

Ask almost anyone and you will discover that person has an intimate knowledge of (and sometimes strong opinions about) one or more classes of artifacts. I have a collection of hats, artifacts for the head. I have hats that function to provide shade; some that protect the head from blows; and others that serve to display fashion. Strictly speaking, most hats have more than one function and reflect a range of beliefs and values of their designers. Nevertheless, all hats have certain basic attributes in common. They all have to sit on a human head that has a standard placement of eyes, ears, hair, etc. From above, the head is an oval that rises to make an elongate, hairy dome. So, even though hats can be designed to do many things, they all have to conform to the restrictions of the human head.

In part, my collection features fire helmets from around the world. In 1995, I was particularly pleased to receive a Yaroslavl (a city in Russia) fire helmet as a birthday present (see Figure 2-5). The helmet was green, made of steel, and had a ridge that ran along the top. This helmet had several of the design features that make a good fire helmet. First, it was made of steel and padded to protect the wearer from falling objects. Secondly, it had a flange that extended from the back with a slight downward angle, which allowed for water to run down off the head and down the back instead of down the collar.

However, other design features did not appear to be useful. The ridge that ran along the top might have given it a little structural support, but really it showed the lineage of the design. The Russian fire helmet looked just like the military helmets that were worn by the French during World War I (Figure 2-6). Then, the top ridge was in place to protect the wearer from a downward saber blow in a cavalry charge by deflecting the sword away from the head and shoulders. By 1995 this relict design feature served more as a statement of fashion than of function.

FIGURE 2-5. Russian fire helmet.

FIGURE 2-6. World War I era French military helmet.

My most prized fire helmets came from my father, whose name was also Jack Holt. He had been a captain on the Tulsa Fire Department before his death in 1986. I inherited his helmets, both of which were of a similar design (see Figure 2-7). They were more rounded

on top with small ridges coming down the dome to help channel water to the brim, which was larger than that of the Russian helmet. Also, my father's helmets had much larger flanges. The real difference was in the materials. My father's helmets were made of fiberglass and plastic, which allowed them to be both strong and light.

My father actually preferred the older fiberglass helmet and used it until he retired although he was supposed to have switched to the plastic helmet years earlier. He said that the plastic helmet was too new and shiny. But I knew that it was because the plastic helmet was plastic. He just didn't like that new-fangled stuff.

FIGURE 2-7. My father's fire helmets: the older fiberglass helmet (top) and the newer (and unused) plastic helmet (bottom).

The fiberglass helmet bears the scars of many years of use. My father often used the helmet as a club, especially to break windows when he arrived at a fire to help prevent explosive situations like backfire. One of the men in his company told me that "ole Jack hated to see unbroken windows." Actually it was because he thought more of his men than he did of the glass. Although he had many nicknames on the Tulsa Fire Department, this habit earned him the name, Crash, and the old helmet is an eloquent testament.

Obviously, the fire helmets had been designed by people to perform several critical functions, particularly those dealing with the safety of the firefighter. Also, the helmets allowed for a means of nonverbal communication. My father's helmets were red, which communicated to all who could see him that he was a captain. Thus, most artifacts like hats, automobiles, clocks, houses, etc. serve multiple purposes - some practical, some aesthetic.

QUEBEC BRIDGE

There can be little doubt that in many ways the story of bridge building is the story of civilization. By it we can measure an important part of a people's progress.

-Franklin Delano Roosevelt (1931)

Many of our artifacts are monumental and large enough to become part of the landscape. Consider bridges. Indeed, it's hard not to consider them here in central Pennsylvania. Aside from the construction of roadways, bridges are among our most obvious engineering marvels. My favorite ones are the old wooden covered bridges. Although they are somewhat abundant here, cement and steel are rapidly replacing them. Most stand as a salute to another time and, with their integrity now in question, allow only foot traffic.

Perhaps, central Pennsylvania's real claim to bridge fame is the Rockville Bridge that crosses the Susquehanna River north of Harrisburg. This is the longest stone arch bridge in the world (3,280 feet long). Most of the newer bridges that cross the river are of arch design, but they are made of steel girders encased in concrete. Regardless of the materials, the arch bridge is an ancient but effective design in which the arch runs from pier to pier and supports the bridge from below (see Figure 2-8). Unfortunately, the arch bridge design requires many piers if the expanse is a long one.

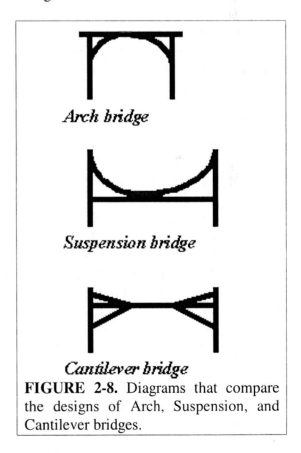

FIGURE 2-8. Diagrams that compare the designs of Arch, Suspension, and Cantilever bridges.

Other bridge designs, the suspension and the cantilever bridges, allow for long expanses with relatively fewer piers.

This is important if the bridge has lots of large boat traffic beneath it. These bridges can be very long like the Brooklyn Bridge (1,595ft), the Verrazano Narrows Bridge (4,260ft), and the Golden Gate Bridge (4,200ft). Also, the suspension bridge is a useful design if it is impossible to have piers for a large extent of its span. For example, the Royal Gorge bridge in Canon City, Colorado is more than 1,000 feet high over a youthful Arkansas River. (I remember once years ago my younger brother spat off the Royal Gorge Bridge so that he could brag to his peers that he could spit a quarter mile).

Usually suspension bridges are somewhat flexible because of their design. Normally, that does not make a difference; however, they can become unstable if the oscillation occurs at a resonating frequency. Such a thing happened to the Tacoma Narrows Bridge (2,800ft), which crosses Puget Sound in Washington. It began to oscillate in a strong prevailing wind and then tear itself apart.

The cantilever bridge design is more stable and very large expanses (though not as large as the suspension bridge) can be spanned. In essence, the cantilever is a crane that is anchored to a pier. In a way, it is a hybrid between the designs of the arch and the suspension bridges with support from above as well as below.

The Quebec Bridge (1,800ft) was one of the most famous of the cantilever bridges. Its construction began around the beginning of the 20th Century in order to allow rail traffic across the St. Lawrence River. Although the finished design was relatively stable, this, like most cantilever bridges was quite unstable during its construction. That coupled with gross underestimates of total weight and substandard materials brought down the bridge twice before it was finished. In all more than 80 men died in the two accidents. The bridge, after nearly 20 years of construction, was finally finished in 1918.

A BRIDGE THAT WALKED

The great dinosaurs strode through their Mesozoic world with the upright gait and carriage that are characteristic of the biggest African elephants today.

-Robert Bakker (1986)

During the time of the construction of the Quebec Bridge, another construction project of sorts was under way. An expedition funded by industrialist Andrew Carnegie discovered an enormous dinosaur on July 4, 1899. The skeleton of the Jurassic dinosaur was nearly complete and was shipped back to the Carnegie Museum of Natural History in Pittsburgh. John Bell Hatcher, director of paleontology at the museum, named the beast *Diplodocus carnegei* for the museum's patron. Carnegie was so taken with the dinosaur and his namesake that he funded other expeditions to collect more and gave them as gifts to the great museums of the world. When he ran out of real fossils, he funded the production of numerous plaster casts so that his dinosaur could be seen the world over. I saw one of Carnegie's plaster skeletons in the Museum National D'Histoire Naturelle, Galerie de Paleontologie, Paris in the summer of 2000.

Hatcher reconstructed the skeleton of *Diplodocus* with pillar-like legs like other large land animals such as elephants and giraffes. Indeed, the reconstruction made it look like a cantilever bridge. It had large pillar-like legs with a cantilever holding the head and the tail. The span between the front and hind legs was supported by a vertebral column that was stiffened by an array of tendons and massive muscles that were anchored on the legs. This animal was a bridge that walked.

The analogy of large terrestrial animals made sense to Hatcher. He could not imagine any other way in which the animal could carry itself on land. Like a bridge, the weight-bearing pilings (legs) were straight columns. Unfortunately, Hatcher died of Typhoid Fever in 1904 just about the time that the controversy over *Diplodocus* began to heat up. A U.S. paleontologist, Oliver Hay, assumed that Hatcher had made a grievous error by giving *Diplodocus* the "unnatural" stance of a mammal. After all, *Diplodocus* was a large reptile, and should assume its "lowly" station. So, he and a German paleontologist named Gustav Tornier gave *Diplodocus* the bent-leg stance of a large lizard (see Figure 2-9) in a paper published in 1908.

William Holland and Henry Fairfield Osborn shot back with anatomical support for Hatcher's upright *Diplodocus*. Holland showed that the Hay-Tornier model of *Diplodocus* could not possibly have been the structure of the animal because it had such a deep rib cage. He added ironically that if the animal had bent lizard knees, it would have had to seek out Mesozoic trenches just to walk around (see Figure 2-10). Osborn went even farther and proposed a model of an active and agile dinosaur that could use its tail as a third leg to allow it to rear up and feed high in the trees (see Figure 2-11).

The lizard model of dinosaur physiology and behavior came back into vogue, though. Long-necked sauropod dinosaurs like *Diplodocus* began to be relegated to the water and marshes. Such places seemed to be more suited to the plodding longnecks because the water allowed for lizard-like legs to support a massive body. Such thinking began to come apart with revelations and new understanding during the last quarter of the 20th Century in which dinosaurs were seen as warm-blooded social animals. We now believe that *Diplodocus* roamed dry land in herds or family groups …just like elephants.

MODELS AND DESIGN

The fact that a nature is only progressively disclosed in experience, and perhaps is never exhaustively understood, makes it especially amenable to study through modeling techniques.

-William A. Wallace (1996)

The use of the elephant to try to understand the structure, physiology, biomechanics, and to a limited extent the behavior of *Diplodocus* turns out to be quite fruitful. The elephant, another large living land-dwelling four-legged animal serves to provide particular insight into *Diplodocus*. Of course, the trick is to make the right connection with an appropriate model organism. In this case, the elephant is a physical model of *Diplodocus*. That is, because they are both large, land-dwelling vertebrates, we can assume that both animals share many characteristics and just treat *Diplodocus* as a scaled-up elephant.

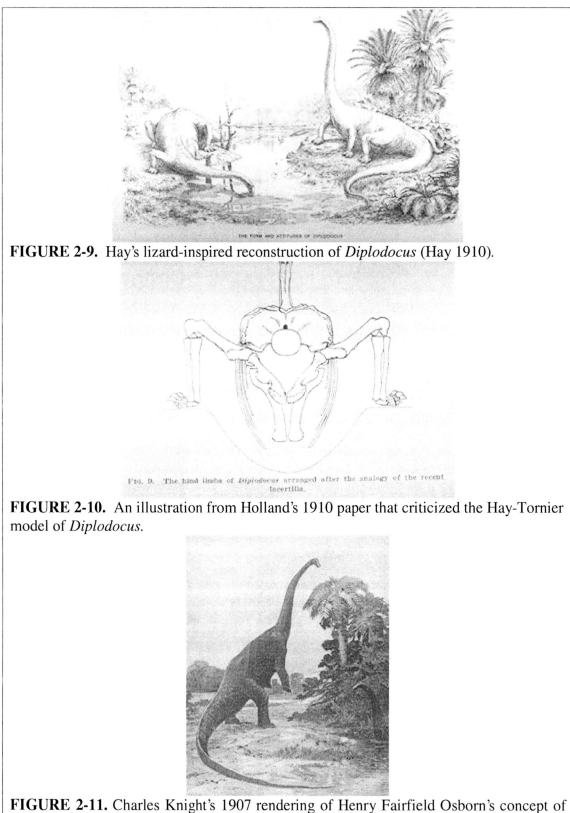

FIGURE 2-9. Hay's lizard-inspired reconstruction of *Diplodocus* (Hay 1910).

FIGURE 2-10. An illustration from Holland's 1910 paper that criticized the Hay-Tornier model of *Diplodocus*.

FIGURE 2-11. Charles Knight's 1907 rendering of Henry Fairfield Osborn's concept of an active and agile *Diplodocus* that could rear up on its hind legs with support from its long tail.

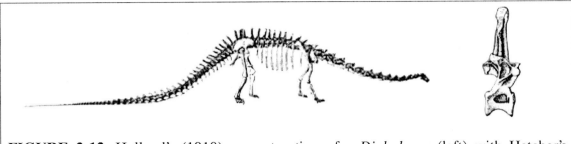

FIGURE 2-12. Holland's (1910) reconstruction of a *Diplodocus* (left) with Hatcher's (1901) detail of a vertebra from the trunk of the animal (right).

Choice of the physical model is very important. *Diplodocus* is a very different animal when the analog is an elephant versus a lizard. Also, the model serves to cause us to ask particular questions that experience with the analog would prompt us to consider. For example, if *Diplodocus* stayed in family groups and moved in herds, how did the individuals recognize each other? What did they sound like? How much care did they give their offspring? How far did their herds forage? Such questions would not occur to the person who considered them to be large lizards, which tend to be solitary.

The engineering aspect of the construction of *Diplodocus* is another matter and requires a different kind of model. I used bridge design to describe the structure of the animal. Now a bridge is not a dinosaur at any scale. In this case, the use of a familiar object to describe an aspect of something completely different is called conceptual modeling.

Consider particular aspects of the structure of *Diplodocus*. The skeleton was made of thick, heavy solid bones in the legs with an open, strut-like weight-saving structure in the vertebral column above (see Figure 2-12). The high dorsal spine on the vertebrae gave a solid place for attachments of muscles, tendons, and ligaments with little additional weight, just like the superstructure of a suspension or cantilever bridge.

Conceptual models such as these are helpful and compelling. The difficulty of models of this type when applied to living things is that they also seem to take on the attribute of being designed like their analogs. Still, *Diplodocus* and elephants conform to about the only body plan that allows a very large animal to move over the earth on four legs. Stephen Jay Gould, evolutionary biologist and paleontologist at Harvard, pointed out this fact of life repeatedly in his essays for *Natural History*. In one of his most memorable essays called *The Panda's Thumb*, Gould explained that pandas have a design flaw. They have a "thumb" that helps them to strip the leaves from bamboo. Upon close examination, the "thumb" is actually an extension of one of the wrist bones. It is an awkward arrangement, but it works. The point is that the ancestors of pandas were animals that had reduced their "hands" to paws. Natural selection[1] was quite limited in the kinds of structures with which to make a thumb, so a makeshift thumb evolved.

---

[1] Please read *Parasites and Darwin's Intellectual Triumph* and *The Mentor and the Heretic* for further explanation of natural selection.

Richard Dawkins, in *Climbing Mount Improbable*, expands that theme. He points out that given long periods of time and small incremental changes in response to natural selection, most wonderful forms can appear. And because they have evolved as a consequence of particular selective pressures, the structures that emerge appear to be designed. Darwin, himself tackled the problem of the eye in *The Origin of Species*. The ability to discern light from dark would be useful and impart an advantage to an organism over those without the sensitivity. Animals (and many other types of organisms) have light-reactive compounds in their cells. If the compound that is involved in another pathway were to give its possessor a rudimentary sense of light-dark, then natural selection could take over and more precise light perception and image formation could evolve. This scenario seems to have repeated itself many times in the Animal Kingdom alone.

However, if we look only at the human eye and ask, how could such a beautifully designed structure appear like that from nothing, the answer would have to be that it could not. But our eyes evolved from structures that could do little more than perceive light or darkness. Dawkin's metaphor was a mountain. Natural selection does not climb of the cliff face; it walks up the mild slopes on the back of the mountain. Thus, the eyes of vertebrates, insects, cephalopods (squid and octopus), etc. only appear to have been designed, but that appearance is an artifact of natural selection and a long history through which it operated.

. Natural selection has its "design" limits, and there are many things that it has not discovered. For example, four-legged animals move by swinging legs and alternately taking weight and lifting their legs. Although a wheel and axle is more efficient, natural selection has not climbed that mountain, so it makes do with structures that once helped fish move through water.

OCCAM'S RAZOR
It is vain to do more with what can be done with less.
                    -William of Occam (1300-1349)

Darwin's (and Wallace's) theory of natural selection was accepted by the scientific community after 1859 because it was the simplest explanation for the diversity of life. It remains the simplest explanation and has become the cornerstone of modern biology. The view that most scientists hold today is that the simplest explanation is the best explanation. This idea is identified with William of Occam, a 14th century philosopher who suggested that although there might be an infinite number of possible solutions to problems in a physical world, the simplest is probably closest to the truth. By simplest, he did not mean the most insipid or naïve explanation, but the explanation that was based firmly on natural law and required the fewest number of axioms or qualifying statements. By the same token, a scientific view that takes into account a universal designer would reject natural law and, thereby, multiply the number of explanatory axioms many times over. This stipulation serves to distinguish scientific explanations from the artistic and religious. Occam's admonition or Occam's Razor is the name given to this philosophy or way of interpreting nature, and it is the application of this concept to problems in nature that causes us to reject nonsense such as alien abductions, ancient astronauts, new age power crystals, and intelligent design.

Indeed, the concept of intelligent design is a very old one and manifests itself in its last scientific vestige as Natural Theology from the 18th through the middle of the 19th Centuries. This view was that nature declares the majesty of its creator through its beautiful and precise design; so, one could come to know of the creator by studying the creation (nature). The philosophers Immanuel Kant and David Hume both explored the question of intelligent design. Kant concluded that although the argument was compelling, that pure reason alone would allow the observer of nature that there was a designer, but it could not say anything about the designer as creator, the designer as omnipotent, or the designer as omniscient. David Hume was less generous. He stated that intelligent design was an illusion brought about by an inadequate knowledge of nature and its underlying laws. Today, the community of Biologists accepts that the "designer" is the blind and uncaring action of natural selection, an answer to both Kant and Hume, and an answer that meets the demands of William of Occam[2].

The application of Occam's Razor does not make nature any less mysterious or interesting. Indeed, the ability to explain natural phenomena and consider their relationships, connected by unbroken natural law only enhances the beauty and wonder of nature. It also helps to connect us in a physical way with the phenomena that we observe.

I began this essay with a reference to clouds, stalagmites, and their accidental similarities to familiar objects. I return to them because they are what they are. Clouds do conform to certain kinds of shapes and textures as a consequence of natural laws. After all, we can identify particular kinds of clouds such as cumulus and cirrus clouds. Stalagmites are the same way.

Our guide through Penns Cave pointed out a very interesting feature. A mineralized shelf of the same material as the stalagmites emerged from the wall of the cave and stuck out nearly a meter over the water. How could such a thing have formed? How could the mineralized water that formed these flowstones move such that it was suspended and parallel with the ground? The guide suggested that the simplest explanation was that there had once been a bank of mud over which the mineral-laden water flowed and formed a layer on top of the mud. Then, as the consequence of a flood through the cave, the mud was washed away, and the shelf was left "suspended" from the wall. This was an Occam's Razor explanation. I immediately accepted how plausible it was and thought, "That's probably it."

I am just as optimistic that Occam's Razor will cut through the veil that surrounds the strange stone. If the answer is good enough and simple enough, I'll likely ask, "Why didn't I think of that?"

-1997, revised 2005

References:

Bakker, Robert T. 1986. *The Dinosaur Heresies.* Zebra Books, Kensington Publishing Corp. New York.

Caws, Peter. 1966. *The Philosophy of Science.* D. Van Nostrand Company, Inc. Princeton.

Darwin, Charles R. 1859. *The Origin of Species by Means of Natural Selection.* The corrected copyright edition (1902). John Murray. London.

---

[2] Further arguments against Intelligent Design can be found in *Nature's Bounty* and *Origins*.

Dawkins, Richard. 1996. *Climbing Mount Improbable.* W.W. Norton & Co. New York.

Dawkins, Richard. 1998. *Unweaving the Rainbow.* Houghton Mifflin Company. New York.

Gould, Stephen Jay. 1982. *The Panda's Thumb.* W.W. Norton & Co. New York.

Hatcher, John Bell. 1901. *Diplodocus: Its Osteology, Taxonomy, and probable Habits, With a Restoration of the Skeleton.* Memoirs of the Carnegie Museum. 1:1-63.

Hay, Oliver P. 1910. *On the Manner of Locomotion of the Dinosaurs, Especially Diplodocus, With Remarks on the Origin of the Birds.* Proceedings of the Washington Academy of Sciences. 12:1-25.

Holland, William J. 1910. *A Review of Some Recent Criticisms of the Restorations of Sauropod Dinosaurs Existing in Museums of the United States, With Special Reference to that of Diplodocus carnegiei in the Carnegie Museum.* American Naturalist 44: 259-283.

Hooker, Clifford A. 1987. *A Realistic Theory of Science.* State University of New York Press. Albany.

Hume, David. 1999. (originally published 1739-40 in 3 vols). *An Inquiry Concerning Human Understanding.* Tom L. Beauchamp, ed. Oxford Philosophical Texts. Oxford University Press. Oxford, UK.

Kant, Immanuel. 1952 (originally published in 1781). *Critique of Pure Reason.* Translated by J.M.D. Meiklejohn. In: Robert Maynard Hutchins. 1952. *The Great Books of the Western World.* Vol 42. University of Chicago and Encyclopedia Britannica, Inc.

Knight, Charles R. 1907. *Diplodocus Restored. The Largest Creature That Ever Roamed the Earth.* Scientific American 96(24): 485.

Kosso, Peter. 1992. *Reading the Book of Nature.* Cambridge University Press. Cambridge.

Loewenberg, Bert J., ed. 1959. *Charles Darwin: Evolution and Natural Selection, an Anthology of the Writings of Charles Darwin.* Beacon Press. Boston.

Mason, Stephen F. 1962. *A History of the Sciences.* Collier Books. New York.

McAllister, James. W. 1996. *Beauty and Revolution in Science.* Cornell University Press. Ithaca.

Nagel, Ernest. 1979. *The Structure of Science.* Hackett Publishing Company. Cambridge.

Roemer, Alfred S. 1966. *Vertebrate Paleontology.* University of Chicago Press. Chicago.

Shanks, Niall. 2004. *God, the Devil, and Darwin, A Critique of Intelligent Design Theory.* Oxford University Press. Oxford, UK.

Suppe, Frederick. 1974. *The Structure of Scientific Theories.* University of Illinois Press. Urbana.

Trefil, James and Robert Hazen. 2000. *The Sciences, An Integrated Approach.* John Wiley & Sons, Inc. New York.

Ulam, S. M. 1976. *Adventures of a Mathematician.* Charles Scribner's & Sons. New York.

Wallace, William A. 1996. *The Modeling of Nature.* The Catholic University of America Press. Washington, D.C.

Acknowledgement: I wish to thank Greg and Grier Wilt for showing me a very interesting rock.

Questions to Think About

1. Comment on the following statement by Richard Dawkins: *Our propensity to see significance and pattern in coincidence, whether or not there is any real significance there, is part of a more general tendency to seek patterns.* (Dawkins, 1998).

2. What are artifacts? Give some examples of some (other than hats) that you use often. What about them might be variable? What about them is characteristic?

3. What are the strengths and weaknesses of the three types of bridges?

4. How might a *Diplodocus* be considered a bridge that walked?

5. What are some analogs for *Diplodocus*? How do they force very different interpretations of the dinosaur?

6. Distinguish between physical and conceptual models. What limits do each of them impose on the interpretation of a phenomenon?

7. What is Occam's Razor? Why is it an appropriate philosophical tool to employ in science?

8. Why do complex structures like eyes appear to be designed?

9. Why would we not assume a designer of complex biological structures?

10. How did Immanuel Kant and David Hume address the question of intelligent design more than 200 years ago?

KILLER ALGAE

A FISHKILL IN TEXAS

The "red tide" reported here consisted of a heavy bloom of a cryptomonad...in a small abandoned catfish pond in Grayson County, Texas.

-Lois Pfiester & Jack Holt

On June 8, 1976 Mr Robert Cunningham, a "catfish farmer" in northern Texas, placed 2,500 one pound catfish in a large holding pond. He worried that the water volume might not be great enough to accommodate so many fish in the pond, so he pumped some more water from a smaller pond on the farm. By morning, most of the fish were either dead or dying.

Mr. Cunningham was nearly in a panic. He called around to find out who might help solve the mystery and save some fish. He ended up calling the director of the University of Oklahoma Biological Station, just over the state line. Ichthyologists (fish biologists) there suggested that the fish were dying because there was not enough oxygen in the water to support so many fish. However, when they visited the farm on that day, the oxygen levels were surprisingly high. Almost as an afterthought, one of the biologists took a sample of the water because it had a strange blue-green tint to it.

That summer, Dr. Lois Pfiester (pronounced feester) was teaching a course about algae (the study of algae is called Phycology). The sample of water from Mr. Cunningham's catfish farm made its way to Lois Pfiester's microscope. In the sample, she saw that it was teeming (>5,000 cells per milliliter) with a particular one-celled organism called *Cyanomonas*

americana[3], a cell with two flagella. Instead of having their own chloroplasts (photosynthetic organelles), *Cyanomonas* had round blue-green algae (photosynthetic bacteria), called cyanelles.

This is where I became involved in the detective story because I was a student in Lois Pfiester's Phycology course that summer. I remember that we drove down to the catfish farm in time to see the last of the catfish dying as they gulped air with flared gills. The appearance of the fish reminded Lois of reports of fish behavior during red tide events. However, red tides occurred in the oceans, not in freshwater ponds.

FIGURE 2-13. Dr. Lois Pfiester

Mr. Cunningham showed us the pond from which he pumped the water on the evening before the fish kill. That pond had a pronounced blue-green surface scum. We collected water from this pond and talked Mr. Cunningham into giving us enough one pound fish to conduct an experiment at the biological station.

---

[3] The generic name, *Cyanomonas*, means the bluegreen unicell.

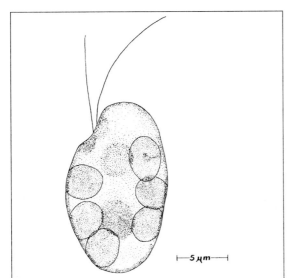

FIGURE 2-14. *Cyanomonas americana.* Note the ball-like photosynthetic cyanelles. Also the size bar is smaller than the diameter of a human red blood cell.

We set up five large aquaria, each with varying concentrations of the *Cyanomonas* pond water (100%, 50%, 25%, 10%, and 0%). We then added 10 catfish to each aquarium and waited, but we did not have to wait very long to see an effect. Within 24 hours, all 10 catfish in the undiluted pond water had died. Within 48 hours, most of the fish had died in the other experimental aquaria while all survived in aquaria that had no pond water and no *Cyanomonas*.

Since *Cyanomonas* was the only dominant organism in the water (besides the catfish), we assumed that it was the causative agent, and, therefore, must have been producing a toxin. A chemist came down from the main campus at the University of Oklahoma to collect the algae in large enough quantities to isolate the toxin. I waded in the water for hours collecting and concentrating the algae. Other students joined in to help, even my sister who was also a student in the same Phycology course. All of us who waded in the water

suffered rashes to varying degrees on our hands and lower legs.

Later, at the university, I set up a small aquarium with pond water and hoped to isolate *Cyanomonas*. Finally, I gave up and set about to clean out the aquarium. As soon as I reached into the water, my hands began to tingle and swell. Later, they were covered with large, watery blisters and became numb for several days.

The next spring we returned to the north Texas catfish farm to collect some more pond water or some mud from which to isolate the algae. However, Mr. Cunningham had drained and bulldozed the pond. We couldn't blame him.

ALGAE IN ARMOR
The biology of algae is a duty or a task,
That consumes the better portion of your time
In the sampling of waters from an ocean, or a flask,
Or a snow-field, or a gutter full of slime.
                                    -Ralph A. Lewin (1971)

Lois Pfiester had become a world expert on a group of one-celled things called dinoflagellates. Most of them live in the oceans where their total living volume exceeds far more than that of all the world's whales. When in abundance (or bloom), some can cause red tide, a situation in which toxin is released into the water causing fish to die. Also, the toxin (which in some species is second only to botulism in its potency) is stored in the tissue of shellfish in the region of the bloom making them poisonous and causing a condition called Paralytic Shellfish Poisoning. In freshwater, the dinoflagellates are more well behaved and rarely cause toxic conditions.

43

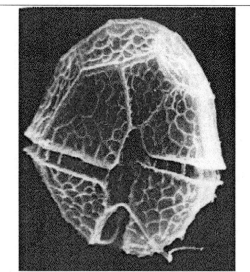

FIGURE 2-15. *A Peridinium willei* cell taken with a Scanning Electron Microscope. The flagella, located in grooves on the surface, are inserted in the center of the cell. Note the overlapping "armor" plates of cellulose.

Lois studied freshwater dinoflagellate species, particularly those in the genus *Peridinium*. These species are covered with interlocking armored plates made of cellulose (the same substance from which wood is made). Many make their own food with brown-green chloroplasts and they store that food within the cell as starch or oil.

Perhaps, the most distinctive aspect of all dinoflagellates is the appearance of the swimming cell. They swim by means of two flagella, each located in a groove on the cell surface. One flagellum encircles the cell and is flattened or ribbon-like; the other is like a whip and extends beyond the posterior end of the cell. Together, the actions of the two flagella cause a characteristic spin as the cell moves forward. Thus, they are called dinoflagellates, the spinning flagellates.

One of Lois' major contributions was to document that these species, particularly *Peridinium*, have life cycles.

That is there are different forms and functions of the cells through the history of the population. Although she was not the first to observe changes in form, she was the first to document cell changes throughout the life cycle using both a light and electron microscope. This required that she isolate the species in question and grow it in large numbers. Then, she had to sit patiently at the microscope and observe the behavior.

The vegetative or photosynthetic swimming cells of *Peridinium* are typical in appearance (Figure 2-16-A). Some of the cells can develop into gametes or sex cells (Figure 2-16-B-C). These fuse to make a new cell with two sets of chromosomes and even two sets of flagella for a time ((Figure 2-16 D-F). Please notice that in one-celled organisms, sexual reproduction does not lead directly to an increase in numbers. Instead, two cells fuse to make one.

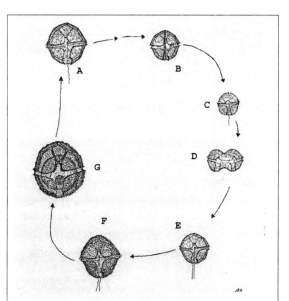

FIGURE 2-16. A life cycle of *Peridinium volzii*. The cell stages (A-G) are drawn to scale. The cyst or hypnozygote (G) is the large, warty form that can sit on the bottom and "wait" for environmental changes before germination.

The swimming zygote enlarges and becomes warty. A red oil droplet develops in the center of the cell and the plates begin to be pushed apart at the edges where they overlap. The zygote eventually loses its flagella and develops one or more walls around the living component inside (Figure 2-16-G). One of those walls is so resistant to change that it has been found in Cretaceous sediments, chemically unchanged! The zygote, then, forms in response to changes in the environment (temperature or chemical changes) and rests on the bottom mud until conditions are right again. Then, the zygote germinates releasing one to four swimming vegetative cells.

This series of cellular changes is called a life cycle. Lois was able to show that many described varieties and even separate species are just different stages in the life cycle of some *Peridinium* species.

PREDATORS IN DISGUISE

This study indicates that earlier descriptions of vegetative reproduction are invalid and suggests the need for systematic revisions in both protozoan and algal taxonomy.

-L. Pfiester & J. Popovsky (1979)

In 1978 Lois went to Prague for four weeks to work with Jiri Popovski, another specialist in freshwater dinoflagellates. On an excursion to the Hubenov Reservoir in the Czech highlands, she collected some stringy, filamentous algae. When she examined their samples in the laboratory, she observed a dinoflagellate called *Cystodinedria*, an organism that she had never encountered before. Although *Cystodinedria* had the characteristic dinoflagellate brown-green color and

produced a dinoflagellate swimming cell, it was usually a lump-like amoeba that sat on the outside of other algae. She was enthusiastic about finding it because it was a dinoflagellate. However, as she watched this one, her enthusiasm turned to wonder and amazement. The brown-green amoeba sat on the outside of a filament of cells. Suddenly, the cell on which the amoeba sat (apparently impassive) shuddered and the cell contents went up into the amoeba! She watched as the amoeba crawled to the next cell and repeated the operation. Each cell it left had a small, round hole in its wall.

She and Popovski studied this thing and identified more than 30 different stages to its elaborate life cycle. The amoeba was just a feeding stage. She soon discovered that other seemingly inactive dinoflagellates had similar appetites and behaviors. One, called *Stylodinium*, sits on filaments as if on a pedestal (see Figure 2-17). However, it, too, feeds and then manifests itself in many forms, most of which are amoeboid. At least one of the forms has a red oil droplet, a feature that is characteristic of dinoflagellate zygotes.

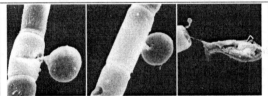

FIGURE 2-17. SEM micrographs of *Stylodinium* feeding on an algal filament. The third micrograph illustrates its amoeboid form.

When she returned from Czechoslovakia (now, the Czech Republic), all of us in her laboratory went out looking for blooms of filamentous algae. We discovered that the feeding dinoflagellates were very common, but easily overlooked. From this experience, she and Popovski proposed that in the classification of dinoflagellates (and other algae) the entire life cycle should be considered, not just the dominant life stage.

She continued her work with freshwater dinoflagellates, particularly *Peridinium*. I even returned to her laboratory during the 1990 academic year and worked with her for a semester. I did not know it then, but Lois was mortally ill. She maintained a high level of research and professional activity until her death in 1992.

THE PHANTOM

Here we describe a new toxic dinoflagellate with 'phantom-like' behaviour that has been identified as the causative agent of a significant portion of the fisk kills in these estuaries, and which may also be active in other geographic regions.-J. Burkholder, et al., 1992

In the same year as Lois' death, there was an unusual fish kill in North Carolina. Fish like Striped Bass and Atlantic Menhaden were dying with oozing sores on their bodies. JoAnn Burkholder, an algal ecologist, had recently received her degree and landed an academic position at the University of North Carolina. She was curious about the fish kill because the oxygen levels were high, and, therefore, a disease or toxic cause was suspected.

In freshly collected water, she saw a very tiny dinoflagellate that was in abundance in the water with the afflicted fish (see Figure 2-18). She identified the dinoflagellate (later called the Phantom or Ambush Dinoflagellate) as the causative agent by using many of the

same methods that had been pioneered by Lois Pfiester.

With painstaking attention, Burkholder and her student Howard Glasgow, determined that the Phantom remains inactive on the bottom mud until it detects the presence of particular fish. Then, it swims free of the cyst and releases a powerful toxin (or set of toxins) that help to immobilize the fish and cause the flesh to begin falling off in pieces (thus, the characteristic open sores). The cells feed on the flesh particles and quickly metamorphose into other forms, most of which are amoeboid.

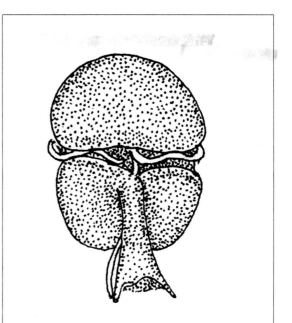

FIGURE 2-18. *Pfiesteria piscidida* in one of its most dangerous stages. It has the typical dinoflagellate swimming cell form. However, the long siphon that extends to the bottom of the picture is a feeding structure. After Burkholder et al. (1992).

While growing these in culture, Howard Glasgow was afflicted with short-term memory loss, mood swings, and neuromuscular impairment. Finally, he was so ill that he was not permitted to return to the culture facility for about six months. Even JoAnn Burkholder suffered from exposure to the cultures of dinoflagellates. At this point, she realized that the toxin could be transmitted through the air. In a display of remarkable courage, she installed appropriate isolation and exhaust equipment and protocols and continued working on this dangerous organism.

Although she had documented evidence to the danger of the dinoflagellate to human health as well as to fish, the North Carolina state agencies were either slow to respond or questioned her evidence. Even as recently as June of this year, the North Carolina Department of Environment, Health and Natural Resources issued the following statement:

There are no substantiated cases of humans who have been made ill by the Phantom Dinoflagellate, except for researchers who were breathing the toxins in a closed environment without proper protective equipment. The jury is still out on whether the dinoflagellate can make people in "real world" situations ill.

Why is a laboratory setting not "a real world situation"? [This sounds remarkably like the sandbagging of the tobacco industry for the past 50 years.] In fact, Burkholder and others did document characteristic oozing sores on local crabbers and on divers for the North Carolina Department of Transportation.

Burkholder identified as many as 19 to 24 different stages in the complex life cycle of the phantom dinoflagellate. This served to compound the difficulty in finding and identifying the phantom dinoflagellate.

Science was not equally receptive to the idea of an organism with so many stages to its life cycle. Particularly, several labs have taken issue with Burkholder that amoeboid stages even exist in dinoflagellates. They argue that the presence of amoebae in samples that already contain fish simply are common contaminants. Furthermore, the molecular data are equivocal to date. This phase of the phantom dinoflagellate story has yet to be completed.

PFIESTER PFIESTERIA
Classically, phycologists divided dinoflagellates into monads, rhizopods, coccals, capsals, and trichals based on morphology. During our studies of freshwater dinoflagellates we have observed and recorded stages transcendent among these forms.
-J. Popovsky and L.A. Pfiester (1990)

While working with the dinoflagellate, Burkholder sent samples to other phycologists. In particular, Karen Steidinger of the Florida Department of Environmental Protection and an expert on toxic dinoflagellates, realized that it was new to science and with Burkholder published its description with a new latin name, Pfiesteria picidida (Pfiester's fish eater).

Now, Pfiesteria has been found from the Gulf Coast to the Delaware Bay. It has also been seen in the Chesapeake Bay. Burkholder speculates it might appear in estuaries that are enriched by careless farming practices. She believes that the main culprit it North Carolina is the massive hog farming operation. I suspect that Pfiesteria could become a problem in estuaries that are enriched with nitrogen[4], regardless of the source. This intuition, too, comes from my experience with Lois Pfiester.

It is a fitting tribute to Lois Pfiester that one of the most enigmatic and complex dinoflagellates should be named for her. She pioneered the methods that Burkholder and Glasgow used in piecing together the life cycle.

Lois served the science as an active and prolific researcher and as President of Phycological Society of America. She was not only a mentor with regard to methods in science, but she was also a stellar teacher. She demonstrated again and again that students learn best when they discover science, not when they are told about it. She won the Regents' Award for Superior Teaching in 1986, the same year that she became a full professor at the University of Oklahoma.

Her legacy lives in the hundreds of undergraduates who were touched by her enthusiasm, in her graduate students and professional colleagues who were touched by her dedication and experience, and in her friends who were touched by her kindness.

-1997, revised 2005

References:

Barker, Rodney. 1997. *And the Waters Turned to Blood.* Simon & Schuster. New York.

Burkholder, JoAnn M. and Howard B. Glasgow. 2002. *The Life Cycle and Toxicity of Pfiesteria piscicida revisited.* Journal of Phycology. 38(6): 1261.

Burkholder, JoAnn M., Harold G. Marshall, Howard B. Glasgow, David W. Seaborn, and Nora J. Deamer-Melia. 2001. *The Standardized Fish Bioassay Procedure for Detecting and Culturing Actively Toxic Pfiesteria, Used by Two Reference Laboratories for Atlantic and Gulf Coast States.* Environmental Health Perspectives. 109(suppl 5):745-756.

Burkholder, JoAnn M., Edward J. Noga, Cecil H. Hobbs, and Howard B. Glasgow. 1992. *New 'Phantom' Dinoflagellate is the Causative Agent of Major Estuarine Fish Kills.* Nature 358:407-410.

Glasgow, Howard B., JoAnn M. Burkholder, Donald E. Schmechel, Particia A. Tester, and Parke A. Rublee. 1995. *Insidious Effects of a Toxic Esturine Dinoflagellate on Fish Survival and Human Health.* Journal of Toxicology and Environmental Health 46: 501-522.

Litaker, R. Wayne, Mark W. Vandersea, Steven R. Kibler, Edward J. Noga, and Patricia A. Tester. 2002. *Life Cycle of the Heterotrophic Dinoflagellate Pfiesteria piscicida* (DINOPHYCEAE). Journal of Phycology. 38: 442-463.

Litaker, R. Wayne, Mark W. Vandersea, Steven R. Kibler, Edward J. Noga, and Patricia A. Tester. 2002. *Reply to Comment on the Life Cycle and Toxicity of Pfiesteria piscicida Revisited.* Journal of Phycology. 38:1268-1272.

Pfiester, Lois A. and Jack R. Holt. 1978. *A Freshwater 'Red Tide' in Texas.* The Southwestern Naturalist 23(1): 103-110.

Pfiester, Lois A. and John J. Skvarla. 1979. *Heterothallism and Thecal Development in the Sexual Life History of Peridinium volzii (Dinophyceae).* Phycologia 18: 13-18.

Pfiester, Lois A. and Jiri Popovski. 1979. *Parasitic, Amoeboid Dinoflagellates.* Nature 279: 421-424.

---

[4] Some other sources claim that the addition of phosphate is the major cause.

Popovsky, Jiri and Lois A. Pfiester. 1982. *Life Histories of Stylodinium sphaera Pascher and Cystodinedria inermis (Geitler) Pascher (Dinophyceae), Two Freshwater Facultative Predator-Autotrophs.* Archiv fur Protistenkunde 125: 115-127.

Popovski, Jiri and Lois A. Pfiester. 1990. *Dinophyceae.* Band 6. Susswasserflora von Mitteleuropa. G. Fischer Verlag, Stuttgart.

Steidinger, Karen A., JoAnn M. Burkholder, Howard B. Glasgow, Cecil W. Hobbs, Julie K. Garrett, Earnest W. Truby, Edward J. Noga, and Stephen A. Smith. 1996. *Pfiesteria piscicida Gen. et Sp. Nov. (Pfiesteriaceae fam nov.), A New Toxic Dinoflagellate with a Complex Life Cycle and Behavior.* Journal of Phycology 32: 157-164.

Steidinger, Karen and Dee Fink. 1996. *Lois Ann Pfiester (1936-1992) Freshwater Microalgal Biologist and Ecologist.* In: Garbary, David J and Michael J. Wynne, eds. *Prominent Phycologists of the 20th Century.* Lancelot Press Limited. Hantsport, Nova Scotia. pp. 271-280.

Timpano, Peter and Lois Pfiester. 1986. *Observations on "Vampyrella Penula-Stylodinium sphaera" and the Ultrastructure of the Reproductive Cyst.* American Journal of Botany 73(9): 1341-1350.

Questions to Think About

1. What is the evidence that *Cyanomonas* caused the fishkill in Texas? What was the first suspect?

2. What is the evidence for the release of a toxin from *Cyanomonas*?

3. Who was Lois Pfiester?

4. What did Pfiester and Popovsky discover in a reservoir in Czechoslovakia? Why was it unusual?

5. What is a dinoflagellate? What is the typical life cycle of a dinoflagellate?

6. Who are JoAnn Burkholder and Howard Glasgow? What did they discover?

7. Why does the phantom dinoflagellate have to be cultured in a CDC level-3 facility?

8. Why is there no unanimous agreement on the nature of the phantom dinoflagellate?

9. Why do you think that the phantom dinoflagellate was named *Pfiesteria*?

10. Why are *Pfiesteria* and *Pfiesteria*-like organisms now being observed?

NIGHT LIGHTS

ASSATEAGUE ISLAND

The sea-shore is a sort of neutral ground, a most advantageous point from which to contemplate this world.

Henry David Thoreau

On October 3, 1997 I accompanied a group of students, former students, and faculty from Susquehanna University to camp on Assateague Island[5], a barrier island off the coast of Maryland (see Figure 2-19). The popularity of this annual event had grown through the years despite several not so pleasant encounters with nature. Last year we camped behind the main dune and endured gale-force north winds. The year before, we camped in the marsh and were descended upon by a plague of mosquitoes. This time, it seemed as though we were being rewarded for our patience with past years. The weather was warm and moderately calm, and there were few insects. Throughout the first evening, the sky continued to clear out under a dome of high pressure.

Phenomena such as weather occur on a global or regional scale. That is why particular predictions are difficult and require much data. At our scale, weather is manifest by the wind blowing sand, leaves and tent flaps that are in our range of vision and within our range of hearing. The temperature of the air, humidity or rain as it strikes our skin are all phenomena that we experience directly from one moment to the next. Such small scale phenomena from day to day and moment to moment collectively produce what we understand as climate.

That evening, another phenomenon at multiple scales began to unfold. The few clouds had begun to give way to a clearing sky with a cheerful red glow as the sunset. As I stood leaning against a picnic table, several of the students came running up to us shouting that the sea and sand were luminescent. I looked up to see a darkening sky and noticed that the moon, a thin crescent about to set soon after the sun, could not be causing an optical illusion by making the whitecap foam reflect its light.

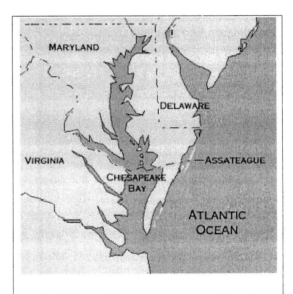

FIGURE 2-19. Assateague Island, a barrier island off the Delmarva Peninsula (from the National Park Service Brochure on Assateague Island).

I ran to the top of the main dune, and, as I stood on the walk that overlooks the beach, watched a magnificent sight of waves, glowing blue-green as they rose and crashed against the sand (see Figure 2-20). The sight was as magnificent as it was unexpected. We all converged on the beach with exclamations of wonder. We

---

[5] Read more about Assateague Island in *Islands and their Lessons in Biogeography.*

laughed. We shouted. Then, out loud, we began to ask what, how and why.

FIGURE 2-20. The glow of the waves visible with a one second exposure.

The backdrop of salt wind and the roar of the crashing waves made it a grand spectacle. Even more mysterious were ghostly glowing shapes that moved parallel to the beach beyond the surf.

It had been a long time ago since I had seen this kind of phenomenon, particularly of this magnitude. It was on Mustang Island, a barrier island near Corpus Christi, Texas. There, about 20 years ago, I saw the sea and sand glow in a similar way. Although it looked like magic or the aftermath of a nuclear waste spill, the *glowing sea* had the same biological cause, the of a bloom of a particular dinoflagellate [6] called *Noctiluca scintillans* (see Figure 2-21).

Noctiluca literally means "night light". This is a very good name for them because they can flash light when disturbed. This phenomenon is called bioluminescence, and it is scattered throughout the kingdoms of life. Although the phenomenon is not universal among dinoflagellates,

bioluminescence is common enough that the formal name for dinoflagellates in some taxonomic systems is Pyrrhophyta, a pair of Greek roots that mean "fire plants". Chemically, the mechanism for the generation of the light flash is essentially the same as that of fireflies.

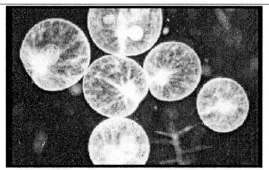

FIGURE 2-21. Microscopic view of *Noctiluca scintillans*, a dinoflagellate that can generate flashes of light.

Noctiluca is rather large as dinoflagellates go, sometimes exceeding 1mm. It is bladder-like with a single tentacle that it uses to capture food. Indeed, this organism, is like another dinoflagellate called *Pfiesteria*[7] in that it gets its food by eating other things rather than by making its food through photosynthesis. The flashes of light are tied closely to the rhythm of the day night cycle. During the day, they barely flash. At night, the intensity and frequency of flashes increases. This phenomenon persists, even when they are brought indoors and kept in constant darkness for several days. This kind of rhythm is called a circadian rhythm and has been studied extensively in dinoflagellates.

Occasionally, prevailing winds and water movements cause an abundance of them to be concentrated into a bloom. The concentration of billions of cells

---

[6] See the essay *Killer Algae* for more information about dinoflagellates.

[7] See *Killer Algae* for a more detailed explanation and description of *Pfiesteria*.

into a relatively small area made a phenomenon composed of single-celled microscopic organisms to become a very macroscopic wonder. That is what we had experienced on the beach at Assateague.

That answers the what and how. The answer to why is much more difficult. The prevailing view among those who study bioluminescent dinoflagellates is that the sudden flashes of light serve to scare away little zooplankton that feed on *Noctiluca* and other single-celled plankton.

JUPITER AND THE MILKY WAY
Even a small star shines in the darkness.
-Finnish proverb

The excitement on the beach began to die down after a time. I stayed for a long time and then began to walk back to camp, on the other side of the main dune. The night had become very clear and about as calm as it ever gets on a barrier island; so, conditions seemed perfect to look at the night sky with my small spotting scope. A student, Matt Wargo, who was much more adept at looking at the heavens than I, set up the scope and trained it on Jupiter. The giant planet was especially bright and nearly overhead. Students crowded around the telescope to get a quick glance at the planet as the rotation of the earth caused Jupiter to "move" across the field of the telescope. That evening the view of Jupiter was spectacular even with a spotting scope. I could resolve the banding of the clouds and see the great red spot.

I could also see three and sometimes four of the largest moons in orbit around the planet. They are called the Galilean moons because he saw them and interpreted their change in position as a product of their movement around Jupiter. He also suggested that Jupiter and its moons could serve as a model for the heavens in describing how the planets move around the sun.

Although Jupiter was impressive, the great band of the Milky Way was far more conspicuous. Galileo was also one of the first to train a telescope on the Milky Way and determine that the broad, glowing cloud was really made of many, many stars. We now understand that the Milky Way is our own galaxy seen from one arm of the great spiral disk that is about 100,000 light years across. (Our solar system is about 26,000 light years from its center).

The phenomenon of the glowing surf was the cumulative effect of billions of *Noctiluca* in a microscopic scale. The Milky Way was the cumulative effect of billions of stars on the cosmic scale. Still, both are manifest as similar phenomena at our scale, the one that I call the scale of the familiar. This is the scale at which nature makes its impressions on us. This is the scale at which we do not need to enhance or extend our senses.

Stars are enormous balls of glowing gas but are very far away, and, therefore, appear as small points of light. Even our sun, a star that is many times larger than the earth, appears to be no larger than the moon. However, the sun is 93 million miles away while the moon is only 250,000 miles away. To understand them, we must construct models that exist in our scale.

Even a celestial structure as small as our solar system cannot be appreciated directly. I can visualize it only in a scale model. Still, if all of the objects and distances are held to the same scale, the distance from the sun to the outer planets must be a kilometer before the model of Pluto emerges from a microscopic size.

I was struck by how impressed most of the students were with the Milky Way. Some had never seen it before. Most had lived in urban areas with lots of extraneous light where the excess light was sufficient to overpower the effect of the Milky Way. I knew how they felt. When I moved to Freeburg, Pennsylvania in 1982, extraneous light was minimal. I could walk out into my back yard and see the Milky Way. Now, there are four, large street lamps in the fair grounds across the street. My neighbors have more "decorative" outdoor lighting. This extra light blots out and overwhelms the Milky Way as well as most other celestial lights. This phenomenon can be seen from the other direction, too. From space, the cumulative effect of millions of human-produced lights shining at night cause large parts of our planet to glow.

Even on Assateague Island we were not immune to the problem of anthropogenic lights. On the second evening of our stay, we waited eagerly for the sunset because we were hoping to see a return of the glowing sea. However, on Saturday, there were many more people camping and fishing. Fires and lights were everywhere on the beach and in the campground. The sea may have been glowing, but we had no way of seeing it. Even the Milky Way was washed out and pale.

A NIGHT LIGHT

Between two worlds life hovers like a star, twixt night and morn, upon the horizon's verge. -Lord Byron

On October 17, two weeks after the Assateague camping trip, I traveled to Puerto Rico with Pat Nelson, two other faculty and a class of 12 students. We landed in San Juan in the early afternoon, got to the hotel, unpacked, and then met in the lobby for a trip to the northeastern corner of the island, to a place called Laguna Grande. As we drove to the east, the sunset and the sky blackened. We arrived at a protected bay with lots of small boats at anchor. There, we donned life jackets and got into kayaks to go through the mangrove swamps at night.

Although I had been in a canoe many times, I had never used a kayak-type double paddle before. That took some time to learn to use (I'm sure that the person who shared the kayak with me would insist that I never quite mastered it).

As we entered a narrow channel through the mangroves, the water began to glow blue with each paddle stroke. After a while, we entered a large lagoon surrounded by mangroves. There, the effect was most intense. We paddled to the middle of the lagoon, and one by one, we slipped into the water. Our movements caused the dinoflagellates to form a glowing boundary layer around us.

Although dinoflagellates, these organisms were very different from *Noctiluca*. They were called *Pyrodinium bahamense* (Greek for "fire-spinner of the Bahamas") and were more typical of dinoflagellates in their form[8]. That is, they moved by means of two flagella, one that encircled the cell in a groove causing the cell to spin as it moved. The other flagellum trailed behind the cell and pushed it along. Like many that I study, *Pyrodinium* was covered with overlapping armor plates. Although I

_____

[8] Go to Figure 2-14 for an image of a similar armored dinoflagellate.

knew of these characteristics, I could not see any of them at my scale in the water.

We swam and played in the water. We laughed and asked what, how and why. We saw many other sights and had many other experiences on that whole trip to Puerto Rico, but swimming with the dinoflagellates seemed to be the most impressive thing for the students and faculty alike (see Figure 2-22).

FIGURE 2-22. Swimming with *Pyrodinium bahamense.*

I pulled myself up onto the kayak and let my hand move lazily back and forth in the water. The agitation caused blue sparkles of light to appear. Then I saw the stars reflected in the water. Superimposed were dinoflagellates and stars, the microscopic and the cosmic together at my fingertips.

-1997

References:

Bixby, W. and G. de Santillana. 1964. *The Universe of Galileo and Newton. A Horizon Caravel Book.* American Heritage Publishing Co. New York.

Horiguchi, T. 1997. *Welcome to the World of Dinoflagellates.* //bio.bio.hokudai.ac.jp/~horig/Eng-Doccumentation/Dinophyceae.html.

Light Pollution Committee. 1997. Royal Astronomical Society of Canada. //www.rasc.ca/light/

Mlot, C. 1997. *The Rise in Toxic Tides. What's Behind the Ocean Blooms?* Science News 152(13): 202-204.

Taylor, F.J.R., ed. 1987. *The Biology of Dinoflagellates.* Blackwell Scientific Publications. Oxford.

Questions to Think About

1. What is the concept of scale and how does it relate to our day-to-day existence? How does it relate to our attempts to understand nature?

2. If the cause of the glow is a microscopic organism, how could it produce a glow bright enough and expansive enough to cause the beach and waves to luminesce?

3. Why do they glow?

4. How is the glowing sea related to the glowing sky?

5. What is the concept of light pollution?

6. How was the Laguna Grande experience similar to that of Assateague Island?

7. Can you think of other small-scale phenomena that manifest themselves at a larger scale?

EVIDENCE AND EINSTEIN'S BRAIN

COMMON MISCONCEPTIONS?

Well, all I know is just what I read in the papers.   -Will Rogers

Especially to a boy growing up in Oklahoma, those words by Will Rogers were everywhere. I'm not sure that I understood them, but I did know that adults used the phrase when they expressed how little they knew about a subject. I thought of that phrase when I pondered several news stories that caught my eye last summer. One reflects a careless and lackadaisical approach to the presentation of data as evidence for a theory about medical accidents. The other presents evidence for anatomical explanations of Einstein's genius with much more bold conclusions than those of the researchers who did the original work. Do these reflect common misconceptions about science, or scientific evidence? I think so, and I am sure that Will Rogers would agree with me.

EVIDENCE

…in science, as in criminology, we speak of discovering - rather than inventing or creating - evidence.   -Laura J. Snyder

Evidence for a theory comes mainly in two forms: explanation and prediction. Consider the question of the extinction of the dinosaurs [9]. It had been an enduring mystery for more than a hundred years. The discovery of Iridium (an element that is rare in the crust, but more common deep within the earth and in meteors) and shocked quartz (quartz grains that bear fine fracture lines as a

---

[9] Consult my essay *Impacts* for more complete background.

consequence of violent pressure like an atomic blast) at the K-T boundary suggested either extended, violent volcanic activity or a very large meteor struck the earth 65 million years ago.

Either scenario could have explained the extended and extreme environmental disruption necessary to cause mass extinctions. However, only the meteoric impact theory could explain the distribution of shocked quartz. Further, the meteoric impact theory predicted that there would be a crater about 180-200 km in diameter dated at about 65 million years old. The meteoric impact theory predicted that tektites would be distributed over much of the earth with the largest number and size near the crater.

A candidate for the crater was found at Chicxulub on the northern edge of the Yucatan peninsula. Independent laboratories dated it at 65+/-4 million years old. The pattern of destruction at the K-T boundary radiated out from that epicenter. So, the evidence best supported an impact theory for the mass extinction at the end of the Cretaceous Period. It was supported because an impact best explained what happened. It best explained shocked quartz, iridium, and the patterns of destruction. The prediction of and discovery of a crater with the appropriate age then clinched the impact theory as the best one.

LIES AND STATISTICS

He uses statistics as a drunken man uses lamp-posts - for support rather than illumination.   -Andrew Lang

Explanation in science does not allow or give equal credence to any and all speculation. A proper scientific explanation requires that the event be tied to physical laws and general, established theories. Sometimes those laws are statistical ones especially when associated with complex phenomena like weather or human health. However, those explanations can be distorted and often abused when part of a media presentation.

A front-page story for the Philadelphia Inquirer (*Sunday, September 12, 1999; 171:104*) was an investigative piece on medical errors or medical mistakes that translate into accidental deaths. The author intended to expose the medical profession as sloppy, careless, and a public menace. A large bar graph (see Figure 2-23) on the front page of the paper seemed to underscore that theme and lend empirical support.

That there were three times as many deaths from medical mistakes as from automobile accidents was a frightening statistic. That is, it was frightening until I began to look at the author's assumptions and methods in creating the numbers. The author had taken the information from the records of a single bankrupt hospital. She had defined all unexpected and procedure-related deaths to be accidental. She found that in 1996 there were 58 *accidental* deaths in that hospital. Then, she assumed that similar accidents occur at the same rate throughout all hospitals in the United States. Through a particular kind of voodoo, she came up with the estimate of 120,000 medically related accidental deaths (see Figure 2-23).

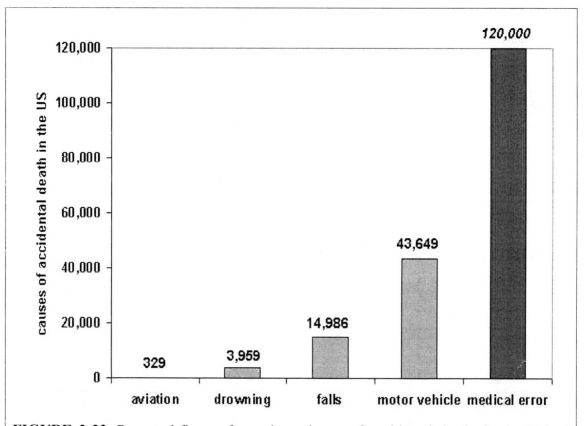

FIGURE 2-23. Reported figures for various classes of accidental deaths in the United States during 1996 with projected figures for accidental death due to medical accidents, a

projection based on accidents reported in one hospital. Adapted from the Philadelphia Inquirer (*Sunday, September 12, 1999; 171:104*)

The numbers for the other accident categories came from reported incidents. That is, they were not estimated values. However, those numbers juxtaposed with the estimated medical accidents served to lend a visual validity to the calculation.

Understand that extrapolation methods are useful and often necessary. However, scientists recognize the inherent error in the particular extrapolation and usually report a range of values. For example, estimates for the number of species on earth are extrapolations from spotty samples and can range from 5 to more than 100 million, an enormous range.

The difficulty with extrapolating from single (perhaps aberrant) events can be illustrated by the storm events here in central Pennsylvania for the past two weeks. Based on that, I could make the assumption that the frequency of flood-producing storms is about one per week. Therefore, I could extrapolate that central Pennsylvania should expect 52 flood-producing storms per year (That would keep FEMA busy).

Another important matter not addressed by the author of the newspaper article is that almost all of the people involved in "medical accidents" are at some medical risk anyway. Indeed, patients represent a high-risk group. Further, all medical procedures represent some level of risk to the patient. In most cases, however, the risk associated with performing the procedure is far lower than the risk associated with taking no action at all. Indeed, it would have been interesting to see the estimate of deaths if no medical procedures were performed.

As if extrapolation were not strong enough in supporting the argument, the paper gave a series of testimonials as solid proof. Often compelling, personal stories are subject to exaggeration and most cannot be corroborated or repeated. This kind of evidence, called anecdotal evidence, is rarely admitted into science as support. Personal anecdotes are stories, the kinds of "solid evidence" usually given in support of UFO's, bigfoot and lake monsters.

Certainly, no one questions that individuals can suffer personal tragedies when it comes to medical misfortunes. However, how these personal stories lend support to the assertion that deadly medical accidents are commonplace is beyond me or my imagination.

A DEATH IN 1955

I want to be cremated so people won't come worship at my bones. -Albert Einstein

On April 17, 1955 Albert Einstein died a not so accidental death due to aortic aneurysm in Princeton Hospital. He knew of the condition but refused corrective surgery. With his death immanent, he expressed the wish that his remains be cremated.

On the 18th of April, Thomas Harvey performed a routine autopsy on the body of Einstein. Then, the plot became quite bizarre after Harvey removed the old man's brain and preserved it (see Figure 2-24 for a labeled image of a human brain). At first the hospital supported Harvey's decision. He even convinced the Einstein family that the brain was too important to be incinerated and should be studied. However, Harvey never undertook a serious study of the brain, and he kept it as a holy relic in a jar in his office. Harvey even chose to be dismissed from the hospital rather than give up the artifact.

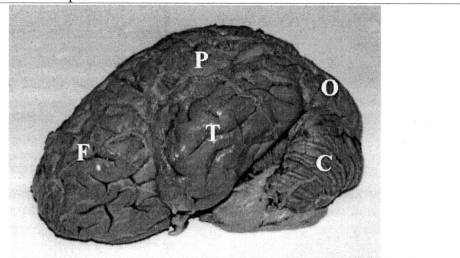

FIGURE 2-24. A photograph of a human brain with the Frontal (F), Parietal (P), Temporal (T) and Occipital (O) lobes of the cerebrum identified. C designates the cerebellar hemisphere. The parietal operculum lies within the parietal lobe.

This could have just remained a bizarre story except that Sandra Witelson, a neurobiologist at McMaster University in Hamilton, Ontario, prevailed on Thomas Harvey to allow her to study the brain. She compared that brain with 90 other normal brains that are housed at McMaster and discovered that there were unique features in the structure of Einstein's brain. On June 19, 1999, Witelson, Kigar and Harvey published their findings in the British medical journal, *The Lancet*.

Simply put, our brains are dominated by a convoluted region called the forebrain. This makes up most of the volume of mammalian brains and is associated with cognitive processing, among other things. Figure 2-24 shows the four lobes of the forebrain (frontal, parietal, temporal, and occipital lobes), the midbrain (cerebellar hemisphere) and the hindbrain (medulla).

The mid-line of the forebrain has a fissure that separates left and right frontal, parietal and occipital lobes.

Witelson reports that Einstein's brain was unusual in that the fissure separating the left and right parietal lobes was shallower than normal. In addition, Witelson noted that the parietal operculum, a structure within the parietal lobe, was missing in Einstein's brain. The volume normally occupied by the parietal operculum was taken up by more parietal lobe. Therefore, Einstein's parietal lobe was about 15% larger than it would have been if the parietal operculum were present.

Einstein said that the concepts related to relativity began to come to him after he asked himself what the world would look like if he were to ride on a beam of light[10]. In general, he tended to think in movements and images rather than in words. This kind of thinking served him well in his thought experiments.

---

[10] See my essay, *One Stone*, for a description of Relativity and its postulates

Modern brain research has produced enough evidence to suggest that various cognitive functions like language, mathematics, spatial relationships, etc. are compartmentalized. Indeed, mathematical and visuospatial cognition and imagery of movement appear to be centered in the parietal lobes. Thus, Witelson and her colleagues predicted that if Einstein's brain showed any deviation from the normal, it would be in the parietal lobes. Their observations and measurements supported their predictions. Curiously, Einstein had an unusually large head when he was born. Also, he did not begin to speak until he was three. The anatomical description of Einstein's brain helps to explain those anomalies. Thus, Witelson used both kinds of evidence, prediction and explanation, to support the localization theory of cognition.

There were several things that disturbed me about the news reports of the incident. By and large, they seemed to concentrate on the structure and how that determined or produced the scientific genius of Einstein. Even Witelson was very careful in pointing out how important environment is in conjunction with the anatomical features. After all, the ability to visualize problems would be very useful to a mechanic, an engineer, or a landscaper. I wonder how rare this ability of Einstein's really was or is.

ART AND SCIENCE

The values he (Einstein) cherished are the values of science no less than of ethics. I do not mean that one must be noble to be creative. I do mean that science as one of the glories of man is animated by the values of a decent society: the love of truth for its own sake,
respect for dissent, independence, free expression.

-James R. Newman

By and large, all general news articles about science ignore how remarkably creative the enterprise of science really is. In fact, it is as creative as art, literature, music, or dance. However, in this enterprise, scientists assume that there is an objective reality that is external to themselves, and that the objective reality is knowable.

This restriction is an important one. We discover, not create, aspects of nature. We use theoretical constructs to visualize unseeable entities like electrons, photons, genes, and the Earth's core. We can travel across time and space in our minds. In one way or another, we all wonder what the world would look like if we rode on a beam of light. Still, we look for real relationships, not those that we can fabricate to "prove our points" about accidental deaths or the determination of brain structure.

Certainly, Einstein was quite unusual, and he probably represented the limit of visuospatial ability in our species. Einstein saw forms interacting as he thought. He may have been more gifted than most, but all scientists do that to a certain degree as they seek and use evidence to understand nature.

- 1999; revised 2005

References:

Achinstein, Peter. 1994. *Explanation v. Prediction: Which Carries More Weight?* IN: Hull, Forbes & Burian, Eds. *PSA 1994 Vol. 2.* Philosophy of Science Association. East Lansing, Michigan.

Gerlin, Andrea. 1999. *Health Care's deadly Secret: Accidents Routinely Happen. Philadelphia* Inquirer. 171 (104; September 12, 1999).

Holton, Gerald. 1996. *Einstein, History, and Other Passions.* Addison-Wesley Publishing Co. New York.

McAllister, James W. 1996. *Beauty and Revolution in Science.* Cornell University Press. Ithaca, NY.

Newman, James R. 1963. *Science and Sensibility.* Anchor Books. Doubleday & Co., Inc. Garden City.

Paulos, John Allen. 1995. *A Mathematician Reads the Newspaper.* BasicBooks. New York.

Snyder, Laura J. 1994. *Is Evidence Historical?* IN: Snyder & Achinstein, eds. *Scientific Methods: Conceptual and Historical Problems.* Krieger Publishing Co. Malabar, FL.

Witelson, Sandra F., Debra L. Kigar, and Thomas Harvey. 1999. *The Exceptional brain of Albert Einstein.* The Lancet 353 (9170): 2149-2153.

Questions to Think About

1. What is a theory in science? How does it differ from a theory in common usage?

   Based upon evidence → not the other way round

2. What is the concept of evidence in science?

   Scientific explanation requires that the event be tied to physical laws

3. What was the problem with the graph published in the Philadelphia Inquirer?

   Estimated v. Scientific Values

4. Although compelling, why are anecdotes rarely admitted as scientific evidence?

   Extrapolation is bad

5. How does the story about Einstein's brain illustrate the use of evidence in science?

   Lots of extra research

6. What do you think about the statement by James Newman: *The values he (Einstein) cherished are the values of science no less than of ethics. I do not mean that one must be noble to be creative. I do mean that science as one of the glories of man is animated by the values of a decent society: the love of truth for its own sake, respect for dissent, independence, free expression.*

7. How does this match your understanding of science and how it works?

GAIA: SCIENCE, PSEUDOSCIENCE, OR FRUITFUL ERROR

AN INTERESTING SEMINAR

The Gaia Hypothesis, in acknowledging this atmospheric disequilibrium, has opted for physiology over miracles.
-Lynn Margulis

Have you ever heard of the Gaia Hypothesis? I must confess that I had heard of such a thing when I was a graduate student during the 1970's, but I had no idea what it was. Then about 12 years ago, Susquehanna University invited a ball of fire named Lynn Margulis to speak. She began by presenting a seminar to the Biology Department and a few students (no more than 10 of us, all told).

That talk was one of those defining moments in my professional life. She presented several ideas that were astonishing, and they all centered on cooperation among microbial species. She popularized the view (now generally accepted) that cells with nuclei (like yours) are bacterial communities. This concept has redefined the way that I look at living things and how I teach my courses on biological diversity. Indeed, the students hear "Lynn Margulis" at least once each class period.

At the end of her seminar, she began to talk about the Gaia Hypothesis, a view that the earth behaves as a superorganism. She began by presenting the Goldilocks Phenomenon, that is, Venus is too hot, Mars is too cold, but the Earth is just right. Why? She proposed that although Venus is closer to the sun than is Earth, the distance does not adequately explain why the surface temperature on Venus is high enough to melt lead. She said that the high temperature was a consequence of an atmosphere that was rich in greenhouse gasses.

Mars was similar in its atmospheric composition, but its smaller mass and smaller gravitational field allowed much of its atmosphere to slip away. So, not only is it farther from the sun than is Earth, but it has a much thinner atmosphere. Then, there is the Earth. It is "just right." Note that in atmospheric composition, surface temperature, and surface pressure, an Earth with life is very different from its sister planets or an Earth without life (see Table 1). Dr. Margulis suggested that the Earth was just right because life saved it from the fate of Venus. Thus, began her explanation of the Gaia Hypothesis.

VIKINGS AND DAISIES

The evidence gathered in support of Gaia is now considerable but as is often the way of science, this is less important than is its use as a kind of looking glass for seeing the world differently, and which makes us ask new questions about the nature of Earth.   -James Lovelock

Lynn Margulis talked about the originator of this theory, an eccentric independent scientist and inventor named James Lovelock. In the late 1950's he had gained a reputation for making devices to measure very small concentrations of gasses. NASA contracted him to work with them on several projects, including a lunar probe (in 1961) and, later, the Viking Lander for the exploration of Mars [11]. He became particularly interested in the Viking project because it was designed to search for life. He was charged to come up with instrumentation for the Viking Lander that would detect signs of life. He thought about the problem for some time and then realized that if life were present, the atmosphere should be full of its by products.

He considered the atmosphere of Earth as it contrasts with that of Mars. The Earth has an atmosphere with a collection of gasses that should not co-exist. How do oxygen and methane (natural gas) occur together? In fact, why is carbon dioxide so low on Earth when it is relatively high in the atmospheres of its sister planets? He estimated how much carbon dioxide would be in the atmosphere if all of the living things and all of the carbonate rocks were converted to gas. Then, he realized that the Earth would be a very different place (see Table 2-1). The atmosphere would be about 98% carbon dioxide. It would weigh about 60 times the present atmosphere. Also, the green house effect caused by so much carbon dioxide would produce a surface temperature between 240 and 340C! That is several times higher than the boiling point of water.

Lovelock then realized that the Earth behaved as a superorganism; that is, the Earth is alive. The atmosphere and the climate are not the consequences of geological processes, but are controlled by life. Just consider photosynthesis. In this process, plants (and other photosynthetic organisms) take in carbon dioxide, split water in the presence of light and produce sugar while releasing oxygen and locking away excess carbon

[11] See my essay, *Inferno and Purgatorio* for a more detailed explanation of the Viking mission.

as carbonates and other carbon-rich rock. This process over millions of years could have produced the oxygen-rich and carbon dioxide-poor atmosphere the earth has today. It also began to explain why such gasses could co-exist in an atmosphere. The air is a dumping ground for the by-products of life.

Lovelock used a spectroscope to analyze the major gasses on Mars; he saw that the gasses there were in chemical equilibrium. Therefore, the atmosphere of Mars was not being used as a dump for life. He then, confidently pronounced that there was no life on Mars. He remained the nay-sayer on the Viking project until 1975 when the Lander touched down on Mars, performed some experiments, and confirmed that, indeed, there was no life there.

If the early atmosphere was like that of a lifeless Earth, how did it provide a suitable site for the formation of life? That is, why didn't an intense greenhouse earth develop 3.5 billions years ago? Lovelock looked to research in stellar evolution for an answer. The "Faint Young Sun Hypothesis" estimated that our sun was about 25% cooler when it first ignited and has been warming slowly since then. A cooler sun would allow a planetary surface with liquid water even with an atmosphere of 98% carbon dioxide.

In the Gaian view, life evolved just in time. As life incorporated carbon to make its building blocks, the reservoir of atmospheric carbon dioxide was reduced. Then, prior to 3.2 billion years ago, the kind of photosynthesis that liberated oxygen evolved. The atmosphere and oceans began to have significant amounts of oxygen. This led to many other kinds of chemical changes in the atmosphere and the oceans.

TABLE 2-1. PLANETARY ATMOSPHERES: Composition by major gasses, surface pressure, and surface temperature for Venus, Earth, and Mars. Estimates for a lifeless Earth are also given. From Lovelock (1988).

	Venus	Earth No life	Earth As it is	Mars
carbon dioxide	96.5%	98.0%	0.03%	95.0%
nitrogen	3.5%	1.9%	79.0%	2.7%
oxygen	trace	0.0	21.0%	0.13%
methane	0.0	0.0	1.7ppm	0.0
pressure	90bars	60bars	1bar	0.0064bars
surface temperature	459C	240-340C	13C	-53C

What is central to the Gaian view in this story is that life acts as a kind of thermostat for the planet. When the planet warms up, more of the surface can harbor life (rather than be frozen out of the poles). The increased life then pumps down carbon dioxide. That causes the atmosphere to hold less heat and the planet cools down. So, Lovelock envisaged this kind of passive control with cycles of many millennia.

In some of his early tests of Gaia, Lovelock wrote a computer program called Daisyworld (see Figure 2-25). This world is very simple. It has two species of daisies, a black daisy and a white daisy. In this world, the atmosphere is similar to that of Earth

Consider a thought experiment. Place a white piece of paper and a black piece of paper on a lawn at mid-day during the summer. What do you suppose will happen (assume that there are no clouds)? Which one will be warmer to the touch in 30 minutes? The black paper absorbs more light and therefore, more energy which it radiates as heat. Thus, the difference in albedo of the two substances can have a great impact on the differences in temperature.

with enough carbon dioxide to allow daisies to grow; however, carbon dioxide does not vary. Instead the relative growth of the two species of daisies can affect the planet's albedo (reflectance).

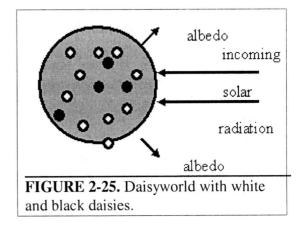

FIGURE 2-25. Daisyworld with white and black daisies.

According to Lovelock's initial conditions, daisies do not grow below 5C. They grow best at 20C, and they wilt and die above 40C. High temperatures favor white daisies and low temperatures favor black daisies. With these conditions in place, the temperature of Daisyworld remains fairly constant even when the amount of light from the sun increases from 60% to more than 120%.

Lovelock argued that if a simple system of two species with very simple interactions maintain constant conditions over such a wide range of solar luminosity, how much more capable Gaia would be to the task. She has between 5 and 30 million species, and uncounted numbers of individuals, all with very complex interactions.

James Lovelock suggested in a tongue-in-cheek way that Mars could be converted to an environment suitable for life with the following steps.

1. Begin by sending greenhouse gasses, particularly Chlorofluorocarbons (CFC's) and carbon tetrachloride to Mars with old Intercontinental Ballistic Missiles (ICBM's). These compounds are more than 10,000 times more powerful as greenhouse gasses than carbon dioxide.
2. After bases are established on Mars, tap into underground water and brine. Factories could begin to use that and other native materials and pump more greenhouse gasses into the Martian atmosphere.
3. Introduce microbial communities when the temperature stabilizes. The microbes should be engineered to withstand extremes in temperature. Also, they should be dark-colored like the black daisies to decrease the planet's albedo.
4. Then wait for millions of years.

Obviously, Lovelock was only partly serious when he proposed this idea. However, Lord Young of Britain has started a group called the Argo Adventurers whose mission is to terraform (make like Earth) Mars. It is a daunting task and one that is provided here on Earth for free.

GEOPHYSIOLOGY AND EARTH

The controversial hypothesis that the living earth can best be understood as a self-regulating biochemical system which controls, or at least strongly influences the mean state of the planet has stimulated recent research which might be called "geophysiology" or "biochemical climatology".

-Richard H. Gammon

James Lovelock worked on this theory that he came to call Gaia, after the Greek Earth mother goddess. He published some of his first articles about Gaia in the early 1970's, but he was met by silence from the academic community. Although it didn't help that he had named his theory after a goddess, there were (and remain) two major objections to Gaia. First, the Gaia Hypothesis seemed to give the Earth the ability to plan for the future or have a collective consciousness. Lovelock countered that Gaia can no more see into the future than a home thermostat does. Like the thermostat, Gaia simply responds to changes in a mechanistic way. Sometimes Gaia makes mistakes, and the thermostat is reset, as it is during an ice age.

The second objection came from evolutionary biologists who asked how could Gaia change or evolve? If the Earth really is a superorganism, how can there be natural selection in a population of one? He and Lynn Margulis answered that Gaia is a complex community. Those species (including our own) that do not tend to expand life on the planet are cast out by the Gaian community and become extinct.

A few reputable scientists, most notably Lynn Margulis began to take his theory seriously. Margulis understood that the Gaian view was a view of a global microbial community. In her view, the planet is governed by microbial metabolism and that the atmospheric gasses (including higher than expected oxygen and methane and lower than expected carbon dioxide levels) could be explained as a consequence of the global microbial communities functioning as a single organism. More and more Lovelock began to view the planet as a living, but constantly changing entity. He said that Gaia really represents a way of studying the physiology of the Earth; therefore, he called this study Geophysiology.

Lovelock (1988) said that Gaia includes the following postulates:

1. Living organisms that grow vigorously, and exploit any environmental opportunities that open.
2. Organisms are subject to the rules of Darwinian natural selection: the species of organisms that leave the most offspring survive.
3. Organisms affect their immediate physical and chemical environments. For example, animals change the atmosphere by breathing: taking in oxygen and letting off carbon dioxide. Plants and algae do the reverse. In numerous other ways, all forms of life incessantly modify their immediate physical and chemical environments.
4. Life is constrained within certain limits. The environment can be too hot or too cold; with a preferred temperature range for each species. Likewise, the environment can be too acid or too alkaline. Almost all chemicals have a range of concentrations that are tolerated or required for life. For some elements like iodine, selenium and iron, too much is a poison and too little causes starvation. Pure uncontaminated water

will support little; but neither will the saturated brine of the Dead Sea.

Gaia or Geophysiology finally came into its own with a conference devoted entirely to the concept in March 1988 at an American Geophysical Union conference in San Diego. Stephen Schneider of the National center for Atmospheric Research, Glenn Shaw of the University of Alaska and Penelope Boston of NASA served as the convenors of the meeting. They began their proposal for this conference with the following statement:

A question of fundamental intellectual importance to the geosciences is whether the earth's climate is regulated. The Gaia Hypothesis, introduced by Jim Lovelock from England and Lynn Margulis from the united States, surmises that interaction between the biota and the physical and chemical environment is of large enough intensity to serve in an active feedback capacity for biogeoclimatological control. On the other hand, geochemical arguments have been advanced to explain many of the environmental changes over geological time, regardless of the contribution of life. Clearly, the possibility of active climatic regulation systems and the relative importance of feedback processes between organic and inorganic components need to be examined in a frank, interdisciplinary setting.

At that point, Gaia entered the larger conversation of science.

LIFE & THE LIVING EARTH
The earth is more than just a home, it's a living system and we are part of it.
                                    -James Lovelock

In his March 1996 essay for Natural History, Stephen Jay Gould reported some amazing data for bacteria and where they grow on this planet. The bacteria of the deep oceanic vents called black smokers tolerate temperatures several times the boiling point of water. In the laboratory some of them were heated to more than 600F at a pressure of 265 atmospheres, and they survived!

He also reports the research of Tom Gold of Cornell University, who believes water that percolates deep within the crust and the upper 3 to 6 miles supports a thriving microbial community [12]. This is not a trivial handful of bacterial cells. Gold estimates that the underground biomass of bacteria approaches 2×10^{14} tons. That is enough to cover the entire land mass 5 feet deep with bacterial cells. If true, that represents far more life than exists on the surface. Gold, then defines the skin of the living Earth, a planet that is alive in a real sense. In some ways this confirms the Gaian view that the Earth is alive, and particularly the view of Lynn Margulis that Gaia is a microbial community. However, if Gaia operates in planetary regulation, then most life does not care if the mean surface temperature is 13C. It could be much hotter (or colder) on the surface and the subterranean bacteria would be just fine. Perhaps Lovelock's 4 attributes of Gaia need to be modified.

Lovelock himself proposed that his idea might be in error when he began one of his chapters with a quote from Vilfredo Parteo (in a comment on Kepler), *"Give me a fruitful error any time, full of seeds, bursting with its own corrections."* Clearly, the Gaia

---

[12] See my essay, *Origins,* for more about Tom Gold and implications of his views.

Hypothesis or Geophysiology is not pseudoscience, regardless how it is portrayed in the popular press and Saturday morning cartoons. It has started a serious conversation between evolutionary biologists, biogeochemists, ecologists, and climatologists. As an idea, Gaia has sparked questions that would not have been answered. So far it has been fruitful. It is too early to judge if the Gaia Hypothesis is in error.

-1997, revised 2004

References:

Goody, R. 1995. *Principles of Atmospheric Physics and Chemistry.* Oxford University Press. New York.

Gould, S.J. 1996. *This View of Life: Microcosmos.* Natural History 105(3):20ff.

Gribbon, J. 1990. *Hothouse Earth, The Greenhouse Effect and Gaia.* Grove Weidenfeld. New York.

Joseph, L.E. 1990. *Gaia, The Growth of an Idea.* St. Martin's Press. New York.

Kirchner, James W. 1989. *The Gaia Hypothesis: Can it be Tested?* Reviews of Geophysics 27 (2): 223-235.

Lovelock, J. 1979. *Gaia, A new Look at Life on Earth.* Oxford University Press. new York.

Lovelock, J. 1988. *The Ages of Gaia, A Biography of our Living Earth.* Bantam Books. New York.

Lovelock, J. 1988. *The Earth as a Living Organism.* In: Wilson, E.O., ed. *Biodiversity.* National Academy Press. Washington D.C. pp 486-489.

Lovelock, J. 1991. *Healing Gaia, Practical Medicine for the Planet.* Harmony Books. New York.

Margulis, L. 1997. *A Pox Called Man.* In: L. Margulis and D. Sagan. *Slanted Truths, Essays on Gaia,*

Symbiosis, and Evolution. Springer-Verlag. New York. Pp. 247-261.

Margulis, L. and D. Sagan. 1986. *Microcosmos, Four Billion Years of Microbial Evolution.* Touchstone Books. New York.

Margulis, L. and G. Hinkle. 1997. *The Biota and Gaia.* In: L. Margulis and D. Sagan. *Slanted Truths, Essays on Gaia, Symbiosis, and Evolution.* Springer-Verlag. New York. Pp. 207-220.

Margulis, L. and J.E. Lovelock. 1997. *The Atmosphere as Circulatory System of the Biosphere – The Gaia Hypothesis.* In: L. Margulis and D. Sagan. *Slanted Truths, Essays on Gaia, Symbiosis, and Evolution.* Springer-Verlag. New York. Pp. 127-143.

Margulis, L. and Oona West. 1997. *Gaia and the Colonization of Mars.* In: L. Margulis and D. Sagan. *Slanted Truths, Essays on Gaia, Symbiosis,* *and Evolution.* Springer-Verlag. New York. Pp. 221-224.

Sagan, D. and L. Margulis. 1993. *God, Gaia, and Biophilia.* In: Kellert, S.R. and E.O. Wilson, eds. *The Biophilia Hypothesis.* Island Press. Washington D.C. pp 345-364.

Sagan, D. and L. Margulis. 1997. *Gaia and Philosophy.* In: L. Margulis and D. Sagan. *Slanted Truths, Essays on Gaia, Symbiosis, and Evolution.* Springer-Verlag. New York. Pp. 145-157.

Sagan, D. and L. Margulis. 1997. *A Good Four-Letter Word.* In: L. Margulis and D. Sagan. *Slanted Truths, Essays on Gaia, Symbiosis, and Evolution.* Springer-Verlag. New York. Pp. 201-206.

Trefil, James and Robert Hazen. 2000. *The Sciences, An Integrated Approach.* 3rd Edition. John Wiley & Sons, Inc. New York.

Questions to Think About

1. What is the Gaia Hypothesis?

   Earth is alive

2. Who are Lynn Margulis and James Lovelock?

   US   UK

3. Why did Lovelock suppose that Mars was devoid of life before the Viking lander even went there?

   Atmosphere isn't full of byproducts

4. What is the Daisyworld thought experiment? What does it demonstrate?

   White v black daisies, Earth controls

5. What is the importance of Table 1? What does it illustrate about the Gaia concept?

   Earth gave us ability for life

6. What are positive and negative feedback mechanisms? How do they work? Which one describes a thermostat?

   negative - mistake/reset

7. How could Mars be terraformed?

   CFCs, plants, ammonia, trees, wait

8. What are Lovelock's four postulates of Gaia?

   1) orgs grow   3) orgs affect environment
   2) Darwin   4) life limits

9. Why have scientists been slow to accept Gaia as a scientific theory?

   Seems crazy, new

10. What is Tom Gold's hypothesis about the norm for the location of life? What implications might it have for a Gaian explanation? What implications might it have for the exploration of Mars?

    water percolates, millions of bacteria - supports next on
    could be stuff under surface

11. Comment on the statement by Vilfredo Parteo (in reference to Kepler), "*Give me a fruitful error any time, full of seeds, bursting with its own corrections.*" How does it describe the scientific process?

    one of error

PSEUDOSCIENCE, THE SCIENCE OF THE GULLIBLE

A U.F.O.

As amusing as some of pseudoscience may seem, as confident as we may be that we would never be so gullible as to be swept up by such a doctrine, we know it's happening all around us.-Carl Sagan

When I was in Junior High School, I had a friend whose oldest brother had procured a weather balloon. The balloon was silvery and even looked impressive in the box. I was invited to the launch of the balloon. Because I was a spectator, I don't remember many details except that we went to the banks of the Arkansas River. The sun had just set and there was a heavy, humid sweetness in the air. That meant that the breeze was blowing toward the oil refineries across the river.

In preparation for the launch, someone had made a platform that hung from the balloon and held several (4, I think) flares. The balloon was inflated, the flares were lit and the balloon rose quickly with its silvered sides reflecting the flares so that it appeared to have blinking lights on its sides. We were wrapped in awe at our accomplishment and stood in silence as the shining object danced in the darkening sky.

Suddenly, a man came driving up, jumped out of his car and ran down the sand path toward us. He was pointing and shouting. At first we thought that he was angry with us, and then we realized that the balloon was the focus of his attention. When he was close enough, I heard him shout, "Boys! Boys! Look at that. Up there. That's a U.F.O. I know. I'm a pilot." We said nothing that would convince him otherwise. All of us watched the "U.F.O." as it moved over the city of Tulsa. It seemed to circle the tallest building and then vanished into the clouds. The pilot cursed his luck at not having a camera. He left convinced that he had witnessed a close encounter with space aliens.

We were wild with delight at our good fortune. In our zeal to make some wonderful contrivance, we created a U.F.O. and a mystery. What was better, only we knew the answer to the mystery.

Now, I reflect on that event of nearly 30 years ago. I am surprised that the pilot was so gullible. Why did he assume that the object was an alien space ship? Why didn't he assume a more rational explanation? I consider the same question as I flip through the channels on cable TV. Consider serious documentaries about lake monsters, big foot, and alien abductions. There is even a Psychic Friends Network (Its something to watch if you find yourself up wandering around at 3 in the morning). Why are more rational explanations not even considered? For example, if a large *Plesiosaur* is in Loch Ness, it must exist in a population of such creatures. Now, if the species breathes air, it would be impossible for it to remain hidden. Anyway, why would such a large aquatic animal be so reclusive? But the Loch Ness monster is a mystery, and we love mysteries...even if there is a more rational and simpler explanation. Sometimes its just fun to be gullible.

Carl Sagan described our penchant to accept irrational solutions as our demon-haunted world. This, his newest book, is a look at pseudoscience, particularly nonsense about alien abductions. As we accept irrational solutions, our universe is ruled more and more by demons of the imagination.

Scientists are trained to be skeptics[13]. They are trained to look for alternative explanations. The real danger of pseudoscience is that it blunts the effectiveness of scientific skepticism in the eyes of the public. Particularly when wild claims like the Loch Ness monster and alien abductions are explained by phrases like: ANYTHING IS POSSIBLE. Any scientist knows that anything is not possible.

Well, if scientists are such skeptics and doubt everything, how can they accept any explanations? They follow a set of methods that are based on the observation of the phenomenon. Then, they consider explanations and alternative explanations. Those ideas or hypotheses that seem most likely are tested by experiment (or some other test). This way scientists can reject or eliminate possibilities and thus provide stronger support for the hypotheses that remain.

Sometimes the pseudoscientist tries to appear in the disguise of the skeptical scientist. Consider the problem that many public school districts face today with regard to evolution. Some schools are required to say that evolution is only a theory and that alternative explanations should be considered. In particular, the schools require that Creation Science be given equal time. The truth of the matter is that the theory of Creation Science was considered as an explanation, and it was rejected *more than 135 years ago*. Indeed, it is intellectually dishonest to present evolution (the unifying principle of the science of biology) and creation science as alternative explanations.

This kind of intellectual dishonesty is very evident in the struggle to present information about cigarettes and cancer. In 1953 (the same year that Watson and Crick published the structure of DNA), the first report that made the connection between cigarette tar and cancer was reported. The work was fairly simple. All mice in the study had a patch of hair shaved from their backs. Half of the mice were painted with cigarette tar and the other half (the control group) were untreated. The untreated group showed no tumors while the treated group showed a very high rate of malignancies.

Of course, tumors on the backs of mice are very different from tumors in the lungs of people. In a series of publications in the 1960's, British researcher Richard Doll confirmed the connection between smoking cigarettes and lung cancer. The tobacco companies countered with a campaign to cast doubt on the results (while their own researchers were confirming Doll's research). Their alternative explanation was that people who are compelled to smoke also have a genetic weakness that induces lung cancer (thus, tobacco smoke does not cause cancer, and the companies are blameless). Although the scientific community rejected such a convoluted hypothesis, the tobacco companies preyed upon the gullibility of the public and kept this alternative explanation alive in the halls of congress.

Now, even the most conservative researchers estimate that nearly 400,000 deaths per year can be attributed to cigarette smoking in the United States alone. According to the World Health Organization, that number increases to nearly 3 million deaths world-wide. In the words of Carl Sagan, "Gullibility kills."

---

[13] Read more about the philosophy of skepticism in *Succession in a Skeptic's Garden*.

INTO THE GREENHOUSE

Increasing numbers of climate experts have recently concluded that the "signature" of man-made global warming has been detected. -Carl Sagan

The question of global warming[14] is much more complex than that of smoking. This is based on the assumption that the atmosphere and its constituent gasses determine how much heat the earth's surface traps. Thus, the atmosphere acts like a blanket and helps to trap heat.

How can the atmosphere work that way? Well, the gasses in the air are mostly clear so that little light coming from the sun is absorbed. However, after the light hits objects on the earth's surface, some of it is reflected as light and can escape back into space. The absorbed light is reemitted from the surface as heat or infrared radiation which is absorbed by certain gasses in the atmosphere. As gasses absorb energy, they warm up. So, the atmosphere warms up just like a greenhouse or a car with its windows rolled up in bright sunlight (see Figure 2-26).

The gasses that are most effective at absorbing heat are carbon dioxide, water vapor, methane, and CFC's. Most of the atmosphere is made of nitrogen and oxygen, gasses that do not function in the "greenhouse effect." Thus, most heat absorption is done by a few, relatively rare gasses. Even so, the planet would be about 60F (-20C) cooler

than it is if there were no greenhouse gasses.

Water vapor is the most abundant greenhouse gas and accounts for more than 70% of the trapped heat. You can observe its influence directly. Consider the temperature on a clear, calm night in mid winter. Without a cloud layer to trap and hold heat, much of it radiates to space and the night cools. However, if there is a cloud cover, the night will not cool as quickly.

Carbon dioxide accounts for about 10-12% of the greenhouse effect. That would seem minor compared to water. However, water varies according to relative humidity and readily evaporates into the atmosphere from the oceans and other reservoirs (recall the hydrologic cycle). Thus, we can have little impact on the amount of water in the atmosphere. But we seem to be able to have an impact on the amount of carbon dioxide in the atmosphere. Estimates are that the atmosphere contained about 280 parts per million (ppm) carbon dioxide prior to the industrial revolution. In 1995, the atmosphere contained about 360ppm carbon dioxide. It seems that the extra 80ppm carbon dioxide is a consequence of burning fossil fuels like coal and gasoline.

Some atmospheric scientists like Stephen Schneider believe that there is a connection between the increased carbon dioxide and an increased temperature of about 0.6C over the past 100 years. Indeed, Klaus Hasselmann, director of the Max Planck Institute for Meteorology claims that there is a 95% chance that the temperature rise over the past 100 years is due to an increase in carbon dioxide. If this is correct, increased burning of fossil fuels could have an even greater impact on climate in the next 100 years.

---

[14] I wrote this essay in 1996. Since then, the evidence for climate change has been mounting and discussed in other essays: *Gaia: Science, Pseudoscience , or Fruitful Error; Red Planets and Microbes;* and *Clouds: The Keys to Understanding Climate, Weather, and the Hydrologic Cycle.*

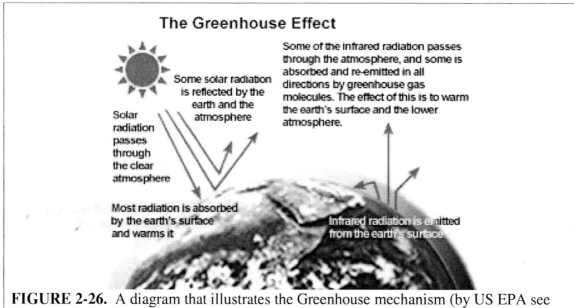

The Greenhouse Effect

Some solar radiation is reflected by the earth and the atmosphere

Solar radiation passes through the clear atmosphere

Some of the infrared radiation passes through the atmosphere, and some is absorbed and re-emitted in all directions by greenhouse gas molecules. The effect of this is to warm the earth's surface and the lower atmosphere.

Most radiation is absorbed by the earth's surface and warms it

Infrared radiation is emitted from the earth's surface

FIGURE 2-26. A diagram that illustrates the Greenhouse mechanism (by US EPA see http://www.epa.gov/globalwarming/climate/index.html).

For every temperature rise of 1C, a global line of equal temperature will move north about 200 miles. That means that the climate in Selinsgrove will be about like that of Richmond, Virginia. The current computer-generated scenarios predict a global temperature rise of 0.8-3.5C by 2100.

What is the support for the global warming hypothesis? As of 1996[15]:

1. The 10 warmest years in the past 100 years have been since 1980 (see Figure 2-26).
2. The warming of the central Pacific (an event called El Nino) is longer and more frequent (in the past they occurred every 3-7 years and lasted 12-18 months). The last El Nino lasted from 1991 to the middle of 1995.
3. Last year a piece of the Antarctic ice sheet the size of Rhode Island broke away and floated into the south Atlantic.

4. Siberia is now warmer than at any time since the Medieval Period.
5. Northern Europe has experienced a string of warm winters and severe winter storms.
6. Alpine glaciers have been retreating and have exposed ice and rocks that have been buried for thousands of years.
7. India has experienced devastating heat waves in recent years.
8. The orbiting radar gun has detected an annual rise in sea level of about 3mm. This should happen if the oceans warm and expand as they heat up.
9. Recent analysis of records that go back to the 13th century shows that the onset of the seasons was remarkably constant until around 1940 when a significant shift began to occur.
10. The past 5 years have witnessed a string of weather-related disasters on a global scale. That includes the most active hurricane season since the 1930's.

---

[15] The list of supporting evidence has grown very long since 1996. JH (2005)

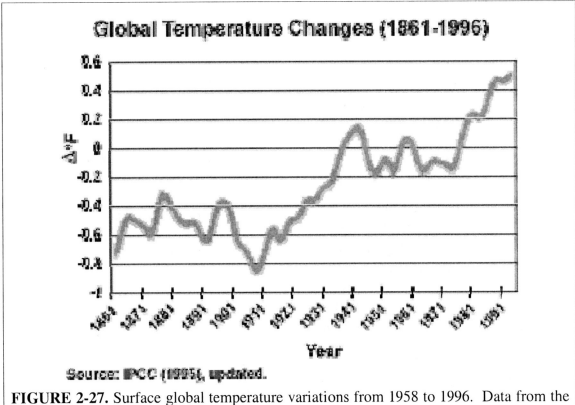

FIGURE 2-27. Surface global temperature variations from 1958 to 1996. Data from the US EPA. http://www.epa.gov/globalwarming/climate/index.htm

Certainly, some of these observations can be explained by alternate hypotheses. However, these are not "Just So" stories. Ten years ago presentations of global warming theories were presented in a very cautious way. In the past three years I have become a little alarmed at the almost matter-of-fact certainty with which the scientists present scenarios of climate change. Like the scientific community, insurance companies are becoming interested in the question of global warming. The risks of economic and political instability as a consequence of changes in climate are too great to ignore.

It is curious that the strongest recent evidence for the connection between rare atmospheric gasses and global climate comes from a cooling event. In June 1991 Pinatubo, a volcano in the Phillipines, erupted explosively and sent 25-30 million tons of sulfate aerosol into the upper atmosphere. Jim Hansen, head of the NASA Goddard Institute for Space Studies, predicted that the eruption would cause a cooling of 0.5C compared with the year before Pinatubo. Satellite-measured temperatures of the lower atmosphere confirmed a depression of 0.6C compared with 1991.

I again look at an editorial in the local paper dated February 11, 1996. The author claims that global warming is a myth perpetrated by academics who promote themselves and get grants by predicting disasters.

When I consider questions of global warming, I have to keep asking myself, "Am I looking at a weather balloon or a U.F.O? Am I gullible when it comes to the question of global warming? Is global warming an appropriate, rational explanation for recent climatic events and trends? Perhaps, but if I am to be turned from this point of view, it will be by rational argument and appropriate interpretation of observations. I'll not allow the demons of pseudoscience to capture me.

-1996

References:

Easterbrook, G. 1995. *A Moment on the Earth, the Upcoming Age of Environmental Optimism.* Penguin Books. New York.

Flavin, C. 1996. *Facing Up to the Risks of Climate Change.* In: L. Brown et al. *State of the World 1996.* W.W. Norton and Co. New York. pp 21-39.

Goody, R. 1995. *Principles of Atmospheric Physics and Chemistry.* Oxford University Press. New York.

Kerr, R.A. 1993. *Pinatubo Global Cooling on Target.* Science 259: 594.

Monastersky, R. 1995. *World Climate Panel Charts Path for Action.* Science news 148: 293.

Monastersky, R. 1996. *1995 Captures Record as Warmest Year Yet.* Science News 149: 23.

Monastersky, R. 1996. *The Loitering El Nino: Greenhouse Guest?* Science news 149: 54.

Paulos, J.A. 1995. *A Mathematician Reads the Newspaper.* BasicBooks. New York.

Pendick, D. 1996. *Hurricane Mean Season.* Earth 5(3): 24-32.

Sagan, C. 1995. *The Demon-Haunted World, Science as a Candle in the Dark.* Random House. New York.

Trefil, James and Robert Hazen. 1995. *The Sciences, An Integrated Approach.* John Wiley & Sons, Inc. New York.

Zimmer, C. 1995. *El Grande.* Discover 16(1): 68.

Questions to Think About

1. What is pseudoscience? Why is it more like a religion?

   Cult following

2. Why is UFology a pseudoscience?

   Not real

3. How can pseudoscience be dangerous?

   blunts skepticism

4. How does the greenhouse effect work?

   like a greenhouse

5. What is the most effective greenhouse gas in the atmosphere?

   CO_2 Water

6. What evidence as of 1996 suggested that anthropogenic greenhouse gasses were producing a warming, then called Global Warming?

   warm years, el Niño ↓ Ice blocks, Siberia

7. How did the eruption of Mount Pinatubo in 1991 serve to confirm some of the predictions concerning global warming?

   0.5°C change predicted

8. In what ways are scientists skeptics?

   Doubting. Socratic method

RED PLANETS AND MICROBES

A ROCK FROM MARS[16]

Although there are alternative explanations for each of these phenomena taken individually, when considered collectively...we conclude that they are evidence for primitive life on early Mars.
    -David McKay et al. 1996

Last May I celebrated my 50th birthday while working on a project at Johnson Space Center (JSC) in Houston. The project involved adapting some of the center's materials for use in my courses. To augment our visit there, the staff at JSC had gone all out to provide us with an education by tours and a parade of speakers.

It so happened that on the day that I turned 50, I sat in a conference room (the same room that the Mercury, Gemini, and Apollo astronauts gave their first press conferences after quarantine) to hear Dr. David McKay speak (Figure 2-28). This was the man who in 1996 led the team that announced the evidence of possible life from examination of a meteorite that had come from Mars.

I was thrilled when McKay entered the room and placed a piece of the very same meteorite on the table in front of me. He then began his talk by carefully laying out the evidences for the meteorite coming from Mars and then the telltale signs of life that he and his team detected in it. The most compelling bits of evidence, however, came from scanning electron microscopic examination that revealed structures, which could have been fossils of bacteria (see Figure 1-4).

origin. Structures appeared to be rods and filaments of cells. Such fossils have been found on earth. Indeed, I have some

---

[16] This essay expands on information in *On a Performance of Durufle.*

of them in a siliceous rock of the Gunflint chert from the northern shore of Lake Superior in southern Ontario, Canada (see Figure 2-29).

FIGURE 2-28. David McKay at Johnson Space Center, May 2001.

FOOD AND HISTORY

Unlike neighboring Mars and Venus, whose atmospheres settled down to become stable chemical mixtures of carbon dioxide, the Earth had gotten energized.
    -Lynn Margulis and Dorian Sagan, 1986

The Gunflint Chert was discovered by Elso Barghoorn and Stanley Tyler in the 1950's, but the discovery languished in Barghoorn's lab until he was pushed to publish when Preston Cloud threatened to scoop him in the 1960's. The discovery and clear presentation of bacterial fossils in the gunflint chert pushed direct evidence of life back to about 2 billion years ago, well into the Proterozoic Era (see Table 2-2).

Most fossils come from the last half billion years of earth's 5 billion year history, an eon called the Phanerozoic. As ancient as trilobites and their associates in the Cambrian Period may seem, they appeared after more than 85% of earth's history had elapsed. The dinosaurs came much later than that.

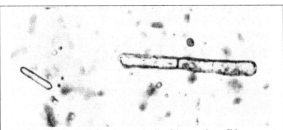

FIGURE 2-29. A rod (left) and a filament of cells (right) from a thin section of the Gunflint Chert.

The earliest eon, the Hadean, was marked by a time of heavy meteor bombardment as the planetary bodies accreted, and the earth-moon system appeared. High energy impacts repeatedly liquefied the earth's surface allowing lighter elements to float to the surface and accumulate there. As the bombardment abated, the surface solidified, and atmospheric gasses and liquid water began to accumulate.

The next eon, the Archean, was marked by the presence of land masses, oceans, and a stable atmosphere. It was during this era that life likely began. The Proterozoic Eon saw increasingly complex forms of bacteria arise (By complex, I mean physiological rather than structural complexity).

Perhaps the most important physiological pathway to evolve was that of oxygenic (oxygen-producing) photosynthesis. Recall that the process of photosynthesis used light energy to convert inorganic substances to food. By and large, the energy within food was stored in the carbon-hydrogen bond. Thus, the production of food required an inorganic carbon source like carbon dioxide (CO_2) and a hydrogen source like water (H_2O).

Chlorophyll absorbs light energy to power the process of reducing carbon dioxide (The process of making food is a reduction process in which electrons, or hydrogens, are added to carbon. Conversely, respiration is an oxidation process in which hydrogens or electrons are stripped from food to provide for metabolic energy). Special proteins called enzymes mediate the whole process of photosynthesis and respiration. With a few modifications, the general pathway of photosynthesis is the reverse of the general pathway of respiration. This whole business of food production and food use is an important one to consider. Early life had organic compounds available through nonliving means (abiotic synthesis and additions from comets and meteors). That would have formed a limit to the amount of life possible on the earth and led to intense competition. In that do-or-die period, Bacteria invented (evolutionarily speaking) a variety of other food making pathways which persist today. Some glean energy from reduced inorganic compounds (chemosynthesis; this is the source of food in deep ocean thermal vents). Some use other sources of hydrogens along with a range of bacterial chlorophylls (bacteriochlorophylls) to make food [17]. With the advent of biologically-created food life could expand to much greater mass until particular elements such as nitrogen or phosphorus became limiting.

---

[17] One of the most common hydrogen sources for this kind of bacterial photosynthesis is hydrogen sulfide (H_2S). In this case, the resulting waste product is sulfur. Such organisms still exist and are abundant in high sulfur environments. They need light, carbon dioxide, and reduced sulfur. Also, they need an environment with little or no oxygen.

TABLE 2-2. An Abbreviated Geological Time Scale.

EON	BILLIONS OF YEARS AGO
PHANEROZOIC	0 - 0.59
PROTEROZOIC	0.59-2.6
ARCHEAN	2.6-3.9
HADEAN	3.9-5.0

The switch to oxygenic photosynthesis seems to have begun around the time of the Gunflint fossils and likely evolved from a line of hydrogen sulfide bacteria. As a source of hydrogen, hydrogen sulfide was pretty good. The organism did not have to invest very much energy to wrench the hydrogens from sulfur. Unfortunately, hydrogen sulfide and similar reduced compounds also were in limited supply. For hydrogen-hungry microbes, water, one of the most abundant sources of hydrogen on earth, was an ideal solution. However, water required much more energy to separate its hydrogens from oxygen. Chlorophyll, slightly different from bacteriochlorophylls, could absorb sunlight energy at more energetic wavelengths and, therefore, succeeded in breaking apart water. Then, the microbes had to deal with water's toxic waste product, molecular oxygen.

Rocks from Gunflint times also testify to a change in the atmosphere. Iron, one of the most abundant elements on earth, shows striking differences when in reduced or oxidizing conditions. Iron in its oxidized form (Fe^{+3}) generally is insoluble and is reddish, or rust-colored. In its reduced form (Fe^{+2}), iron is quite soluble and is black or blue-black. Only when combined with the sulfide ion does reduced iron readily come out of solution. Then, it imparts a black or gray color to the rock. When oxidized, iron imparts a reddish color to rock.

Proterozoic aged rocks (beginning about 2.8 billion years ago) frequently show a peculiar banded iron formation (see Figure 2-30). This is alternating bands of black and red iron-rich rock. The interpretation is that molecular oxygen, released by oxygenic photosynthesis, built up and then combined with available iron. This continued for many millions of years until most of the elements with which oxygen could combine had been swept free. During this period the ocean (and planet earth) would have had a decidedly reddish cast. For a time, the earth was a large red ball.

MICROBIAL MATS

The Precambrian would have been a fascinating period for the cyanophytologist, since vast areas of stromatolitic rocks are known, hundreds of feet thick and hundreds of miles in extent.

-Thomas Brock, 1973

So, oxygen began to accumulate in the oceans and the atmosphere by Gunflint times. Curiously, the rise in oxygen was accompanied by an increase in the occurrence of stromatolites, pillow-like layered structures. Stromatolites came in a variety of sizes (ranging from a centimeter to meters across; see Figure 2-31), and generally were associated with limestone. In fact, they were the principle components of reefs until the advent of newcomers like red algae and corals.

FIGURE 2-30. Banded iron pebble (ca. 2.4 billion years old) collected by Ben Hayes in South Africa.

FIGURE 2-31. Models of stromatolites at Kew Gardens.

The stromatolite structure was the consequence of a whole microbial community. The upper-most part of it was populated by cyanobacteria like *Lyngbya*. These produced oxygen while a layer of photosynthetic sulfur bacteria beneath them (and safely out of the way of the oxygen) absorbed light not used by the cyanobacteria. Layers beneath them were populated by chemosynthetic and decomposer bacteria. Similar arrangements of microbes exist in structures called microbial mats. Still, stromatolites were much more than

platforms for microbial growth. They were made by the actions of the microbial community itself.

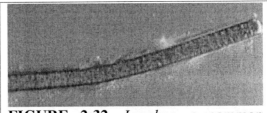

FIGURE 2-32. *Lyngbya*, a common cyanobacterium in microbial mats and stromatolites.

Cyanobacteria like *Lyngbya* often have an outer slime or mucilage coating. Figure 2-32 illustrates the filament and its slime outer covering with some debris caught in it. Now consider that these organisms take up carbon dioxide during the course of photosynthesis, and in so doing, they affect the solubility of calcium carbonate which causes it to precipitate out of solution [18]. So, in calcium carbonate rich waters, active photosynthesizers run the risk of encasing themselves in a tomb of limestone. Cyanobacteria can grow quickly but also many of the filamentous ones (like *Lyngbya*) can crawl out of their slime tubes and move toward the light. Thus, the stromatolite can be made layer by layer by the constituent members of its microbial community.

Consider the Gunflint chert again (see Figure 2-29). This was made in an environment rich in silica. Thus, organisms within the mat became preserved as fossils, an exceedingly rare event. Barghoorn, Tyler, and Shopf showed that the microbial community represented in the Gunflint was similar those that must have produced the more common (but barren of microbial fossils) limestone stromatolites.

---

[18] See *In Hot Water* for an explanation of this phenomenon.

FIGURE 2-33. A typical microbial mat in the salt marsh at Assateague Island.

FIGURE 2-34. Top a polished section of the Gunflint chert. Below is a prepared thin section from which I took the photograph of Figure 2-29.

The Gunflint Chert was the first reported incidence of precambrian microfossils. To date, they have been found in suitable precambrian rocks all over the world. In 1993 J. William Schopf reported the discovery of microbial fossils in the Apex Chert of Australia. These dated to about 3.5 billion years old. Stromatolites of a similar age have been found, also in Australia, although almost certainly they were made by communities that lacked cyanobacteria.

Although rare today due to the pressures of marine grazers like snails and sea urchins, living stromatolites can be found in certain places that tend to exclude or inhibit such animals. Such a place is Shark Bay in Australia. There, an enclosed lagoon becomes hypersaline and tends to exclude organisms that prey on the microbial mat that covers the outside.

Jennifer Elick, a Geologist at Susquehanna University studied Pennsylvanian aged (about 300 million years old) stromatolites from an area near Manhattan, Kansas. There, the shapes and arrangements of the stromatolites allowed her to make broad interpretations of the environment at large. For example, the orientation of the structures suggested that they were subjected to tidal current flow within a, hypersaline environment very much like that of Shark Bay (see Figures 2-35 and 2-36).

FIGURE 2-35. The arrangement of stromatolites at Jennifer Elick's study site in Kansas. The scale in the center is 1 meter long.

FIGURE 2-36. A longitudinal section through one of the Kansas stromatolites to show the typical laminations.

RETURN TO MARS[19]

NASA scientists are already working out ways to tell real stromatolites from "foolers" as they tool up to search the returned rocky debris for signs of martian life. - J. William Schopf, 1999

Thus, it seems that stromatolites as well as all other forms of microbial mats have been around almost since life began. Indeed, no sooner had the earth cooled to allow for the existence of life (around 3.9 billion years ago) than stromatolites and rock bearing microfossils (3.5 billion years ago) began to appear. Such structures testify to the occurrence of microbial communities and relatively complex structures almost as early as they could possibly appear on earth.

This brings us back to that meteor from Mars. The isotopic evidence of the rock indicates that it was formed about 4.5 billion years ago as part of the original Martian crust. Then it received a severe shock around 4 billion years ago (probably through meteor bombardment of Mars). About that time carbonates were laid down within cracks in the rock. The simplest scenario for the formation of carbonates requires liquid water at temperatures that could support life. In addition to the apparent microfossils in ALH84001, the rock has organic compounds and grains of magnetite that are similar to those produced by living iron bacteria. The rock then was ejected from Mars by a meteor impact about 17 million years ago and landed on an Antarctic ice sheet about 11,000 years ago.

Suppose that life did appear on Mars by 4 billion years ago and other rocks were ejected then (as ALH84001 was much later). If the bacteria survived the shock of the ejection and landing and the cold and vacuum of space, then life could have been transferred here from Mars. The scenario is possible and would help to explain the rather sudden appearance of life on earth. As compelling as this scenario might be, it is not sufficient to accept as proof. Indeed, because something is possible does not mean that it happened (an approach that my children tried to take with me many times). As Carl Sagan often said, "Extraordinary claims require extraordinary evidence." I believe that the only suitable evidence could be obtained by collecting samples directly from Mars. The discovery of microfossils or possibly even living microbes could answer the question. That would be the extraordinary evidence needed.

-2001

References:

Boggs, Sam. 1987. *Principles of Sedimentology and Stratigraphy.* Merrill Publishing Co. Columbus, OH.

Bowler, Peter J. 1992. *The Fontana History of the Environmental Sciences.* Fontana Press. London.

Carr, N.G, and B.A. Whitton, eds. 1973. *The Biology of Blue-Green Algae.* Botanical Monographs. Vol 9. University of California Press. Berkeley.

Elick, Jennifer. *The Significance of the Howe Limestone, Red Eagle Limestone (Pennsylvanian) as a Paleoecological Unit.* Student Thesis. Kansas State University.

Fogg, G. E., W.D.P. Stewart, P. Fay, and A.E. Walsby,eds. 1973. *The Blue-*

---

[19] Please read *Inferno and Purgatorio* for a list of Mars missions, past and present.

Green Algae. Academic Press. New York.

Huggett, Richard John. 1997. *Environmental Change: The Evolving Ecosphere.* Routledge. New York.

Margulis, Lynn and Dorian Sagan. 1986. *Microcosmos, Four Billion Years of Microbial Evolution.* Simon and Schuster. New York.

Margulis, Lynn and Dorian Sagan. 1997. *Slanted Truths, Essays on Gaia, Symbiosis, and Evolution.* Springer-Verlag. New York.

McKay, D.S.,E.K. Gibson, K.L. Thomas-Keprta, H. Vali, C.S. Romanek, S.J. Clemett, X.D.F. Chiller, C.R. Maechling, R.N. Zare. 1996. *Search for Past Life on Mars: Possible Relic Biogenic Activity in Martian Meteorite ALH84001.* Science. 273(5277): 924-931.

Raymo, Chet and Maureen E, Raymo. 1989. *Written in Stone, A Geological History of the Northeastern United States.*The Globe Pequot Press. Chester, CT.

Schopf, J. William. 1999. *Cradle of Life, The Discovery of Earth's Earliest Fossils.* Princeton University Press. Princeton, NJ.

Questions to Think About

1. Who is David MacKay?

2. What is the importance of the Gunflint Chert?

3. Describe the contributions of Elso Barghoorn and Preston Cloud.

4. How did photosynthesis change the earth?

5. What was the source of food before the advent of photosynthesis?

6. How can we interpret banded iron formations?

7. Why are stromatolites layered?

8. What are microbial mats and stromatolites? Where would you go to observe living microbial mats and stromatolites?

9. Why did Jennifer Elick conclude that her study site had been similar to Shark Bay?

10. How can the study of stromatolites (both present and ancient) support our exploration of Mars?

DRAKE'S EQUATION AND FERMI'S PARADOX, LOGIC BEHIND THE SEARCH FOR EXTRATERRESTRIAL INTELLIGENCE

A DINNER SPEAKER

The aim of science is to seek the simplest explanation of complex facts.

-Alfred North Whitehead

On October 1, 2003 at a regional meeting of the Space Grant affiliates, we were treated to an after dinner talk by an astronomer. The topic of his talk was life in the universe and what is the likelihood that we could contact communicating beings elsewhere in our galaxy. He used the Drake Equation (see Figure 2-37) and Fermi's Paradox as vehicles to explore this question.

$$N = N_* * f_p * n_e * f_l * f_i * f_c * f_L$$

N = the number of communicating civilizations in our galaxy at present.

N_* = the number of stars in the galaxy.

f_p = the fraction of stars with planets.

n_e = the number of planets per solar system with earth-like planets.

f_l = the fraction of earth-like planets that developed life.

f_i = the fraction of life-bearing planets that develop intelligent life.

f_c = the fraction of planets with intelligent life that develop means of interstellar communication.

f_L = the fraction of a planet's history occupied by intelligent, technological, communicating life.

FIGURE 2-37. The Drake Equation.

Of course I had heard of the Drake Equation. That was one of the most memorable parts of *Cosmos,* a series for television that later came out as a book in 1980. Carl Sagan, astronomer, educator, skeptic, and apologist for the SETI (Search for Extraterrestrial Intelligence) Project, was ideally positioned to make a plausible argument for how and why we should look for ET. Frank Drake, made a fundamental contribution to this question when in 1961, at a gathering of scientists interested in looking for signals from space, he pondered the question of the likelihood of communicating intelligent life in our galaxy. That is should we even be looking for communicating civilizations and what would be the factors that would determine their occurrences? Or put another way, could we estimate the number of communicating intelligent technological races in our galaxy? He pondered the question and put down the variables that would determine their existence. This became known as the Drake Equation.

HOW MANY?

As long as you live in this universe, and have a modest talent for mathematics, sooner or later you'll find it.

-Carl Sagan (*Contact,* 1985)

We know that the number of stars in the Milky Way Galaxy (N_*) is approximatcly 100 billion. Although this is a huge number, it is not infinite. Also, most of those stars have life spans on the order of billions of years, long enough for life to get started and develop intelligence. Drake began there and considered how many of those suns could have solar systems. In 1961 astronomers could only guess as to whether other stars had planets. It seemed unlikely that our solar system was unique in the galaxy, but other planets had not been observed. For the past 7 years, however, a steady stream of observations has confirmed many stars with planets circling them. One of the first found was a large gas planet orbiting alpha draconis. Unfortunately, almost all of the extra solar planets have been similar large, Jupiter-sized or larger, not rocky water-bearing earth-like planets. This almost certainly is a product of sampling. Large planets are much more likely to be detected. Still, some small, earth-like planets have been found which supports the assumption that earth-like planets must be common, but much too small to detect routinely at interstellar distances.

What do these assumptions have to say about the Drake Equation? Well, the fraction of stars with planets (f_p) is greater than 0. Estimates generally range from 20->90%. Part of the problem is whether systems with two stars (called binary systems) can have planets in stable orbits. Since most of the star systems in our galaxy seem to be binarys, this is an important consideration. Recently, computer models have shown that planets can have stable orbits in such a system. So, my estimate for f_p is 50%. That makes the number of stars with solar systems around 50 billion (0.5 * 100 billion).

How many earth-type planets are there in each of the 50 billion solar systems? Given what we know, and using our own solar system as a model the range could be anything from 1 to 10. Technically, our solar system has four inner earth-type planets. However, the larger planets have moons (e.g. Europa and Titan) that qualify as earth-like. So, our own system has at least 6 such bodies (Mercury, Venus, Earth, Mars, Europa, and Titan). I take a conservative position in my estimate of n_e and make the assumption that each solar

system would average 2 earth-like planets. So, given a fairly conservative estimate, there are as many as 100 billion earth-like planets in the Milky Way Galaxy.

Of the estimated 100 billion earth-like planets, how many could develop and sustain life? Well, ideally, a planet would have to have liquid water for life to allow for the development and maintenance of life. Again, back to our own solar system only the Earth and Europa seem to have large amounts of liquid water. However, Mars shows signs of having had liquid water move across its surface and may have water trapped underground. Experience with microbial life on earth suggests that *anywhere* liquid water occurs so does microbial life. That would make the search for extraterrestrial life quite hopeful. Also, the building blocks of life, carbon molecules, are quite common on comets and other extraterrestrial objects. I have no doubt that the early Earth was a soup of organic molecules in its early ocean. However, a soup of organic molecules is a far cry from life, and, although the simplest answer is that life developed from that mix here on Earth in a fairly short time (We have fossils that date back to 3.5 billion years and our Earth-Moon system evolved only a billion years earlier). Still, I do not believe that the development of life on Earth was inevitable. It happened, yes, but I think that life was still very unlikely. Estimates of Earth-like planets that actually evolve life range from nearly impossible to 100%. I again take a conservative position and estimate that no more than 1 in a thousand such planets actually evolved life. That makes my estimate of f_l around 0.001. Given the number of potential earth-like planets, however, the number of life-bearing planets could be in the neighborhood of 100 million (see Figure 2-38 for an illustration of microbial life).

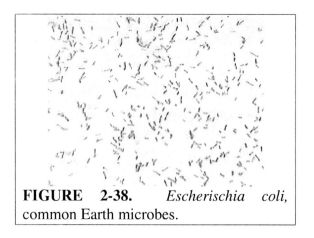

FIGURE 2-38. *Escherischia coli,* common Earth microbes.

HOW MANY CARE?

An interstellar message, intended to be understood by an emerging civilization, should be easy to decode. -Carl Sagan

Although our galaxy may teem with life, how many of its planets would house intelligent life? That is an even more difficult question. Is intelligence inevitable? I do not think so. Consider the multiple millions (that's right we don't even know how many different species of living things that we live together with on our own planet) of species here on Earth. Of those, only a handful of species are intelligent. By intelligent, I mean that they communicate with others of their own kind and have developed cultures. I feel that the requirement for communication is a fairly strong one in that intelligence would have little need otherwise. Certainly, I do not mean that all species that communicate are intelligent. Spiders and some plants communicate in certain ways. I require that the communication manifest itself in unique interactions that we could interpret as culture. Arguably, the other great apes, cetaceans, elephants, etc. join us in this. During the bulk of the history of life on Earth, life remained microbial. Even now, most of the life on Earth likely is microbial (small and without nuclei) and many of the living things with nuclei also are unicellular. Some organisms have become multicellular. This seems to be an important prerequisite for the complexity necessary for the development of intelligence. Such a step does not seem inevitable to me. Then, the step of multicellular life becoming intelligent is very unlikely. Indeed, consider the multicellular fungi, kelps, plants, seaweeds (there are even some multicellular microbes), animals, etc. Given the example of life on Earth, 1% of life-bearing planets producing intelligent species seems optimistic to me. Still, that means with f_i at 0.01, our galaxy has 1 million planets on which intelligent life has evolved.

How many of those species that develop intelligence also develop the technical capability to communicate by radio or other electromagnetic radiation? These are forms of communication that travel at the speed of light and most likely to be developed or recognized by a technological civilization as an "instantaneous" means of communicating over long distances. While developing the technology, their signals would likely leak into space and travel through the interstellar reaches. Perhaps some of them will want to send signals that would allow them to be noticed by other such technological civilizations. That is the hope of Frank Drake, a founder of SETI. He began to look for extraterrestrials with radiotelescopes. In fact, for a time he was the director of the world's largest radiotelescope at Arecibo[20] in Puerto Rico (see Figure 2-39).

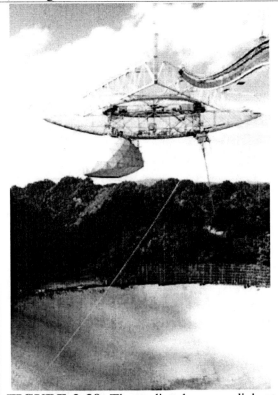

FIGURE 2-39. The radiotelescope dish at Arecibo in Puerto Rico.

Estimates of intelligent civilizations that have the means to communicate and might wish to communicate through interstellar space vary, but are on the low end (10-20%). I feel that the low end is still too high as I try to imagine a whale constructing a means of interstellar communication. Still, I allow for a communicating technological species per 10 intelligent species. The f_c factor therefore equals about 0.10, which brings the number of communicating races in our galaxy down to 100 thousand.

The last consideration is what is the faction of the lifespan of a planet during which technological, communicating races live? That is, if civilizations exist for short periods of time (relatively speaking), they might not ever overlap to communicate with each other. Consider the example of our own species on Earth. We have not been around for the whole life of our planet, much less the lifespan of our galaxy. Our species has been on the planet for 100,000 years. However, we have been communicating so that outside civilizations could detect us for around 100 years. That period of time is a tiny fraction of the age of the earth. Even if our species persists at a high technological level for 10,000 years, the Earth's age is 2 million times the period of communication. This is something that I cannot estimate well especially since we are still at the beginning of our own technological period. Anyway, if I assume that our species is in its infancy and could continue as a technological species for another 100,000 years, we would endure for only about 0.002% of the Earth's 4.5 billion year history. That would make the value of f_L only about 0.00002 and thereby reduce the number of coexisting technological communicating races to 2 in the Milky Way Galaxy. Considering that we are one of the two, which would leave just one other civilization to look for, we could be looking for a needle in a haystack.

Most estimates that employ the Drake Equation produce much more optimistic results. The speaker's own calculations were in the double digits. If the high range estimates for the factors in the Drake Equation are employed, then the number of communicating, technological species in the galaxy could be as high as 10 million or one per 10,000 stars in our galaxy. Clearly, there is plenty of room for error[21].

---

[20] For more about radiotelescopes, read *A Man with a Telescope.*

[21] See the table at the end of this essay. Try to generate your own estimate by plugging your numbers into the Drake Equation.

FERMI'S PARADOX

Where are they?   -Enrico Fermi

Then the speaker took another approach in his talk and introduced Fermi's Paradox. I had heard of it before but had not paid much attention to it. Enrico Fermi, a physicist of many scientific accomplishments, was asked once if he thought that there were extraterrestrial civilizations. He is supposed to have done a quick calculation in his head and answered, "Where are they?" This was not as flippant as it appears. He based his answer on a few assumptions, but certainly many fewer than are contained in the Drake Equation. He assumed that such a civilization would seek to explore and colonize habitable portions of the galaxy. Suppose that the length of time a civilization of high technology persists before it establishes its first interstellar colony is 10,000 years. Also, suppose that it then continues to colonize other stars at the same rate. Then, it should have 4 colonies in 20,000 years, eight colonies in 30,000 years, etc. In about a third of a million years, at such exponential growth, the entire galaxy should be colonized. Even if the colonization process took 10 million years, a prodigiously long time for an earthly species, it would be only 0.07% of the entire history of the universe. Fermi's point was that such a technological civilization should be here or at least have left evidence of its having been here. The truth of the matter is that they are not here and there is no credible evidence that they have ever been here. We might truly be quite alone.

I reconsidered my values for the Drake Equation in light of the age of the universe. In particular, I realized that our own planet is in its middle age, and, therefore, my calculation for f_L was too large. In fact, it was twice as big as it should be if the total age of the Earth is factored in. The solution for N in that case was 1. The Milky Way should have only 1 technologically advanced civilization. Perhaps, then there really is a reason why we have not contacted a sentient alien race. As suggested by the Fermi Paradox, they are not there. This, too, was the speaker's conclusion.

As I sat following the talk and listened to the discussion afterward, I was a bit shaken by my back of the envelope calculation and the logic of Fermi's Paradox. I, who had been raised on a steady diet of science fiction and still partake whenever possible, hoped that a signal was about to be discovered, that we would make contact. I had always had to suspend such belief whenever I read or watched science fiction. Very little of it conformed to science except perhaps Carl Sagan's *Contact* and Arthur C. Clarke's *2001, A Space Odyssey*. Those, too required considerable suspension of what I knew to be a stretch or untrue.

Then, why do I support SETI and its goals? Why do I see Drake's Equation as much more than a waste of time? First of all, the assumptions that I made for most of the components of the calculation were guesses, informed guesses, but guesses nonetheless. Drake's Equation as do similar vehicles, helps us to concentrate on important features as of the overall question. Thus, there are some parts that can be tested and subjected to scientific scrutiny. For example, we can now confirm that stars have planets. We have some evidence that some of those planets are earth-like. Thus, we might be able to know f_p and n_e as well as we know the number of stars in the galaxy.

The search assumes that technological races would want to be found or are curious about the universe. The search assumes that technological civilizations might persist 10-100 thousand years. Perhaps they could last for millions of years. Fermi's Paradox also assumes that technological races would choose to colonize. Certainly, this whole essay is fraught with assumptions on both sides.

Also, I do not mean to give the least bit of comfort to those who accept in an unskeptical way the claims of UFOlogists and parapsychologists. The Drake Equation is not a recipe that *proves* the existence of aliens. It does not show that we must be and have been visited. I view their claims of cover-up and eyewitness testimony as nothing more than anecdote and self-delusion brought on by sincere belief that we are not alone.

As a biologist, however, I do see a hopeful message in my pessimistic calculations. That message is that life might be quite common (100 million planets) in our galaxy. That number could be ramped up considerably if life were to be found on Mars or Europa, in which case we would have to assume that life could appear almost any place that is suitable. Fermi's Paradox notwithstanding, I do hope that our species never stops looking, but in its search accepts only evidence that could qualify as extraordinary.

-2003

References:

Ball, Philip. 2003. *Earth-like Planets Probably Water-logged, Simulation Suggests Formation of Wet Worlds Easy.* http://www.nature.com/nsu/030818-10.html

Gold, Thomas. 1999. *The Deep, Hot Biosphere.* Springer-Verlag. New York.

Mullen, Leslie. 2001. *Extrasolar Planets With Earth-like Orbits.* http://nai.arc.nasa.gov/news_stories/news_print.cfm

PBS. (n.d.). *Life Beyond Earth, The Drake Equation.* http://www.pbs.org/lifebeyondearth/listening/drake.html

Sagan, Carl. 1980. *Cosmos.* Random House. New York

Seti Institute. 2003. *Drake Equation.* http://www.seti-inst.edu/science/drake-bg.html

Shostack, Seth. 2001. *Our Galaxy Should Be Teeming With Life, But Where Are They?* http://www.space.com/searchforlife/shostack_paradox_011024.html

Swimme, Brian and Thomas Berry. 1992. *The Universe Story.* Harper Collins. New York.

Trefil, James. 1997. *Are We Unique? A Scientist Explores the Unparalleled Intelligence of the Human Mind.* John Wiley and Sons, Inc. New York.

Zinnecker, Hans. 2003. *Chances For Earth-like Planets And Life Around Metal-poor Stars.* In: R. Norris, C. Oliver, and F. Stootman, eds. *Bioastronomy 2002: Life Among the Stars Proceedings IAU Symposium No. 213.*

Questions to Think About

1. Who are Carl Sagan and Frank Drake?

2. What is the importance of the Drake Equation?

3. Of the different factors used by the Drake Equation, what seems to be the most well known? The least well known?

4. What does SETI stand for? Is its premise scientific?

5. How does SETI differ from other groups searching for ET?

6. What is Fermi's Paradox? Why does it seem to suggest that we must be alone?

TRY YOUR OWN VALUES AND CALCULATE N		
$N = N_* * f_p * n_e * f_l * f_i * f_c * f_L$		
FACTOR OF THE DRAKE EQUATION	**MY VALUE**	**YOUR VALUE**
N_* = the number of stars in the galaxy.	100 BILLION	100 BILLION
f_p = the fraction of stars with planets.	0.5	
n_e = the number of planets per solar system with earth-like planets.	2	
f_l = the fraction of earth-like planets that developed life.	0.001	
f_i = the fraction of life-bearing planets that develop intelligent life.	0.01	
f_c = the fraction of planets with intelligent life that develop means of interstellar communication.	0.10	
f_L = the fraction of a planet's history occupied by intelligent, technological, communicating life.	0.00002 (reduced to 0.00001 if the full age of the earth is considered)	

A MAN WITH A TELESCOPE

A CANOE TRIP

Just because you can find a similarity between your claim and one that scientists accept, it does not follow that your claim is consistent with what scientists believe.- Radner & Radner, 1982

I take an annual trip to Assateague Island[22] with students from the Biology Club each fall. I find these trips to particularly fun because I learn so much each time I go there. Some years ago on one of those treks the cool October weather had discouraged most campers so the marsh side campground was relatively empty. In one of the only occupied campsites, I encountered a man who had set up a large reflecting telescope and struck up a conversation with him. With enthusiasm the man with the telescope described the clear skies and calm nights that had prevailed over the time that he had been camping there. He was happy to show our group some of the things that his large telescope could resolve. In particular, I remember having a very good look at the Andromeda Galaxy

The man with the telescope had been there several days before we arrived so he had become acquainted with some of the particular wonders that the island had conjured up that time. He happened to mention in passing that he had observed bioluminescence in the marsh before the full moon rose very high into the sky. Well, bioluminescence was exactly what I had been looking for, I alerted the students to it and made plans to go out in the canoe at night to collect some of the causative organisms. The man with the telescope

asked to go, so I said "Sure." After all, he had done so much for us.

I'm not sure why, but we left without a flashlight. The residual glow of the fading sun made the canoe trip through the calm waters of the marsh quite easy. With each dip of the paddle, I saw large and small glowing blobs of the jellyfish and comb jellies. The most impressive part for me was the continuous background glow of the bioluminescent algae. I dragged my plankton net behind me concentrating the one-celled glowing algae. After a time, the night sky had become black and filled with stars, and we parked the canoe on a sandbar to wait for the guiding light of the moon that was to rise in a short time.

I pulled up the plankton net and took care of its contents and rinsed the net. With a wait ahead of me, I began to talk about the space program and where it might be going (this was in the mid 1980's). The man sat quietly and remained distant for a time. Then he said that the space program was a waste of money and was completely unnecessary. I was astounded. He had seemed so interested in astronomical objects. I sputtered for a moment and then asked, "Don't you want to know what things are like on Mercury or Mars?" I started to continue the list, but he cut me off with, "I have been there." I said, "Ohhhh." as my mind raced about trying to understand what he had said. At the same time, I looked at the horizon where the moon was to rise.

He began to explain that he and others had traveled to the various planets and moons of our solar system by astral projection. He began to describe his trips to Mercury and his walks along the twilight zone (the band around Mercury

---

[22] Read *Night Lights* and *Islands and their Lessons in Biogeography* for more about Assateague Island.

93

between the hot, sunlit side and the cold nighttime side). I felt as though I was in the Twilight Zone at the moment. Finally, the moon peeked above the horizon and gave us enough light to navigate back to our campsites. On the way back he described his astrology business in Philadelphia and explained that he had come to Assateague Island to make observations for some of his clients.

FIGURE 2-40. Moonrise over Assateague Island.

Astrology is the belief that the "stars" (planets, stars, etc.) all influence our lives and our destinies. That is, our futures are predetermined. We just have to live and discover the scripts intended for us.

The zeal with which he pointed out the constellations, planets, etc. all began to make sense to me. The students never suspected. They assumed that his telescope and knowledge made him an astronomer, as had I. How had he and I both seen the same sky, but observed it so differently?

GEOCENTRIC UNIVERSES

It is not once nor twice but times without number that the same ideas make their appearance in the world.

    -Aristotle of Stagira, On the Heavens

That is the question that comes to mind when I look at the changing views of the nature of the universe. The earliest and longest held view was that the earth occupied the center of the universe. The earth was fixed and had no motion while the planets, sun and stars moved around it.

The Greeks accepted that there was a difference between how the universe actually was and the use of a mathematical device to predict the positions of the planets, phases of the moon, etc. The theoretical description of the universe was called cosmology while the mathematical device was called astronomy. The distinctions between the two concepts remained strong through the first two millennia of science.

The cosmology of the earth-centered universe came in several forms. Thales of Miletus (c. 625-c.550 B.C.) thought that the earth was a cylinder floating in a cosmic sea. A cylinder that contained the moon surrounded the cylinder of the earth. Those cylinders rested in a nested array with the outermost cylinder being that of the fixed stars.

Pythagoras (c.560-480 B.C.) adopted an unusual cosmology in which the earth did not reside in the center. Instead, the center of the universe contained a central fire (this was not the sun). He argued that the earth was not noble enough to occupy the center. Also, the central fire could not be seen from earth because a counter earth obscured its light. Some Pythagoreans believed that the earth moved around the center. The other planets and fixed stars were affixed to nested spheres that culminated in the furthermost sphere of the fixed stars.

Plato (c.428-c.348 B.C.) and his student, Eudoxus of Cnidus (408-353 B.C.), created the most persistent cosmology. It had a fixed, spherical earth at its center and a nested series of crystalline spheres with planets embedded in them. As before, the outermost sphere was that of the fixed stars. All spheres moved about the earth in uniform circular motion, the simplest motion possible.

Aristotle (384-322 B.C.) adopted the Eudoxan cosmology and made it the cornerstone of his physics. In the Aristotelean universe, there was an earth-heaven dichotomy with the physics and compositions of the two being completely different. Celestial bodies were made of a substance, called the quintessence, which did not occur on earth. It was uniformly bright, unblemished and moved in simple circles with uniform motion. The crystalline sphere of the moon marked the boundary between the earth and heavens. The upshot of this was that Aristotelians did not observe celestial bodies to study them because a full understanding of a body made of a completely foreign substance was impossible and made no sense. Besides, if the celestial bodies were made of the quintessence, no structure could be discerned anyway. It would be comparable to you trying to discern structure by staring at a lit light bulb.

Aristotle was a mechanical thinker. He did not reduce his ideas to mathematics in the familiar manner of modern physics. The Eudoxan-Aristotelian cosmology remained the dominant description of the cosmos in the tradition of Western Science for 2,000 years. Nevertheless, the predictive power of Aristotle's theory was zero. So, Astronomers, mathematicians in the tradition of the Babylonians and other non-science cultures, began to make numerical devices that could predict the relative positions of the planets and other bodies in the heavens within the framework of the Aristotelian universe.

HEAVENLY MATH
Those who have been true philosophers, Syrus, seem to me to have very wisely separated the theoretical part of philosophy from the practical.
-Claudius Ptolemy, Almagest

Perhaps, the most influential Astronomer was Claudius Ptolemy (c.100-c.178 A.D), an astronomer from Alexandrian Egypt in the second century A.D. He wrote a treatise that codified the theories of astronomy in a book that we call *Almagest* (See Figure 2-41). He made the earth (E) slightly eccentric with planets (P) circling the center (C) along a deferent (B). The particular planets occupied one or more epicycles that rotated around a point (F) on the deferent. He had to add another point called the equant (Q) around which a point on the deferent moves with the same angular velocity. Thus, in this astronomy, there is no uniform circular motion of the individual planets.

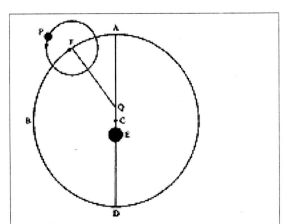

FIGURE 2-41. A diagram of the main components of Ptolemy's astronomy: Earth (E), Center (C), Equant (Q), Deferent (B), Diameter of the Deferent (A-D), Center of Epicycle (F).

Ptolemy had to make these mathematical adjustments because the heavens, particularly the planets of the heavens, move in strange ways. For example, if you go outside and observe Mars at the same time each night and mark its position, you will observe a general movement against the background of the fixed stars. The planet will appear to advance across the sky relative to the stars with occasional backward loops and altered rates of motion. A properly calibrated epicycle could emulate the motion of a planet such as Mars and allow accurate prediction of its future positions.

Because of the epicycles and equant, the planetary motions in the astronomy of Ptolemy adopted an elliptical orbit. Ptolemy recognized that his astronomy would be easier to construct if the earth were to move, but he accepted the physics of Aristotle. In fact, the Eudoxan-Aristotelian Cosmology persisted alongside the astronomy of Ptolemy until significant challenges of the 15th and 16th centuries precipitated a change in view.

A POLISH CLERIC

For what could be more beautiful than the heavens which contain all beautiful things? -Nicolaus Copernicus, 1542

The first serious challenge of the astronomy and cosmology of the ancients came through Nicolaus Copernicus (Nikolai Koppernigk -1473-1543) who was born in Poland and raised by a powerful uncle. Copernicus attended Krakow University where he became educated in the astronomy of the day, that is the astronomy of Ptolemy. He then attended universities in Italy where he took degrees in Arts and Sciences, Church Law, and Medicine. He became a Cannon of the Church, which made him eligible for a life-long annuity to spend his days in study.

The philosophy of the ancient Greeks came to the attention of the West in the 12th Century through an accident of history. The church, the primary seat of philosophy and learning in Western Europe, embraced the cosmology and physics of Aristotle. The accommodation of Christian theology and Aristotelian philosophy began with the writings of Thomas Aquinas.

By the beginning of the 16th Century the astronomical tables of Ptolemy had become woefully out of sync with the heavens and their motions. Also, the calendars, which had been based on astronomical tables, had drifted significantly. Copernicus set about to fix the problem.

He laid out his basic ideas of a new astronomy in which the earth moved along with the planets. Copernicus did this because he was a mathematician who embraced the philosophy of Pythagoras, a philosophy in which the earth did not occupy the center and did move. Mainly, he attempted to save the concept of uniform circular motion and abandon the equant, which he regarded as a cheat. In the astronomy of Copernicus, the earth assumed three motions:

1) Rotation on its axis.
2) Orbital motion around the sun.
3) Conical (or wobbling) motion of the earth's axis. This supposition is not necessary.

Copernicus made the sun stationary and moved it to a place near the center of the universe. Retrograde motion could be explained by the relative motions and velocities of the planets as they circled the sun in their respective spheres. Still, he required uniform circular motion so that observed planetary positions did not correlate with his mathematical scheme without the addition of epicycles. Although his astronomy required smaller epicycles (an additional motion),

Copernicus' system was as complicated as that of Ptolemy in the end.

Copernicus presented his astronomy in *On the Revolutions of the Heavenly Spheres* (1542), but he went beyond an explanation of the universe with a certain mathematical motion. He considered cosmological questions like why an object falls straight down on a moving earth. Also, he considered the problem of parallax. That is, why do the stars not seem to shift position if the earth moves around the sun. He concluded that the sphere of the fixed stars must be very far away from the sphere of the earth. Clearly, such questions and considerations indicated that he believed that the earth really did move.

As a cosmology, Copernicus' view seemed absurd. The earth did not move. Experience indicated that it was stationary. So, Copernicus did not simplify the astronomy of Ptolemy nor did he offer a suitable substitute for the cosmology of Aristotle and Eudoxus. Copernicus made little impact on science of the day. In fact, his book seems to have been considered only twice in the fifty years following its publication.

YET IT MOVES

In questions of science the authority of a thousand is not worth the humble reasoning of a single individual.

-Galileo Galilei

Galileo Galilei (1564-1642) was born 21 years after the publication of Copernicus' system. He began to study medicine at the University of Pisa in 1581 but did not care for it and left without a degree. While there, however, he did become very interested in the study of mathematics and music. Through this experience and the influence of his father who was a Pythagorean and one of the founders of opera, Galileo embraced the philosophy of Pythagoras. He began to experiment with pendulums and motion. His research indicated that Aristotle had been wrong about motion (a conclusion that angered the Aristotelian faculty at Pisa) so he had to leave.

Galileo then went to Padua (1592-1610) where he taught mathematics, military engineering, and astronomy to medical students so that they could use the tool of astrology in their practice. Further, he made a name for himself as a scientist. In 1609 Galileo constructed a telescope based on lenses that had been made by Dutch spectacle makers. He may have heard that the Dutch also had begun to make telescopes by placing two convex lenses in a tube. He may have obtained a small telescope or just heard of one and applied his mathematical and technical skills to its construction. Anyway, he made a series of telescopes and began to look at objects in the heavens.

As Galileo tinkered with the telescope and its design, he began to understand that the image depended more on the light-gathering ability of the lens system. Generally, larger lenses gather more light, but they also have longer focal lengths. Figure 2-42 shows a diagram of a simple telescope. Lens A gathers the light and focuses it (f). The eyepiece (B) enlarges and focuses the image for the eye. This depends upon the refraction or bending of light as it enters and leaves the denser medium of the glass lens.

Because lenses bend light, they tend to separate the colors of white light as a prism does. So, lenses with a strong curvature, those with the greatest magnifying ability, also produce problems with rainbow rings of color around the images. These chromatic aberrations could be addressed simply by using large lenses with little curvature and very long focal lengths. Galileo never overcame the problem of chromatic aberration.

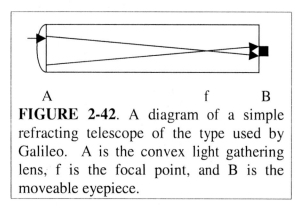

A   f   B

FIGURE 2-42. A diagram of a simple refracting telescope of the type used by Galileo. A is the convex light gathering lens, f is the focal point, and B is the moveable eyepiece.

His initial observations revealed that the moon's surface had mountains, valleys, and seas. He saw that the Milky Way was made of stars and that Jupiter had moons that went around it. His telescope, though better than any produced by the Dutch, suffered severe chromatic aberrations so some of his interpretations were quite strange. For example, he saw the rings of Saturn as bulges, an image that he interpreted as three spheres. Regardless of the problems, his telescope revealed that the planets had blemishes and that crystalline spheres could not exist. In short, Aristotle was wrong.

Galileo published his observations in a book called *Siderius Nuncius (Heavenly Messenger)* in 1610 and received almost immediate acclaim. He dedicated the work to the Grand Duke of Tuscany, Cosimo II, a member of the Medici family. He also named the newly discovered moons of Jupiter the Medician stars. For this flattery, Galileo received a heavy gold chain and an appointment to the court.

Galileo continued his telescopic observations of the heavens. By 1614 he became an open defender of the Copernican system and began to be attacked by priests throughout Catholic Europe. Offended by this treatment, Galileo remarked, "The Holy Spirit intended to teach us in the Bible how to go to the heavens, not how the heavens go."

The Holy Office told him to remain silent on the subject, and he did so until 1627 when he published *Il Saggiatore*. Galileo dedicated the book to his friend, former patron, and newly-elected Pope Urban VIII. The text described new discoveries of the heavens that pointed more to a sun-centered universe. In the writings of Galileo, the Astronomy-Cosmology dichotomy disappeared. He described the cosmos as he interpreted it to be in drawings and mathematical terms. Nevertheless, his book was well received and caused little stir.

With newfound confidence, Galileo began to work on another book that he published in 1632 called *Dialogue of the Two Principal Systems of the World*. In this book, Galileo presented the Aristotelian and Copernican cosmologies in a dialogue format. The conversation was between an Aristotelian named Simplicio, a Copernican named Salviati, and an educated non-philosopher named Sagredo. He ridiculed the Aristotelian system through the character of Simplicio (literally meaning simpleton) often using the words of the Pope himself. This brought the church squarely down on Galileo almost immediately. He was taken by the Inquisition and charged with:
1) Breaking the agreement of 1616.
2) Teaching Copernicanism as truth.
3) Believing the truth of the Copernican system.

He was convicted of the suspicion of heresy and placed under house arrest for the rest of his life. As the story goes,

Galileo recanted his belief in the Copernican system but muttered under his breath, "And yet it moves." The change that Galileo produced in the scientific community caused it to move rapidly away from the philosophical stranglehold of Aristotle. Contemporaries like Johannes Kepler (1651-1631) took the heliocentric universe and eliminated the need for uniform circular motion. Galileo died in 1642, the year of the birth of Isaac Newton (1642-1727) who devised the law of gravity and used it to explain the laws of planetary motion as defined by Kepler. The universe of Aristotle became untenable and unneeded[23].

TELESCOPES

The range and power of the main sense organ of Homo sapiens had suddenly started to grow in leaps to thirty times, a hundred times, a thousand times its natural capacity. -Arthur Koestler, 1959

I have no doubt that Galileo became the principal architect of the new view of the heavens. His telescope made heavenly objects more than points in the geometry of space. The telescope turned them into individual objects by bringing them to our scale.

Larger and larger refracting telescopes began to be built and used. Some were more than 100 feet long, but very unwieldy and unstable. Newton attempted to solve the problems of refracting telescopes by collecting the light with a curved parabolic mirror instead of a lens (see Figure 2-43). This solution eliminated the problem of chromatic aberration and allowed for the creation of the large reflecting telescopes in the observatories of today. Even the Hubble Space Telescope uses the same design.

Similar parabolic reflectors can be used to gather other forms of electromagnetic radiation such as radio waves by facilities such as Arecibo in Puerto Rico (see Figure 2-39[24]).

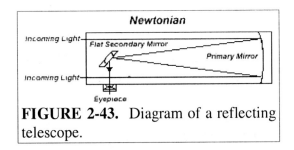

FIGURE 2-43. Diagram of a reflecting telescope.

Through these instruments, we have come to abandon the sun-centered universe and accept a universe that is infinite in all directions, a universe without a center. We now occupy the third planet of a solar system that resides in an arm of a disk-shaped galaxy in a sea of billions of galaxies. The telescope removed us from the privileged position of the center and made us part of the whole.

THE MAN WITH THE TELESCOPE
Only when the historical and social aspects of science are neglected does it become plausible that pseudoscience is an unchanging category.
-Paul R. Thagard, 1978

How is it, then that astrology can thrive in this time of science? Astrological charts and predictions bedeck almost all newspapers and are the mainstay of the tabloids that drape the checkout stands. Why should I care if people allow themselves to be duped into believing foolishness at the fringe of science? Certainly, astrology was part of the belief systems of many to whom I referred in this essay. Kepler, for one,

---

[23] Read more about this in *Principia Mathematica: The Foundation of Modern Physics.*

[24] Find this in *The Drake Equation and Fermi's Paradox.*

fed himself by casting horoscopes. If it was part of science then, why can't we consider it part of science now? Mainly because science seeks to understand nature rather than try to proselytize for a particular worldview. By that I mean that the community of scientists has to be convinced that one explanation is more useful than another. Thus, there is a sociology as well as a history that defines the enterprise that we call science. As for astrology, science abandoned it hundreds of years ago as an explanation for the impact of the heavens on individuals. The history of science is littered with discarded ideas and parts of theories. Rarely are they revisited. Those who insist that astrology (or any other discarded theory like creationism) is a science in light of the current views of cosmology and astronomy by members of the scientific community, place themselves outside of science in a shadowy realm called pseudoscience. This type of anachronistic thinking is characteristic of those who participate in the pseudosciences.

Personally, as a scientist and as a member of a free society, I object strongly when religion and politics attempt to interfere with the operation of science or the teaching of science. Certainly science's interpretations of nature can be wrong, but arguments from anachronistic points of view cannot be admitted as evidence. For example, the Jesuit objection to Galileo's interpretation of what he saw in the telescope was justified at the time. However, as better lenses without distortion began to give clearer views of the heavens, their objections evaporated from the realm of natural philosophy.

When I view the sky through a telescope, I often think of that encounter in the marsh and wonder what became of the man with the telescope. Clearly, the accouterments of science do not make a scientist. In a way, his astrology attempts to place us at the center, a position that science abandoned over 400 years ago. That was precipitated by Galileo, another man with a telescope and the first modern astronomer.

-2000, revised in 2004

References:

Bolles, Edmund Blair, ed. 1997. *Galileo's Commandment, An Anthology of Great Science Writing.* W.H. Freeman. New York.

Carey, John, ed. 1995. *Eyewitness to Science.* Harvard University Press. Cambridge.

Drake, Stillman, translator. 1957. *The Discoveries and Opinions of Galileo.* Doubleday. New York.

Ferris, Timothy. 1988. *Coming of Age in the Milky Way.* Anchor Books, Doubleday. New York.

Gribben, John. 2002. *The Scientists, A History of Science Told Through the Lives of its Greatest Inventors.* Random House. New York.

Hutchins, Robert Maynard, editor-in-chief. 1952. *Great Books of the Western World.* Vol 16: Ptolemy, Copernicus, Kepler; Vol 28: Gilbert, Galileo, Harvey; Vol 34: Newton, Huygens. Encyclopaedia Britannica, Inc. Chicago.

Koestler, Arthur. 1959. *The Sleepwalkers, A History of Man's Changing Vision of the Universe.* Grosset and Dunlap. New York.

Radner, Daisie and Michael Radner. 1982. *Science and Unreason.* Wadsworth Publishing Co. Belmont, CA.

Thagard, Paul R. 1978. *Why Astrology is a Pseudoscience.* In: Martin Curd and J.A. Cover. 1998. *Philosophy of Science.* W.W. Norton and Co., Inc. New York.

Questions to Think About

1. What are the differences between Astrology, Astronomy, and Cosmology?

2. What was the dominant cosmology until the time of Galileo?

3. Why did Claudius Ptolemy create an astronomy that used deferents?

4. Do you think that Copernicus created an astronomy or a cosmology?

5. Why did Galileo reject the Aristotelean cosmology?

6. Why was Galileo in trouble with Pope Urban VIII?

7. What are the two general types of telescopes? Which provides the image with least distortion?

8. What did I mean when I wrote that there is a sociology as well as a history that defines science? What are some consequences to that concept?

9. Why is Astrology a pseudoscience?

10. Can you think of examples other than Astrology that are supported by anachronistic thinking?

CHAPTER 3: SOLVING PROBLEMS

If a man...make a better mousetrap than his neighbor, ...the world will make a beaten path to his door.

Ralph Waldo Emerson. Attributed to him

I walked this street in Old San Juan, Puerto Rico. The regular lines and symmetry of the buildings down to the bricks in the pavement reminded me of the self-similarity of complex systems. This is, indeed, a beaten path, hundreds of years old laid with bricks imported by the Spanish to make a better path. This kind of improvement is the function of technology.

The essays in this chapter consider mathematics (*Mathematics and Science*) and applications of science to solve particular problems (*Butterflies, A Trinity, A Wright Solution, Maps as Models,* and *A Human Presence*). Two essays about Stonehenge (*Observatory, Clock, or Temple* and *Sunrise, Sunset*) explore the interface between science, technology and religion.

MATHEMATICS AND SCIENCE, PARTNERS IN THE EXPLORATION OF NATURE

BOTANISTS AND ZOOLOGISTS

There isn't a scientific community. It is a culture. It is a very undisciplined organization.   -I.I. Rabi

In 1976 I began to work on my PhD program at the University of Oklahoma. Before that I had been working on a project in the Zoology Department that required that I know algae very well. In particular, I had become interested in the phytoplankton (free-floating algae) of Lake Thunderbird, a reservoir in Norman, Oklahoma in order to document whether or not the algae migrated up and down in the lake every day. Because of this question, I had to be able to distinguish them at the species level. Now, at that time, aquatic ecologists only distinguished algae as general groups. After all, most aquatic ecologists were trained in Departments of Zoology and algae were plants. Fortunately, these algae swam with little whip-like extensions and so were also claimed by Zoologists as "protozoa." Because of that, I did have some help with identifications even though they were algae, and I was in a zoology department. As luck would have it, one of the things that I was studying was a dinoflagellate and Dr. Lois Pfiester[1], a world expert on freshwater dinoflagellates, had been hired as part of the faculty of Botany and Microbiology at the University of Oklahoma. I talked to her about my project and some of my results. Then, I convinced her to be on my thesis committee. This was a little

unusual because I had gone beyond the territory of the zoology department and sought advice from a member of another community. One of her first requirements was that I take a course in phycology (the study of algae). It just so happened that she was teaching a phycology course at the University of Oklahoma Biological Station on Lake Texoma (an impoundment of the Red River between Texas and Oklahoma).

A field station experience is great for almost any aspect of biology, ecology, or environmental science. In this setting, nature truly is the laboratory. I spent eight weeks learning to recognize algae and to use keys in the determination of unknown algal species. We even did a side project that we later published. I think that this was the first time that I began to feel less like a student and more like a scientist.

Whether I worked in the zoology or the botany department, the fundamental methods were the same. I had to collect the samples and examine them such that numbers could be applied to them. How many per milliliter? Could they be graphed according to the depth at which they occurred? Could I apply a numerical diversity index number to them? Would this reduction to number help me to make sense of the vertical migration of the dinoflagellates? Anyway, the time at the field station allowed me to focus on these problems.

Even though I had thrown myself into the study of algae, I couldn't collect samples or sit at a microscope all of the time. The routine at the Biological Station was marked by the dinner bell at

---

[1] Read *Killer Algae* for an introduction to Dr. Lois Pfiester and her scientific legacy.

7a.m., noon and 5p.m. Following dinner, the tradition was to play volleyball. I did this several times, but the competition was cutthroat, and I did not enjoy being yelled at (or watching poor undergrads become the object of scorn). More often than not, I chose the alternative of returning to the laboratory rather than to sit and watch this disgraceful scene.

MUSIC & DANCE

Why do you look at me like that? That's how I am. There's a devil in me who shouts, and I do what he says. Whenever I feel I'm choking with some emotion, he says 'Dance!' and I dance. And I feel better!

-Nikos Kazantzakis, *Zorba the Greek*

Fortunately, I discovered another outlet when Doug Butcher, a fellow zoology graduate student introduced me to another diversion. He had been an instructor in the International Folkdancing Club at the University of Oklahoma and offered to teach dances two nights a week. Doug concentrated on the dances of Eastern Europe, particularly those of the Balkan region. I fell in love with the haunting melodies and the unusual meters of the music.

By meter, I mean that we hear music in phrases or bars (Figure 3-1). Take most popular music in the Western European tradition for example. A march usually has four regular beats per measure of music. In this case, a quarter note gets 1 beat and there are 4 beats to a measure. The musical designation for this meter is 4/4 (see Figure 3-2). A waltz is written in ¾ time. That is, there are 3 beats per measure and a quarter note gets one beat. However, in the waltz, there is a slight stress on the first beat of the measure. So, it would feel

funny to try to march to a waltz. The polka (and many other dances in the western European tradition) is danced in a 2/4 meter. It has the feel of four eighth notes per measure with a slight stress given to beats 2 and four. Thus, the feel of a polka is slightly syncopated.

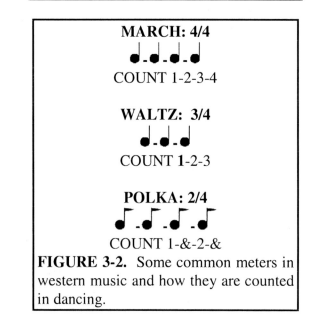

FIGURE 3-1. Bar of music from *Won't You Play a Simple Melody* (from Figure 1-1). This has a 2/2 meter. That is, there are two beats to a measure and a half note (♩) gets one beat.

MARCH: 4/4

COUNT 1-2-3-4

WALTZ: 3/4

COUNT 1-2-3

POLKA: 2/4

COUNT 1-&-2-&

FIGURE 3-2. Some common meters in western music and how they are counted in dancing.

All in all, the connection between movement and music is the real beauty of dance. When the two are in synchrony, and everyone in the room moves together, all senses seem to be affected. Before long my fondness for Balkan dance matched my love for its music. In particular, I enjoyed the dances of Greece, Serbia, Romania, Bulgaria, and Macedonia. Soon, I began to generalize certain aspects of the music and dances, and the taxonomist in me began to classify them according to common features. For example, I noticed that most Macedonian dance moved to a 7/8 *lesnoto* rhythm. That is, each measure had 7 beats and an 8th note got one beat. The resulting music was a combination of 8th notes such that the dance rhythm was slow-quick-quick. That was because the 8th notes were tied this way: 1-2-3; 1-2; 1-2 (see Figure 3-3). In form, Macedonian dances tended to be line dances with dancers' hands joined at shoulder level. The line always moved to the right.

Croatian dance, on the other hand, was usually danced in a circle to a 2/4 rhythm, called a kolo or dermish rhythm. The dancers held hands across the people next to them in a complex hold called basket hold. The circle almost always moved to the left. Curiously, the Croats and the French were the only ethnic groups in Europe that consistently danced to the left. [I wonder if this helps to explain why the Serbs and Croats never seem to *dance* together in a political sense].

MACEDONIAN LESNOTO METER 7/8

COUNT: slow-quick-quick

FIGURE 3-3. The 7/8 meter of the Macedonian Lesnoto that produces a slow-quick-quick rhythm for singing and dancing.

BALKAN STATES

FIGURE 3-4. A Map of the Balkan States. Map taken from IMSI Clip Art.

Quickly, my favorite dances became those of Bulgaria with an array of odd meters, complex syncopated steps, and interesting hand holds. Like the Macedonian *lesnoto*, the dance rhythms of most Bulgarian music were made of combinations of eighth or sixteenth notes such that they were sequences of quick and slow steps (see Figure 3-5). Dances like *pajdushko* had a simple quick-slow dance rhythm so that the feel of the dance was like limping (the meaning of the word pajdushko). Others like ruchenitsa (7/16 with a quick-quick-slow dance rhythm) and gankino (11/16 with a quick-quick-slow-quick-quick dance rhythm) were dynamic and physically challenging.

Before long, the folkdance alternative attracted a relatively large group away from the volleyballers. We then began to dance three times a week. By the end of the summer session, I had learned about 30 dances, most of which came from the Balkan region. I was hooked.

After I returned to the main campus I found myself part of the International dance community as well as the graduate student community. More and more I became drawn to events that were put on by the international dancers.

As I continued to learn more and more dances, I noticed that many of them were almost modified walking. Others were so complex that I was surprised that I could learn them at all. The most complex dances we learned to perform in local exhibitions and competitions in places like San Antonio, Texas. As the dances began to pile up, I had to generalize them to keep from being confused. For example, I needed to be able to anticipate the rhythm way, the way in which the dancers joined in a line, and the styling of the body and footwork of dances such as ruchenitsa. As I learned them better, I began to understand what movements were most conservative and which ones could vary.

I could hear the music for a waltz or a ruchenitsa and recognize the particular class of dance to which it belonged because I had a model of those dances in my mind. That is, I had a generalized image that allowed me to anticipate the overall framework of the dance. For example, a Bulgarian ruchenitsa was danced in short lines with the dancers holding their neighbors' belts. They were dynamic or physical with rhythmic bouncing of the legs and the upper torso slightly stooped. If there were a stamp, the Bulgarian styling is a flourish with the foot but not with an earth-shaking sound. This model was somewhat nebulous and served to define a general form and those variations of the fundamental ruchenitsa step that might be possible in the particular dance sequence. This "model" of the dance was descriptive and much less proscriptive than the 7/16 dance music in

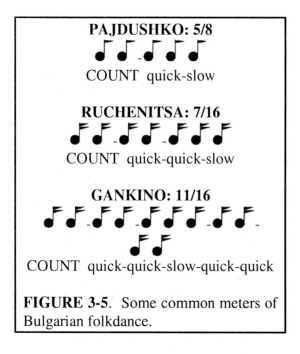

PAJDUSHKO: 5/8

COUNT quick-slow

RUCHENITSA: 7/16

COUNT quick-quick-slow

GANKINO: 11/16

COUNT quick-quick-slow-quick-quick

FIGURE 3-5. Some common meters of Bulgarian folkdance.

phrases of 8 measures (see Figure 3-5).

My friends and I were able to learn so many dances like ruchenitsa because we applied such models to the dances, which we broke down into steps. We learned them as algorithms or sequential solutions. Then, after we repeated them often enough, the steps became almost automatic. I was reminded of this when I tried to recall a Bulgarian ruchenitsa called *Kopceto*. It was a complex dance that took weeks to learn nearly 25 years ago. I had not danced it very often since I moved to Pennsylvania. Still, I had to hear the music only a few times before the music triggered my memories of the steps and their particular sequences. In some ways, this memory of dance as a sequence of movements was similar to the sequence of steps taken in solutions to complex problems. By the time I moved to Pennsylvania in 1981, I had learned nearly 300 dances, more than half of which were from the Balkans. As a new faculty member at Susquehanna University, I made an effort to become part of the campus community and the local community. Still, as busy as I was, I did not want to lose my connection with music and dance. Fortunately, there I found another group of dancers.

A REDUCTION TO NUMBERS[*]
They [the Pythagoreans] supposed the elements of number to be the elements of all things, and the whole heavens to be a musical scale and a number. -Aristotle

Dance and the music on which it is based has an almost mathematical quality. Not only are the meters and rhythms numerically based but scales, and harmonies also have a foundation in number. These relationships had been discovered and explored by one of the earliest natural philosophers called Pythagoras of Samos (580-500 B.C.E.). He was a mathematician who supposed that the underlying reality of nature was number. Born on the Greek island of Samos, Pythagoras seemed to have been such a trouble maker that he moved from place to place until he settled in the city state called Croton in what is now southern Italy. There he seemed to have created a mystical number cult religion with quite a following.

Pythagoras and his followers applied an array of abstract concepts to numbers. For example, odd numbers were male and even numbers were female. Thus, the number 5, the sum of the male number 3 and the female number 2 represented marriage. [Note that this works just as well for the combination of 4 and 1].

One of the most fundamental confirmations of the Pythagorean concept was the relationship between number and music in which the Pythagoreans expressed musical intervals as ratios of whole numbers. For example, a ratio of 1:2 represents an octave-level difference. That is, a vibrating string (or a pan pipe) of two units is an octave lower than a vibrating string (or pan pipe) of 1 unit (see Figure 3-6). A fifth ratio is 3:2 and a fourth ratio is 4:3. Pythagoreans supposed that the intervals of the planets, etc. in the heavens were related in a similar way and resonated in a great heavenly harmonic.[2]

Plato (427-347 B.C.E.), although not a mathematician, encouraged mathematics in the Academy. His student, Eudoxus of Cnidus (408-355 B.C.E.), was one of the

---

[*] I have expanded on most of the information in this section in other essays. If you wish further background, go to *A Man and a Telescope*; and *Principia Mathematica: The Foundation of Modern Physics*.

---

[2] See the essay, *On a Performance of Durufle* for an explanation of resonance.

greatest original mathematicians of the ancient world. Among other things, he sought to provide a geometrical foundation for the earth-centered universe that dominated Greek thought. He supposed that the earth occupied the center of the heavens with a series of nested crystalline spheres surrounding it. He supposed that the uniform circular motion of two or more spheres could explain the complex motions of each of the planets. This concept was so compelling that it became the cosmological concept for the Greeks. Even Aristotle, who had a great mistrust of mathematics, accepted the Eudoxan cosmology and incorporated it into his great theory of everything.

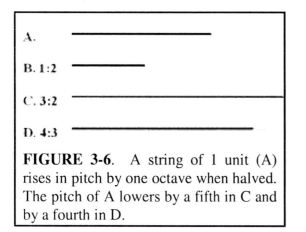

FIGURE 3-6. A string of 1 unit (A) rises in pitch by one octave when halved. The pitch of A lowers by a fifth in C and by a fourth in D.

The Greeks accepted that the cosmology of Eudoxus was a conceptual model of the universe as it really was. Thus, the Eudoxan model was explanatory in that it served to explain how the universe worked. However, the mathematics of that particular model did not accurately predict the motions of the planets; so, more and more, authors of mathematical models of the universe added geometrical tricks to force the Eudoxan model to work. The Greeks recognized that the mathematical model did not really represent reality, but included conventions that allowed

prediction. This mathematical model of the universe was called astronomy. For more than 2,000 years the explanatory conceptual model (cosmology) and the predictive mathematical model (astronomy) existed side by side in the Greek tradition of Natural Philosophy.

The mathematical model of the Eudoxan universe reached its zenith in the work of Claudius Ptolemy (90-168 A.D.) of Alexandria. He assumed that the Earth occupied a position that was nearly but not quite, the center of the universe. Around that spheres moved by uniform circular motion. Then he made some mathematical adjustments. He assumed that a planet occupied a position on a sphere called an epicycle that turned about a point on the fundamental sphere called a deferent.

The Ptolemaic mathematical model worked fairly well to predict planetary positions, but clearly it was not meant as a description of reality. If a planet really went careening about an epicycle centered on a crystalline sphere, the heavenly harmonic would sound like the explosion of shattered glass. The mathematical model worked well enough, though. Ptolemy published the results in a book of tables and description of the mathematical method that we know as *The Almagest*, a corruption of the Arabic translation of the first words of his text. The planetary tables (including lunar tables) were more than idle curiosities. The planets and their positions helped to confirm and determine the calendars of the day.

As useful as they were, the Ptolemaic tables were so far out of whack by the fifteenth century that they were no longer useful. Thus, Nicolas Copernicus (1473-1543) was given the task to produce another *mathematical model* or astronomy that would aid in the creation of a new calendar. Copernicus supposed that the problems with the Ptolemaic geometry would be less pronounced if the sun were stationary in the center of the universe with a series of planets (including the earth) circling the sun. Because he made the orbits obey the old Greek dictum of uniform circular motion, he had to include epicycles in his system, also.

Much had happened in Europe between the time of Ptolemy (ca. 200 A.D) and Copernicus (ca. 1500 A.D.). Following the collapse of the Roman Empire in the west, Christian Europe descended into intellectual darkness. The mathematics and Natural Philosophy of the Greek tradition was kept alive in the Eastern Roman Empire and the Islamic Empire. Through the latter, the writings of the ancients were introduced to Western Europe. Initially, the philosophy of Aristotle was adopted by the western church and adapted to its doctrines. Thus, by the time of Copernicus, the Aristolelian-Eudoxan Cosmology was not just a conceptual model of reality, it was religious dogma. So, to propose that the universe was anything other than earth-centered was dangerous. Still, Copernicus, a Canon of the Church had nothing to fear because the church understood that he was producing an astronomy (Many indications in the text of his book, however, suggest that he thought of his system as a mathematical model and as a cosmology).

The real problem with Copernicus for the church in Rome came long after his death when when Galileo Galilei (1564-1642) and Johannes Kepler (1571-1630), both mathematicians and Pythagoreans, began to convert the Copernican astronomy to a cosmology. They not only stated that the predictions would be easier if the sun were in the center of the universe. They said that the sun really was in the center of the universe and that the mathematical model was a predictive model of reality. Thus, the astronomy-cosmology dichotomy disappeared at the dawn of the modern period of science.

Galileo invented the concept of the experimental method in which he sought to reduce the explanation of physical phenomena like falling bodies to mathematical models. Then, the philosophy of Rene Descartes (1596-1650) suggested that the universe was a mechanism and mechanical mathematical models could be created to explain and predict natural phenomena.

The Pythagorean ideal and Cartesian mechanics came together in the work of Isaac Newton (1642-1727), who defined a law of gravity and a relationship (F=ma) that together explained the motions of the planets and interactions of objects on earth. The Newtonian mathematical model was powerful and compelling because it was both explanatory and predictive. Indeed, the concept of a physical law was (and remains) the general mathematical expression of a phenomenon, and all explanations of that phenomenon must be consistent with the laws that govern it. The success of the mechanical philosophy then supported the fledgling science of what was to become chemistry. The well-established mathematical models of both physics and chemistry became the physical laws of science.

COMPLEXITY AND GAMES

Biologists, it is said, suffer from physics envy. They build physics-like models that lead from the microscopic to the macroscopic, but find it difficult to match them with the messy systems that they find in the real world.

-E. O. Wilson (1998)

The translation of more complex phenomena like climate, geology, and living systems into the mode of the mathematical law-explanation model of the physical sciences was very difficult. Biological laws were formulated, but they were rarely mathematical in form and almost entirely explanatory. Consider, for example, Darwin's great Law of Natural Selection. This had enormous explanatory power in that it served as an explanation for the amazing diversity of life on earth. However, it could not begin to predict the course of evolutionary change that any single line might take. So, the law that served as the explanatory foundation for the unifying Principle of Evolution could not function in explanation and prediction as mathematical laws within the physical sciences did. Nevertheless, all explanations of complex phenomena in biology had to be reducible to and consistent with the laws of chemistry and physics. Thus, all of the sciences became a community in the sense that they were united by the logic of explanation.

Biological and environmental phenomena began to be quantified in a real sense after the creation of the mathematics of probability, also called statistics. This area of mathematics seemed to have grown from an attempt to better understand games of chance. Blaise Pascal (1623-1662) and Pierre de Fermat (1601-1665) began to consider a problem put to them by some dice-playing friends of theirs. If a game of dice were interrupted prematurely, what should be the pay off to the players? In a series of letters exchanged by the mathematicians probability theory evolved.

Consider a simple system, a coin toss of heads or tails. The probability of tossing heads is 1 of 2 or 50%. This does not mean that the coin will land heads then tails then heads, etc. Instead, it means that of a population of coin tosses 50% should be heads and 50% should be tails. However, if two independent events are tied together, the probability becomes the product of the two probabilities. That is, the probability of tossing heads twice in a row is ½ times ½ or ¼. Similarly, the probability of tossing 3 consecutive heads is ½ X ½ X ½ or 1/8. The problem of the dice was even more complex because each die had 6 faces, each with an equal chance (1/6) to be face up. Thus, the likelihood of rolling two sixes or snake eyes (two ones) was 1/36 for each one.

By the 19th Century, an understanding of probability had produced sophisticated tests that could aid in discriminating between the variation within a group and that between groups. Gregor Mendel (1822-1844) used an understanding of probability to establish his laws of heredity. However, his probabilistic laws explained patterns of inheritance in populations of peas, but could not predict the inheritance of any particular pea plant with the same exactness that the law of gravity could predict the gravitational attraction between the sun and a planet. Then, the great edifice of the mechanical Newtonian universe began to crumble. Even problems in physics like turbulence and later the problems of Quantum Mechanics required probabilistic explanations and predictions. Statistics became a necessary mathematical tool for exploring these and other complex systems such as ecology, weather, epidemiology, etc. Still, the ability to model such systems required the creation of new kinds of mathematics and new technologies.

PRISONER'S DILEMMA

If people do not believe that mathematics is simple, it is only because they do not realize how complicated life is.

-John von Neumann

Only Albert Einstein influenced the interface of science, technology, and mathematics as much as John von Neumann (1903-1957) did during the first half of the 20th Century. By and large, he did not create areas of mathematics or technology, but frequently he did see ways to improve and expand existing processes. He was born in Budapest, Hungary in 1903, and very early displayed the nature of his genius. Everything seemed to fascinate him as he explored history, languages, and of course mathematics. Once when he was six, von Neumann saw his mother in a daydream staring into space. The boy asked her what she was calculating. His love for numbers and mathematics stayed with him for the rest of his life.

His father, a practical man, encouraged his son's genius but also pushed young Johnny to take a degree in chemical engineering at the Universities of Berlin and Zurich. At the same time, von Neumann entered the University of Budapest to pursue a Ph.D. in mathematics. He received his B.S. in Chemical Engineering and his Ph.D. in Mathematics in 1926, when he was 22. He received both degrees with highest honors.

With the rise of fascism Europe, the Jewish academic found the doors of opportunity closed to him. In 1929 Princeton University invited von Neumann to join its faculty as a visiting lecturer, and he accepted. In 1933 he became one of the charter members of Princeton's Institute of Advanced Study (IAS).

Von Neumann's agile mind helped to create and formalize the mathematics necessary to describe Quantum Mechanics. In addition, he explored almost all aspects of mathematics. Later, he served on the Manhattan Project where his expertise in the mathematics of complex systems such as hydrodynamics, ballistics, meteorology, game theory, and statistics made him invaluable. He contributed to the implosion mechanism necessary for the detonation of the plutonium bomb (the fat boy bomb) and made it work.

While still in Europe, von Neumann became intrigued by the complex bluff and counter bluff of games like poker. He decided to model the process and helped to found an area of mathematics called game theory. One of the models of game theory that explored decisions and interactions between two competing parties (like competitors in a poker game) was known as the Prisoner's Dilemma. The scenario for this model was that two men were taken prisoner, both suspected of being in on a robbery. They were taken into separate rooms for interrogation where each one was offered a lighter sentence if he will testify against the other one. Because there was insufficient evidence, the prisoners might go free or serve a light sentence if they cooperate and do not testify. However, if they both defect, both will serve the full sentence. Von Neumann modeled the process by payoff tables like those in Tables 3-1 and 3-2.

Models of behavior like Prisoner's Dilemma, illustrated that given an array of advantages and penalties, even the most selfish competitors benefit by cooperation *most of the time*. He realized quickly that this theory would explain far more than just how competitors behave in a game. He saw that it could explain complex interactions like the distribution of resources in economic systems, strategies of war, diplomatic interactions between governments, etc. Further, the model also served to explain other relationships like predator-prey interactions; host-parasite relationships, social behavior of animals, plant pollination strategies, symbiotic associations as in the fungus and alga in a lichen, and the interplay between genetics and environment in Natural Selection. This was a very powerful theory for the interplay of complex entities.

TABLE 3-1. A potential payoff scheme for Prisoner's Dilemma in which the advantage (and penalty) for defection is great.

	Cooperate	Defect
Cooperate	3,3	5,0
Defect	0,5	-1,-1

TABLE 3-2. A potential payoff scheme for Prisoner's Dilemma in which there is almost no advantage or penalty for defection.

	Cooperate	Defect
Cooperate	3,3	4,2
Defect	2,4	2,2

Iterations of the Prisoner's Dilemma scenario suggested that the strategy of cooperation was good one. However, an occasional defection might give the greatest benefit to one of the players. A way to counter that was to adopt a policy of repeated retaliation against a defector.

Still, even when the advantage for defection was almost nonexistent as in Table 2, players still defected at least once in more than half of the games. Knowing this, and the consequences of a single defection in the "game" of thermonuclear war, von Neumann advocated *Preventative War* against the Soviet Union after it gained a nuclear capability.

The incredible number of calculations necessary to model aspects of a weapon of mass destruction (particular experiments were not only destructive and dangerous, they were also very expensive) brought von Neumann and others to the question of automating the millions of calculations that were necessary to provide speed and accuracy. Von Neumann commented that the number of calculations required for the Manhattan Project and the development of the thermonuclear bomb required more calculations than had been calculated up to that point in the history of humanity. He later repented of that hyperbole, but his point was well taken. The more calculations, the more time required and the greater opportunity for human error.

To address this and other computational problems, Von Neumann, who earlier had had Alan Turing (1912-1954) as a student, helped to define the current architecture that we identify as the modern computer. In essence he said that a computer had to have the following "major organs":
1. arithmetic
2. memory
3. control
4. connection with a human operator

Most anyone who uses a computer would recognize the organs as common components of a typical computer. Arithmetic refers to the kinds of operations performed by a computer with its binary code. Memory refers to the ability to store information, both programs and data. Control refers to a central unit (now called a central processing unit or CPU) that manages the fundamental sequence of steps necessary to perform the arithmetic operations on the program and the data. The fourth organ, connection with the human operator, is called input and output. Perhaps the most important contribution was that the program would be stored like the data and, therefore, easily modified or changed. Up to that time, the instructions were hard wired into the calculating machines.

Von Neumann died prematurely of cancer, almost certainly brought on by nuclear weapons testing. Always the workaholic, he spent the last year of his life in a wheelchair but remained active as an advisor to corporations (IBM, Rand, etc.) and government (the Atomic Energy Commission, etc). He used the platform of the computer to model the process of thought and to explore the essential logic of what makes a living thing. He had a dream that the computer would help to make all areas of science more precise and logical. Whether or not that dream has come true is up to question. Certainly, the computer has become an essential component of all scientific disciplines and many others beyond science.

NEW MODELS

...in real life mistakes are likely to be irrevocable. Computer simulation, however, makes it economically practical to make mistakes on purpose.
-John McLeod and John Osborn (1966)

With the advent of the computer, mathematical models become very powerful in that they allowed their users to explore questions at different scales in time and space. Such models even

allowed interaction with the program and experiment with a range of possibilities. Thus, through the use of computer-based mathematical models, science can make complex calculations of the movements of comets, predict the positions of the continental plates in the next 50 million years, consider credible scenarios of climate change, compare thousands of DNA base sequences, and explain the collapse of the twin towers of the World Trade Center.

One of the first applications of computer models to science was in the understanding of ecosystems. Figure 3-7 illustrates a model of a grassland ecosystem published in 1969. The model attempts to describe the flow of energy within the ecosystem and between its components. Figure 3-7a shows the different components (or compartments) for which measured values of living mass can be inserted and predicted. The arrows indicate the rate of movement of organic matter from one compartment to the next. Figure 3-7b indicates the rate equations applied to each of the arrows.

VanDyne reported that the output of the model mimicked actual field data very well. The agreement between the model and observations in Figure 3-7 indicates that VanDyne succeeded in abstracting the important features of the grassland. Thus, the model could serve as a means to explain the grassland ecosystem. The power of a computer model is that VanDyne then could "experiment" with the components and test hypotheses that would be impossible or unethical to do in real life. Thus, this model could be used to predict changes in the grassland in response to particular perturbations, both catastrophic (like fire) and long-term (like an increase in community respiration due to climate change). The grassland ecosystem model can be generalized and applied to other ecosystems and even to   economic systems.

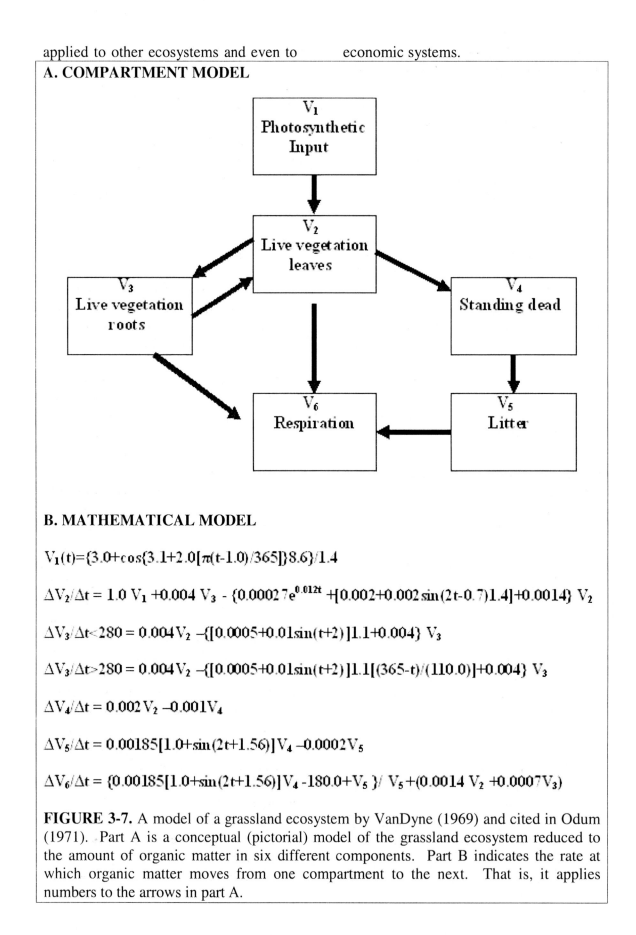

A. COMPARTMENT MODEL

V_1
Photosynthetic
Input

V_2
Live vegetation
leaves

V_3
Live vegetation
roots

V_4
Standing dead

V_6
Respiration

V_5
Litter

B. MATHEMATICAL MODEL

$V_1(t) = \{3.0 + \cos\{3.1 + 2.0[\pi(t-1.0)/365]\}8.6\}/1.4$

$\Delta V_2/\Delta t = 1.0\ V_1 + 0.004\ V_3 - \{0.00027e^{0.012t} + [0.002 + 0.002\sin(2t-0.7)1.4] + 0.0014\}\ V_2$

$\Delta V_3/\Delta t < 280 = 0.004\ V_2 - \{[0.0005 + 0.01\sin(t+2)]1.1 + 0.004\}\ V_3$

$\Delta V_3/\Delta t > 280 = 0.004\ V_2 - \{[0.0005 + 0.01\sin(t+2)]1.1[(365-t)/(110.0)] + 0.004\}\ V_3$

$\Delta V_4/\Delta t = 0.002\ V_2 - 0.001 V_4$

$\Delta V_5/\Delta t = 0.00185[1.0 + \sin(2t+1.56)]V_4 - 0.0002 V_5$

$\Delta V_6/\Delta t = \{0.00185[1.0 + \sin(2t+1.56)]V_4 - 180.0 + V_5\}/\ V_5 + (0.0014\ V_2 + 0.0007 V_3)$

FIGURE 3-7. A model of a grassland ecosystem by VanDyne (1969) and cited in Odum (1971). Part A is a conceptual (pictorial) model of the grassland ecosystem reduced to the amount of organic matter in six different components. Part B indicates the rate at which organic matter moves from one compartment to the next. That is, it applies numbers to the arrows in part A.

Nowhere are such models more important than in predicting weather and weather-related events. These are very complex and require a whole battery of equations that take into account the turbulent movements of air, both vertically and horizontally, and the movements of heat, and water. The equations then rely on the input of an array of local weather data like wind, temperature, atmospheric pressure, and relative humidity, all of which literally change from moment to moment. Of course, such models cannot give precise solutions. Indeed, even for a particular storm event, the same model can give more than one solution as a range of probability. Still, the utility of such models is easy to see in the prediction and mitigation of flood events, hurricane tracks and the likelihood of severe storms.

I recall about five years ago in the wake of flooding in the Red River basin of the northern plains, I heard one official who was angry with the National Weather Service because their prediction for the crest of the Red River was off by 2 feet. On the other hand, I was amazed that they could get within 10 feet.

MODELS GOOD AND BAD

For purposes here, a model will be taken to be an analogue or analogy that assists or promotes the gradual understanding of something not readily grasped in sense experience.

-William A. Wallace (1996)

Models practical or esoteric have to satisfy particular functions. How well they do that depends on an understanding of the phenomenon and on the ability to abstract that phenomenon. John Casti points out that a good scientific model has three important attributes:

1. Simplicity
2. Clarity
3. Bias-free

Simplicity speaks for itself. The purpose of a model is to define the salient features that govern or define a particular phenomenon. By necessity, that means the elimination of the least important components of that phenomenon. Clarity goes hand in hand with the concept of simplicity. Useful models must be understood by the group of scientists, policy makers, etc. for which it was created. The components have to be clearly defined so that they provide the same answers to all who use the model. A model free of bias is one in the components can be measured objectively. The last two characteristics, clarity and bias-free, aside from being attributes of good models, also serve to distinguish scientific models from religion and pseudoscience.

In Table 3-3 I have attempted to evaluate some of the models presented in this essay according to Casti's criteria for good models. Clearly, models do not have to be correct to be good. For example, Ptolemy's model of the universe passed all of Casti's criteria. It even passed the prediction criterion. As a model, therefore, it was a good one. However, it did not model reality.

Newton's model for universal gravitation also passed all of Casti's requirements. Its explanatory and predictive powers are prodigious. That is why the gravitation model is a physical law. Nevertheless, the nature of gravity itself remains a mystery (thus the question mark).

More complex models like Prisoner's Dilemma, ecosystem models and weather models do not really pass all of Casti's criteria. Nevertheless, I would

115

argue that they still are useful to science, and society. The simplicity criterion, the basis on which ecosystem and weather models fail, is mitigated by the use of the computer.

Of course, I did not expect my model of Bulgarian ruchenitsa to fare well. Although it is simple, the model is not clear. No words can express the footwork combined with the styling. A student might actually learn the dance only in the traditional folk style. That is, directly from the movements of an experienced dancer. Also, the model is not bias-free. I hear the music, and I am transported. On the other hand, my children, want to be transported when they hear a Bulgarian gaida and frula.

Bulgarian music and dance, however, can be compared with the dances of the other Balkan countries. In a general sense, the music of Greece, Bulgaria, and Macedonia tend to have odd meters and the dances elsewhere tend to be variations of 2/4 meters. If one were to overlay the extent of the Ottoman Empire onto Europe, the longest unbroken Turkish occupation would be up into the Balkans and engulf northern Greece, Macedonia, and Bulgaria. Turkish music also tends to be in odd meters. Thus, a musicologist can explain the similarities of the music from these regions based on their histories. The dance model is not less good than the other ones because it is not mathematical (except in a Pythagorean sense), it is less good because it relies on trying to generalize value judgments and arbitrary aspects of culture.

TABLE 3-3. An evaluation of some models according to John Casti's criteria for good models. I added whether or not the models can predict or explain the phenomena.

MODEL	SIMPLICITY	CLARITY	BIAS-FREE	PREDICTION	EXPLANATION
PTOLEMY	YES	YES	YES	YES	NO
GRAVITY	YES	YES	YES	YES	YES?
PRISONER'S DILEMMA	YES	MAYBE	MAYBE	YES	MAYBE
ECOSYSTEM	NO	YES	YES	YES	YES
WEATHER	NO	YES	YES	YES	MAYBE
MY DANCE	YES	NO	NO	MAYBE	YES

From the time of Galileo when experimentation and the reduction of nature to mathematics began to happen, it seemed as though the Pythagorean ideal would come to fruition. However, many aspects of nature simply cannot reduce to number except in a descriptive sense. Consider the following: a fast ruchenitsa, a swimming dinoflagellate, and parallel lines. All three are real. However, they occupy different realities. The swimming dinoflagellate is a type of organism that has occupied the earth for hundreds of millions of years. The ruchenitsa has been part of culture for hundreds or maybe a thousand years. Both of these occupy the realm of nature. They were not determined to be and nature will continue without them. The matter of parallel lines, on the other hand, is independent of nature. In Euclidian geometry, parallel lines never meet, that is an axiom, a fundamental truth. In non-Euclidian geometries, parallel lines may meet, also an axiom for that mathematical system. Which is correct? They both are, each within its own system. Nature exists in only one system, and science must make sense of it through observation. As Albert Einstein put it, "As far as the laws of mathematics refer to reality, they are not certain; and as far as they are certain, they do not refer to reality."

Consider the Ptolemaic Model of the universe. It made no pretense to emulate reality. Thus, it was not explanatory. Mathematically it was internally consistent and analytically correct. It just did not describe the particular nature of this universe. So, mathematics can describe this universe and many others (the basis of quite a few computer games and questions in pure mathematics). Like partners in dance, though, mathematics and science can move together. When they do, the result can be a thing of beauty like the ecosystem and the law of gravity.

-1997; revised 2002

FIGURE 3-8. The finale of a partner dance from the Ukraine called Hopak.

References:

Casti, John L. *Five Golden Rules, Great Theories of 20th Century Mathematics - and Why They Matter.* John Wiley and Sons, Inc. New York.

Casti, John L. 1997. *Would-Be Worlds.* John Wiley and Sons, Inc. New York.

Fundenberg, Drew and Jean Tirole. 1992. *Game Theory.* MIT Press. Cambridge, Mass.

Gardner, Martin. 1996. *How Not to Talk About Mathematics.* In: *The Night is Large, Collected Essays, 1938-1995.* St. Martin's Press. New York. pp 280-293.

Grattan-Guiness, Ivor. 1998. *The Norton History of the Mathematical Sciences.* W.W. Norton & Co. New York.

Hilborn, Ray and Marc Mangel. 1997. *The Ecological Detective, Confronting Models With Data.* Monographs in Population Biology no. 28. Princeton University Press. Princeton, New Jersey.

Hollingdale, Stuart. 1989. *Makers of Mathematics.* Penguin Books USA, Inc. New York.

Odum, Eugene P. 1971. *Fundamentals of Ecology.* Third ed. W.B. Saunders Co. Philadelphia.

Poundstone, William.1992. *Prisoner's Dilemma.* Doubleday. New York.

Porter, Theodore M. 1995. *Trust in Numbers, The Pursuit of Objectivity in Science and Public Life.* Princeton University Press. Princeton, New Jersey.

Von Neumann, John and Oskar Morgenstern. 1944. *Theory of Games and Economic Behavior.* John Wiley & Sons, Inc. New York.

Wallace, William A. 1996. *The Modeling of Nature.* The Catholic University of America Press. Washington, D.C.

Weibull, Jorgen W. 1995. *Evolutionary Game Theory.* MIT Press. Cambridge, Mass.

Wilson, Edward O. 1998. *Consilience, The Unity of Knowledge.* Alfred A. Knopf. New York.

Questions to Think About

1. What is meant by meter in music?

2. I said that the steps of a dance were a kind of algorithm. What did I mean by that?

3. Who was Pythagoras? How did he use mathematics to model music?

4. What was the major difference between the Eudoxan and Copernican models of the universe? Which one was an attempt to mimic reality by a mathematical model?

5. What are the differences between the laws of the physical sciences and the laws of the natural sciences (e.g. biology, geology, ecology)?

6. What is the probability of rolling a four with a 6-sided die? What is the probability of rolling a four and a six with a pair of 6-sided dice?

7. Who was John von Neumann? What did he define as the necessary "organs" of the electronic computer?

8. What is the concept of Prisoner's Dilemma? How can this game be applied to other situations? What does it suggest about the interactions of complex phenomena?

9. Why are complex phenomena like ecosystems often subjected to mathematical

models? Why would a researcher choose to create a model rather than do an experiment with an ecosystem?

10. What are John Casti's attributes of useful models?

11. How are prediction and explanation different?

MAPS AS MODELS

A STONE MAP

As one drives along secondary roads in the rolling country in northeastern Oklahoma, in the environs of the Delaware powwow grounds near Copan, he will see here and there an isolated cedar, the gnarled limbs of old peach and apple trees, or the decaying logs that were once part of the walls of a cabin.

-C. A. Weslager (1972)

In the mid 1970's I went on a trek through land that had been granted to the Delaware Nation (also known as Lene Lenape) when they were moved into Oklahoma (then called Indian Territory; see Figure 3-9). A reservoir then under construction was to inundate some of their important sites, not the least of which were the remains of their last working long house. Anyway, I recall that we were side tracked by dinner and extended conversation with a colorful local rancher whom I knew only as Uncle Joe. He was a large man with flowing white hair and deep creases in his weathered face. He was one of the first settlers to move into Oklahoma Territory and had become something of a legend in the area. After our lunch and talk Joe happened to mention a stone map on his land. The archeologist could barely contain himself and prevailed upon the old man to take us there. He walked us up a clearing that had been cut for a power line right of way and then led us into a cross timber forest of mixed black jack and post oak. We fought to keep up with him as he guided us through the wooded hillside to an area covered by oak leaves that for all the world looked like the rest of the woods. He pulled out a rake that he had stashed next to a rock. He gave me the handle and told me where to remove the leaves. Soon I had exposed what looked like a small stone patio. Some of the features of the stone had been enhanced by a chisel to illustrate hills and streams. Joe said that the map had been shown to him by an old Delaware who claimed that it was at least as old as he was.

Joe said that he had spent some time studying that map and tried to correlate it with local surface features, but no place seemed to fit. The archeologist studied the map for some time and then became very excited. He asked for a boost up into a tree and studied the map some time longer. Finally he announced that he thought that we had been trying to interpret the map at the wrong scale. He suggested that if the carved hills represented the Appalachian Mountains and the creek were the Mississippi River, then the stone map might represent most of the eastern half of the United States. I stood in awe as the rock patio transformed itself before my eyes.

The world transforms itself when it presents itself in two dimensions as a map. The pictorial representation of surface features of the earth or part of it imparts knowledge and power over the unknown. Consider your own use of maps in navigating your car or perhaps even a boat. The ability to know where you are demands that you accept the lines on a sheet of paper as a conceptual model of the reality of a place.

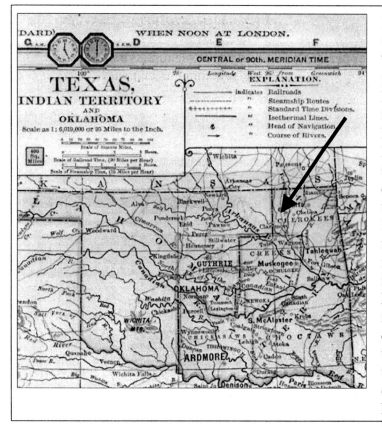

FIGURE 3-9. A map of Oklahoma and Indian Territories from 1899 published by the Philadelphia Inquirer. The arrow indicates the location of the stone map. By this time, the Delaware Nation had become part of the Cherokee Nation in an economic confederation. Note the gridwork of latitude and longitude in which the map is framed. Note also that the map indicates the differences in time between that of London and the time in that zone. All of these conventions were centuries in the making and the story of their development is the theme of this essay.

From The Philadelphia Inquirer Co. (1899)

TO MEASURE THE EARTH

There was among them a man of genius but as he was working in a new field they were too stupid to recognize him. As usual in those cases they proved not his second-rateness but only their own.

-George Sarton (1964)

Similarly, the world transformed itself in the minds of ancient philosophers as they accepted the concept of the earth as a sphere. Pythagoras first proposed it. Plato, Eudoxus, and Aristotle conceptualized it and Eratosthenes demonstrated it at the time of a summer solstice in ancient Alexandria.

Eratosthenes of Cyrene (c. 276-194 B.C.E) was a versatile natural philosopher of his time. He contributed to geography, and mathematics, literature, etc. Because of his versatility, the newly installed Greek rulers of Egypt asked him to be the head of the Library at Alexandria. This library, also known as the Museum because it was dedicated to the Muses, the deities of inspiration, was more than a collection of books. It was a government-sponsored site for research and contemplation. The site quickly attracted the great minds in mathematics and natural philosophy throughout the Mediterranean region. The setting seemed to foster specialists rather than a generalist like Eratosthenes. He bore the scorn often heaped upon an administrator by members of an institution and began to be called "Beta" or second rate and "Pentatholos", one who excels in many things but is master of none. Still, this generalist made some contributions to science that cannot be ignored even today.

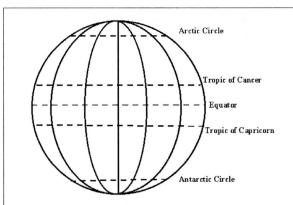

FIGURE 3-10. The globe of the earth with the relative positions of the Tropic of Cancer, Tropic of Capricorn, the Arctic and Antarctic Circles, and the Equator. Eratosthenes used a knowledge of the Tropic of Cancer to determine the size and shape of the earth.

It seems that Eratosthenes helped to establish the apparent seasonal path of the sun (and stars) across the sky. He and others at Alexandria assumed that the paths of the sun and planets (called the ecliptic) were inclined to the equatorial plane of the earth by about 24° (Note that today we say that the earth is inclined 23.5^O to the ecliptic of the solar system). Thus, the sun seemed to be directly over the equator at the times of the fall and spring equinoxes. It was over a line about 24° north of the equator (Tropic of Cancer) on the day of the summer solstice before it began its trip south to a line over 24° south of the equator (the Tropic of Capricorn) at the time of the Winter Solstice (see Figure 3-10).

Probably while contemplating this problem, Eratosthenes heard that the town of Syene had a well that was illuminated all the way to the bottom around noon on the day of the summer solstice. He reasoned that Syene must lie on the Tropic of Cancer and that at noon on the Summer Solstice, the sun shone from directly overhead. Thus, a well could be illuminated and vertical sticks cast no shadows. He did know that on the same day, a large stone obelisk called a gnomon

did cast a shadow in Alexandria. That was all that he needed to know to demonstrate that the earth was a sphere and to determine its diameter.

Eratosthenes knew the height of the gnomon and measured the length of the shadow that it cast at noon on the Summer Solstice. That meant that he knew two sides of a right triangle (a triangle in which one of the three angles is 90°) and could calculate the other side. More importantly, he could calculate the angle that the ray of the sun made with the top of the Gnomon which is the same as the angle at the center of the earth between Syene and Alexandria (See Figures 3-11 and 3-12).

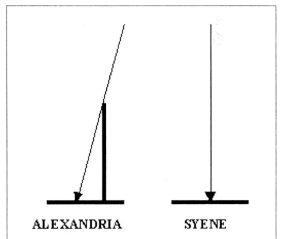

ALEXANDRIA   **SYENE**

FIGURE 3-11. At noon on the day of the Summer Solstice (the longest day of the year in the northern hemisphere), an obelisk casts a shadow in Alexandria while on the same day, the sun shines to the bottom of a well in Syene.

He knew that a camel caravan took about 50 days to make the trip from Syene to Alexandria. Furthermore, he knew that a caravan traveled at about 100 stadia per day. Thus, the total distance was about 5,000 stadia (or about 725 km). He knew from his measurements of the angle of the shadow from the top of the Gnomon (see Figures 3-11 and 3-12) in Alexandria that the arc from Syene to Alexandria was just over 7° (or 1/50th of a circle). Thus, the circumference of the earth must be about 50 times 5,000 stadia or 250,000 stadia (1 km approximately equaled 5.4 stadia) thus 46,300 km (actually it is about 40,000 km). Remarkably, Eratosthenes produced a number that was unsurpassed in accuracy for the next 20 centuries.

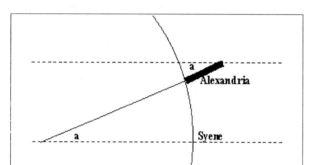

FIGURE 3-12. The angle (a) at the top of the gnomon is equal to the angle (a) between Alexandria and Syene at the center of the earth.

This was a breathtaking example of the ability of the human mind to create a conceptual model of the earth and then use that model to come to an answer. Sadly because Eratosthenes was derided as second rate by the other natural philosophers of the Library, his numbers were not accepted and his conclusions were suspect. Others confirmed the spherical nature of the earth also by the use of celestial observations. Thus, the technique of taking measurements of stars, moon, and sun to determine geography had been established.

PTOLEMY'S GEOGRAPHICA

The task of Geography is to survey the whole in its just proportions, as one would the entire head.

-Claudius Ptolemy (ca. 90-170)

One of the most celebrated members of the Library (nearly five centuries after the time of Eratosthenes) was Claudius Ptolemy. He is most well known for the mathematical model of the universe that he published in the book that we know as *The Almagest*. He also wrote a book that we know as *Geographica* or *Geography*. This work was a major influence on the way that those who followed in the Greek philosophical tradition viewed the earth for the next 1,000 years.

Geographica was a careful compilation of Greek geographic speculation. In it he defined the discipline of geography and the methods by which maps should be drawn. In addition, he added a compendium of place names and their descriptions. Most importantly, he included a collection of 26 maps, one of which was a map of the known inhabited world.

Ptolemy accepted a revision of Eratosthenes' estimate of the global circumference. This put it at 25% smaller than the current globe. Furthermore, he assumed that the known inhabited lands occupied 1/2 or 180° of the globe. So, he stretched the continents of Europe and Asia over half of the earth.

Ptolemy used the known positions of major cities as benchmarks in drawing his maps. These positions had been determined by astronomical observations and filled in the coast lines and terrestrial features by using descriptions from travelogues, mariners, etc. Ptolemy also indicated that his maps should be modified as more accurate geographical information became available.

He recognized that the spherical nature of the earth required that any map of a large area must be a projection that distorted the surface. He chose to use a conic projection that showed the known world from the Atlantic Ocean in the west to Asia in the east. He showed most of the known northern hemisphere and part of the southern hemisphere including part of Africa. He assumed that the earth must be balanced so the southern hemisphere should have a land mass at least comparable to that in the north. He called the unknown continent Terra Australis (the southern land).

In the tradition of Greek geography and cartography, Ptolemy thought of the earth's sphere as being covered by a regular grid of east-west and north-south lines. The lines divided the globe along 360° in the north-south plane and the east-west plane. The equator made a natural line from which to begin the designation of the east west parallels of latitude. He designated the equator as 0° and the poles as 90°.

Perpendicular to the parallels of latitude, Ptolemy set up lines or meridians of longitude. These lines were not parallel. Instead, they converged at the poles and exhibited greatest divergence at the equator. Unlike the lines of latitude, the starting point or 0° longitude was arbitrary. Ptolemy placed it in the Atlantic Ocean just west of all landmasses. He numbered the longitudinal lines from that point eastward. Thus, Ptolemy could designate any point on earth by two sets of numbers in the grid. Not only could he designate the position by degrees, but each degree was divided into 60 minutes and each minute was divided into 60 seconds. Thus he could designate particular sites on earth with great precision.

The grid as described was regular on the globe of the earth, but it became distorted as it was flattened out into two dimensions as a map. If distortion was a natural result of projecting the 3 dimensions onto 2, why would anyone do it? Well, globes are cumbersome and anything but portable. Maps can be rolled, folded and are very portable. Besides, to have a globe that is as detailed as a typical road map would require a sphere many stories in diameter. Thus, the utility of maps is evident, despite the necessary distortions.

Still, Ptolemy sought to minimize the level of distortion in the world maps by producing a projection that translated the globe of the earth into a cone and then just unrolled the cone into a flat sheet. The parallels of latitude were low, sweeping u's and the longitudinal lines diverged from a parallel near the pole to the equator where they began to converge again in the southern hemisphere. His projections of the world allowed for a distortion that retained the relative sizes of the land masses. However, it did distort directions and distances. Thus, it was useful as a picture of the earth but not very helpful as a navigational tool. However, he did add other regional maps that had little distortion and could be used to estimate direction and distance.

Because his *Geography* was so comprehensive and carefully written, it served as the model for cartography from that point on. With it began cartographic conventions such as placing north on the top and east on the right of maps, and the division of degrees by minutes and seconds (rather than the old fractional method). The successors of Greek learning in the Islamic Empire augmented maps of Ptolemy but kept the cartographic conventions in place. They followed Ptolemy's methods and added to his maps by the methods that Ptolemy described. Maps and collections of maps appeared all over the Islamic Empire housed in great libraries that were patterned after the library at Alexandria.

MERCATOR'S ATLAS

[Mercator] set out, for scholars, travelers, and seafarers to see with their own eyes, a most accurate description of the world in large format, projecting the globe on to a flat surface by a new and convenient device, which corresponded so closely to the squaring of the circle that nothing, as I have often heard from his own mouth, seemed to be lacking except formal proof

.-Walter Ghim (1569)[3]

Western Europe became introduced to philosophy in the tradition of the Greeks when one of the great Islamic libraries fell in 1089 to a Christian army in Toledo. In this way, the impoverished Europeans began to appreciate the intellectual riches of the Greeks and Arabs. Educated Europeans from this point on were schooled in the tradition that the earth was a sphere. Thus, Columbus never believed that he might fall off the edge of a flat earth. However, he did accept the Ptomlemaic view that the inhabited world stretched halfway across the globe. Also, he seemed to have calculated the remaining ocean between the Canary Islands and Asia was only about 4,300 km (the actual distance from Spain westward to Asia was almost 20,000 km). Fortunately for Columbus, the Americas happened to be about where he expected to find Asia. The discovery of the New World set off a flurry of exploration by Europeans. In order to accomplish the discovery in a successful and profitable way, however, maps that were more accurate had to be generated. Flanders was one of the principle map-making areas during the 16th Century and one of its most innovative map makers was

Gerardus Mercator (born Gerhard Kremer; 1512-1594). He was the son of an impoverished German immigrant to Flanders and was raised by a more well to do uncle who determined the course of the rest of his life. Mercator graduated from the University of Louvain and then traveled Europe before he returned to Louvain and studied mathematics and its applications to astronomy and geography. Later he learned methods of engraving and making instruments. All of these methods served him well as a successful mapmaker. After 1535 Mercator began to make globes and maps. In 1538 he produced a map with a new projection. It was somewhat similar to the map of Ptolemy but it showed the whole earth.

Mercator understood that projections such as his 1538 map, although innovative, perpetuated some of the problems that had been common to maps of all projections up to that point. In particular the distortion necessary to "flatten the globe" made most world maps poorly suited for navigation., something that the dawning Age of Discovery required. Mercator realized that he could do that but would have to introduce distortions in distance and size, particularly for land masses near the poles. Thus Mercator created his most famous map projection (see Figure 3-13). The great modification for which Mercator is remembered allowed navigators to plot straight line courses. So, the angles relative to north (or any other cardinal direction) were constant. However, distances varied as one plotted courses farther from the equator. Still, the advantages far outweighed the disadvantages. Besides, smaller more local maps could be used to judge distance.

---

[3] This was quoted in Wilford (2000).

He used this philosophy when he published his collection of maps, much like that of Ptolemy and other mapmakers. He published a Mercactor projection of the earth with a collection of regional maps and began his book with a genealogy of the Titan named Atlas, the Greco-Roman God who had the task of supporting the heavens on his shoulders. Ever since then such a collection of maps has been called an atlas.

The synergy between maps and navigation helped to improve the general understanding of the earth, its oceans, and continental boundaries at an accelerating rate. Exploration of the kind fostered by better maps also supported colonial expansion of the Western powers and helped to reap fantastic wealth from trade and conquest. Thus, colonial, economic, and military prowess depended upon accurate maps and the means of finding oneself on those maps. Those could be achieved only by the careful use of precision instruments that could measure both earth and sky.

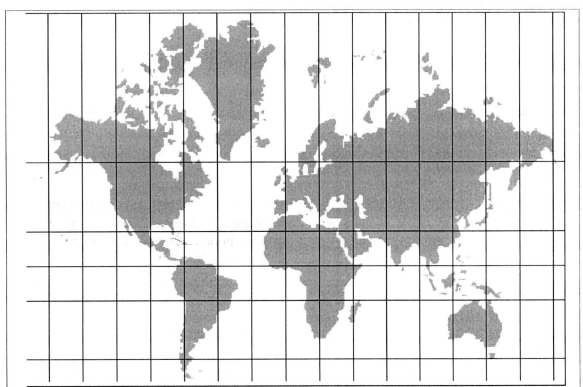

FIGURE 3-13. The modern outline map of the earth illustrates the Mercator projection with gradual elongation of the longitudinal lines toward the poles. In this projection, the latitudinal and longitudinal lines are always perpendicular to each other. Also, the lines of longitude are always parallel. The poles cannot be shown in this projection. The Greenland problem illustrates the distortion inherent to this kind of projection. The surface area of South America is about eight times that of Greenland; however, because of size distortion near the poles, Greenland appears to about the same size as South America on a Mercator projection.

MAPMAKER'S TOOLS

In the seventeenth and eighteenth centuries, surveying assumed a more integral role in geodesy and cartography.... No longer were mapmakers dependent almost solely on the meager fare that came their way from traveler's tales, explorer's crude sketches, and mariner's random compass bearings.

-John Noble Wilford (2000)

The tools for making maps had changed little from the time of Ptolemy. Specifically, the mapmaker had to determine specific locations and then plot them on a coordinate grid system. He then had to fill in between the known points with other kinds of measurements and information. The most accurate positions could be determined by standard astronomical observations. For example, latitude in the northern hemisphere could be determined quite precisely by taking the angle of a place relative to the north star. That angle was the parallel of latitude (see Figure 3-14).

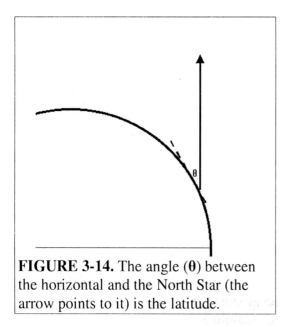

FIGURE 3-14. The angle (θ) between the horizontal and the North Star (the arrow points to it) is the latitude.

A magnetic compass allowed the mapmaker to orient relative to north even if the skies were overcast. It was not long, however, before the precision of measurements demonstrated that the magnetic north was not quite the same as true north, which even varied from one place to the next on the earth.

Navigators and surveyors employed the methods of both locating places on maps and making maps. For both groups, maps and measurements were the arts of the trade. Surveyors needed to depict an area as accurately as possible because they measured land and land was money. They employed chains and wheels to estimate overland distances. They developed methods of triangulation to find distances and angular positions relative to north from a known point. They employed similar means to measure elevation in relation to known points. Thus, more accurate and detailed depictions of place could be made. Tools of the surveyor resembled those of the astronomer in which precise determinations of angles became the all-important task.

Simple triangulation could be done using a flat or plane table. The surveyor lined up the table relative to north and mounted an arbitrary point on the table over a known point on the ground. Consider Figure 3-15A. Suppose that the squares are known points; then the interesting features (the circles) can be determined by triangulation. As the positions of the circles become known, then their baselines can be used in turn to determine the positions of the other circles (see Figure 3-15B). If the baseline is of a measured distance, then all lines on the map are drawn proportional to that line and true to the compass directions. Thus, triangulation and instruments designed for that task allowed surveyors to map local areas with great precision.

The determination of longitude proved to be a more difficult problem. Longitude

128

has no astronomical object against which to measure because the earth turns on an axis where the lines of longitude converge at the poles. The most obvious way of telling longitude would be to consider what happens as the earth turns on its axis. In a 24 hour period the sun appears to travel across the sky and then to disappear during the night. Thus, the earth turns a full 360° in 24 hours or 15° per hour. Suppose that you know that local time is noon when it is 1pm at the Royal Observatory at Greenwich, then you know that you are 15° west of Greenwich. However, in the seventeenth and eighteenth centuries clocks just were not accurate enough to determine time at another place. So, astronomical methods were used. For example, Galileo had suggested that the transit of the moons of Jupiter and their relative positions might be used as a great clock in the heavens.

Giovanni Domenico Cassini (1625-1712), astronomer to the Pope, began the task of mapping France. First, he worked out the appropriate tables for Jupiter's moons so that he could read the time in Paris. He then compared that time (determined at night) against local time (determined during the day). Pendulum clocks could be trusted to keep the time from the night observations to the daytime determination. The difference in time could be interpreted as longitude. The mapping project became the work for the rest of his life. He did not finish it and its completion fell to his son and then to his grandson. The map of France finally was completed in 1745 in the first great precision surveying effort.

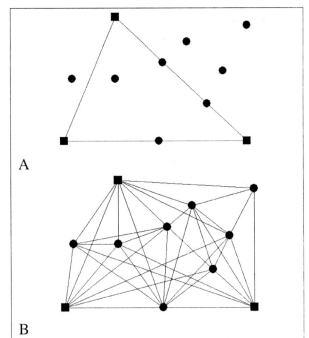

FIGURE 3-15. A shows three known positions (squares) and distances between them. The circles represent features hat need to be mapped. B shows the result of triangulation in which the circles can be accurately determined according to distance and direction.

THE LONGITUDE PRIZE

I have treated about matters pertaining to the strictness of measuring time...; and I have also treated of the improper, troublesome, erroneous - tedious method, which the professors at Cambridge and Oxford would have to be for the longitude at sea.

-John Harrison (1775)

Astronomical methods like those employed by the Cassinis were very useful in surveying and cartographic projects on land. However, they did not work well at sea. Trying to make sightings of Jupiter's moons on the rolling decks of ships was nearly impossible. Another method had to be established for the accurate determination of longitude. For states such as Great Britain this problem was a very serious one.

By the 18th Century Great Britain had emerged as the most powerful and wealthy sea-faring nation on earth. Its position as an island nation and colonial power depended on a strong and effective navy whose capability depended on good navigation. The nautical charts had been much improved over those of Mercator and his contemporary mapmakers. The instruments for navigation also had been improved and developed to allow the determination of accurate positions, particularly with regard to latitude. However, precise methods for the determination of longitude still eluded navigators with many mishaps at sea as a consequence. Dead reckoning remained the standard method, a method by which ships could be off by as much as 10° or more even with the most experienced navigators. For example, Magellan's pilot with his experience and all of the scientific equipment available to him at that time placed the Philippines correctly with respect to latitude, but was off by 53° (or 1/7 of the distance around the earth) in his determination of longitude.

In recognition of the problem and the importance of its solution, the British Parliament passed the Longitude Act of 1714 in the wake of several navigation-related naval disasters. The rules of the prize stipulated that Parliament would award £10,000 for a method by which the determination of longitude would be accurate to within 1^O ; £15,000 for a method accurate to within $2/3^O$, and £20,000 for a method that was accurate to within $1/2^O$ of longitude. These were princely sums (£20,000 then would be more than one million dollars in today's money). This just showed how important, some said insoluble, the problem was.

The Longitude Act called for the creation of a Board of Longitude. This was stacked with astronomers, naval officers, and members of Parliament. In general, the scientific-minded of the day favored an astronomical solution. The moons of Jupiter were too small, but some, like Edmond Halley (1656-1742), believed that the time at the Greenwich Observatory could be determined by observing the position of the moon and its proximity to major stars because the moon moves about 13° with respect to the "fixed stars" each day. This method held promise, but it required much work to construct tables for its implementation.

Meanwhile, other methods were explored, but few believed that the answer would be the production of a clock that could hold its time and not be affected by the rolling motion of a ship, the changes in humidity and temperature, or the corrosive sea salt while under sail. Indeed, the mechanical solution was seen as impossible and likened to our response to the possibility of constructing a perpetual motion machine. Still, the prize attracted many hopeful incompetents and the records attest to a plethora of hair-brained schemes.

In this atmosphere of incredulity John Harrison (1693-1776), a self-taught clockmaker and instrument maker began to see the possibility of achieving the prize. He had a particular genius with clockworks and managed early on to make clocks that required no lubrication nor were they affected by changes in temperature. In 1835, Harrison produced a large clock whose moving parts were balanced such that the motion of a rolling ship did not alter its regular action. Harrison presented this to the Board of Longitude, which although it wanted an astronomical solution, saw that Harrison's clock, which was called H-1, might work. It was subjected to a short sea trial in which it performed very well.

However, Harrison, ever the perfectionist, saw that his clock could be improved and withdrew it from competition. He worked to make the clock smaller (H-1 stood nearly 1 meter high). He improved its design through H-2, and H-3. Unsatisfied, Harrison withdrew H-3 right after he submitted it to the Board of Longitude.

Harrison began a different approach to the clock and completed H-4 in 1761 (for a more modern version see Figure 3-16). This was a departure from the earlier timepieces in that H-4 was made as a large pocket watch about 15cm across. Its reliability and accuracy during a sea trial to the West Indies and back was well within the $1/2^O$ of longitude specified by the Longitude Act. The Board, however, refused to give the full amount and required Harrison to make two duplicates of H-4 without the plans or the original clock to use as a guide. Then, Parliament changed the rules and required a whole battery of sea trials. In the mean time, the astronomers were working hard to complete their lunar tables.

Harrison struggled to make the duplicate clocks (now called chronometers) while the original H-4 had been taken by his chief rival to the Royal Observatory at Greenwich for extended accuracy trials which, of course, it failed. Fed up with the manipulation of his father by the Board of Longitude, Harrison's son petitioned King George III for an audience and related the entire affair. The king became incensed by Harrison's treatment and performed his own trials of the newest timepiece called H-5. This one performed beautifully and the king demanded that Harrison be acknowledged as the winner. Finally, Harrison was given the full amount that

he sought. Although his award did equal about £20,000 in its various increments, Parliament had changed the rules of the longitude prize so that technically the award was never claimed.

FIGURE 3-16. A Rail Road watch is little changed from the type of H-4. The watch is designed so that the time can not be changed without unscrewing the face.

Captain James Cook took a copy of H-4 with him on his second (1772-1775) and unlucky third (1776-1779) voyages around the world. Although he tried both the chronometer and lunar methods of longitude, Cook certainly preferred the chronometer. He referred to the H-4 copy as "our faithful guide through all the vicissitudes of climates." John Harrison, finally vindicated, died within the year of Cook's return from his second voyage.

A single chronometer might cost £200 or more while a sextant and a book of lunar tables could cost a tenth of that. Still, the advantages of the clock method were obvious. The navigator could determine longitude independently of clouds and the times of the month when the moon was close to the sun (periods of the new moon). The glaring disadvantage was what would happen if the clock stopped or malfunctioned.

The chronometer method became the standard for the British Navy. To counteract the prospect that a chronometer might malfunction, British exploration and mapping vessels often had multiple chronometers aboard, each serving as a check for the others. Captain Fitzroy of The Beagle, had the charge of mapping the coastline of South America. To support this, he had more than 40 chronometers on ship. Usually such mapping expeditions also engaged in geological and biological surveys to coordinate with the maps that they produced. Fitzroy's second expedition (1831-1836) to map the coastline of South America introduced a young naturalist named Charles Darwin to the diversity of life.

Even though little of the earth's surface had been surveyed in a scientific way, the methods available by the early 19th Century assured that it could be. The only remaining problem was the matter of standardizing aspects of cartography. In particular, there was no standard of international measurement and there was no agreement on the location of the Prime Meridian, the line of longitude against which all others would be determined.

MODERN MAP MAKERS

That the Conference proposes to the Governments here represented the adoption of the meridian passing through the centre of the transit instrument at the Observatory of Greenwich as the initial meridian for longitude.
-Resolution of the International Meridian
   Conference, Washington D.C. (1884).

Prior to 1875 maps and measurements came in a cacophony of units. In many cases, standard measurements changed from one region of a country to another. No country suffered more from this than France in the latter part of the 18th Century. After the French Revolution, sweeping reforms of almost all of the old systems caused the new government to look at a scientific standard for the unit of length. After much debate, 1 ten-millionth of the distance from the pole to the equator was adopted as the meter, the foundation of the whole metric system. Gradually, science and commerce adopted France's system. Finally, the Meter System Treaty of 1875 established the metric system as the standard means of measurement for international transactions and a common unit of distance for international charts and maps.

The problem of the Prime Meridian was a significant issue in the mid 19th Century. Because of rising nationalism throughout Europe and the Americas, there were at least 14 different Prime meridians in use. Because of their accuracy and pervasive use, the British sea charts with their reference to the longitude at Greenwich Royal Observatory as $0°$ longitude were well-known internationally. Thus, when the United States called for a standardization of longitude and hosted a meeting (International Meridian Conference Washington, D.C.) on the issue in 1884, Greenwich was adopted as the International Prime Meridian with longitude numbered to $180°$ both east and west from that line. With the establishment of a Prime Meridian, International Time Zones could be created, a move that fostered commerce, particularly by rail.

The next major step in cartography was the use of aerial photography to support on the ground surveys. This method was first used in mapping parts of the Pocono region in Pennsylvania. Since then it proved to very valuable, particularly when mapping rugged terrain and when updating existing maps. The photographs also suffered from lateral distortions. One solution to the distortion problem was to get very far away and take the photos straight down. With the advent of the space age, the problem of distance and the computer power to make maximum use of the information came together. Now, satellite images of the earth can be downloaded routinely. For example, satellites in the Landsat series (1972-present under the authority of NASA and the USGS) can view the earth with a variety of sensors and provide valuable information for "global change research and applications in agriculture, geology, forestry, regional planning, education and national security."

Similarly, the U.S. military put aloft a series of 24 satellites (called Space Vehicles or SVs). They orbit the earth at 20,200 km in a particular pattern of 6 orbital planes, 4 satellites in each plane. They form the ideal technology for navigation and survey (see Figure 3-17). With a Global Positioning System (GPS) receiver, anyone could know latitude, longitude, and elevation that the Cassinis and Harrisons could not dream possible. With the GPS system, we once again look to the heavens to find where we are.

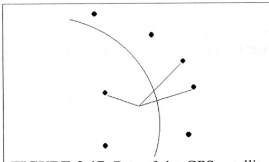

FIGURE 3-17. Part of the GPS satellite system that allows for precise triangulation in the determination of place (latitude, longitude, and elevation).

MAPS AS MODELS

Watcher was chief; he looked toward the sea.

At this time, from north and south, the whites came.

They are peaceful; they have great things; who are they?

      -End of the Walam Olum[4]

Our ability to know and map the earth has increased in leaps and bounds. The methods that we can employ have been used to map the moon and Mars so that we know them better than we knew the earth only a century ago. Maps are useful because they obey the rules of Ptolemy and conform to the standardized conventions that have developed over the centuries. Such conceptual models as maps are powerful tools because they tell of where we have been and might go.

There are other kinds of conceptual models that portray the earth, too. The predecessor of the stone map on Delaware land in Oklahoma was a much older mythology, an oral text that accompanied a series of pictographs often written in red ochre on bark called the Walam Olum (or Red Scribe). The pictures depict Delaware history from the mythic times of the origin of the world to their ancestors' travels across a land from the west to the eastern ocean. Liberal interpretations of the stories suggest that the Delaware describe their life in Asia and the crossing of the frozen waters of the Bearing Straits.

Curiously, the Walam Olum ends with a bittersweet statement about the coming of the whites and closes with the question, " They are peaceful; they have great things; who are they?" The last pictograph of the Walam Olum illustrates a ship on the eastern ocean, a ship that arrived by means of charts and instruments, which allowed its inhabitants to find their way across the sea. After that the Delaware added no further pictographs to the Walam Olum. The U.S. government moved them out of Pennsylvania to Ohio, then Indiana, Kansas,

---

[4] These lines accompany the pictographs of Figure 3-18

and finally into Northeastern Oklahoma. In one of life's ironies, I now live in a house that sits on land inhabited by the Delaware when they created that last pictograph. Maps were one of those "great things" that those who came from the north and south brought with them. Perhaps the stone map was an attempt to tell a new story with a new model of the earth, a western-style pictograph, the map.

-2002, revised 2006

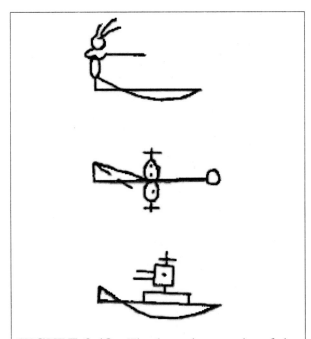

FIGURE 3-18. The last pictographs of the Walam Olum. Note the bottom figure illustrates a ship on the sea. Redrawn from Brinton (1999).

References:

Brinton, Daniel G. 1999 (originally published 1885). *The Lenape and their Legends; With the Complete Text and Symbols of the Walam Olum.* Wennawoods Publishing. Lewisburg, PA.

Philadelphia Inquirer. 1899. *Pictoral Atlas of the Greater United States and the World.* The Philadelphia Inquirer Co. Philadelphia.

Ptolemy, Claudius. 1991 (from a 2nd Century text). *The Geography.* Trans & ed. Edward Luther Stevenson. Dover Publications, Inc. New York.

Sheffner, Ed. 1999. *Welcome to the Landsat Program.*

http://geo.arc.nasa.gov/sge/landsat/landsat.html date accessed: March 29, 2002.

Sobel, Dava. 1995. *Longitude. The True Story of a Lone Genius Who Solved the Greatest Scientific Problem of His Time.* Penguin Books. New York.

Weslager, Clinton A. 1972. *The Delaware Indians, A History.* Rutgers University Press. New Brunswick, NJ.

Wilford, John Noble. 2000. *The Mapmakers.* Revised Edition. Alfred A. Knopf. New York.

Questions to Think About

1. Can you think of a conceptual model other than a map?

2. Why was Eratosthenes considered by his peers to be mediocre? How did he calculate the circumference of the earth?

3. What underlying belief (other than the earth is a sphere) did Ptolemy use in creating his map of the world?

4. What is the advantage of the Mercator projection? What is at least one disadvantage?

5. How does triangulation work to produce a map?

6. Why was determination of latitude relatively easy compared to longitude?

7. How did John Harrison win the longitude prize? Why were the authorities reluctant to award him the prize?

8. Why was the concept of the prime meridian so important to map mapmakers as well as to the railroads?

9. How does the GPS system work?

10. How were the pictographs of the Walam Olum conceptual models?

BUTTERFLIES

CALDER'S BUTTERFLIES
I paint with shapes. -Alexander Calder

On one of my visits to Washington, D.C. a friend suggested that I should see the Alexander Calder exhibit in the East Building of the National Gallery of Art. I have to confess that I did not know of Calder, but I took her advice and was enriched for it.

Alexander "Sandy" Calder came from a family of artists. As a child, he showed considerable creativity in making toys and small sculptures. However, he enjoyed making things and took a degree in mechanical engineering. It wasn't long before he joined an artist's group and then moved to Paris where he began to experiment with moveable sculptures. Some of them were delicate wire structures that moved by a small motor or hand crank. Others hung down and fluttered gently in the light air currents of a room.

It was these hanging sculptures, later dubbed *mobiles* by Marcel Duchamp in 1932, that I found so interesting. Calder said that he changed from motor-driven sculptures to wind-driven mobiles in order to introduce chance and irregularity into the movements of his sculptures. He later wrote, "To most people who look at a mobile, it's no more than a series of flat objects that move. To a few, though, it may be poetry."

Later, Calder moved back to the U.S. and experimented with larger, monumental works, both mobiles and stabiles (large, open sculptures that suggested form with little mass). One of his last works was a monumental mobile that now hangs on permanent display in the East Building of the National Gallery of Art.

I stood looking at the enormous mobile as it hung from the metal framework in the large, open atrium of the East Building. Even though it was hundreds of pounds of metal, it was so delicately engineered that the subtle air movements of convection gave it life like a flight of butterflies in slow motion.

BUTTERFLIES & ATTRACTORS
In weather, for example, this translates into what is only half-jokingly known as the Butterfly Effect- the notion that a butterfly stirring the air today in Peking can transform storm systems next month in New York. -James Gleick

The motions exhibited by that and all his mobiles were very complex. They followed a pattern of movement whose magnitude was determined by the engineering constraints of the structure, but particular directions were quite unpredictable. This was very much like the atmospheric forces that drove them.

Think of weather and its prediction. It, too, is determined in that average temperatures, rainfalls, etc. can be calculated for particular months (or weeks or days for that matter). So, a weather forecaster can say with certainty that the temperature will be colder in the winter than in the summer. However, that is not enough. When we refer to weather prediction we mean what the weather will be like at temporal scales much shorter than a year. We want to know with some precision if it will rain a week from Saturday or on what date the first frost will come. In 1961 Edward Lorenz, a meteorologist at MIT whom James Gleick described as a mathematician in the guise of a meteorologist, had written a computer program to look at the feasibility of long-range weather forecasting. The program relied on the interactions of 12 different functions (mathematical statements that modeled different atmospheric parameters) to produce simulated weather patterns. This was long before the days of PC's. He had to wait for print outs and interpret the rise and fall of numbers and letters on the paper. Still, the simulation engaged the interest of most others in his lab. They watched as the temperature line rose and fell in unpredictable ways, just like real weather data.

One day Lorenz said that he wanted to repeat another particularly interesting run. He entered the particular values as indicated by the printout and watched with interest as the program began to repeat the run. Initially, the two runs were identical; however, they began to diverge in subtle ways and then became completely different (Figure 3-19).

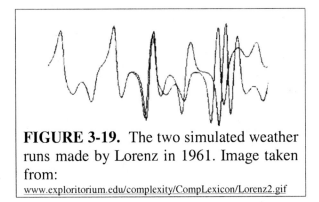

FIGURE 3-19. The two simulated weather runs made by Lorenz in 1961. Image taken from:

www.exploritorium.edu/complexity/CompLexicon/Lorenz2.gif

He struggled to come up with an explanation for this odd outcome. Finally, he discovered that the difference was due to a rounding error. He had used numbers rounded to six places to the right of the decimal point rather than the nine-place accuracy of the machine. Still, the numbers were within one part per thousand. Lorenz quickly grasped that even these small differences in initial conditions could produce great differences within a short time. Thus, he understood why phenomena like tides could be predicted with great accuracy for long periods and weather could not. Tides, even though they are part of a fluid dynamic system like the atmosphere, are periodic phenomena. On the other hand, weather patterns are aperiodic at scales of time much less than a year. Unlike the tides, each weather pattern is influenced by the preceding conditions in myriad and complex ways. Therefore, the implications for long-range forecasting were not good. He realized that very long range could mean as few as five days because weather, like his simulation, also was sensitive to initial conditions. He wrote it up and submitted his paper to a meteorology journal with the title: "Predictability: Does the Flap of a Butterfly's Wings in Brazil Set Off a Tornado in Texas?"

In an attempt to further understand and model air movements, Lorenz created a mathematical description of a very simple system in which a rectangular box held a simple (elemental) gas. The box was heated on one side so that the gas rose on one side and fell on the other. This should have been predictable; however, the gas rolled in one direction for a while and then reversed direction again and again, in a seemingly random pattern.

He reduced the phenomenon to three equations from fluid dynamics and plotted it in three dimensions. The dimensions represent: rate of rotation of the gas (X), difference in temperature between the opposite sides of the gas (Y), and the deviation of the system from a linear, vertical graphed line representing temperature (Z). When plotted, the point whips around a region and then jumps to another "orbit" in a random pattern. The graph resembles a butterfly when viewed from the X-Z plane (see Figure 3-20).

The equations used to generate the Lorenz attractor were non-linear. Unlike simple algebraic equations where a particular X-value always makes a particular Y-value, non-linear equations have no particular solutions. Each solution (or point) depends on the numbers generated during the previous "solution" or iteration. Thus, the overall solution to a non-linear equation must be generated over many iterations.

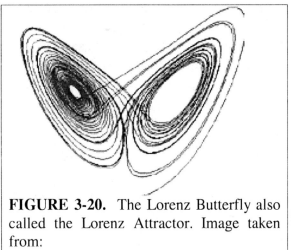

FIGURE 3-20. The Lorenz Butterfly also called the Lorenz Attractor. Image taken from:

www.exploritorium.edu/complexity/CompLexicon/Lorenz2.gif

James Yorke, a professor of mathematics and physics, discovered in Lorenz' paper an explanation that he had been searching for. He photocopied the paper and gave it to anyone who would read it. Then, in his own publication about non-linear systems that are sensitive to initial conditions in 1975, he coined the term Chaos. The name stuck.

FRACTALS AND SCALING

It is by logic we prove, it is by intuition that we invent. Henri Poincaré

Edward Lorenz was not the first to notice the strange behavior of aperiodic or non-linear phenomena. Henri Poincaré (1854-1912) of France had noticed the same thing more than half a century earlier. In 1889 he had entered a contest given by Olaf II, the King of Sweden and Norway, to come up with a proof that the solar system is dynamically stable. Poincaré entered the contest and produced a body of inspired work that won him the prize even though he did not generate the outcome that the King expected.

In essence, Poincaré said that the future of the universe could be predicted if we knew the initial conditions exactly. However, because the initial conditions and all measurements made after that are only approximations of the true conditions, we could not predict the outcome. Thus, "small differences in the initial conditions

produce very great ones in the final phenomena." This is exactly what Lorenz was to demonstrate nearly 70 years later.

Similarly, Poincaré was mathematical genius with an interest in everything. Indeed, his influence on mathematics was as great as it was on the sciences. (For example, he is credited along with Einstein as a co-discoverer of relativity). However, much of his mathematical work relied on his astounding intuition and ability to reduce problems to certain geometric forms in his mind. Mathematicians who followed him, particularly in France, rebelled against his intuitive methods and sought to restore mathematics to its pristine logic. They viewed geometry as the lowest of the mathematical disciplines and abhorred any practical applications in science or technology. The movement was called Bourbaki and dominated western mathematics through the middle of the 20th century.

Benoit B. Mandelbrot (b.1924 in Poland) moved to France during the 1930's. There, he came under the tutelage of his uncle, a professor of mathematics and a founder of the Bourbaki movement, at the Collège de France. With a mind and interests more like Poincaré, Mandelbrot chafed under the restrictions in what mathematics could be studied. At the outset of WWII, his family escaped to the south of France. He returned to Paris after its liberation where he was accepted into the elite Ecole Normale but left for the Ecole Polytechnique to escape the mental prison of the Bourbaki. After the completion of his degree he left for the U.S. where he was hired by IBM to pursue mathematical problems. During this time he threw himself into a number of applied and pure mathematical problems. He retired from IBM and moved to Harvard (economics), Yale (engineering), and the Einstein School of Medicine (physiology). Something of a jack-of-all-trades, he remarked after an introduction listing his positions:

Very often when I listen to the list of my previous jobs I wonder if I exist. The intersection of such sets is surely empty.

Mandelbrot's main contribution to Chaos Theory was the concept of fractional dimensions, something that he termed fractals. Let me explain fractals by building on the illustration of a spleenwort fern leaf (Figure 3-21). Like the Lorenz attractor, the Spleenwort Fern Fractal emerged from the interactions of four sets of matrices, also non-linear. What's more, the mathematical spleenwort leaf has infinitely fine resolution with infinite complexity. It is more than a line (one dimension) and less than a plane (two dimensions). The spleenwort fern leaf occupies a fractional dimension or fractal between dimensions 1 and 2.

FIGURE 3-21. The Spleenwort Fern Fractal generated by a program produced by Steve Benner (1989) of Microcomputer Applications.

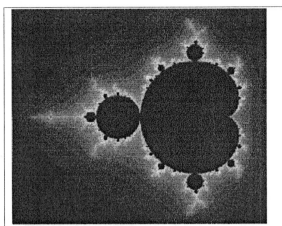

Image A.

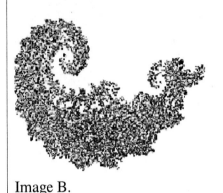

Image B.
FIGURE 3-22. Mandelbrot Set at two scales. Image A represents the set at the largest scale while Image B is a portion of one of the small curls that emerge from Image A. Images taken from:
www.exploritorium.edu/complexity/CompLexicon/Lorenz2.gif

Perhaps the most famous group of fractals is known as the Mandelbrot Set. This was created by Benoit B. Mandelbrot during WWII when he was trying to work with an older group of fractals called the Julia Set. The Mandelbrot Set is infinitely complex because it appears equally complex at any scale. At large scale (Figure 3-22A), the Mandelbrot Set appears complex with unfragmented Julia Sets in the center and fragmented Julia Sets over the outside. When viewed in smaller scale (Figure 3-22B), the level of complexity remains. At each scale, the Mandelbrot Set appears similar but not identical.

This aspect of self-similarity is characteristic of fractals and is typical of many aspects of nature. Consider mountain landscapes that can be seen on large planetary scales and in the scale of a grain of sand. Coastlines, trees, clouds, etc. all exhibit the property of self-similarity. Look at the photo below of cirrocumulus clouds taken outside of the science building in May (Figure 3-23). It almost looks like a Mandelbrot picture with a large cloud made of many smaller, self-similar clouds.

FIGURE 3-23. Cirrocumulus clouds displaying absence of scale.

FIGURE 3-24. The plume of smoke from a stick of incense with simple, laminar flow at the bottom and chaotic flow at the top.

WHY TURBULENCE?

...why turbulence? Werner Heisenberg

One of the most perplexing questions for physicists has been the nature of turbulence mainly because it does not seem to follow simple Newtonian laws. Consider the rise of a plume of smoke (Figure 3-24). The smoke begins to rise in an orderly way with a gradually expanding cone. Then, suddenly, the smoke begins to exhibit erratic, chaotic behavior. This is a phenomenon that displays self-similarity as well. Smoke plumes from a forest fire in Florida or from a stick of incense show the same behavior.

James Gleick in his book, *Chaos*, tells a story about Werner Heisenberg on his deathbed. He was one of the founders of Quantum Physics, the author of the famous Uncertainty Principle, and head of the German atomic bomb program in WWII. Heisenberg is supposed to have said that he had two questions for God: why relativity and why turbulence? "I really think that He may have an answer to the first question."

When fluids (in this case gasses behave as fluids) move in an orderly way, they move as sheets or laminations sliding past each other. During this laminar flow, fluids behave themselves and are easy to model. However, fluids rarely exist in laminar flow. Consider a perfectly smooth pipe 1 cm in diameter that carries water. If the water flow rate is less than 18cm/sec, the flow is laminar. However, it becomes chaotic above that flow rate. Now, consider a similar pipe that is 1 meter in diameter, turbulent flow occurs at velocities greater than 1mm/sec.

The implications are clear for streams, lakes and oceans, all of which are larger than my examples. Turbulent flow is the norm in nature. Water flowing over stones and at velocities above the initiation of chaotic behavior cause unpredictable eddies and currents on a small scale. Some of these eddies remain stable and can travel downstream for a good distance, as if they were influenced by an attractor. For example, consider the photograph of a small stream (Figure 3-25). Deeper, slower moving water is very smooth, almost glassy on its surface. At the riffle, however, water velocity increases and turbulent flow is quite evident.

Water is not the only thing that behaves this way. All substances with fluid motion such as gasses (recall the Lorenz movement of gas in a heated box) exhibit turbulence. This means that the atmosphere also displays chaotic motion more often than nice, neat laminar flow. Eddies and irregularities in the atmosphere can manifest themselves in many ways. Sometimes the motion can become organized into cyclones, hurricanes, etc.

FIGURE 3-25. Turbulence in a small stream behind my house in Freeburg, PA.

One of the most impressive examples of chaotic atmospheric flow can be found in the bands of clouds surrounding Jupiter (see Figure 3-26). Rivers of atmosphere organized into bands scream around the planet at hundreds of miles per hour. Large eddies like giant Mandelbrot figures appear at the margins of the bands where they rub together.

FIGURE 3-26. Cloud bands around Jupiter. Note organized eddies within the bands, particularly, the great red spot. Image taken from:
pds.jpl.nasa.gov/planets/gif/jup/jovian.gif

The most impressive eddies are the organized atmospheric cyclones within the bands. The great red spot is such a structure. The application of chaos mathematics to a theoretical Jupiter produces similar organized, stable cyclones. Thus, underlying complexity can produce simple and quite stable structures.

It seems that turbulence is more than an esoteric problem embedded within an arcane type of mathematics. An understanding of turbulence has implications for a deeper understanding of weather, climate, the oceans, flight, and myriad other problems in science and technology. Heisenberg understood this. I wonder if he has his answer?

MONARCHS OF YESTERYEAR

All things by immortal power
Near or far
Hiddenly
To each other linked are
Thou canst not stir a flower
Without troubling of a star.

          -Francis Thompson
          (*The Mistress of Vision*)

I was thinking about these problems as I stood in my garden last week. My garden, one of the most chaotic places on earth, serves many purposes. It provides some food and endless hours of attention. I enjoy surprises of the appearances of flowers, the first tomatoes, or moss capsules. I chafe at the emergence of unwanted plants such as the amaranth known as red root or unwanted walnuts germinating in a raspberry hedge. Still, the song of an unexpected (or expected in the case of catbirds, wrens, etc.) bird seems to make it worthwhile.

In planting my garden I can be assured that I can set out frost-sensitive plants during the summer. As chaotic as the weather might be, I know that the temperature will not go below freezing during July. There are some things that I can count on like the call of the American Toad on a May night or the wispy flight of firefly beetles on a June evening.

FIGURE 3-27. A group of monarch butterflies on Assateague Island during their fall migration. Detail: An adult Monarch Butterfly in that group.

Also, I tend to leave milkweed if I find it growing in my flowerbeds, much to the chagrin of my neighbors. I have planted other milkweeds on purpose like butterfly weed and swamp milkweed in order to attract butterflies, particularly Monarchs (Figure 3-27). This year, however, I have not seen a single adult or caterpillar in the garden.

Monarchs are very interesting animals in that they, like many birds, migrate sometimes thousands of miles to overwintering grounds in central Mexico. Unlike birds, however, their life span is so short that the particular animal that leaves Pennsylvania will not return. However, its offspring may.

I became interested in the phenomenon of monarch migrations when I found myself in the middle of one of the southward migrations on Assateague Island at the end of September 1997 (see Figure 3-27). The butterflies covered available shrubs giving them unexpected color at that time of year. The fragile creatures in phalanx after phalanx assaulted the wind and storm on their way to the south.

Then, that next winter (1998), *El Nino* created a stable weather pattern that brought unusually cold weather to the Monarch's winter home. Some explained the decline in Monarchs as a consequence of the chaotic weather. Others blamed the extensive logging that occurred in the area where Monarchs wintered. More recently (winter 2002) several weather-related die-offs occurred also (Thus, they were affected by the Butterfly Affect). It appeared, however, that the die-offs were exacerbated by extensive habitat loss in some of the winter home areas. Also, how much of the population decline was due to activities in the United States (pesticides, habitat loss, etc.)?

Population fluctuations, especially populations of animals whose numbers are dependent on the vagaries of the weather and long, dangerous trips, should show fluctuations even in the best of times. Probably, a simple answer pointing to a single cause will not be found. Chaos theory as applied to complex systems like Monarch populations allows for a more realistic explanation of population dynamics. The particular interactions that cause fluctuations in Monarch numbers are probably quite complex and involve the intersections of weather, habitat loss in Mexico and the U.S., disease, etc. Because population dynamics are chaotic does not mean that we do not have to worry about our own impacts on Monarch numbers. Rather, the chaotic nature of population numbers makes our impact potentially even more important because human-related impacts could come on top of random fluctuations that produce catastrophic results. Thus, we cannot do anything about the weather or butterfly diseases, but we do have control over habitat loss. This is where we should center our efforts if the Monarch populations are to recover and remain healthy.

UNCERTAINTY & ART

Omnis ars naturae imitatio est. (All art is but an imitation of nature.) -Seneca

The degree of uncertainty in predicting Monarch populations, turbulent eddies, and next week's weather is not restricted to these phenomena. The normative aspect of nature itself seems to be aperiodic and nonlinear. Thus, we measure approximations of reality and use those approximations to explain approximations of nature. In that sense science, like art, is but an imitation of nature. I do not say this to denigrate science, but to underscore how fascinating and intriguing it is to those of us who practice the art of science. Imagine how uninteresting nature would be if everything were completely predictable. .

Thus, the underlying complexity in nature serves as a unifying principle in understanding it. At the same time events like the survival of a Monarch on the sands of Assateague Island or the particular direction of a Calder mobile at any moment are unpredictable; the overall patterns are determined, and with appropriate study, they can be explained. In 1955, Alexander Calder wrote of his mobile sculptures, "From the beginning of my abstract work, even when it might not have seemed so, I felt there was no better model for me to choose than the Universe." Like the universe, both determined patterns and unpredictable motion come together in Calder's mobiles that model nature in beautiful and elegant ways.

-1998, revised 2003

References:

Carey, John, ed. 1995. *Fractals, Chaos, and Strange Attractors.* In: *Eyewitness to Science, Scientists and Writers Illuminate Natural Phenomena From Fossils to Fractals.* Harvard University Press. Cambridge, Mass. Pp 495-504.

Cohen, Jack and Ian Stewart. 1994. *The Collapse of Chaos, Discovering Simplicity in a Complex World.* Penguin Books. New York.

Gleick, James. 1987. *Chaos, Making a New Science.* Penguin Books. New York.

Goody, Richard. 1995. *Principles of Atmospheric Physics and Chemistry.* Oxford University Press. Oxford.

Hutchinson, G. Evelyn. 1957. *A Treatise on Limnology. Volume 1. Geography, Physics and Chemistry.* John Wiley & Sons, Inc. New York.

Leopold, Luna B. 1997. *Water, Rivers and Creeks.* University Science

Questions to Think About

1. Why did we not see many Monarch butterflies in 1998?

   El Nino → unusual cold

2. What is another name for the Lorenz Attractor?

   Lorenz Butterfly

3. Who invented the mobile?

   Alexander "Sandy" Calder

4. Why does smoke, after it initially rises in an orderly way, begin to exhibit erratic, chaotic behavior?

   Random phenomenon

5. What is chaos?

   Things don't act how they should

6. Self-similarity is characteristic of fractals and is typical of many aspects of nature. What is an example of such a system?

   Spleen worth sem

7. What is an example of chaotic behavior producing a pattern?

   Mandelbrot set / Turbulence

8. How is the Monarch migration different from the migration of birds?

   Life span is shorter

9. Why was Lorenz initially ignored by physicists and mathematicians?

10. How could you demonstrate laminar flow and turbulence?

    water in a pipe

11. In what ways were Lorenz, Poincare, and Mandelbrot alike? How was Calder's approach to art similar to the approaches of Lorenz, Poincare, and Mandelbrot to science?

    Crazy)

OBSERVATORY, CLOCK, OR TEMPLE?

A VISIT

In its presence, within those silent circles, one feels the great past all around

.-Gerald S. Hawkins

In the summer of 1995 I sat in the back of a van and marveled as Pat Nelson successfully negotiated roundabouts and the traffic of London. We navigated our way to Down House, Cambridge and points in between. After we had visited Down, we drove to the west. I was about to doze off when we crested a hill and there before us was Stonehenge in the late afternoon sun. The monument was impressive from the road and majestic as we approached on foot. Even in ruins Stonehenge elicited awe and sent my mind scrambling to try to determine how it was made (see Figure 3-28).

There were lots of helpful diagrams and explanations for its construction. Technically, Stonehenge (which literally means hanging stones) was made of two types of stones: bluestone from the Preseli Mountains in southern Wales and sandstone (called sarsen) from outcrops at the Marlborough Downs, 25 miles north of the monument. The bluestones were smaller. Even so, some weighed as much as 4 tons, and all bluestones were transported nearly 250 miles by land and sea.

It seems that Stonehenge was built several times from 3000 BC to about 1000 BC. The earliest structure had a few of the outlying stones and may have had a wooden structure in the center. Around 2000 BC the bluestones were brought to the site. I seemed that the builders intended to make a double circle of bluestones in the middle. However, the circles were not finished before the large sarsen stones were added.

The sarsens were transported only 20 to 25 miles, but they were colossal compared with the bluestones. The large sandstone blocks weighed 40 tons or more and were harder than granite. The official guidebook for the Stonehenge monument suggests that 500 to 600 people working for one year were required to move the enormous sarsens from Marlborough Downs. After that masons shaped the slabs into rough rectangles.

Edgerton in his June 1960 National Geographic article supposed that 50 masons worked over a month with large round stones of sarsen sandstone and antlers to shape the big stones. As evidence for this supposition, the field around Stonehenge is littered with the chips from sarsen and bluestone (see Figure 3-29).

FIGURE 3-28. Stonehenge as it looks today.

FIGURE 3-29. Samples of the types of stones that make up Stonehenge. The Bluestone on the left came from Wales more than 250 miles away. The Sarsen stone is a quartzite quarried from Marlborough Downs, 20-25 miles from the site.

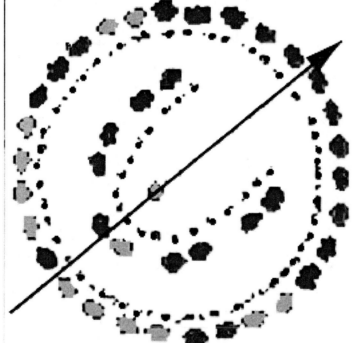

FIGURE 3-30. A diagram of Stonehenge as it was. The stones are shown in their original positions. The larger stones are the sarsens and the smaller stones are bluestones. The dark-colored sarsen stones are still in place. Light gray stones are missing or have fallen. The arrow indicates the direction of sunrise on the morning of the Summer Solstice.

The finished monument had more than 80 bluestones and nearly 80 sarsens. The center of the monument had an outer ring of 30 upright sarsens with 30 sarsens laid across the tops of the uprights as lintels. That made an outer ring of 30 arches or doors. Inside of that was a ring of 60 upright bluestones. In the middle of the two circles of stone were a great horseshoe of sarsens and bluestone. The open ends of the "horseshoes" were aimed toward the northeast (see Figure 3-30).

Why were the stones arranged in a ring? Perhaps, the upright stones supported stone beams for a roof. Such wooden structures, if they existed at all, have long since vanished. The axis of the inner monument lined up with a large upright stone about 70 to 80 meters from the center of the stone circles. That stone has come to be called the Heel Stone.

Although my visit taught me much about how it was built, I really did not learn why it was built. I knew that it was an ancient observatory. I had heard of that since I was a boy. The structure had been built so that the sun could be observed at different periods during the year, particularly at the summer solstice[5].

The builders of Stonehenge aligned the structure along the axis of the midsummer sunrise (Figure 3-30). So, when observers, stood in the center of the inner horseshoe, they saw the sunrise over the Heel Stone through the gap between two upright sarsens on the morning of June 22.

---

[5] The summer solstice or midsummer is the day on which the sun appears furthest north in the northern hemisphere. It is marked by being the longest day of the year and the first day of summer with our calendar. It occurs on or near June 22.

WHAT DOES IT TELL US?
Every age has the Stonehenge it deserves and –desires.   Jacquetta Hawkes

The question, "Why?" rolled over and over in my mind. Certainly, Stonehenge pointed to the summer solstice, but was it an observatory? That is, where was the science? Where was the technology?

According to Robert Fischer, science is accumulated knowledge based on methods that required observation. The accumulated knowledge then helps to explain how the natural universe works. Such explanations are usually called theories or principles. For example, observations made by Benjamin Franklin, James Clerk Maxwell and J.J. Thomson (among others) caused Thomson to propose that electricity came in negatively-charged units called electrons. Do electrons exist? Maybe, but that is the wrong question. What is more important is to ask if the theory of electrons serves to explain electrical phenomena.

On the other hand, technology involves the construction of a device to solve a problem. Stonehenge illustrates many examples of technology. Technical problems related to quarrying the stones, transporting the stones, shaping the stones, and finally placing the stones are not really scientific. The builders of Stonehenge solved these technical problems in the absence of theories.

Was Stonehenge built as a great timepiece? That is, did the ancient Britons require a calendar to know when to plant their crops or move their herds? Although that sounds good, midsummer's morning (the event that defines the axis of Stonehenge) is too late in the year to be reminded when to plant. Regardless, it seems to me that a clock or calendar made of 40 ton stones is overkill. Also, what did they do during the time when the "clock" was under construction?

Erich von Daniken in *Chariots of the Gods?* said that the ancient Britons could not move, shape and position the stones. He believed that they lacked the technology. He then assumed that extraterrestrial beings with their high technology moved the stones and may have helped build the structure. This is not very different from the ancient tradition that Merlin went to Ireland and stole the whole structure of Stonehenge by causing it to fly to its present location.

Von Daniken's assertion is not presented as myth. He gives "scientific" evidence for his explanation. However, his evidence is that the stones are big and that only stupid people would drag such big stones to distant locations. Therefore, technically advanced aliens moved the stones for them. Aliens may even have built the whole thing for the ancient Britons.

Trefil and Hazen (1995) consider this problem as it relates to Stonehenge. First of all, the process of moving the stones was not beyond the technology of the ancients. They just needed ropes, rollers, and lots of people. It is much simpler to assume that the ancients constructed Stonehenge the hard way than to invoke extraterrestrials. Besides, if technologically advanced beings built Stonehenge, why was it so rough and so unstable that many stones have fallen?

The proposal by von Daniken is a perversion of science called pseudoscience. Here, von Daniken and his ilk dress their ideas in scientific language and science-like explanations. One of the identifying marks of pseudoscientists is the notion that their ideas are worth considering because anything is possible. However, in science, anything is not possible. The modern scientist believes that all things in nature must obey the laws of chemistry and physics. Some pseudosciences include modern astrology, biorythms, creation science, lake monsters, bigfoot sightings, alien abductions, etc. Can you think of others?

Does Stonehenge represent science, technology or pseudoscience? Well, it demonstrates considerable technology. However, it is neither science nor pseudoscience. Stonehenge was not built as an observatory with which to make observations of the midsummer sky. It was built as a temple with which to worship the sun. Otherwise why move such enormous stones from distant places to that particular site, a site that was clearly sacred (this is evident from all of the burial mounds around the Stonehenge area). The native stone was chalk and was certainly unsuited to building an enduring structure with which to worship.

In the final analysis, we have the remains of a ruined temple. Most of the original stones have been carried away or have fallen. What is left is a testament to the human spirit. The structure that took generations to build still speaks to us from the distant past. It does not tell us of science, but it does remind us of what it means to be human.

-1996; revised 2005

References:

Atkinson, R.J.C. 1987. *Stonehenge and Neighboring Monuments*. English Heritage. London.

Edgerton, Harold E. 1960. *Stonehenge - new light on an old riddle*. National Geographic. 117 (6): 846-866.

Fischer, Robert B. 1975. *Science, Man, and Society*. W.B. Saunders Co. Philadelphia.

Hawkins, Gerald S. 1965. *Stonehenge Decoded*. Doubleday & Co. New York.

Radner, Daisie and Michael Radner. 1982. *Science and Unreason.* Wadsworth, Inc. Belmont, California.

Trefil, James and Robert Hazen. 1995. *The Sciences, An Integrated Approach.* John Wiley & Sons, Inc. New York.

von Daniken, Erich. 1970. *Chariots of the Gods?* G.P. Putnum's Sons. New York.

Questions to Think About

1. What does "henge" refer to?

    henging

2. Of what was Stonehenge originally constructed? What was the history of its construction?

    Sarsens, wood, Blue stones) 2000 years to make

3. How does Stonehenge work as an observatory?

    Summer solstice through 2 pillars

4. What does Stonehenge teach about the nature of science and of technology?

    It's complex- blurry lines

5. What is pseudoscience and how has Stonehenge been forced to play a role in pseudoscientific claims?

    perversion of science - anything is possible
    - seems so unlikely

6. Was Stonehenge an observatory, a clock, or a temple?

    Temple

SUNRISE, SUNSET

A CALENDAR

Sunrise, sunset
Sunrise, sunset
Swiftly fly the years
One season following another
Laden with happiness and tears
   .-Sheldon Harnick (Fiddler on the Roof)

For Christmas in 1995 my son gave me a Gary Larson desk calendar. It was the perfect gift because the calendar year was nearly over and because I enjoy Larson cartoons very much. Now, on this particular calendar, I recorded the results of observations of a Long Term Project based on the concept of Stonehenge[6]. Recall that Stonehenge was a kind of temple calendar with its primary orientation on sunrise at the summer solstice.

Why is the structure oriented on the summer solstice? That is a good question. Late June is far too late for planting or for any other practical purpose. It seems clear to me the purpose of such an imposing and ancient stone structure was to worship the sun on its most holy day, the day of its northern-most advance. I began my observations of sunrise and sunset on the Susquehanna University campus on the morning of the Winter Solstice and recorded them as an angle from north on the morning of the Winter Solstice (see Figure 3-31). That first attempt on the morning of December 22 was miserably cold. I was nearly half frozen in the snow on the roof of Faylor Lecture Hall at Susquehanna University when the sun crested the ridges across the Susquehanna River. At that point, I recorded sunrise at 142° from north, well into the southeast

(recall that true east is 90° from north). As I expected, sunset was similar (around 135° north to the west). So that the observations would be at approximately equal intervals, I decided to measure sunrise and sunset sometime during the last week of each month.

Through the winter months, I began to appreciate how rare cloudless mornings were in Central Pennsylvania. Often I woke in plenty of time, drove the five miles into school, and then had to abandon the enterprise because a cloud appeared over the ridges. It is interesting (and says much about the weather in Central Pennsylvania) that I was not able to make most observations with a single trip to Susquehanna University. During the spring and fall months, fog banks over the Susquehanna River obscured the disk of the sun completely even though the sky was cloudless. Fortunately, I am a morning person and did not consider the interruption of sleep to be the calamity that others in my house did.

WHAT I LEARNED

Small projects need much more help than great.
   -Dante Alighieri

As an ecologist, I am used to observing a location or a phenomenon for a long period of time. Repeated examination (sometimes called monitoring), is often important in understanding the phenomenon in its annual context. From the repeated observations, I frequently see things that I did not anticipate. This is as true of stream ecosystems as it is of monthly sunrise.

---

[6] For more information about Stonehenge, go to the essay: *Observatory, Clock, or Temple.*

FIGURE 3-31. Sunrise over Faylor Lecture Hall of the Science Building on 22 December 1995.

The month-to-month measurements indicated that the sun seems to change its apparent position about 11.5° each month. Sunrise and sunset appear to change about 0.37°-0.40° per day. After the Winter Solstice, both sunrise and sunset seem to move toward the north, and after the Summer Solstice, they move toward the south.

The sun rises in the north east around the time of the summer solstice. I had just assumed that since I was in the northern hemisphere (and north of the Tropic of Cancer) that the sunrise would always be in the southeast.

If I draw out the angles (Table 3-4) from a fixed position, I get a diagram that looks like a 12-legged spider (see Figure 3-32). This was made by the time of the summer solstice. The measurements from

July through November served to confirm the angles recorded from the first half of the year.

Of course, the sun only appears to change its position in the sky because the earth tilts about 23° on its axis relative to the sun[7]. Like a giant gyroscope, the earth maintains its tilt and the orientation of its tilt independently of the sun. During the Summer Solstice, the North Pole is tilted toward the sun. At the same time, the South Pole is tilted away from the sun. So, summer in the northern hemisphere is winter in the southern hemisphere.

Another consequence of this tilt is that the length of daylight increases to the

---

[7] See *Ice Ages* and *Maps as Models* for more detailed descriptions of the earth's tilt and its consequences.

Summer Solstice (the day with the longest period of daylight) and then decreases until the Winter Solstice (the day with the shortest period of daylight). In addition, the further a place is from the equator, the more pronounced the change. So, here in Selinsgrove, PA (about $40°48'$ North) on December 7, the day length is quite pronounced. Sunrise occurs around 7:19a.m. and sunset is around 4:40p.m (from the U.S. Naval Observatory Astronomical Applications Department).

Today on the equator, the daylength would be about 12 hours long. North of the Arctic Circle ($67°$ N), the sun might not rise at all.

I have been in St Petersburg, Russia ($60°$ N) during the Summer Solstice. This is the time called the "White Nights." I was able to walk through the city at midnight with just a twilight sky as the sun barely dipped below the horizon before it rose again.

TABLE 3-4. Sunrise measurements that were taken approximately a month apart from the campus of Susquehanna University from 22 December 1995 to 27 November 1996. The data are given as degrees from north.

DATE	ANGLE
22 December	142
22 January	130
23 February	118
20 March	108
21 April	97
22 May	85
22 June	77
24 July	88
24 August	100
24 September	111
24 October	122
27 November	132

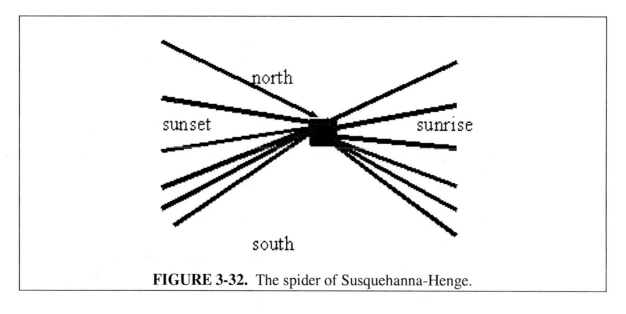

FIGURE 3-32. The spider of Susquehanna-Henge.

CALENDARS

Thirty days hath September,
April, June, and November.
All the rest have thirty-one
Excepting February alone.
That has twenty-eight days clear,
And twenty-nine in each Leap Year.-Anon.

It was while I was trying to measure the angles and thinking about the original Stonehenge builders, that I began to contemplate our calendar system and some of its problems. As you know, our year is divided into 12 months of varying lengths (Remember, thirty days hath September, April, June and November...).

On the other hand, the number of days in a year is set because the year is defined by the length of time that it takes for the earth to go around the sun. A day is the length of time that it takes the earth to rotate on its axis. The two motions are independent of each other so that it takes a little more than 365 days for the earth to complete one orbit.

Why do we have 12 months? Why do the months vary in number of days? Why are the months organized into weeks that do not quite fit? Obviously, our calendar (the Gregorian Calendar) is quite arbitrary. In fact, there are about 46 calendars in use throughout the world today. All of them generally divide the year into units that roughly correspond to our month system. Usually, this division is due to the lunar cycle that is about 28 days long. However, the lunar cycles do not fit evenly in the year, either. There are 13 lunar cycles (plus about 1.25 days) in a solar year.

Julius Caesar was determined to make a reliable calendar; so, he had an Alexandrian astronomer, Sosigines, design a calendar that was independent of the lunar cycle. This "Julian Calendar" went into effect in 45 B.C. By this time, the Roman calendar was so far off that Caesar had to add 90 days just to bring the months back in line with the seasons. It had most of the characteristics that we are used to. There were twelve months and a leap year every fourth year.

The names for our months are still similar to those of the Romans. March is named for the god, Mars; July for Julius, and August for Augustus Caesar. September just means month number seven (March was the first month in the Roman calendar. In our calendar, September is the 9th month). Still the Julian Calendar was flawed and by 1500, it was apparent that the calendar had to be fixed. After all, religious holidays had to be celebrated at the proper times.

In 1514, a secretary of the Pope asked a Polish astronomer-mathematician named Kopernig (his name was Latinized to Copernicus[8]) to try to fix the calendar. However, Copernicus responded that nothing could be done about the calendar until the relationship between the earth, moon and sun had been resolved. As you know, Copernicus resolved that problem by placing the sun in the center of the universe with the earth circling the sun and the moon circling the earth.

In 1582, Pope Gregory adopted the Gregorian calendar which adds the stipulation that centuries are leap years *only if divisible by 400.* Thus, 2000 was a leap year. Britain adopted the Gregorian calendar as the official calendar of the empire in 1782. Interestingly, the United States never officially adopted the Gregorian calendar.

---

[8] See the essay, *Principia Mathematica: The Foundation of Modern Physics,* for more about Copernicus and his contributions.

153

OTHER CALENDARS

Tradition, tradition! Tradition!
Tradition, tradition! Tradition!
  -Sheldon Harnick (Fiddler on the Roof)

I have reviewed a number of ways in which the year is divided in preparation for this essay. Perhaps, my favorite alternative calendar is the 13 month calendar proposed by Auguste Comte in 1849. In his calendar, each of the 13 months is divided into 28 days (4 weeks) plus two blank days at the end of the year.

Moses B. Cotsworth in England improved Comte's idea (see Figure 3-33). He added the new 13th month, called Sol, between June and July. This new calendar eliminated variable lengths of months. Every month would began with a Sunday and ended on a Saturday. The 11th was always a Wednesday, regardless of the month. This revision, called the International Fixed Calendar, received the full support of the American, George Eastman. It never caught on and the effort was abandoned in 1937.

Among human beings, tradition is a stronger force than rationality. Besides, who wants to celebrate the 4th of July on the 17th of Sol? Still, regardless of how we divide the time, the days are what they are. The sunrises and sunsets will continue to occur in regular, predictable patterns and the evening and the morning are just the next day.

S	M	T	W	T	F	S
1	2	3	4	5	6	7
8	9	10	11	12	13	14
15	16	17	18	19	20	21
22	23	24	25	26	27	28

FIGURE 3-33. The Cotsworth Standard Month in the International Fixed Calendar.

-1996, revised 2005

References:

Burke, James. 1985. *The Day the Universe Changed.* Little, Brown and Company. Boston.

Mason, Stephen F. 1962. *A History of the Sciences.* Collier Books. New York.

Trefil, James and Robert Hazen. 1995. *The Sciences, An Integrated Approach.* John Wiley & Sons, Inc. New York.

Questions to Think About

1. Why did I have to make multiple attempts to measure the rising sun on many dates?

2. What was the lesson of the spider of Susquehanna-Henge?

3. How is a calendar a science, and how is it a technology?

4. What was the problem with the Julian calendar that led to its revision?

5. Who was the astronomer most involved with the development of the Gregorian calendar?

6. What is the purpose of a leap year?

7. Why do the months have approximately 30 days each?

8. What is the Cotsworth calendar? What are its advantages? What are its disadvantages?

A WRIGHT SOLUTION

A FOGGY MORNING

And there is a(n)...eagle in some souls that can alike dive down into the blackest gorges, and soar out of them again and become invisible in the sunny spaces. Herman Melville, *Moby Dick*

In the summer of 1972 I traveled to Alaska with my uncle, aunt, cousin, and a Schnauzer named Whiskers in a VW Beetle pulling a camper. My uncle asked me to go along to help with the driving, but he drove almost the whole trip. One morning in British Columbia we had just crossed the mountain range as we headed toward the city of Prince Rupert on the coast. I sat in a morning stupor as my uncle drove us through magnificent mist-shrouded forests and scenery that was almost out of Tolkein. Suddenly a large shape swooped down over the car and soared over a lake we were passing. I noticed that it was a large bird with a white tail. My mind began the deductive exercise of eliminating possibilities, and then I realized that I had seen a Bald Eagle. I shouted to my uncle to stop the car and jumped out with binoculars to admire this spectacle. The bird seemed only too happy to oblige me. It banked and soared over the water. It was close enough that I could see the large flight feathers at the tips of the wings as they spread and vibrated slightly. The bird barely flapped its wings as it surveyed the water. It skimmed the surface and snatched a fish from the water. Then, almost effortlessly, it made several deep strokes of the wings, gained altitude and perched in a lone dead tree at the water's edge.

I have seen hundreds of Bald Eagles since that first encounter. In fact, we saw many more later that day at the harbor at Prince Rupert. Still, the memory of this encounter is one of my most vivid.

HANDS THAT FLY

The modern bird, like an airplane, is structurally and functionally efficient.
-O. S. Pettingill

The wings of birds are modified forelimbs. Indeed, the hands of birds are greatly reduced with most of the bones either lost or fused. Feathers, modified scales that are both light and strong, make the wing surface.

Birds are not the only animals that have evolved powered flight. Among vertebrates (animals with backbones), bats have achieved flight by the elongation of their hands and fingers with skin stretched between them. A similar type of wing had evolved among the extinct pterosaurs during the Mesozoic Era; however, most of the fingers remained small and only one elongated into the strut for the webbed wing (see Figure 3-34 for examples of vertebrate wings). In all three groups of vertebrates, the animals were light and most were small[9].

This is an example of convergent evolution, the independent evolution of similar structures (the vertebrate forelimb) to accomplish similar goals. The forelimbs and their flight surfaces both provide the lift to overcome their weight and to keep them aloft. However, many other gliding animals accomplish this. The notable aspect of bird, bat, and pterosaur flight is that they provide power or thrust by downward motions of their

---

[9] Although some of the pterosaurs were truly giants of the sky, they were still remarkably light for their size. *Quetzalcoatlus* had a 50-foot wingspan but may have weighed less than 190 pounds.

wings. This thrust is great enough to overcome drag or friction with the air and drive them forward. The musculature necessary to provide the power stroke is quite large and well-developed. In birds, the flight muscles can make up the bulk of the weight of the animal.

BIRD

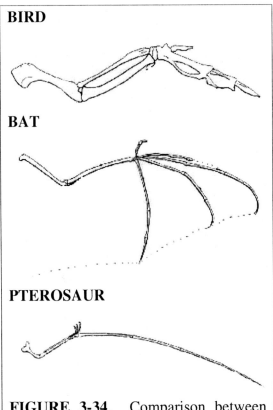

BAT

PTEROSAUR

FIGURE 3-34. Comparison between the forelimb structures of birds, bats, and pterosaurs. They all employ the forelimbs to produce wings; however, each is a unique and independently evolved solution to flight.

Insects, the other major group of animals that evolved powered flight, did not modify an appendage to produce their wings. Instead, they developed elongate scales on their backs as separate structures. Typically, insects have two pairs of wings that are powered by a highly efficient musculature. Overall, their wings are like those of the flying vertebrates; that is, they move up and down (with a complex forward-and-back motion) providing both the surfaces for lift and thrust. Furthermore, their wings seem to get added lift by hairs on the upper surfaces. This has been shown to be the case in the bumblebee, the insect that is not supposed to be able to fly[10].

Flight, although difficult to evolve, offers important advantages to those animals that possess it. This can be seen in the relative numbers of animal species that have this characteristic. There are more bird species than mammals. Among mammals, bats are among the most diverse. However, they cannot hold a candle to the diversity and sheer numbers of insects. Most living animals are insects. This is magnified if we compare only those that live on land (and therefore have a chance of flight).

THE CHALLENGE OF LEONARDO

[10] The story goes that in Germany during the 1930's a biologist asked a Swiss aerodynamics engineer about bees and their flight. The engineer did a "back of the napkin calculation" and determined that bees cannot fly. The engineer assumed that the bee's wing was smooth. He estimated weight and wing area to calculate lift in his calculations and found that lift was insufficient. However, mathematical formulas are models of reality. Until detailed measurements and calculations can be made, those models are flawed. The story should have died at the dinner party, but instead it has become part of our folklore about the failures of science and the foolishness of scientists.

Recent work on insect flight by Dr. Charles Ellington at Cambridge University shows that most of the "back of the napkin" assumptions were false. The bumblebee wing is not smooth. Also, as the wing flaps, air does not stream across it as it does on an airplane wing. Instead, a vortex is created that moves toward the wing tip. The vortex creates an area of low pressure above the wing and provides lift. In fact, this mechanism might increase lift by a factor of 2-3 times. Ellington is seeking ways to apply his discoveries to the design of small propellers.

The great bird will take flight above the ridge...filling the universe with awe, filling all writings with its fame...

Leonardo da Vinci

The mechanics of flight had become a passion of Leonardo da Vinci (1452-1519; a great Renaissance artist who was born in Vinci near the city of Florence. We know him best by his accomplishments as an artist and art theoretician. However, he did many other things, ranging from mapmaker to civil and military engineer.

Da Vinci used dissections to observe the anatomy and mechanics of motion. After 1503, he began a systematic study of birds to understand the mechanics of flight. He compiled his observations on anatomy, wing motion, center of gravity, stability, thrust, and maneuverability in a work called, *Codex on the Flight of Birds.* He then applied his observations to engineer structures that would allow humans to fly. It is not surprising that most of his inspiration came from birds and bats; after all, they were the accomplished flyers of the day. In addition to ornithopters, bat-like contraptions for powered flight (Figure 3-35), da Vinci designed a helicopter-like machine and a fixed-wing glider. Still, he did not bring his dream of flight to fruition. In fact, there is no evidence that he ever built or tried out any of his designs for his "great bird".

Flight seemed to be an elusive dream for da Vinci as well as others. Some attempted to employ bird and bat-like designs, but most experiments ended in disappointment and some in disaster. Joseph Montgolphier made a lighter-than-air balloon based on an observation that his wife made when her petticoat filled with smoke and began to rise one day. She suggested that if they could capture enough smoke, perhaps they could send a man aloft. With several companions, Montgolphier rose above Paris and flew for about 20 minutes on November 21, 1783. (There is some dispute as to the first balloon flight. The town of Santos, Brazil celebrates the balloon flight of Bartolomeu de Gusamao on August 8, 1709, 74 years before Montgolphier.)

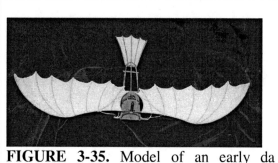

FIGURE 3-35. Model of an early da Vinci flyer that hangs in my office.

Even though it was a flight of a human being, this was not powered flight. The balloon flew according to the concept of density difference. That is, hot air is less dense than cold air and would rise relative to cooler air. If the difference in temperature were great enough, the volume of warmer air would carry aloft a balloon and associated people (or any other payload). Although height could be manipulated by controlling the temperature of the bagged air, direction was generally at the mercy of the wind.

True powered flight required a return to the pioneering work of Leonardo in order to place it on a scientific footing. In particular, just how does a wing work to provide lift? The first good answer came from Daniel Bernoulli (1700-1782) more than 200 years after Leonardo's *Codex.* Bernoulli had a varied career in science and won prizes for work in astronomy, gravity, tides, magnetism, ocean currents, and the behavior of ships at sea. He taught anatomy, botany, physiology and physics most of his life in Basel, Switzerland.

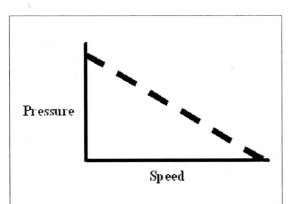

FIGURE 3-36. The fundamental relationship between speed of a medium and its pressure, called Bernoulli's Principle.

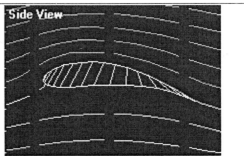

FIGURE 3-37. Bernoulli's Principle as it applies to an airfoil or wing. Air passing over the wing moves faster than air moving beneath the wing. Higher speed means lower pressure on the upper wing surface than on the lower wing surface. Thus the wing rises. I generated this airfoil with FoilSim (1997) from NASA Lewis Research Center.

His eclectic career culminated in a book called *Hydrodynamica*, which explored the properties of fluid flow, pressure, density, and velocity. The book then defined their fundamental relationships, now called Bernoulli's Principle.

Bernoulli's Principle as it applies to a wing is simply that a wing is rounded on top and flattened on the bottom (called a cambered wing; see Figure 3-37). As the wing slices through the air, the air moving across the upper surface has farther to travel and therefore moves faster than the air on the bottom of the wing. The consequence is that the pressure on the top is less than that on the bottom of the wing. Thus, the wing is forced up or lifted by the relatively low pressure on the upper surface of the wing. This cross section of a wing (Figure 3-37) is called an airfoil.

Sir George Cayley (1773-1857) of Scarborough, England is sometimes called the Father of Aviation. He was inspired by the Montgolphier flight; however, he saw the practical limitation of balloons particularly that they flew at the mercy of the winds. He wanted to develop a directed method of flight, one that could be controlled. To that end, like Leonardo, he studied birds, particularly gliding birds, and noticed that the camber of the bird's wing allowed for lift. Then he began to experiment with wing shapes in kites and fixed-wing gliders. Unlike Leonardo's ornithopters, his wings did not move, and the power for lift came from the constant falling motion of the glider. Also, unlike Leonardo, Cayley built and flew his designs. In one case he even forced the cooperation of his coachman to fly 200 yards across a valley in 1853. This was a great day for aviation history and Cayley, even though it was somewhat hair-raising for his coachman.

REALIZATION OF THE DREAM

Success. Four flights Thursday morning all against twenty one mile wind. Started from level with engine power alone...

Portion of telegram from Orville Wright to his father, 17 Dec 1903.

Otto Lilienthal (1848-1896), a prolific aeronautical researcher from Germany, designed numerous experiments to test the shapes of various wing designs. Like Leonardo da Vinci, he studied birds, but unlike da Vinci, Lilianthal studied dynamic bird flight with its range of wing twist and camber (the degree to which the wing arches in cross section). In addition, he designed experiments to compute lift and drag.

Mostly, Lilianthal flew in his heavier-than-air fixed-wing gliders, some of which achieved speeds of 25 miles per hour or more. He logged more than 2,500 flights in his gliders when on August 9, 1896, a cross wind caught him 50 feet in the air. His glider side-slipped and crashed, breaking Lilianthal's back. He is supposed to have said, "Sacrifices must be made," before he died.

Lilianthal had explored the possibility of flying gliders with flapping wings and even explored the possibility of a motorized flapping device. He abandoned that idea in favor of a rotating wing (we call it a propeller) in 1893, but he died before he could build such a device.

In the summer of 1896, Orville Wright caught Typhoid fever and nearly died. His brother, Wilbur, nursed him back to health. The news of Lilianthal's death had affected both of them and spurred them to continue their research in aeronautics. This was not particularly easy for them. Orville and Wilbur ran a bicycle shop and were interested in flight as an avocation. However, their interest grew so that Wilbur, in a letter to an aeronautical engineer in 1900 said, "I have been afflicted with the belief that flight is possible. My disease has increased in severity and I feel that it soon will cost me...increased money...if not my life."

They followed in the wake of Lilianthal and continued experimentation on fixed-wing gliders. They were particularly interested in wing design and how the airfoil of the wing affected lift and drag. This meant that they had to calculate or measure the various forces on the wing. Such numbers had been published, but they varied enormously. The Wright brothers decided to construct a wind tunnel, an apparatus that would allow them to test and measure the various forces.

A wind tunnel is an apparatus that blows air over an object in laminar flow. This way, turbulence and other distortions of the airflow can be observed and measured. Further, scale models can be used to test effects on large, life-sized structures. In fact, a dimensionless number called the Reynolds Number determines whether or not a scale model can be used. The Reynolds Number is a ratio between momentum and viscosity of the medium. In this case, air is the medium both for the model and the life-sized wing. If the model has the same Reynolds Number as the full sized structure, then its measurements can be taken as if it were full size.

The Wrights experimented with models in the controlled setting of the wind tunnel and made careful measurements. They determined that a biplane with two propellers (of their design) turning in opposite directions driven by an 8 horsepower gasoline engine would be sufficient if the plane and pilot together weighed no more than 600 pounds.

At last they were ready to try it out at Kitty Hawk, North Carolina on December 17, 1903. Only five people showed up for this attempt even though a general invitation had been issued to all within a five-mile radius. The first flight lasted 12 seconds. It was especially important because the plane had been lifted off the ground by its own power. Moreover, the flight ended with a controlled decent and landing.

They flew the machine four times that day. The last flight lasted 59 seconds and covered 852 feet. After the fourth flight, a gust of wind caught the flyer and rolled it across the sand. The first four controlled, people had accomplished powered flights.

WHY BIRDS CAN'T FLY LIKE PLANES

Given that there is forward movement through the air, the wings of a bird provide lift in approximately the same way as those of an aeroplane, albeit aeroplane wings are simpler because fixed.

-Richard Dawkins

Now I come back to the question of flight by living things. Why don't birds fly like airplanes? Mainly because animals did not evolve wheels or propellers, they had to employ moving wings in flight. This is true even though flapping wings, compared to the fixed wing designs of airplanes, impart particular problems relative to stability and drag. The important thing to remember when considering this issue is that animals do not always evolve the best mechanisms or solutions. However, flight, no matter how inefficient or unsteady, still imparts an advantage to living things.

Since 1903 humans have been flying. Their flight, unlike that of birds, bats, and insects came about through an understanding of nature (science) and applying that understanding to the problem of flight (engineering). With the marriage of science and technology, so beautifully illustrated by the magnificent advances in aerospace designs over the last century, we contracted millions of years of evolution and surpassed the eagle. That fact became blaringly obvious when on July 20, 1969, a few years before I saw my first bald eagle, I first heard the phrase:

Houston, Tranquility Base here.
The Eagle has landed.
-2000, revised 2003

References:

Brady, Tim. 2000. *The American Aviation Experience, A History.* Southern Illinois University Press. Carbondale.

Dawkins, Richard. 1996. *Climbing Mount Improbable.* W.W. Norton & Co. New York.

Hart, Clive. 1985. *The Prehistory of Flight.* University of California Press. Berkeley, CA.

Jakab, Peter L. and Rick Young, eds. 2000. *The Published Writings of Wilbur and Orville Wright.* Smithsonian Institution Press. Washington.

Pettingill, Olin S. 1970. *Ornithology in Laboratory and Field.* Burgess Publishing Co. Minneapolis, Minn.

Sarton, George. 1957. *Six Wings, Men of Science in the Renaissance.* Indiana University Press. Bloomington, Indiana.

Shapiro, Ascher H. 1961. *Shape and Flow, The Fluid Dynamics of Drag.* Science Study Series. Doubleday & Co., Inc. New York.

Trefil, James and Robert Hazen. 2004. *The Sciences, An Integrated Approach.* 4th ed. John Wiley & Sons, Inc. New York.

Wilson, Edward O. 1992. *The Diversity of Life.* W.W. Norton & Co. New York.

Questions to Think About

1. How are the wings of vertebrates (birds, bats, and pterosaurs) similar?

   All are modified forelimbs.

2. How are the wings of insects different from those of vertebrates?

   • Not a modified appendage
   • Elongated scales as a separate structure

3. What are the contributions of Leonardo da Vinci to the understanding of powered flight?

   • Analysis of analysis and mechanics of motion • Designed structures
   • Wing motion thrust center of gravity   • Copies of the flight birds

4. What did Montgolphier do? How did he get his idea?

   • Blimps!
   • wife's petticoat

5. Why is Sir George Cayley (and not Leonardo da Vinci) called the "Father of Aviation"?

   • wings about more
   • Gliders
   • Actually built & tried something

6. Daniel Bernoulli did not study flight per se, but his name is always connected with the history of aviation. Why?

   • Airflow   • wing design
   • Lift   • Relationship of pressure, density, velocity

7. One author suggested that if Cayley is the "Father of Aviation" then surely Otto Lilianthal must be its uncle. What did he mean by that?

   • Also gliders - broken back
   • Motorized flapping wings — propeller

8. What is the importance of the Reynold's number in testing aviation designs?

   If model has same Reynolds # as full structure, then measurements can be taken as if it were full size.

9. Where, when, and by whom did the first powered flight occur?

   Wright Bros
   Kittyhawk, NC   12/17/1903

10. What allows for lift on a bumblebee's wing?

    Rough edges / Vortex

A TRINITY:
INVENTION, SCIENCE, AND DREAMS IN THE DEVELOPMENT OF ROCKET TECHNOLOGY

AN UNSUCCESSFUL FLIGHT

God protects children and fools.
                                    -American Proverb

When I was a boy in Oklahoma, I was very interested in chemistry and some of its ramifications (especially those that make noise). I worked hard to perfect black gunpowder so that it would sound as good as the firecrackers that were so easily obtained in Oklahoma in those days. Bottle rockets, too, were some of my favorite pastimes. It was just a small step from there to an interest in model rockets. Not only because I enjoyed working with cardboard tubes, glue, and balsa wood, but also because the space race was in full swing during the later years of the 1960's. Thus, I built and launched a number of model rockets. A group of us became interested in building our own rocket, not "just one from a kit". So, we secured a large cardboard tube that carpet came rolled on, and we cut it into about a 4 foot section to make a really big rocket.

We had been experimenting with a standard rocket fuel of sulfur and zinc. We measured small aliquots (about a square centimeter) to a lid to measure a timed burn. We had having trouble keeping a sustained burn, and the speed of the combustion was disappointing. So, one of us had the idea of mixing the zinc-sulfur with the flash powder that we had perfected earlier. After a few experiments with the burning rate, we were ready to go. We had invented a new rocket fuel.

FIGURE 3-38. A more recent rocket flight.

The next step was to fill the tube with the new chemical mixture. The volume of the components that we needed for the carpet tube rocket were expensive, so we all worked and contributed to the purchase of chemicals for this project. We used an evil-smelling solvent to allow for the even mixture of the components, which we poured into the tube in liter-sized aliquots. We needed to allow the solvent to evaporate between our repeated applications of the same procedure. The evaporation occurred at about the same rate that we earned money to buy more supplies. Anyway, after several trips to the local chemical supply house, we had finished filling the rocket motor compartment in the carpet tube. We packed the fuel around a metal rod down the center of the tube to provide for an empty column through the solid fuel for an even burn. After nearly a week more, the solid fuel had hardened and was ready for the application of fins and a nose cone. We even had grandiose schemes of using a hollow nose cone and launching a mouse. Fortunately for the mouse, we did not have time.

Anyway, after attaching the fins of heavy cardboard and a solid wooden nose cone, we drove to a launching site outside of Tulsa. After we admired the impressive rocket, we slipped a long piece of dynamite fuse up through the hole in the solid fuel (yes, you could order such things as dynamite fuse through the mail in those days). We made sure that a generous amount of fuse stuck out of the rocket so that we could be well protected in case the fuel exploded. I can't recall who lit the fuse, but I do remember waiting an eternity until the sputtering flame approached the rocket. The fuel ignited, and a large flame enveloped the whole lower part of the rocket which then began to rise very slowly. Then, it turned on its side and began to fly parallel to the ground, skipping over it in an irregular way. By that time the fins were bent and on fire, too. After it bounced off the ground, rocks, and a tree or two, the prodigal rocket came to rest with its nose cone stuck in the ground at a 45-degree angle. What remained of the crumpled tube billowed smoke and flame until at last, mercifully, only the cardboard was burning.

We emerged from our protection cautiously, and advanced slowly toward the wreck. Our initial reconnoiter revealed several of our mistakes - not the least of which was that we started too big, too grand with our first experimental rocket.

Also, although we spent much time in our research of rocket fuel, we had spent little to no time on the mechanics of rocket flight and rocket design. After all, the kits had always determined the design. We just assumed that if we made a bigger rocket, it would fly higher than its smaller counterparts. We should have made an effort to learn something about rocket stability. Anyway, I don't know about the others, but this experience made such an impression on me that I stopped building model rockets altogether for more than 20 years. Had we not given up, one or more of us might have taken the path described by Homer Hickam in *Rocket Boys*. His group called the "Big Creek Missile Agency" suffered many more profound setbacks than we did, but learned from their difficulties. We did not. Our great intentions like our great invention went up in smoke that day in the summer of 1967.

BY THE GRACE OF INVENTION

Thus we live only by the grace of invention: not merely by such invention as has already been made, but by our hope of new and nonexisting inventions for the future. -Norbert Wiener (1954)

About the same time as the great rocket debacle, my grandfather perfected a locking mechanism that could move easily over a rod, but lock in place with the movement of the hand. This could be applied to music stands, lab stools, and nutcrackers, just to name a few. He applied for and received a patent on the invention, but nothing came of it. I still have the prototype of the nutcracker that produces whole pecan kernels with almost every pull of the lever. All of us in the family were excited about his invention, but the world did not seem to be.

Many inventions, even successful ones, are ultimately failures and go up in smoke. Norbert Wiener (1894-1964), an American mathematician who among other things worked on the mathematics of and their applications to rocket guidance systems during World War II, considered the problem of invention and the means to nurture it. He wrote the manuscript of his ideas about invention in 1954, but it languished among his papers until 1993, 29 years after his death. Wiener considered the useful modern inventions to be applications of scientific concepts. Indeed, he did not seem to differentiate between science and technology, but saw them as part of a continuum. Wiener defined four stages in the process of invention: the intellectual, technical, social, and economic stages. He contended that these had to occur in this order for them to be successful, a success based on the invention's benefit to society rather than to the individual inventor or entrepreneur. Except for a few outdated examples, and repeated references to the antagonism between the Soviet Union and the United States, Wiener's ideas are as relevant today as they were in 1954.

At its most fundamental level, the intellectual stage is the idea, the concept. The idea of my grandfather's locking device (and less so for our solid fuel rocket) is the insight in how to solve a practical problem. Here, I refer to the theoretician as the thinker or the person with the idea but not necessarily the means to bring that idea to fruition. By and large, scientists, engineers, and all manner of technicians are used to this type of thinking. Most of their ideas are tossed about and thrown away. Some ideas survive.

FIRE ARROWS

Invention is a heroic thing and placed above the reach of a low and vulgar genius. It requires an active, a bold, a nimble, a restless min; a thousand difficulties condemned with which a mean heart would be broken.

-Thomas Sprat (1667)

The one or ones who first had the idea of the rocket are lost in a time without science, but they seem to have appeared in China, probably not long after the invention of gunpowder. The first Chinese rockets probably evolved from firecrackers made from sections of bamboo stuffed with black gunpowder and were as unpredictable as mine was. Likely, these were thrown into fires to make the explosive bang required during festivals and celebrations. Some probably did not explode, but shot out of the fire as small rockets. The Chinese made use of this to make propelled arrows that spat flame and startled their enemies. This was recorded in 1232 when the Chinese repelled the Mongols in battle. The fire arrow was a larger version of the bottle rocket that I used as a boy. It had a tube filled with black gunpowder and used a trailing stick as a guidance mechanism. Anyway, the fire arrows were not effective in repelling the Mongols because of their accuracy, but because of the terror that flying fire and smoke created.

Wan-Hu, a Chinese official, got the idea that he could fly if he sat in a chair propelled by fire arrows. The story goes that he attached 47 fire arrow rockets to a chair with two large kite-like wings mounted above it. After the arrows were lit, Wan-Hu disappeared in a thunderclap of fire and smoke.

The Chinese and Mongols perfected the rocket, in part as a military weapon.

However, it saw most use as a means of celebration. Probably, the Mongols carried the knowledge of rockets to the Arabs and Indians who introduced them to the Europeans. There, the step rocket or multiple staged rocket was invented. Still, the rocket was a plaything or a weapon for effect. There was little or no scientific basis for rocket design, particularly stability and guidance (both attributes were lacking in my experimental rocket, as well).

However it was made, the Chinese rocket had become a successful invention. It began as an idea. Then the technical climate developed through the perfection of gunpowder and materials to construct fire arrows. The social climate for the invention grew as the technical skill of making gunpowder developed and flourished in a caste of artisans who provided the propellant, while others, also thorough trial and error, perfected the fire arrow for maximum effect. Thus, the rocket had gone through the first three of Wiener's stages of invention.

I argue that for large government-funded projects, the economic stage is combined with that of the social stage. The government provides the economic incentive and the framework for the communication between the theoreticians and those with adequate technical skill (technicians). In China, there really were no theoreticians in the modern scientific sense. The rocket worked and developed through trial and error.

During the Enlightenment in Europe, the philosophers had gone beyond the science of the ancients. This development, particularly in physics, led to a theoretical framework from which new ideas could arise and provided a common language, one of mathematics, in which theoreticians and technicians could communicate.

NEWTON'S LAWS AND ROCKETS

Although Newton derived the theories appearing in the Principia over 300 years before the beginning of the space age, they serve as the foundation of modern spaceflight mechanics, more popularly known as rocket science.

-Wayne Lee

Isaac Newton (1642-1727) followed the leads of Rene Descartes and Galileo Galilei who envisioned the physical universe as a mechanism with definable mechanical laws. Newton stated three Laws of Motion in his book, *Principia Mathematica Philosophiae Naturalis.* His first law was really a statement of motion as defined by Galileo who said that an object continues in its particular state of motion unless it was acted upon by a force. This idea ran counter to those of pre-Galilean philosophers who said that objects remain in motion because they were acted upon by a force. In the earlier view, objects like balls rolling across a floor stop moving naturally because the mover's hand no longer pushed it. Galileo said that the ball would remain in motion and slow down only as it was acted upon by friction. In this case, friction was a force and its action on a rolling ball was to change its velocity. In a more general sense, Galileo said that all objects possessed an "inertia" that kept them moving in uniform motion. For this reason, Newton's first law is usually called the Law of Inertia. He defined this law with these words: "Every body persists in its state of rest or uniform motion in a straight line unless it is compelled to change that state by forces impressed upon it." In Newton's view, both a state of constant motion and a state of rest were "natural" and could not be distinguished from each other.

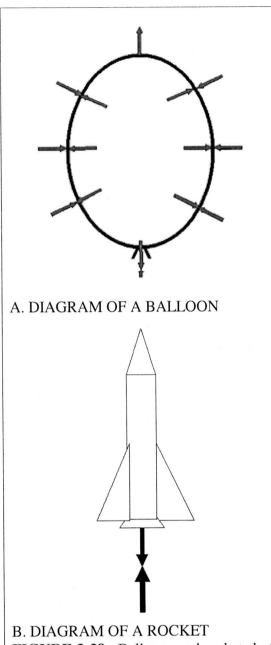

A. DIAGRAM OF A BALLOON

B. DIAGRAM OF A ROCKET
FIGURE 3-39. Balloons and rockets both obey the third law of motion. **A.** shows the paired forces on a balloon. The force of the air leaving the balloon causes it to travel forward. **B** The paired forces on a rocket.

If a force is applied to an object, its velocity changes. A change in velocity is called acceleration. So, a force applied to an object causes it to accelerate. (Note

that here acceleration does not mean speed up. It could mean slow down as the force of friction on a rolling ball). What if the same force is applied to two different bodies like a baseball and a bowling ball? Do they accelerate at the same rate? No, because a force is the product of its mass and its acceleration. The more massive object will have a smaller acceleration (and vice versa). So, the mass of an object is a way of expressing its inertia or tendency to remain in its current state of motion. This is Newton's second law of motion.

Newton's third law of motion states that forces come in pairs such that for every action there is an equal and opposite reaction. The most common example is that of an inflated balloon (Figure 3-39A). When air is allowed to escape, the stream of air is an action that causes the balloon to fly about in reaction. The third law has an obvious connection with model rockets in which thrust, a force or an action, is the consequence of the consumption of propellant and the velocity of the escaping gasses. Thrust then induces a reaction in which the rocket moves in the opposite direction from the escaping gasses (Figure 3-39B). In the case of a model rocket, gasses escape from the nozzle of the rocket engine at about 800 meters per second. [My experimental rocket also did not have a nozzle. However, this is probably fortunate since the confined gasses would likely have exploded.].

In the metric scale, the Newton is a unit of force in which 1 kilogram accelerates at the rate of 1 meter per second per second. Model rocket engines typically specify the total impulse force (Newton-seconds; that is the total force over the length of the burn) by letter followed by a number that indicates the average force in Newtons. For example, a C6 rocket engine produces a total impulse of 5-10 Newton-seconds and an average force of 6 Newtons

TABLE 3-5. The code used on model rocket engines and its meaning in average thrust.

CODE	Newton-seconds
¼ A	0.000 – 0.625
½ A	0.625 – 1.250
A	1.250 – 2.500
B	2.500 – 5.000
C	5.000 – 10.000

So, a rocket that has a mass of 25 grams (with the rocket engine) will have higher acceleration with the same rocket engine than will a rocket that has a mass of 100 grams. In fact, the smaller rocket should accelerate four times faster than the larger one. Greater acceleration means greater altitude in the case of rockets.

Newton's laws of motion began to be used by engineers to perfect the rocket. Particularly, in Germany and Russia, application of Newton's laws allowed for larger and more stable rockets. A British artillery officer, Colonel William Congreve at the turn of the 19th century, observed the effect of fire arrows in the hands if Indian nationals during Britain's conquest of India. He realized that rockets could provide massive firepower that would exceed that of the muzzle-loading cannon of the day. His invention, called the Congreve rocket, was successful militarily and was employed by the British in many campaigns. In fact, Congreve's rockets were used in the siege of Fort McHenry and prompted Francis Scott Key to include the phrase, *the rockets' red glare* in the poem that would later become the words of our national anthem.

Rockets were useful in that thousands of them could be fired upon an enemy without heavy artillery pieces and the delay that muzzle loading required. Later, that advantage began to disappear with the advent of breech-loading cannons. Also, cannons were much more accurate than rockets.

A few improvements allowed slightly increased control over where a rocket went, but it still required a good bit of luck to hit an intended target. Much earlier, fins had replaced the stick of the fire arrow. In the 19th century, fins were placed in the nozzle, the bell at the back of Figure 3-39B. These fins were angled slightly to cause the rocket to spin. A spinning rocket was more stable and tended to go in a straighter line.

There is a point on a rocket at which the mass in front equals the mass in back. This is called the center of mass or center of gravity. A rocket tends to rotate, tumble, or oscillate about the center of gravity, just like a stick will when it is thrown. This will happen to a model rocket if it has no fins. In a way, a rocket is like a weather vane. As it picks up speed, and slices through the air, the fins hold it steady.

Why are fins at the back of the rocket? As air moves past the rocket, drag is created by friction. This is (in an aerodynamic design) related to the surface area of the rocket. The greater the surface across which air must travel, the greater its drag. Like the center of gravity, a rocket has a point called the center of pressure about which the surface area in the front equals the surface area in the back. A rocket is stable when the center of pressure is well back of the center of gravity. That is why fins must be at the back of the rocket.

Aerodynamic design is useful for any object that travels through the atmosphere at high speed. However, some dreamers began to think of moving at high speed beyond our atmosphere into the unknown reaches of space. The first dreamers were science fiction writers like Jules Verne and H.G. Wells. Others had their characters explore space with balloons, and all manner of exotic devices to fling the human-bearing craft into space. Many like H.G. Wells in *The First Men in the Moon* employed antigravity substances. Jules Verne was more straightforward and shot his characters from an enormous cannon in Florida. Although these particular methods were hopelessly counter to natural law or common sense, both of which science fiction writers seem to avoid at all cost, the dream of travel through space and to other worlds had begun. This inspiration in the age of technical growth through the application of Newtonian physics, gave rise to a collection of inventors with the goal of space exploration.

A DEAF TEACHER

All men dream; but not equally. ...The dreamers of the day are dangerous men for they may act their dream with open eyes to make it possible.

-T. E. Lawrence;
The Seven Pillars of Wisdom

Among the dreamers of the day, none was more important in laying the scientific foundation for space exploration than Konstantin Eduardovich Tsiolkovsky (1857-1935). Born near Moscow in the Russian Empire, he grew up in a family of 17 brothers and sisters. When he was 10, Tsiolkovsky was stricken by scarlet fever and lost his hearing as a consequence. Being deaf, he could no longer attend school so he taught himself by reading.

Later, the Russian philosopher and proponent of space exploration, Nikolai Fedorov, tutored him. Besides the influence of Federov, Tsiolkovsky said that he was inspired by the influence the novels of Jules Verne to produce vehicles for living in space, not just travel.

Tsiolkovsky passed exams to earn a teaching certificate and began to experiment with balloon design. During this time, he realized that the only mechanism with the force necessary to allow humans to escape the earth was the rocket. This was no small step to take. The conventional wisdom of the day concerning Newton's third law and rockets was that a rocket moved forward by pushing against the air. Because there was no air in the vacuum of space, a rocket could not work there. Tsiolkovsky realized that the thrust came from the velocity and mass of the escaping gasses, thus a rocket would work even more efficiently in a vacuum. Tsiolkovsky published this concept in 1903 as his rocket equation that he derived from Newton's laws (see Figure 3-40).

$$u = v \ln (M_0 / M) + u_0$$

FIGURE 3-40. Tsiolkovsky's rocket equation. u is the final velocity of the rocket; v is the velocity of the exhaust gasses; M_0 is the initial mass and the M is the final mass; u_0 is the initial velocity.

Tsiolkovsky attacked the problems of rocketry and human habitation in space from a theoretical point of view. He determined that solid fuel rockets were not very practical for use in space. For one thing, solid fuels were heavy compared to the thrust that they produced. Liquid fuels were much more efficient and allowed for the speeds necessary to escape the gravitational pull of the earth (called escape velocity). In addition, solid fuel rockets could not be controlled after ignition because, once lit, they burned to the end. Liquid fuel rockets could be ignited, stopped and ignited again and again. This kind of control would be necessary to navigate in space. Tsiolkovsky set about designing liquid fuel rockets, multiple stage rockets, air locks, etc. Unfortunately, all of his work was theoretical. He was not able to build and test any of his designs until much later in life. Still, as a scientist he was prolific and published more than 500 articles on the theory of rocketry and space flight.

ROCKETS IN PRACTICE
As I looked toward the fields to the east, I imagined how wonderful it would be to make some device which had even the possibility of landing on Mars, and how it might look on a small scale if I sent it up from the meadow at my feet.
-Robert H. Goddard, from Clarke (1968)

Robert Hutchings. Goddard (1882-1945), was born in Massachusetts and, like Tsiolkovsky, was inspired by the science fiction of H. G. Wells and Jules Verne. He independently arrived at the need for a liquid fuel rocket to explore space. Unlike Tsiolkovsky, however, Goddard began to build and test rocket designs [One early design nearly blew up a physics lab at Clark University in 1907 while he was a student. Fortunately, he was not expelled.] Thus, he was not only a theoretician, but used and developed necessary technical methods, materials, and machines.

Goddard funded himself and acquired two patents for rocket design in 1914 (a liquid fuel rocket design and a design for a multistage solid fuel rocket). Later, he received funding from the Smithsonian Institution in 1916 to continue his work. In 1920, Goddard submitted a report to the Smithsonian Institution detailing his experiments and how money was spent. Toward the end of the report, he suggested that a rocket could be built and fired at the moon with a payload of flashpowder. Upon its arrival, its explosion could be detected by telescopic examination. The press picked up this last part of his report and ridiculed him. After that experience, Goddard remained somewhat secretive and refused to join or communicate with the American Rocketry Society.

On the morning of March 16, 1926, Robert Goddard flew the first liquid fuel rocket at his aunt's farm in Auburn, Massachusetts. The rocket flew only 152 feet high (about the same distance as the first flight of the Wright brothers 13 years earlier).

Goddard's practical achievements were many. He demonstrated Tsiolkovsky's assertion that a rocket would work in a vacuum. In 1929, he sent aloft a barometer and a camera as the first scientific payloads. He built and developed the use of gyroscopic control and guidance of rockets, and in 1937, he launched a liquid fuel rocket that was guided by gyro-controlled gimbals.

In 1936, Goddard published an account of his work through the Smithsonian Institution. Although he worked for the U.S. Navy during both World Wars and accumulated more than 200 patents on rocket design, Goddard's work and its potential was ignored by the U.S. military. However, his work was not ignored by his counterparts in Germany.

A DOCTOR DENIED

Never mind. I will prove that I am able to become a greater scientist than some of you, even without the title of doctor.

-Hermann Oberth

Hermann Julius Oberth (1894-1989) was born in Romania and became interested in space travel, like Tsiolkovsky and Goddard, after reading Jules Verne's *From the Earth to the Moon.* After service in the medical corps during World War I, he continued his studies at the University of Munich. His experience during the war convinced him that he did not want to be a ` hysiccian so he began to study physics. His dissertation in 1922 on the use of rockets for space travel was rejected because the old-school German physicists could not accept that a rocket would work in the vacuum of space. Oberth did not try to write another dissertation, but continued his interest in rocketry. In 1923, he reworked his dissertation and published it as *The Rocket into Planetary Space.* He published a much longer version in 1929.

As an impoverished teacher of mathematics, Oberth, like Tsiolkovsky, was unable to fund the application of his ideas. However, he helped to found the German Rocket Society. As a group, the rocket society raised money to fund the research and development of their rockets. Unlike the secrecy of Goddard's work, the rocket society held highly publicized launches. A Captain Dornberger of the newly organized German Army witnessed one of the launches in 1932. A few months later the society disbanded as its members began to work for the German military.

Werner von Braun (1912-1977), inspired by Oberth's writings, worked as Oberth's assistant from 1930-32. Thereafter, von Braun, who always referred to Oberth as "my teacher", became the leader of the military rocket research program. Later, they worked together again during World War II in the construction and development of the vengeance weapons (the V1 and V2). The V2 was a larger and improved version of the rocket built by Goddard in 1937. After the war, both Oberth and von Braun were brought to the U.S. to get our program off the ground. The Soviet program under the influence of the followers of Tsiolkovsky was alive and well at the time.

The inventions associated with rocketry mounted through the 20th century. In this process, invention supported invention. The technical foundations already laid in physics, chemistry, metallurgy, mechanical engineering, etc., allowed the development of components of rockets that made them more reliable, more stable, and more accurate. The giant Saturn V, the rocket that carried the Apollo program to the moon was the crowning achievement of von Braun and, thereby of Oberth, Goddard, and Tsiolkovsky.

A TRINITY

God loves a trinity. -A Russian Proverb

A Russian proverb says that God loves a trinity. That is, important things come in threes. Isaac Newton defined a trinity of laws that gave a scientific basis to rocketry. Three 20th century scientists with dreams of human space exploration and Newton's laws saw rockets as necessary means to those ends. Often working in isolation from the rest of the scientific community and from each other, they taught others who carried on their quest. Of the three, only Oberth witnessed a human presence in space.

The steps required for human entry into space were painful and, at times, faltering. There were many missteps, many failures as in the history of powered flight. Indeed, my misadventure with a rocket pales next to some of the rocket-related disasters. Fortunately, the climate of invention supported the growth of dreams into practical ideas. These, in turn, spawned more ideas until the development of the space shuttle, the most complex machine ever devised. However, it is only the last in a developing set of machines produced through the trinity of science, technical advance, and ideas. The shuttle is just a step in the path to the stars, for as long as there are dreamers, the ideas will not cease to fly. On April 12, 1961, the dreams of Tsiolkovsky, Goddard, and Oberth took flight after cosmonaut Yuri Gagarin sitting in a space capsule atop a rocket called out "**Поехали! (Let's go!)**"

-2004; Revised from 2000 and 2002

References:

Clarke, Arthur C. 1968. *The Promise of Space.* Pyramid Books. New York.

Halliday, David and Robert Resnick. 1970. *Fundamentals of Physics..* John Wiley and Sons, Inc. New York.

Hickam, Homer H. 1998. *Rocket Boys.* Delta Books. New York.

Kosmodemyansky, A. 2000. (from 1954 edition). *Konstantin Tsiolkovsky, His Life and Work.* University Press of the Pacific. Honolulu, Hawaii.

Lee, Wayne.(no date). *To Rise From Earth.* Facts On File, Inc. New York.

NASA. *Robert H. Goddard: American Rocket Pioneer.* NASA FACTS. http://pao.gsfc.nasa.gov/gsfc/service/gallery/fact_sheets/general/goddard/goddard.htm

NASA. *A Brief History of Rocketry.* NASA Spacelink. http://www.ksc.nasa.gov/history/rocket-history.txt

Rosenberg, Carla, editor. 1996. *Rockets, A Teacher's Guide with Activities In Science, Mathematics, and Technology.* NASA. EG-1996-09-108-HQ.

Wiener, Norbert. 1994. *Invention, The Care and Feeding of Ideas.* MIT Press. Cambridge, Mass.

Questions to Think About

1. Think of at least one reason why the carpet tube rocket went out of control.

   Center of mass, poor fins, -Surface Area

2. Who was Norbert Wiener and what were his four stages in the process of invention?

   1) Intellectual 3) Social
   2) Technical 4) Economic
   USA - mathematician
   -rocket guidance

3. Where were rockets invented? What were they used for?

   China - celebration

4. Who was Wan-Hu and what was his fate?

   Rocket Man Chinese Official

5. What is a difference between the science of the ancients and the science of the Enlightenment?

- Theoretical framework
- General understanding,

6. What is Newton 's First Law? Who really defined it as a law of motion?

Law of Inertia
Object in motion stays in motion   → Galileo

7. What is Newton 's Second Law of Motion?

If a force is applied to object it will change its path

8. Newton 's Third Law of Motion usually is the one applied to the principles of rocketry, why?

= and opposite reaction
explains thrust

9. What is the difference between center of mass and center of pressure? How should they be related to make a stable rocket?

Center of mass → mass in front = mass in back
Center of pressure → SA in front = surface area in back
→ Center of pressure should be well behind center of gravity

10. Who were the writers most responsible for igniting the dreams of 20th Century rocket inventors and engineers?

Jules verne & HG wells

11. Who was Konstantin Eduardovich Tsiolkovsky and what did he contribute to rocket technology? *Deaf teacher → vehicles for space*   *·Liquid fuel for space*
Rockets are only mechanism w/ enough force to reach space,
Rocket would work even more efficiently in a vacuum,

12. Who was Robert Hutchings. Goddard and what did he contribute to rocket technology? *USA*
· Developed technology for rockets
Rockets work in a vacuum
· Gyroscopic control & science of rockets

13. Who was Hermann Julius Oberth? How did he indirectly influence the US space program? *Romanian*
- founded German Rocket Society
- taught Werner von Braun

14. Who was the first person to make the dream of human spaceflight come to fruition?

Yuri Gagarin

A HUMAN PRESENCE

THOSE WERE HAPPY DAYS

An old gentleman t'other day in discourse with a friend of his, (reflecting upon some adventures they had in youth together) cry'd out, Oh Jack, those were happy days!
　　　　　　-Sir Richard Steele
　　　　　　The Spectator, 1711

When I was in high school, a friend introduced me to the wonders of life below ground. Andy had gone into the local storm sewer on the north side of Tulsa and was delighted to discover that it took him all the way to the river. On my first trip I found the unfamiliar sounds and odors to be nearly overwhelming. However, I did it a second time and then a third. Within a fairly short time I went through it without the aid of a flashlight. I could determine where I was by the combination of sounds and feel of the wall.

Andy and I had an array of adventures including the time that a family on a picnic saw us walk out to the center of a local pond and drop out of sight. We had gone through the grating of a drain into the storm sewer. From their perspective, we disappeared into the water. We returned from the river to find the local police and fire department dredging the pond for the bodies of three boys.

One sultry spring evening, Andy and some others of us worked up the courage to explore some of the side pipes. We had avoided them because they required that we stoop as we sloshed along. This one came to a branch followed by another branch. At each node, the diameter of the pipe became smaller and smaller. Soon, we found ourselves crawling on our elbows. I began to fell

the subtle panic of claustrophobia trickle over me and then wash over me in waves. All that I could think of was the air and sky, open space. At last we arrived a bricked cavity with very small pipes emptying into it. Far over our heads sat a manhole cover with a long set of rusty metal rungs going up to it. We took this option of escape. I was first up the ladder and forced the hatch open. Dry, sweet air flooded over me as I heard the terrified screams of some local kids who had been playing in the road. I looked up just in time to see their backs disappear into the night.

Although we did not repeat this particular adventure, trips into the storm sewer continued through the second half of the decade of the 1960's. We became somewhat snobbish about those who could go through it in the dark. Indeed, for a time, it became something of a phenomenon. Several groups of parents asked to be guided through the blackness.

FIRST STEPS

Let's go!　　　-Yuri A. Gagarin[11], 1961

Why did we do that? I guess that we did it for the challenge, the adventure and the sense of accomplishment. During the same decade, however, a much grander adventure unfolded on an extraterrestrial scale. Then we, humanity, took the first steps toward the human habitation of space.

The Soviets took the very first, and the hardest step. Yuri A. Gagarin (Figure 3-41) was a test pilot with little more than 200 hours of flight time when he entered the cosmonaut-training

---

[11] I referred to this in *A Trinity*.

program in 1960. Chosen just 4 days before the flight Gagarin climbed into the Vostok 1 space capsule and waited. During the extended delay he was promoted to major, and finally unable to contain himself called out, "Let's go!"

FIGURE 3-41. Yuri Gagarin at the time of his historic space flight. Photo from a Soviet era post card dated 1969.

The first man in space began his adventure at 9:07AM local time. The flight itself made a single orbit of the earth and lasted only 108 minutes. Nevertheless, he did have time to eat and drink and show that it was possible to do so in the state of free-fall or weightlessness. Besides that, Gagarin went almost as a passenger. The control panels had been locked, and all aspects of the flight were controlled from the ground. However, this in no way diminished the difficulty or importance of the achievement. After his capsule made a soft landing in a pasture near Saratov, he became a world-wide celebrity, and the Soviet Union a clear

victor in the first round of what was to become known as the Space Race.

The United States had been somewhat sluggish in its pursuit of space travel, but the Gagarin flight gave it a needed push. The Mercury capsule was ready, but an appropriate rocket booster had not been perfected. So, the US placed the Mercury capsule atop a Redstone rocket. Alan B. Shepard, an accomplished test pilot, was the first US astronaut to go into space on May 5, 1961. Because the redstone did not provide sufficient force, his Mercury capsule, called Freedom 7, made a parabolic suborbital flight with only 15 minutes in space. He did have some control of the capsule and verified that the vehicle could be controlled to perform maneuvers necessary for reentry on an orbital flight. The second US flight, flown 10 weeks later by Gus Grissom, repeated the first.

Only on February 20, 1962 did the US really repeat the achievement of the Soviets. John Glenn, after nearly a month-long delay, circled the earth 3 times aboard Friendship 7. This time, a more powerful Atlas missile carried the capsule into orbit.

In the mean time, the Soviets racked up an impressive series of firsts. Aleksei Leonov was the first to walk in space, and Valentina Tereshkova was the first woman in space.

John F. Kennedy voiced the goal of the US space program on May 25, 1961, just days after Shepard's flight. He said that we would take on the challenge of sending a man to the moon and returning him safely to the earth, "and do it before this decade is out." In a speech at Rice University on September 12, 1962, Kennedy gave the reason for this push:

To be sure, we are behind, and will be behind for some time in manned flight. But we do not intend to stay behind, and in this decade, we shall make up and move ahead.

Thus, the space race heated up.

HUMANS ON THE MOON

We choose to go to the moon in this decade and to do the other things not because they are easy but because they are hard... -John F. Kennedy, 1962.

The Soviets had an impressive lead. Less than a year after the first space walk, Luna 9, an unmanned lunar lander, made a safe touchdown on the moon. In fact, the Soviets had been sending Luna probes to the moon since 1959. It appeared that they had the upper hand there, too.

Wernher von Braun and his team of rocket engineers worked to perfect a large rocket capable of sending a lunar lander to the moon. He had been one of the developers of the V or vengeance weapons used by Germany during World War II. Von Braun and 117 of his fellow scientists surrendered to the Americans at the end of the war in Germany and were brought to the US to continue their work where they developed the Redstone, a larger version of the German V-2 rocket. Von Braun's Saturn V was an enormous rocket that could develop thrust sufficient to the task of delivering a payload to the moon.

In the mean time, the space programs of both nations progressed and faltered. The US evolved to the Gemini program, a two-person capsule that experimented with space walks and docking procedures that would be needed by the lunar lander. Then, the Apollo program began with the disaster of the deaths of three astronauts and the US program languished for a time.

Similar problems and disappointments beset the Soviet program. In particular, they could not get their super booster called the N-1 to work reliably. The solution seemed to be to use a smaller booster with a lighter capsule called Zond. This would not have a lander but could navigate to the moon, circle it and return to the earth *as early as 1968.* Two unmanned Zonds were sent, but Moscow delayed the implementation of a manned mission to the dismay of the flight engineers and team of cosmonauts. Then, during the Christmas season of 1968, the US succeeded in sending a crew to the moon in lunar orbit and return to earth thus stealing the thunder of Zond.

Within a half year on July 16, 1969, the US successfully launched Apollo 11 with its crew of three men, Neil Armstrong, Buz Aldrin, and Mike Collins. Armstrong and Aldrin landed on the moon's surface four days later. They had met Kennedy's challenge.

Public interest in the space program began to wane. It seemed that the goal had been met and there were other things to do. The last Apollo mission to the moon landed on December 11, 1972. The Soviets attempted to launch an unmanned probe to the moon during that mission, but the N-1 exploded on liftoff. The race to the moon ended with that explosion.

HUMAN PRESENCE IN ORBIT

Men who have worked together to reach the stars are not likely to descend together into the depths of war and desolation. - Lyndon Baines Johnson, 1958.

In the mean time, the Soviet Union had been "racing" ahead with the development of orbiting platforms, and space stations. They launched and deployed the first space station called Salyut 1 on April 19, 1971. The first crew arrived at Salyut three days later but could not open its hatch and had to return to earth. A second crew did manage to enter and stayed for 24 days, longer than anyone had spent in space up to that point. Tragically, the second crew died during its return to earth as a consequence of an error with an open valve that caused decompression of the capsule.

Salyut 2 launched in April 1973. Before it could be occupied, however, an engine exploded and the structure fell to earth in May. A similar fate befell a secret space station called Cosmos 557 in the same month.

The US used one of its enormous Saturn V boosters to use as the structure of its first space station called Skylab. Curiously, it launched during the same month that saw the destruction of Salyut 2 and Cosmos 557. Still, Skylab became crippled on its deployment. It suffered from problems of overheating and limited power.

The heat problem was solved by unfurling a nylon umbrella over the body of the space station. This low tech solution worked well enough to allow Skylab to be habitable. A short space walk helped to free the solar panels and restore sufficient power.

In the end, the US had to abandon Skylab in February of 1974. The platform remained usable, but the US had run out of Apollo vehicles. It had used the last one in a joint Soviet-US mission called Apollo-Soyuz. The space shuttle would not be ready for another 7 years.

In rapid succession, the Soviets launched Salyut stations 3-6 through the mid 1970's. Salyut 7 launched in 1982 but suffered a variety of problems including leaky pipes, power failures, and broken radios. They managed to solve the problems but the atmosphere began to expand as a consequence of increased solar activity. The larger atmospheric envelope began to create drag on the space station. The Soviets added a few more years to the usefulness of Salyut 7 by boosting it into a higher orbit. Finally, they abandoned it in 1986, and the station fell to earth in 1991.

The Soviets began to think differently about space station design. They constructed a new kind of structure that could have modules added to it. The new space station was launched in 1986 and was called Mir, the Russian word for both peace and earth.

Mir became a very successful space platform. It could house up to 6 in a crew and allow for stays of more than a year by continuous restocking with robotic supply vessels. More importantly, it had larger rocket engines that could maintain its position more effectively than the old Salyut series.

Mir survived the breakup of the Soviet Union despite some accidents and breakdowns that occurred as consequences of old age. In fact, Mir lasted more than twice as long as its intended life span. During that time protocols and procedures for the successful operation of a larger space station had been worked out.

The International Space Station (ISS) is a result of partnership between 16 countries in the construction and assembly of more than 100 components. In fact, it is the largest international cooperative project in history. Its construction began in 1998 when a Russian Proton rocket delivered the Zarya module into orbit. Then, the US Space Shuttle brought and attached the Utility Module. Zvezda, the third major unit to be attached launched in July 2000.

On October 31, 2000, a Russian Soyuz launch vehicle delivered the Expedition 1 crew launched to occupy the new International Space Station. The four month mission of this crew was to shake it down and make it work. The assembly continued almost without interruption through Phase I with the installation of 8 expedition crews.

The US and Russia have been the primary players since 1994 with the joint Mir-Shuttle missions. The two countries have used what they learned during the joint missions to provide aspects of team work and cooperation necessary for the construction and maintenance of such a complex structure. So far, the modules, some of which have been constructed by other countries, must be delivered by the Russian Soyuz or Proton rockets, or the US Space Shuttle.

When the ISS is in full operation, it will house a crew of seven and will have a volume about the size of a 747 jumbo jet. It is scheduled to be completed sometime in 2008.

INTO THE FUTURE

We shall go to Mars, not just to study its physics and chemistry but to bring a dead planet to life. In bringing a dead planet to life, even more than in the pursuit of scientific knowledge, the name of the game is ecology.

-Freeman Dyson, 1988

Curiously, von Braun and his team favored the construction of an orbiting platform from which to launch humans to the Moon or Mars in the early days of the space program. Thus, the delivery system needed to be powerful enough to get the components into orbit. Assembly of the components could produce a very large structure that need not have to waste its mass on support necessary to

withstand the stresses of moving from the earth's surface to space.

Von Braun presented his vision in a book called *The Mars Project*. The scenario required a Berlin airlift-style series of flights into orbit to provide the components, supplies and men. His project required about 50 men to be on board for the occupation and conquest of the red planet.

The paradox is that his team was given the task of developing the Saturn V, the large delivery system that allowed the deployment of a much smaller module to the moon. A left-over Saturn V became the only space station that the US attempted. Also, the Soviets conceived and nearly implemented a Mars Project-like scenario (to assemble smaller components in orbit) to send the Zond module to the moon long before the US could.

Well, we are back in orbit. We are assembling a space station or orbiting platform that will serve many purposes for many peoples of the earth. We will meet and overcome the challenges of supplying and maintaining the ISS. Indeed, we will find uses for it that no one has envisioned yet. It may serve as a platform from which to launch and supply a base on the Moon or Mars.

I see the technical problems of such enterprises as solvable. The lessons of Salyut, Skylab, and Mir have taught us how to inhabit space and supply an external base. The problems of a Moon base are similar, but greater in scale. Instead of waiting a day for the delivery of supplies, the Moon base will require the wait of several days to a week.

A base on Mars requires a whole new way of thinking. The trip there could take more than a year. Provisions simply could not be sent reliably. Such a base would have to be self-sustaining. It would have to provide its own oxygen and its own food. As an ecologist I understand the difficulties.

Living things already do many of the operations that we take for granted. Such stable working ecosystems are absolutely necessary to the operation and success of a Martian colony. Living communities recycle waste, generate oxygen, remove carbon dioxide and make food. We could dump the waste and use chemical means to scrub the air of carbon dioxide and make oxygen. However, only living things can make food.

The solution would appear to be simple. We just have to assemble the appropriate organisms, and they will do the necessary work. However, ecosystems are complex entities with many species interacting, some of which have obligate relationships and most of which are microbes. That is why ecologists are used to examining ecosystems and explaining their operation. They are not good at assembling ecosystems to perform particular functions. A mistake in such an assembly would be inconvenient on earth but fatal on Mars. The real irony of such preparations for a Martian base might be that we come to know the earth and its ecosystems with a more profound understanding than we know them now.

When I crawled around in the Tulsa storm sewers, I recognized that there was a slight danger. Mainly, there was the discomfort of dank air and wet feet. I knew that I would emerge to sweet air and would be warm and dry within an hour. Inhabitants of a space station run much greater risks and extended discomfort. Mars colonists face even more dangers and uncertainties. Still, I am sure that there are plenty of volunteers who would be willing to endure hardship and danger in the name of adventure and discovery.

-2004

References:

Baker, Wendy. 1986. *America in Space.* Crescent Books. New York.

Caidin, Martin, and Jay Barbree. 1997. Penguin Putnam, Inc. New York.

Carpenter, M. Scott, L. Gordon Cooper, Jr., John H. Glenn, Jr., Virgil I. Grissom, Walter M. Schirra, Jr., Alan B. Shepard, Jr., and Donald K. Slayton. 1962. *We Seven.* Simon and Schuster, Inc. New York.

Dille, John. 1965. *Americans in Space.* American Heritage Publishing Co. New York.

Dyson, Freeman. 1992. *From Eros to Gaia.* Penguin Books. London.

Lee, Wayne. 1995. *To Rise From Earth.* Facts On File, Inc. New York.

Shepard, Alan, and Deke Slayton. 1994. *Moon Shot, The Inside Story of America's Race to the Moon.* Turner Publishing. Atlanta.

Von Braun, Wernher. 1991 (originally published in 1952). *The Mars Project.* University of Illinois. Chicago.

Zubrin, Robert. 1996. *The Case for Mars.* The Free Press. New York.

FIGURE 3-42. In a mockup of a module of the ISS at Johnson Space Center, Houston.

FIGURE 3-43. Inside the International Space Station Mission Control, Johnson Space Center, Houston.

Questions to Think About

1. Who was the first astronaut into space? Who was the first cosmonaut into space? Of the two, who was the first man into space?

2. Who was the first woman into space? Where was she from?

3. Who set the goal of the U.S. space program in the 1960's?

4. What was the significance of the Luna-9 probe?

5. Who first set foot on the surface of the moon?

6. What prevented the soviets from landing a human on the moon?

7. What was the first space station? Who launched it?

8. Why was Mir so important?

9. What was Expedition 1?

10. What was von Braun's vision of a mission to Mars?

11. Why would a mission to Mars be fundamentally different from an orbital mission or a mission to the moon?

12. Why are enclosed ecosystems important for our understanding of a long-term presence on Mars?

13. Why is an understanding of basal metabolism necessary for any mission into space?

CHAPTER 4: CHANGING IDEAS IN THE PHYSICAL SCIENCES

I know not what I may appear to the world, but to myself I seem to have been only like a little boy playing on the sea-shore, and diverting myself in now and then finding a smoother pebble or a prettier shell than ordinary, whilst the great ocean of truth lay all undiscovered before me.   Isaac Newton; from D. Brewster *Memoirs of Newton* (1855)

My colleague, John Clark, stoops to find a prettier shell on a path along the bay side of Assateague Island. Newton's words in a simple way indicate the exhilaration and frustration that those who practice science feel. On the one hand, they pursue ideas that are of intense interest to them. On the other hand, there is so much to discover.

Essays in this chapter consider the discovery of fundamental laws of nature in Physics (*Principia Mathematica: The Foundation of Modern Physics, Electricity? What Good is It? An Experiment that Failed, One Stone, Boyle, Boltzmann, and Banya,*), Astronomy (*The Planets, Moon Stories, Inferno and Purgatorio, Impacts, and Stars and the Beauty of Science*), and Chemistry (*Burning Questions and Revolutions, In Hot Water, Old Books and Atoms, Chance and the Prepared Mind,* and *Seeking Patterns*).

PRINCIPIA MATHEMATICA: THE FOUNDATION OF MODERN PHYSICS

ARISTOTLE'S SOLUTION

It is not once or twice but times without number that the same ideas make their appearance in the world. -Aristotle

What is gravity? I asked a class of college students that question several years ago. Here are some of the responses: It is what holds us on the earth; it is absent in space; it is a force. The question of gravity is a difficult one and the search for its solution gave rise to modern physics.

Aristotle (384-322 B.C.), a Greek philosopher, explained that objects fall to earth because they are made of different amounts of each of the four elements: earth, water, air and fire. For example, a stick falls because it has more earth and water than air and fire. Thus, the stick seeks its "natural" position by falling through the air to the ground. That same stick might fall into the water and float. So, a stick does not contain enough earth to cause it to sink.

Is there any evidence for this Aristotelian view? Certainly. Put that stick into a fire and watch it turn into its component elements. You will see the element fire emerge from the stick as well as smoke (a form of the element air). You might observe a small amount of sap (a liquid which is a form of the element water). When the stick has finished burning, you will observe that ash (a form of the element earth) is left behind.

So, in the Aristotelian view, things fall, float, or fly as a consequence of their constituent elements. Thus, things seek their natural place by this "natural" motion. Also, according to Aristotle, the speed with which things fall is dependent upon their constituent elements.

The Aristotelean theory of the universe also explained the planets and their motions very differently. All bodies in the heavens were made of a different substance (a fifth element or quintessence), which was uniformly bright and unblemished. Natural motion of the heavens was uniform circular motion. Thus, the planets and stars stayed where they were and moved as they did according to their own natural laws. The heaven-earth dichotomy was a very strong and important part of the Aristotelian theory of the universe. Natural philosophers for nearly 2,000 years adopted the Aristotelian view, a view that seemed to have great explanatory power.

A FIRST CHALLENGE

I confess that I shall expound many things differently from my predecessors-although with their aid, for it was they who first opened the road of inquiry into these things. -Nicolaus Copernicus.

The first significant challenge to the Aristotelian Universe came in the 15th Century when the old Julian calendar, a calendar defined by the tables of Cladius Ptolemy using the Aristotelian concept, had begun to drift significantly. The church viewed this development as a problem because Easter and other holy days had to be determined accurately. In 1514, the secretary to the Pope asked a mathematically-minded Polish cleric named Nikolai Kopernig (Nicolaus Copernicus; 1473-1543) to come up with a more accurate calendar[1]. In his study of the astronomical tables of the day, par-

---

[1] See *Sunrise, Sunset* for more about his role in the creation of the Gregorian calendar.

ticularly those produced by Ptolemy in his book (actually 13 books) called *The Mathematical Composition* or *Almagest* [The Arabs called it *Al Megiste (The Greatest),* a corruption of which became *Almagest*].

Copernicus realized that the relationships between observations of the heavens and structure of the heavens would be much simpler if the sun occupied the center of the universe. Given that change, predictions of the heavens would be simpler, too. He was a follower of the philosophies of Pythagoras and Plato, who defined the world mathematically. In addition, the cosmology of Pythagoras even allowed for the earth to move in a small orbit.

FIGURE 4-1. An illustration of Copernicus' universe from his *On the Revolutions of the Heavenly Spheres.*

Copernicus occupied much of the rest of his life with the production of a manuscript called *On the Revolutions of the Heavenly Spheres* to illustrate the heliocentric (sun-centered) concept. The greatest objection to the book, and an objection

that Copernicus anticipated, was that the sun-centered universe required that the earth move on an axis and around the sun [He also added other motions to the earth including a wobble of the axis]. This flew in the face of common sense and everyday experience. Andreas Oseander, a Lutheran theologian and friend of Copernicus who wrote the introductory dedication to the Pope, indicated that the motion was not real but a mathematical hypothesis necessity to make the computations work out. The story goes that Copernicus received a copy of the text while on his deathbed. After reading Oseander's Prologue, Copernicus expired.

GALILEO'S CHALLENGE
Nature is written in mathematical language. -Galileo Galilei

Copernicus' book excited little interest over the next 50 years. During that time, the Revolutions struggled through three editions and was cited only a handful of times. The truth of matter was that Copernicus had little impact except to provide the mathematical construct for Pope Gregory to adopt a new calendar, the one we are under today. It took another Pythagorean with bolder ideas and a flair for experimental philosophy to make the scientific community pay attention to the Copernican system and to reject the Aristotelian worldview. That natural philosopher was Galileo Galilei (1564-1642). Another follower of Pythagoras fifty years earlier had redefined the heavens with the sun in the center of the universe

While studying at Pisa, Galileo began his investigations of mathematics and mechanics. One of his first investigations was a study of pendulums in which he discovered that although a pen-

pendulum could vary in its period (the length of time required for a complete swing), the period depended only upon the radius of the pendulum arm, not on the weight at the end of the arm. Today, we know this as Galileo's *Law of the Pendulum* (see Figure 4-2). The most amazing part of this result was that the swing of the pendulum was like free-fall, and it was independent of the weight at the end of the pendulum arm. This was certainly counter to what was predicted by Aristotle.

Law of the Pendulum:

$$T = 2\pi \sqrt{l/g}$$

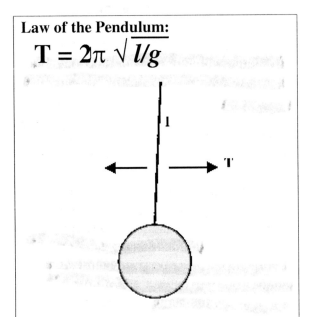

FIGURE 4-2. A diagram of a pendulum. The period (T) is related to the square root of the radius (l) or length of the pendulum arm. The amazing aspect of it is that the period is independent of the mass of the weight at the end of the pendulum arm.

The importance of Galileo's discovery was threefold:

1) He expressed a law in mathematical terms (something that the Aristotelians did not do).
2) He was able to show that the period was independent of mass (note that mass is not part of the equation).
3) The period is dependent upon a constant (the square root of g, acceleration due to gravity on earth or 9.8 m/sec^2).

It seems that Galileo became intrigued by the results, particularly the implications for falling objects. He began to experiment with gravity by rolling balls down slopes of different angles and timing their descent with his pendulums. As with the pendulum, he discovered that the time required for a ball to roll down a given slope depended only on the angle of the slope. The weights of the balls did not matter.

More importantly, he saw that the balls accelerated as they rolled down the incline. That is, their speed increased as they rolled. He also noticed that the rate at which they increased was related to the constant (*g*) that he had found when working with the pendulums. Indeed, he measured the constant with great accuracy and found that objects fall at 32 feet per second per second. That is, after falling for one second, a falling object is moving at 32 feet per second; after two seconds, the same object moves at 64 feet per second, etc.

Legend has it that Galileo proved his point by dropping cannonballs of different weights from the Leaning Tower of Pisa. As he predicted, they hit the ground at the same time and accelerated as they fell. Actually, Galileo made little impact at the time because his results seemed absurd. Why should different weights fall at the same rate? Didn't that predict that cannonballs and feathers should fall at the same rate? Galileo and his contemporaries answered that challenge by saying that since air has substance, air resistance affects light objects. (Indeed, if we put a feather and a steel ball in a vacuum, the objects fall at the same rate).

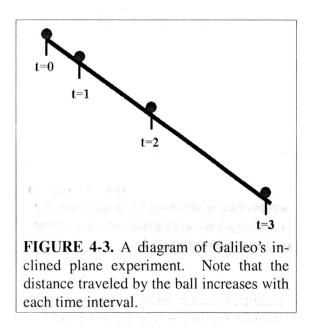

FIGURE 4-3. A diagram of Galileo's inclined plane experiment. Note that the distance traveled by the ball increases with each time interval.

Galileo is better known as a champion of the Copernican system. Mainly, he based that support on direct observations that he made with a telescope (also something that an Aristotelian would not do). He noticed that the moon had mountains and valleys. The Milky Way was made of stars and was not a meteorological phenomenon as proposed by Aristotle. The planet Saturn had a large bulge at its equator (he could not resolve the rings with his telescope). Venus has phases like the moon. Most interesting of all, he noticed that Jupiter had small stars that moved about it [He called these the Medician Stars to curry favor of the powerful Medici family]. Such things were not consistent with the Aristotelian universe. These observations appeared in an influential book called *Siderius Nuncius* (*The Heavenly Messenger*) in 1610.

Finally, Galileo's brash and unorthodox support of the Copernican system got him into trouble. He published a book called *Dialogue of the two Principal Systems of the World (1632)*. In this book, he compared the Aristotelian and Copernican systems. However, his caricature of the

Aristotelian (named Simplicio) was offensive to the Holy Office, especially since many of the phrases attributed to Simplicio were direct quotes from the Pope. Galileo was put under arrest for the suspicion of heresy and forced to recant his views.

While under house arrest and nearly blind, Galileo returned to the study of motion. In addition to falling bodies, Galileo studied objects in projectile motion. Aristotle claimed that objects must have natural motion (that is, seek their natural place on earth) or violent motion (any motion that is not natural motion). Aristotle claimed that an object could not have both types of motion at the same time. So, an Aristotelian description of the flight of a cannonball would be that the gunpowder in the cannon imparted impetus to the cannonball. It would fly in a straight line until the impetus ran out. After that, the cannonball would fall back to earth according to its natural motion. Galileo, however, described the motion of a projectile as a parabola in which both the push of the gunpowder and the attraction of gravity operate simultaneously. He published his results and explanations of uniform motion, accelerated motion, and projectile motion in his last great book called *The Dialogue of the Two New Sciences* (1638).

Galileo had challenged the nature of the universe and Aristotle's description of motion. His attacks on both had been based on careful observations. However, he had applied experimentation to questions of motion and then expressed the outcome mathematically. His observations of the heavens, although detailed were not sufficient to apply the same level of mathematical rigor. That would require an enormous number of careful observations. Just such a treasure-trove of data were being examined by a contemporary named Johannes Kepler (1571-1630) in Prague.

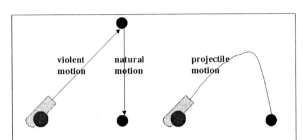

FIGURE 4-4. Diagrams of the flight of a cannonball according to an Aristotelian explanation (left) and Galileo's explanation (right).

A WOULD-BE ALLY

These properties of an ellipse are exhibited in the planetary orbit.

-Johannes Kepler

Kelpler, a Lutheran mathematician, had been selected by Tycho Brahe (1546-1601) to make sense of his astronomical observations. Tycho had established the first real observatory in Europe on the island of Hven in Denmark. There, he designed, built, calibrated and used his instruments to observe the planets, stars, and other phenomena like comets. He set up a regular schedule of research and data collection. Tycho was a fanatic for precise measurements and amassed an enormous amount of valuable data over a 20 year period. After he had a falling out with the king of Denmark, Tycho traveled through Europe and settled in Prague as the Imperial Mathematician to the Holy Roman Emperor Rudolph II in 1599.

Brahe was not a follower of Aristotle, but neither did he accept the Copernican universe. Instead, he had a theory of the heavens that kept the stationary earth of Aristotle with the sun revolving around it. However, the planets all revolved around the sun. This hybrid never did excite attention, but the quality of his data did. He employed Kepler as an assistant to use the data and prove the reality of his Tychonic Universe.

Kepler realized quickly that the mass of observations did not support the theory of Tycho Brahe. Only two years later Brahe died and, after a fight with the family over the right to the data, Kepler became free to make sense of them. Like Galileo, Kepler was a Pythagorean and adopted the Copernican view. Unlike Galileo, Kepler abandoned the concept of uniform circular motion in the heavens. He published his first two laws of planetary motion in the book, *Astronomia Nova* (1609). His first law stated that planets move in elliptical orbits with the sun as one focus of the ellipse.

The data further suggested that the planets vary in speed as they go around the sun. When closer, they moved faster. When farther, they moved slower. From this, he defined his second law of planetary motion, *The Equal Area Law*.

Consider Figure 4-5. The planet follows an elliptical orbit around the sun. The time spent going from **a** to **b** is equal to the time spent going from **c** to **d**. In addition, he calculated that the areas **A** and **B** are equal.

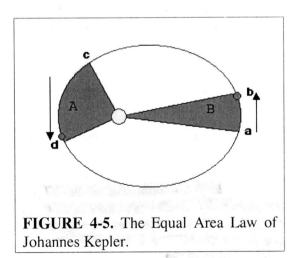

FIGURE 4-5. The Equal Area Law of Johannes Kepler.

His third law was published in *De Harmonice Mundi (On the Harmonies of the World; 1619)* in 1619. In that law, he defined a relationship between the mean radii of the orbits (**r**) and the periods of the orbits (**t**). In particular, he said that the squares of the periods of the orbits (t^2) divided by the cubes of the mean radii of the orbits (r^3) equal a constant for all planets (see Figure 4-6).

The *Harminice Mundi* explains that the sun and the heavens are embedded in a fluid. As the sun turns, it imparts motion to the fluid that, in turn, moves the planets. He explains that the planets stay in their orbits due to a kind of magnetic gravitational force between the sun and planets. Thus, in Kepler's universe, the heavens and the earth obey the same physical laws.

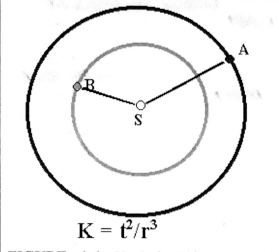

$$K = t^2/r^3$$

FIGURE 4-6. Kepler's Third Law of Planetary Motion. The relationship between t^2 and r^3 is the same for planet A and for planet B.

Although Kepler tried to establish meaningful contact with Galileo, they never did form a scientific alliance. Mainly, Galileo did not trust Kepler. Also, given Galileo's situation with the Catholic Church, he would have been in even greater trouble if he had allied himself with a Lutheran. Furthermore, Galileo just did not believe in the elliptical orbits.

in the elliptical orbits. Galileo believed that the planets remained where they did because uniform circular motion was their natural motion.

SHOULDERS OF GIANTS
If I seem to see farther than anyone else, it is because I stand on the shoulders of giants. -Isaac Newton

Through most of the 17th Century natural philosophers contemplated the works of Galileo and Kepler. The old Aristotelian universe had finally died, but there did not seem to be a suitable replacement. Galileo's laws of motion and Kepler's laws of planetary motion did not seem to be compatible. Rene Descartes (1596-1650) had produced an influential model of the universe in which the sun and planets were not attracted to each other (indeed, he said that mass did not exist and the only reality was motion). He said that attraction was not necessary to keep the planets in their orbits. The sun moves and creates great vortices in the effluvium, which in turn keep the planets in their respective orbits.

The question of gravity had become a great topic of speculation and debate in The Royal Society of London, a society dedicated to the experimental philosophy of the sciences. At a meeting of the Royal Society in January of 1684 Robert Hooke (1635-1703), Christopher Wren (1632-1723), and Edmund Halley (1656-1742) engaged the problem of celestial mechanics, particularly concerning the nature of gravity. All had deduced that gravity must attract according to the inverse square of the distance of the sun and planet (see Figure 4-7). Halley claims to have deduced that from Kepler's third law. Still, Halley could not prove that the relationship existed on mathematical grounds. Robert Hooke, a brilliant experimentalist and designer of instrumentation, always seemed to claim more than he could prove. At that meeting, he claimed to have proven the relationship, but could not produce his proof. Halley remembered the encounter and made his way to Cambridge the next August to ask Isaac Newton (1642-1727) about the gravity problem. In particular, Halley asked Newton what would the orbit of a planet look like if the attractive force of gravity varied according to the inverse square of the distance. Newton said that the orbit would be an ellipse, and that he had solved the problem nearly 20 years earlier.

Newton had solved the problem after he left Cambridge in 1665 to escape The Great Plague. He returned to his mother's farm at Woolsthorpe Manor near Grantham. Although his mother expected him to help out on the farm, Isaac did very little work. Thirty years later he claimed that during this time it occurred to him that falling apples, flying cannonballs and planets circling the sun must obey the same law of gravitation. His astounding insight had allowed him to bring together Galileo's laws of motion and Keplers laws of planetary motion. The heaven-earth dichotomy vanished.

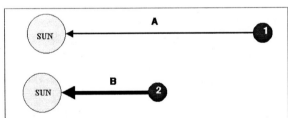

FIGURE 4-7. The inverse square relationship says that if **Planet 1** is twice as far from the sun as **Planet 2**, then the gravitational attraction **A** is one-fourth that of **B**.

Newton explained that gravity, whether on the earth or in the heavens, is a property of mass, and objects attract each other relative to their mass. That is, just as you are attracted to the earth, the earth is attracted to you. So, if you jump off of a step, the earth accelerates toward you while you are accelerating toward the earth! Since the earth is so much more massive than you are, it moves only a tiny amount.

He, too, used Kepler's laws of planetary motion to deduce the inverse square nature of gravity. Newton determined that the behavior of the planets could be explained if the gravitational force decreases by the square of the distance from the center of mass of each planet to the center of mass of the sun.

All objects of mass behave the same way. Suppose that the earth and moon were 2 times as far from each other as now. Then the gravitational force between the earth and moon would be reduced to 1/4th the current force. This is called the inverse square law, a law that is so fundamental that it is true for light intensity, and the force of magnetic attraction and electrical charge as well as gravity. Newton used these assumptions about gravity to explain the orbit of the moon and the planets as well as why things fell on earth. He even estimated how fast things might fall on the moon!

Halley was so taken with the mathematical proof that Newton presented to him, that he encouraged Newton to publish. Newton worked hard through many drafts, and arduous geometric, and trigonometric proofs of his assertions. He even developed a new kind of infinite series mathematics that he called fluxions (we call it calculus) to aid in the mathematics. Finally, he finished the work, *Principia Mathematica,* in three books: *The Motion of Bodies, The Mo-*

tion of Bodies in Resisting Mediums, and *The System of the World in Mathematical Treatment.*

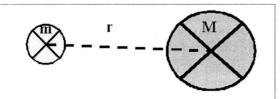

$F = GmM/r^2$

FIGURE 4-8. A digram that illustrates Newton's Law of Gravity. Note that the force is the product of the gravitational constant (G) times the product of the two masses (m and M, respectively) divided by the square of the distance between the two masses.

The Royal Society was nearly bankrupt so it could not underwrite the publication of the work. Edmund Halley personally encouraged Newton with words, deeds, and money and personally underwrote its publication. In many ways Hally was as important to the production of the *Principia* as Newton himself. When the first books appeared in 1687, the Royal Society acted as its sponsor. Here, again Halley wrote critical reviews for the society and an explanation for King James himself (a paper on the cause of the tides). Even devout followers of Descartes like Christiaan Huygens said that the mathematics was sound.

Modern physics began in 1687 with the publication of the *Principia*, and it begins with definitions in which the characteristics of gravity are assumed. Newton then defined the *Laws of Motion:*

1. The First Law of Motion: Bodies continue in the state of uniform motion or rest unless acted upon by a force. This is sometimes called the Law of Inertia. In this, he clearly stated that an object will remain in unchanging motion as a

natural state. Also, he said that bodies tend to move in straight lines as a universal form of natural motion.

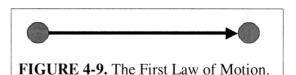

FIGURE 4-9. The First Law of Motion.

2. THE SECOND LAW OF MOTION: The change in motion is relative to the force applied. This law clearly defined the quantity of matter called mass and the nature of a force. Newton a force as that which causes a mass to accelerate (**acceleration** is the rate which the velocity changes). This is sometimes called the **force** law.

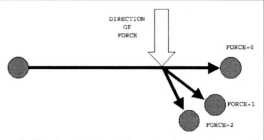

FIGURE 4-10. The Second Law of Motion. The same body and its deflection from a straight line when subjected to a force of 0, 1, and 2 units.

3. THE THIRD LAW OF MOTION: To every action there is an equal and opposite reaction or forces come in pairs. Newton describes this to say that a body cannot affect another body without itself being changed. He even describes a magnet that attracts iron which is itself equally attracted to the magnet. In the case of a rocket, the force of the ex-

pelled gasses from the rocket engine forces the rocket to move in an opposite direction.

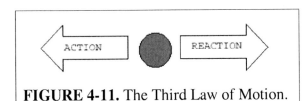

FIGURE 4-11. The Third Law of Motion.

He then used the laws of motion and the nature of gravity to describe the motions of the moon, planets, and their moons. For example, Newton explained that the moon orbits the earth even though it would tend to move in a straight line. However, the force of the gravitational attraction pulls the moon toward the earth. Because the earth is spherical, the surface of the earth falls away from the moon as the moon falls toward the earth. The same thing is true for orbiting space shuttles.

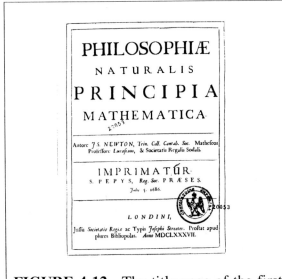

FIGURE 4-12. The title page of the first edition of the *Principia Mathematica.*

The apparent weightlessness of astronauts in orbit is a consequence of this constant state of free-fall. The space shuttle (or International Space Station) also is in a state of free-fall and cannot push against the astronauts. Thus, they do not experience the resistance to their fall as the surface of the earth resists us (the Third Law).

Almost immediately upon the publication of the *Principia* Newton became embroiled in another fight with Robert Hooke. Indeed, there was no love lost between the two men. Years earlier, Hooke had ridiculed Newton's early paper on the nature of light. Newton became so incensed that he did not participate in the Royal Society in any significant way until the publication of the *Principia.* This time, Hooke claimed priority with regard to the inverse square law and, therefore, to the whole law of gravity. Newton and his allies held off Hooke's attacks, but this time Newton left the society until after Hooke died in 1703.

The next year Newton once again became active in the society. This time he became president, a post that he held for nearly 25 years.

Later, during a renovation of the building that housed the Royal Society, he had the large portrait of Hooke removed for "safe keeping". After that, the portrait disappeared. To this day, no one has found an image of Robert Hooke.

Indeed, Newton may have had Hooke in mind when he made his "on the shoulders of giants" remark. Generally, we assume that he was referring to the writings of Galileo and Kepler on whose experiments and speculations his own work was based. Indeed, without such giant ideas, Newton could not have seen very far. There is a more interesting interpretation. It seems that Robert Hooke was a very short man with a somewhat crooked back. Probably Newton meant the remark both as praise for the earlier scientists like Galileo and as a sarcastic dig at Hooke.

Newton had many other controversies through his life. The most notable ones were feuds with John Flamsteed (1646-1719), the Astronomer Royal at Greenwich and Gottfried Leibniz (1646-1716). Always jealous of his reputation, both personal and scientific, Newton went to great lengths to crush a rival any way that he could.

Halley remained an important confederate for Newton throughout his life. In an ultimate triumph of the Newtonian Revolution, Halley used the principles of Newtonian Mechanics and predicted in 1705 that the comet of 1531, 1607, and 1682, would return in 1758 (after the deaths of both Halley and Newton). It has been called Halley's Comet ever since.

NEWTON'S REVOLUTION

Hypotheses non fingo. (I do not feign hypotheses).   -Isaac Newton

Although highly predictive and useful, Newton never seemed to be completely satisfied with the *Principia*. He took it through three editions and made numerous notes on the margins of his own copies. The small errors he corrected. He engaged the followers of Descartes in philosophical debate about gravity. However, inwardly, he was never content with a law of gravity that did not explain what gravity was. The law just described gravity as a force. More importantly, the force of gravity acted at a distance so that bodies of mass did not have to encounter each other in order to have an effect. The mysterious aspect of action at a distance worried Newton who refused to speculate in public as to why gravity behaved that way.

Given those problems and Newton's own objections, why did the *Principia* have such an influence? Only about ten people in Europe even understood the mathematical proofs. For one thing, the mathematics worked and described a universe as a mechanism that followed clear, predictable laws. Newton had made mathematical abstraction the "reality" of physics. Unlike the giants on whose shoulders he stood, Newton provided a universe that was a clear alternative to that of Aristotle. The *Principia* with its mathematical, mechanical approach defined the nature of physics and guaranteed the dominance of mathematics, physics, and astronomy well into the 19th Century.

2001; revised 2004

References:

Christianson, Gale E. 1984. *In the Presence of the Creator, Isaac newton and His Times.* The Free Press. New York.

Copernicus, Nicolaus. 1543. *On the Revolutions of the Heavenly Spheres.* In: Hutchins, Robert Maynard, editor. 1952. Great Books of the Western World. Vol 16. Encyclopaedia Brittannica, Inc. Chicago.

Cohen, I. Bernard. 1980. *The Newtonian Revolution.* Cambridge University Press. Cambridge.

Galilei, Galileo. 1638. *Dialogues Concerning the Two New Sciences* In: Hutchins, Robert Maynard, editor. 1952. Great Books of the Western World. Vol 28. Encyclopaedia Brittannica, Inc. Chicago.

Halliday, David and Robert Resnick. 1970. *Fundamentals of Physics.* John Wiley and Sons, Inc. New York.

Kepler, Johannes. 1619. *The Harmonies of the World.* In: Hutchins, Robert Maynard, editor. 1952. Great Books of the Western World. Vol 16. Encyclopaedia Brittannica, Inc. Chicago.

Koestler, Arthur. 1959. *The Sleepwalkers.* The Universal Library, Grosset & Dunlap. New York.

Newton, Isaac. 1686. *Mathematical Principles of Natural Philosophy.* In: Hutchins, Robert Maynard, editor. 1952.

Great Books of the Western World. Vol 34. Encyclopaedia Brittannica, Inc. Chicago.

Westfall, Richard. 1993. *The Life of Isaac Newton.* Cambridge University Press. Cambridge.

Questions to Think About

1. How was Aristotle's universe different from that of Newton?

   Geo vs. Heliocentrism → Orbits

2. How did Copernicus really challenge the Aristotelian universe? *Helio centrism*

3. Why did Copernicus write *On the Revolutions of the Heavenly Spheres*?

   illustrate heliocentrism

   new center

4. How did Galileo use Copernicus to challenge the Aristotelian paradigm?

   Bresh support - telescope

5. Why was Galileo predisposed to challenge Aristotle?

   Careful observation, didn't agree

6. Why was Galileo put under house arrest?

   Simplicio - quote pope.

7. Johannes Kepler also supported the Copernican view. Why?

   Pythagorean Ellipse

8. What were Kepler's Laws?

   1.) Planets - ellipse
   2.) Equal Area
   3.) $K = t^2/r^3$

9. How did Newton use Kepler's Laws to change physics?

   Inverse² nature of gravity

10. What was Newton's solution to the gravity problem? How did he run into problems with Hooke over it?

    property of mass/attract / Hooke claimed prt of it

11. What are Newton's Laws of Motion?

    1) At rest stay at rest   *3) Eq. Opp reaction*
    2) Change relative force

12. How did Newton's physics support a concept of the universe as a great clock?

13. Even though Newton formulated a Law of Gravity that was very predictive, he remained unsatisfied with it. Why?

14. What did Newton really mean by the "shoulders of giants" remar.

194

ELECTRICITY? WHAT GOOD IS IT?

WHAT GOOD IS IT?

Tongues in trees, books in the running brooks,
Sermons in stones, and good in everything?

-quoted by Michael Faraday

When I was growing up, I spent most weekends with my two cousins, Steve and Stan. Their interests were fairly different from mine, and sometimes I just stayed in their room and read or worked on some project. One project in particular was the construction of a strobe light. This was before they were integral parts of cameras, discos or even of the psychedelic scene. I had read about them and how they could seem to stop fast action. I wanted to build one and use it at night to see how moths fly. Anyway, I recall sitting on the floor trying to wire the parts together from a diagram. I was frustrated and Stan asked me to tell to him once again what I was doing. After I tried to explain it, he just looked at me and asked, "What good is it?" I must have muttered something in reply, but it was not very memorable. I tried to build the strobe because I found it fascinating. Even today, although I am often asked to justify the practical purposes of my research, I do not think about it very much. That is not why I do research.

Many of the modern miracles that we all take for granted began as observations, toys, or hobbies. They then were taken by science and studied for the sake of knowledge with practical technologies flying from them along the way. No phenomena follow this description better than those of electricity and magnetism.

Look around you. Observe how much your world is influenced by electricity and magnetism. A modern American home must have electricity just to operate. Its walls are filled with wires that provide energy to electrical outlets, lights, and air-conditioning systems. Porch lights, streetlights, and the occasional diabolical bug zapper will punctuate even a stroll down most streets. In the homes, we cook and prepare our meals, heat our water, and dry our hair by electricity. We entertain ourselves with electronic televisions, radios, and stereos. In fact, electricity has insinuated itself so completely into our lives, that we would have a very hard time living without it.

When I was in Russia this past summer I visited a small village called Bykee. It had about 10 houses with a single, deeply rutted road that passed through it. All of the village houses got their water from a well, but they all had electricity.

ELECTRICITY & MAGNETISM

I feel a Want of Terms here and doubt much whether I shall be able to make this intelligible. *-Benjamin Franklin*

The phenomenon of electricity, at least static electricity, had been known for millennia. In fact, electron is Greek for amber, one of the substances famous for producing a static charge when rubbed. Although known, static electricity was nothing more than a curiosity until the 18th Century.

Benjamin Franklin (1706-1790, USA), was one of the first to explore electricity. He did so after he was given a static electricity generator by a friend in Britain. He became so immersed in the study of electricity in 1746 that almost everything else in his life took second place. He began a set of experiments that led him to write a series of papers that were well-received (after some initial jokes about a colonial yokel) at the Royal Society and elsewhere in Europe. In 1752, he conducted his most famous experiment with the kite, which helped to confirm that that lightning and electricity were the same things. Based on that, he initiated experiments that led to the practical application of the lightning rod, an invention that saved and continues to save many buildings from destruction. Those and other experiments with electricity convinced Franklin that electricity moved from one place to another as a fluid. He was not sure which way the fluid went, but he guessed that the fluid moved from an object of excess to an object of deficiency. This was his explanation for why oppositely charged objects seemed to cancel each other out. He invented the terms positive and negative charge to differentiate between the two conditions.

Although little was really known about the new, mysterious force of electricity, it did exert a force (or charge) that could either attract or repel another charged object. Charles Augustin de Coulomb (1736-1806, France) examined the force between charged particles and discovered that electricity acted at a distance, and, like gravity, diminished according to the inverse square of the distance between the charges. That is, the charge of object 1 times the charge of object 2 divided by the distance between them squared can be expressed in units of force. This became known as Coulomb's Law (see Figure 4-13).

Electricity works for us because we make it move in a circuit. In this sense, the movement of electricity is similar to the movement of water. In fact, the similarity does not stop there nor is it superficial. Electricity conducts through a metal wire like water moves through a pipe. If the pipe is smaller, less water gets through the pipe each second. Simi-

larly, if a wire gets smaller, less electricity moves through it each second. Water moves downhill or as a consequence of water pressure in a pipe. Electric current moves as a consequence of electrical pressure from the power source. This is called the voltage.

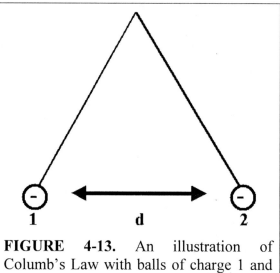

FIGURE 4-13. An illustration of Columb's Law with balls of charge 1 and charge 2 repelling with a force to push them distance d apart.

Volt is named after Allesandro Volta (1745-1827), the man who invented the first chemical battery. His battery (or pile as he called it) was a layer cake of different metal disks with felt soaked in a weak acid between the metal disks. Volta tried to impress Napoleon with his idea, but he was unsuccessful at first. However, Volta did impress the scientific community with a reliable source of electrical power. This led to the use of electricity for many explorations in physics, chemistry, etc. Now, the battery is a necessary component of many things in the household, including the computer on which I am writing this.

The power of a battery was its ability to make positive and negative charges at the poles of the battery; the greater the difference in charge, the greater the voltage. It was the voltage that provided the electrical pressure to move an electrical current in a wire. Andre-Marie Ampere (1775-1836 France) studied this movement of electrical charges in an electrical circuit. We now refer to the flow of electrical charge as amp (short for Ampere). Throughout the initial period of study, the Franklin theory of electrical fluid remained the prevailing view.

While electricity had been known for only a short time, magnetism had been studied for millennia. Magnetite, a naturally occurring magnetic ore or lodestone is relatively common and, like any other magnet, causes nails and other iron objects to jump. William Gilbert (1544-1603; England), physician to Queen Elizabeth I also studied and wrote about magnets. He concluded that all magnets have two poles. Also, like magnetic poles repel each other while opposite magnetic poles attract.

It wasn't until Hans Christian Oersted (1770-1851, Denmark) was switching a current on and off during a lecture in Denmark in 1820 that he saw evidence of the relationship between electricity and magnetism. When current flowed through a wire that was suspended over a compass, the needle in the compass moved to a position perpendicular to the wire. Ampere interpreted Oersted's observation of the interactions between electricity and magnetism in a Newtonian way. He described, mathematically, point forces acting at a distance from each other. In what is now called Ampere's Law, which stated that a changing electrical charge or current produced a magnetic effect. In England, however, Oersted's observation led to a revolutionary new way of viewing electrical and magnetic phenomena by a brilliant self-taught experimental genius.

ELECTROMAGNETISM

Several important results may be deduced from the properties of lines of force. — James Clerk Maxwell

Michael Faraday (1791-1867, England) did not have proper schooling. In fact, he was self-educated. He worked in a bookbindery and read many of the books that came through his shop. One happened to be a portion of the third edition of the Encyclopedia Britannica. In particular, he read the 127-page article about electricity. At that point he became interested in science.

By 1810 he began to attend lectures by the renowned chemist, Sir Humphry Davy (1778-1829, England). About a year later, Davy became temporarily blinded by an explosion in his laboratory and hired Faraday to be his eyes and his hands. Soon, Faraday was performing his own experiments in Davy's laboratory. He discovered benzene, made the first chlorinated hydrocarbon and ethylene. He did pioneering work in the field of steel alloys and produced heavy optical glass.

In 1821 Faraday heard of Oersted's work and began to explore the strange connection between electricity and magnetism. He made a wire that circled a magnet when a current was passed through it. He also showed that a magnet would rotate around a wire carrying current. Because he did not have a background in mathematics, he did not understand Ampere's explanation of electromagnetism. Instead, Faraday began to describe the phenomena in terms of physical models. He began to think of electricity and magnetism as fields or lines of force that extended from the wire or from the magnet. The lines of force interacted to create the electromagnetic phenomena that he had observed.

Later, Faraday used a bar magnet and passed it through a coil of wire and noticed that the magnet induced a current in the wire (see Figure 4-14). However, when the magnet was stationary, the current stopped. He speculated that as the magnetic lines of force cut through the wire, they set into motion an electrical force. Likewise, he discovered that when a current flows in a wire, it creates a magnetic field that circles that wire. Thus, Faraday, using his physical model to visualize the phenomenon, defined the Law of Induction or the electrical effect of changing a magnetic field. In addition, he used the concept of induction to create the first electric motor.

Carl Friedrich Gauss (1777-1855, Germany) was a mathematician whose interests ranged from pure mathematics to astronomy and physics. In 1832 Gauss used the concept of the field to generalize Coulomb's Law into what is now called Gauss' Law for Electricity. Later, he became very interested in magnetism and magnetic fields. He attempted to measure magnetic field strengths over a large area in an attempt to map the Earth's magnetic field. While doing so, he formulated a mathematical law intended to describe the magnetic field called Gauss' Law for Magnetism. The most important outcome of which was that there are no magnetic monopoles. That is, no matter how small, a magnet always has both a north and south pole.

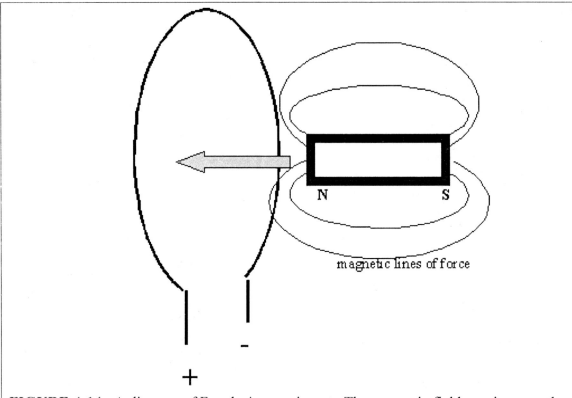

FIGURE 4-14. A diagram of Faraday's experiment. The magnetic field moving past the wire induced a current to move in the wire.

James Clerk Maxwell (1831-1879, United Kingdom) had one of the most expansive minds of the 19th Century. His interests covered almost all aspects of physics, and his influence was re-markable for one with such a short life. Not only was he a careful experimentalist with an obsession for exact measurements, but he also was an influential writer because of his extraordinary ability to synthesize information. Thus, he influenced mechanics and thermodynamics. However, he was best known for his synthesis of electromagnetic theory.

Like Faraday, Maxwell attempted to model physical phenomena. He viewed the ether as a field filled with hexagons of magnetic force each surrounded by small spheres of electrical force (Figure 4-15). As the electrical spheres moved, the wheels of magnetic force turned thus producing vortices of magnetism within the ether. Conversely, if the ether were subjected to a magnetic force, the turning wheels would push along the electrical spheres. He used this to explain the relationship between electricity and magnetism and to show how a single ether medium could accommodate both of them.

Like Gauss, though, Maxwell generalized electromagnetic phenomena mathematically. In fact he distilled electromagnetism into four elegant differential equations that he published in 1873. The four equations were: Gauss' Law for Electricity, Gauss' Law for Magnetism, Ampere's Law, and Faraday's Law of Induction (Table 4-1). He put them all into the same form and several unexpected consequences emerged. The most important one was a calculation for the speed of electromagnetic wave propagation, which turned out to be about the experimentally derived speed of light. Because of that and other relationships between light, magnetism, and electricity, Maxwell theorized that visible light must also be an electromagnetic wave. This simplified things very much in that only a single ether would be required to transmit all of three of them. Other very far-reaching outcomes were the possibilities of electromagnetic waves with frequencies longer and

shorter than those of visible light. This led to a search for what we now call the electromagnetic spectrum (Figure 4-16). The other more subtle, but ultimately more revolutionary outcome was the apparent constancy of the speed of light.

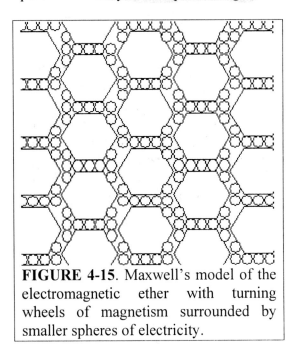

FIGURE 4-15. Maxwell's model of the electromagnetic ether with turning wheels of magnetism surrounded by smaller spheres of electricity.

After the publication of his electromagnetic theory, Maxwell was appointed Cavendish Professor at Cambridge where he spent time designing and building the influential Cavendish Laboratory. In addition, he spent five years editing and compiling the unpublished electrical papers of Henry Cavendish (1731-1810, England). By the time he was finished, Maxwell was overcome with a debilitating illness that finally killed him in 1879. Maxwell never saw the outcomes of his electromagnetic theory either from the perspectives of pure or applied science. Nevertheless, his theory ultimately led to inventions like the radio and radar. It also provided Albert Einstein with the impetus to formulate the Special Theory of Relativity and to Albert Michelson (1852-1931, USA) to seek to detect the movement of the earth through the ether.

SCIENCE, PURE AND APPLIED

Why, sir, there is every possibility that you will soon be able to tax it. The supposed response by Michael Faraday to Prime Minister William Gladstone's question, *"What good is an electric motor?"*

The exchange between Gladstone and Faraday likely is apocryphal because there are no contemporary accounts of such a conversation. However, it does illustrate the tension between the nonscientist's wish for a better or more comfortable world and the scientist's desire to understand. The motives of pure science, admittedly, are selfish. However, in the end, a society is better off knowing more about electromagnetism than the invention of a whole pile of new electrical gadgets. Thomas Alva Edison (1847-1931, USA), the Wizard of Menlo Park, amazed the world with a whole string of inventions whose impacts certainly changed the ways that we live. Still, when he wanted to improve and generalize the light bulb, his most notable invention, Edison called on a mathematician to model it according to electromagnetic formulas. Even though Edison held more than 1,000 patents, Norbert Wiener claimed that Edison's most enduring "invention" was the discovery that in a hot light bulb even a vacuum conducts electricity, a phenomenon now known as the Edison Effect, his only real scientific discovery

TABLE 4-1 Maxwell's Equations of Electromagnetism modified from Halliday and Resnick (1970).

Gauss' Law for Electricity describes the electric field.	$\oint \mathbf{E} \cdot d\mathbf{A} = \dfrac{q_{enclosed}}{\epsilon_o}$
Gauss' Law for Magnetism describes the magnetic field.	$\oint \mathbf{B} \cdot d\mathbf{A} = 0$
Ampere's Law describes the magnetic effect of a changing electric field or current.	$\oint \mathbf{B} \cdot d\mathbf{s} = \mu_o I_{enclosed} + \mu_o \epsilon_o \dfrac{d\Phi_{E\ enclosed}}{dt}$
Faraday's Law of Induction describes the electric effect of a changing magnetic field.	$\oint \mathbf{E} \cdot d\mathbf{s} = -\dfrac{d\Phi_{B\ enclosed}}{dt}$

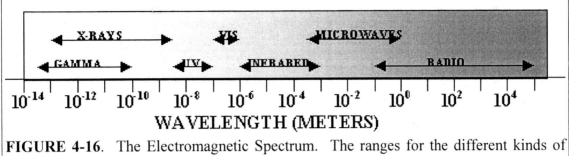

FIGURE 4-16. The Electromagnetic Spectrum. The ranges for the different kinds of waves are approximate and given in logarithmic scale in meters. Overlaps indicate how the waves are used or treated, because electromagnetic phenomena come in a continuum of wavelengths. The background shading indicates the relative energy of the waves.

Applied Science generally provides temporary solutions to permanent problems. The light bulbs of today are not the same as those of Edison's day, nor will the lamps of the future necessarily be familiar to you who read this today. What I am certain of, though, is that the laws of electromagnetism will govern the lamps of the future. So, what good was immediately realized by the work of Franklin, Coulomb, Ampere, Oersted, Faraday, Gauss, and Maxwell? It is difficult for us in our electrical world to look back at a time when electricity was a source of scientific curiosity. Some, like Benjamin Franklin put his observations to use in the form of lightening rods. However, most were curious and were just attempting to answer the riddles of nature.

I intended this story about electricity to illustrate the importance of primary research to a society. Many times the primary research leads down blind alleys and into dark rooms. But, sometimes research can lead to a well-lit room and a brighter future for us all.

- 1996, revised 2004

References:

Billington, David P. 1996. *The Innovators, The Engineering Pioneers Who Made America Modern.* John Wiley and Sons, Inc. New York

Boorstin, Daniel J. 1983. *The Discoverers, A History of Man's Search to Know his World and Himself.* Vintage Books, A Division of Random House, New York.

Burke, James. 1985. *The Day the Universe Changed.* Little, Brown and Company. Boston

Einstein, Albert and Leopold Infeld. 1938. *The Evolution of Physics, The Growth of Ideas From Early Concepts to Relativity and Quanta.* Simon and Schuster. New York.

Faraday, Michael. (1910, reprinted 1993). *The Forces of Matter.* Promethius Books. Buffalo, NY.

Fay, Bernard. 1929. *Franklin.* Little, Brown, & Co. Boston.

Gribben, John. 2002. *The Scientists.* Random House. New York.

Halliday, David and Robert Resnick. 1970. *Fundamentals of Physics.* John Wiley and Sons, Inc. New York

Harre, Rom. 1981. Great Scientific Experiments, *20 Experiments that Changed Our View of the World.* Phaidon Press, Ltd. Oxford.

Mason, Stephen F. 1962. *A History of the Sciences*, Collier Books. New York.

Mahon, Basil. 2003. *The Man Who Changed Everything, The Life of James Clerk Maxwell.* John Wiley & Sons. Hoboken, NJ.

Maxwell, James C. 1873 (reprinted 2002). *A Treatise on Electricity and Magnetism.* Oxford University Press. Oxford, UK.

Wiener, Norbert. 1993. *Invention.* The MIT Press. Cambridge, Mass.

Questions to Think About

1. What are some distinctions between the pure and applied sciences?

2. Beyond flying a kite, what did Benjamin Franklin contribute to science?

   · Lightning rod   · + & - charges
   · Electricity as a fluid

3. Coulomb defined the electrical force mathematically and showed that it was like gravity in what ways?

   Diminished according to the inverse square of the distance btwn the 2 points

4. Why was the battery so important in the new study of electricity?

   · made + & - charges at ends of the battery.   · Allowed electricity in physics
   · Creates voltage

5. What phenomenon did Oersted observe? How did his observation cause Faraday to change physics?

   · Relationship btwn electricity & magnetism
   · View things as lines of force

6. How is the magnetic force different from the electrical force?

   · Magnetic force can set off an electrical one
   · Electric current creates a magnetic field

7. What is the importance of Maxwell's equations? What two unexpected predictions came from them?

   → 4 equations
   · Speed of Electromagnetic wave - light
   · Electromagnetic Spectrum

8. Would you consider Edison to be a scientist?

   more of an inventor

AN EXPERIMENT THAT FAILED

EXPERIMENTS AND DEAD FISH

Youth is wholly experimental.

-R.L. Stevenson

Some years ago I sat as a judge for the Junior Academy of Science. The presentations were, for the most part quite good and reflected much thought and guidance. One, in particular stood out. A young man had performed an experiment with fish and an aquarium to test the effect of pollution. Well, first he added some ammonia, then some vinegar, and finally some chlorine bleach. The fish died. So, he concluded that pollution could be deadly to fish. I sat there trying to be generous as I scored his presentation. I realized that the boy had put in time and had prepared very well for his presentation. Why, then, could I feel a growing anger as I put down my comments? Mainly, my harsh comments were aimed at the person who directed the project. That person should have helped to steer the child into a fruitful direction.

The rules for the experimental method are taught at almost all levels of education. In fact they are so important that they are often (and erroneously) called the scientific method. I don't want to digress very much here, but I do want the reader to understand that science employs many methods other than the experimental method. Nevertheless, the steps for the experimental method are:

- Observe a phenomenon. That is, all phenomena that can be subjected to experiment have to be observable or measurable.
- From that observation, devise a statement, or hypothesis, that can be tested.
- Try to manipulate only one variable.
- Do a parallel run in which the variable is not manipulated. This is the control.
- Then, observe whether the outcome differs from the control.

Those steps are defined by and their results are explained by the theory or theoretical framework within which the phenomenon is studied.

Now, let's reconsider the fish experiment. In this case, the main problem was that a whole parade of different pollutants had been introduced into the aquarium. What caused the death of the fish? Any one of the pollutants could have, but the interactions of the pollutants could not have been ruled out.

If I had to choose an immediate cause for the death of the fish, it would be the chlorine bleach. I had performed my own "experiment to that effect many years earlier in Oklahoma. I wanted to see what would happen if I poured chlorine bleach into one of my grandmother's small fishponds. Almost instantly the fish began to gyrate and flop at the surface. Then followed a terrible silence. The fish in the pond next to it showed no such response. What did my "experiment" demonstrate? It showed that chlorine bleach could be deadly to adult goldfish. The result could be explained according to theories of fish physiology or biochemistry. The outcome suggested a whole string of possible spin-off hypotheses about the levels of chlorine bleach, other forms of chlorine and related elements, the impact on smaller goldfish, etc. Fortunately, I did not try any of these in my grandmother's ponds. I couldn't. My great aunt had the ponds filled with earth not long after my "experiment".

Of course, I did not try to explain it. In fact, I was not really working from a hypothesis. In that sense both of the fish "experiments" were flawed. However, even when flawed, the power of the experimental method is obvious. Science is replete with examples of great experiments, those whose results changed the ways in which we viewed nature. The famous experiments in the history of science succeeded in demonstrating or confirming their hypotheses (note that I did not say prove their hypothesis because proof exists only in the realms of philosophy and mathematics) and, at the same time, challenged the prevailing theories.

Curiously, in the grand catalogue of experiments and their impacts on science, there is an example of an experiment, which, as a failure, made a major contribution to our understanding of light and other electromagnetic phenomena. That was the Michelson–Morley experiment of 1887, which was intended to detect the motion of the earth through the luminiferous ether. Because that experiment was designed within the late 19th Century theory of light, and its results were explained within that theory, I have to explain the development of the theory of light as it was accepted in 1887.

REFLECTIONS ON REFRACTIONS
Light seeking light doth light of light beguile.
　　　　　-Shakespeare (Love's Labour's Lost)

What do you know about light? I'm sure that any of you could describe some of its properties. For example, light can vary in brightness (intensity), and color (wavelength). It bounces off of mirrors (reflection), bends as it goes through lenses (refraction), and goes very fast (299,792,458 meters per second in a vacuum). Like gravity and electrical charge, the strength or intensity of light obeys the inverse square law. Still, this is a description of light rather than an answer to the "what" question. That is a statement of theory.

Through the ages there have been attempts to explain the phenomenon of light. For example, Pythagoras (c.582-500 B.C.; Croton-Southern Italy) believed that light was the eye's sense of touch. Euclid (c.330-260 B.C. Alexandria-Egypt), who complied a book of geometry, accepted the Pythagorean view of light. He noticed that as it reflected and bounced off of water and other reflective surfaces, light followed strict geometric patterns. That is, the angle in equals the angle out. This later was formalized and became known as the Law of Reflection (see Figure 4-17). Note that reflection worked as a theory whether the light comes from a source or it emanated from the eye.

The Pythagorean view had one major flaw.

That is, how could the "touch hypothesis" account for shadows? How could it account for the differences between day and night? Epicurus (c.342-270 B.C.), a philosopher from the island of Samos, said that light is transmitted from a source and reflected by objects. The reflected light then enters the eye to give the sensation of sight. Still, this begged the question of the nature of light. The Epicurean view really was a description, and the Greek Natural Philosophers did not accept the theory of vision.

An Alexandrian Greek, Claude Ptolemy (85-168 A.D.), wrestled with the problem of light bending as it entered water. He described this phenomenon that we call refraction with the precision of Geometry. He noticed that as light goes from a thin medium like air to a thick medium like water, light always bends in a characteristic way. That is, as light goes from air to water, the light ray is bent toward an imaginary line that is perpendicular to the surface of the water (Figure 4-18).

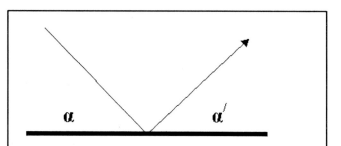

FIGURE 4-17. An illustration of the Law of Reflection. Here the angle of incidence α equals the angle of reflectance α'.

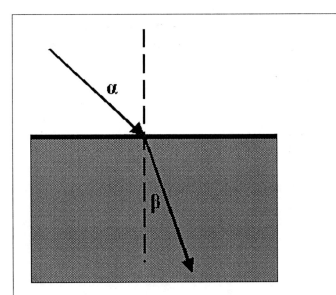

FIGURE 4-18. An illustration of the Law of Refraction. Here, a ray of light bends toward the normal (the perpendicular dashed line) as it goes from a rarified to a denser medium.

During the Roman period, science languished and nearly was extinguished through lack of interest in fundamental questions. The flame sputtered and remained alive in the Eastern Roman Empire. Then, it was rekindled by the Islamic Empire, which began to establish libraries and seats of learning. They did much more than just collect the works of the Greeks, they made significant contributions to science, building on and often contradicting the theories of the Greeks. Arab scientists did much work on light in attempting to describe it by Geometry and Mathematics. Most notable was Abu Ali Hasan, Ibn al-Haitham (965-1040; Iraq and Egypt), known in the West as Alhazan. He is attributed with having written more that 200 books, including a large and influential treatise on optics. He, too, worked out the Law of Refraction and recorded the separation of white light into its constituent colors. Alhazan made the first detailed study of the eye and developed a theory of vision like that of the Epicureans.

Western Europe finally captured one of the Islamic libraries in Toledo, Spain in 1089, not long after Alhazen's death. From the time of the fall of the Western Roman Empire books were scarce. Even Charlemagne in his search for books to establish universities could only muster about 100 books. Here were thousands of books. The period of translating the materials from Arabic into Latin took nearly a century. However, the literature itself launched a rebirth of philosophy, science and a reexamination of the fundamentals of western Christianity. Albertus Magnus and Thomas Aquinas worked to accommodate the new knowledge with Christianity from which emerged a new climate of learning and exploration. The writings of Alhazen, especially his advocacy of experimentation possibly influenced the methods of science in the coming centuries.

Knowledge of refraction and its application to make lenses, pieces of glass that are ground such that their continuous curvature causes light to bend such that it converges (in convex lenses, Figure 4-19) or diverges (in concave lenses, Figure 4-20). Both Galileo Galilei and Johannes Kepler used their understanding of refraction to perfect the lenses of the telescope and other optical instruments. However, such instruments allowed the exploration of other aspects of nature but begged the question of the fundamental nature of light itself.

PARTICLES OR WAVES?
Come forth into the light of things,
Let Nature be your teacher.-William Wordsworth

Although its properties had been described with greater precision, the nature of light was not considered until Rene Descartes (1596-1650, France) published his law of refraction. Descartes supposed that light was a particle or corpuscle in linear motion. That is, it was like a little bullet that bounced off of objects (reflection) and changed its path when it went into a medium of different density (refraction). Descartes believed that light corpuscles went faster as they penetrated a denser medium just as a ball rolls faster on a hard floor than on a carpet.

According to this bullet or corpuscular theory, we see objects because the light particles exert a pressure on our eyes. Also, planets remained in their orbits because the pressure from solar light particles balanced the light pressure from the stars. He explained colors as a manifestation of the rate at which the light particles were spinning. Red light was a consequence of particles spinning rapidly while blue light was particles spinning slowly.

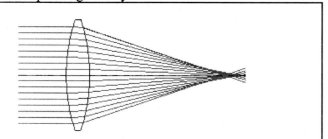

FIGURE 4-19. A diagram of a convex or converging lens. The continuous curvature of the glass works by the Law of Refraction to cause incoming parallel rays to converge at a focal point.

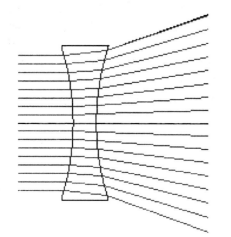

FIGURE 4-20. A diagram of a concave or diverging lens. Here, the continuous curvature of the glass causes incoming parallel rays of light to diverge and not come together at a focal point.

In 1705 Isaac Newton (1642-1727) published his corpuscular theory in his book, *Optics*. This particle theory was based on the ideas of Descartes, but he rejected the light pressure hypothesis. Also, he said that white light is a mixture of colored corpuscles. That is, each color of the rainbow (red, orange, yellow, green, blue, indigo, and violet) had its own corpuscle that moved through the universal background fluid called the ether.

The ether was an old idea. Since the beginning of Greek philosophy the concept of the vacuum was rejected. It was generally believed that the space between the planets was filled with a substance that transmitted light called the ether. Most scientists didn't question its existence. Newton employed the ether by saying that light corpuscles moved through it and set up vibrations. These vibrations helped to give corpuscles a periodic push (Figure 4-21). He used this to explain why some light reflected and other light penetrated the surface of water. Light with low energy bounced off of the water while light with higher energy penetrated the water's surface.

FIGURE 4-21. Ether Vibrations caused by the movement of light corpuscles. Where the vibrations come together, they impart a push to the corpuscle. Where the vibrations are apart, the ether provides less energy to the light corpuscle.

An alternative explanation had appeared earlier in the 17th century after a Jesuit Priest, Francesco Grimaldi (1618-1663, Italy) noticed that shadows cast by large buildings often were fuzzy and sometimes had rings of color. The particle view of light predicted that shadows would have very sharp edges. Grimaldi said that his observations could be explained only if light were a very fast wave in a fluid medium.

Christiaan Huygens (1629-1695, Netherlands) adopted Grimaldi's view and expanded it in his book, *Treatise on Light*, in 1690. Huygens was troubled by Descartes' particle theory of light. For example, light appeared to be matter in rapid motion because it could heat up things and cause them to burst into flame. In the mechanical philosophy of Huygens, this could only be caused by motion. However, it could be explained if light was the motion of matter, or waves in the ether.

Huygens also asked why strong light beams could cross and not deflect each other. That is, they did not behave as streams of bullets. In fact, Huygens believed that light behaved very much like sound, which was accepted as a kind of wave that was transmitted through the ether.

In 1801 Thomas Young (1773-1829, England), a British physician whose accomplishments included translation of the Rosetta Stone, was interested in the cause of astigmatism. He began to conduct a series of brilliantly simple experiments with light and discovered that light behaved very strangely when a strong beam was passed through a very small hole. The corpuscular theory predicted that the projected hole would be the size of the hole and had sharply-defined edges (Figure 4-22). However, the projected point of light was larger than the hole and had fuzzy edges (Figure 4-23). Young explained his results by assuming that light was a wave. As the waves went through the slit, they spread out forming a fuzzy-edged disk of light with a bright center.

He tested the wave hypothesis by passing light through two very close holes. The resulting projection had stripes of alternating bright light and no light (Figure 4-24). He interpreted this as the product of waves hitting each other in a process called interference. When two wave crests met, they reinforced each other and made the light brighter. When a wave crest and a wave trough met, they interfered with each other and canceled each other out. This spreading property of light is called diffraction and can be accounted for only if light is a wave. Thus, it seemed that the wave explanation of light had won the day.

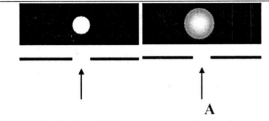

FIGURE 4-22. Light emitted through a small hole casts a spot of light on a screen. **A.** is predicted by the corpuscular theory. **B.** is predicted by the wave theory of light.

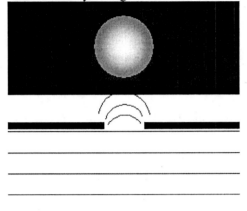

FIGURE 4-23. An explanation of the fuzzy-edged light spot. If light is a series of waves and the crests are given as lines, then the waves bend as they go through the hole. They spread out making a bright spot that is larger than the hole with fuzzy edges.

Many natural philosophers still were unconvinced. The British scientists accused Young of being unscientific, illogical, and, most importantly, unpatriotic. After all, he had challenged the optical theory of the great British hero, Isaac Newton. The French and other scientists of the European continent were concerned that wave theory was supported by analogy and lacked mathematical support. Augustin Jean Fresnel (1788-1827, France) provided the mathematical rigor to show that diffraction and interference phenomena could be explained as products of wave action. Furthermore, Fresnel, Young, and others through the study of polarized light concluded that light was a transverse wave like those on the surface of the ocean rather than the compression waves of sound. Thus, it could be defined as wavelength (distance between the crests) and amplitude or brightness (height of the wave from trough to crest; see Figure 4-25).

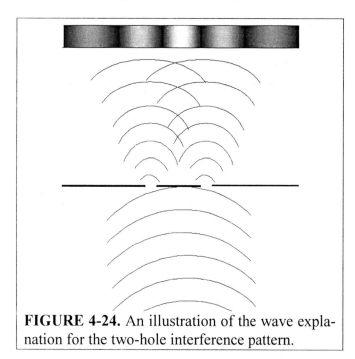

FIGURE 4-24. An illustration of the wave explanation for the two-hole interference pattern.

This theory also simplified the need for corpuscles of many different colors. Young explained that exhibited color as a manifestation of its wavelength alone. Corpuscles were not needed at all.

When Michael Faraday conducted his experiments on electromagnetism, he believed that electricity and magnetism were wave-like manifestations in their own ether-like fluid. In fact, he believed that the lines of force around a magnet were visualizations of the ether itself.

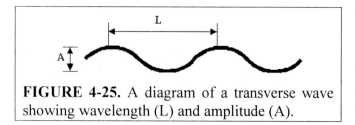

FIGURE 4-25. A diagram of a transverse wave showing wavelength (L) and amplitude (A).

Faraday began to wonder whether light might not be an electromagnetic phenomenon as well. He noticed that polarized light (light with its waves all aligned in the same direction) was af-fected as it passed through a strong magnetic field.

James Clerk Maxwell (1831-1879) began to consider Faraday's work and united electromagnetic phenomena by a set of four elegant equations. Also, he was struck by how both light and electric current had the same speed. They were all wave-like and propagated through an ether. The simplest explanation was that light, magnetism and electricity were manifestations of the same phenomenon. Light became a wave in the ether. The waves had an electrical component and a magnetic component. Also, the lines of force in the ether connected everything; so, there was no action at a distance, a concept that had bothered Isaac Newton.

This theory was so complete that it explained nearly all of the behaviors of light. There were just a few details to mop up. One detail was the photoelectric effect. When a zinc plate was hit by high energy light such as ultraviolet, the zinc plate became charged. This seemed that the light was behaving as a series of bullets knocking the recently discovered electrons out. The other detail was the demonstration of the ether itself.

THE EXPERIMENT

The only real difficulty lies in this measurement.
        -Albert Michelson & Edward Morley

The ether had certain properties that could be deduced from the properties of light and other electromagnetic phenomena. First, it had to be everywhere in the universe, at least everywhere that electromagnetic waves propagated. Second, because the vibrations of light were so small, the ether must act like a very stiff fluid. Third, it could not offer any resistance to bodies of mass as they move through it. Most importantly, Newtonian physics suggested that there should be an absolute state of rest, just as there is motion. If the ether filled all space, then it could be the entity against which absolute motion could be measured.

It was with these properties of ether that Albert Michelson (1852-1931, Germany & USA), an American physicist set out to detect the absolute motion of the earth. He had developed a reputation for precise measurements and designing instruments to do so. He had already measured the speed of light with much greater accuracy than had been achieved thus far in 1881. Then, it occurred to Michelson that if the earth were moving through the ether, then it should be possible to detect its motion and, therefore, demonstrate the reality of the ether. While in Germany, Michelson built an instrument called an interferometer (see Figure 4-26). This instrument took a beam of light and split it with a half-silvered mirror. The two beams bounced off of mirrors oriented at right angles and came together to form a characteristic interference pattern. Michelson oriented one beam in the direction of the earth's motion and the other beam perpendicular to the direction of the earth's motion. When the two beams came back together, they showed an interference pattern. He expected the pattern to change as he changed the orientation of the interferometer arms.

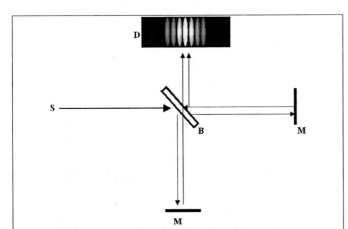

FIGURE 4-26. The Michelson interferometer. Light enter from a source (S) and is split by the beamsplitter (B). Each beam reflects from a mirror (M) and is reconstituted at the beamsplitter which directs the two mixed beams to a detector which shows a characteristic double beam interference pattern.

Michelson's reasoning went like this. Suppose two swimmers who swim at exactly the same speed begin to race. One swims across a river and the other swims the same distance upstream and turns around and swims back. The swimmer who swam upstream actually went farther from the perspective of the water. Thus, the swimmer who swam across the current should win.

The split light beams were like the swimmers. The earth moving through the stationary ether created a kind of ether wind or current on the earth's surface. Thus, the light beam oriented in the direction of the earth's motion should have taken slightly longer than that oriented perpendicularly to the earth's motion. Also, the interference patterns should have changed as the arms of the interferometer were moved relative to the ether wind. These predictions were made within the Maxwell Electromagnetic Theory, the culmination of the Greek, Arabic, and Western Science theories of light.

Even his earliest instruments were so sensitive that they could detect people walking outside. But he saw no ether effect. When he returned to the U.S., Michelson asked a colleague Edward Morley (1838-1923, USA) to help him build an even more sensitive interferometer. This new instrument was built in Cleveland at the Case School of Applied Science (now, Case-Western University). This interferometer was mounted on a large piece of sandstone that floated in mercury to eliminate vibration. The path lengths of the split beams were lengthened to amplify the erther wind effect. The instrument was ready in 1887 and certainly was precise enough to detect the motion of the earth. As Michelson and Morley turned the sandstone block, they noticed no change in the interference pattern. Michelson was scrambling for ideas. He knew that this new instrument was sensitive enough to detect the motion of the earth through the ether. Why didn't it?

He thought that the ether on the earth became stagnant near the surface. So, he climbed a mountain with his instrument. Still, there was no effect. How could this be reconciled? Light was obviously a wave and waves are disturbances in a medium. Where was the medium? George Fitzgerald (1851-1901, Ireland) came up with the idea that the arm of the interferometer that was aimed in the direction of the earth's motion contracted just enough to prevent a change in the interference pattern. Hendrik Anton Lorentz (1853-1928) developed the Fitzgerald explanation with a set of equations that related transformation in length along the direction of motion relative to the velocity. Michelson continued to measure the speed of light with increasing precision and even measured the diameter of Betelgeuse, a red giant star in the constellation Orion. In 1907 he became the first American Scientist to win a Nobel Prize. Still, he never accepted the results of his experiment.

THE PROGRESS OF SCIENCE
The first principle is that you must not fool yourself, and you're the easiest person to fool.   - *Richard Feynman*

Certainly, some experiments are failures. The two goldfish experiments recounted at the beginning of this essay were failures for a number of reasons. Some fail because the hypothesis is faulty or the phenomena cannot be observed or measured (most pseudosciences suffer from this problem). Did the Michelson-Morley experiment really fail? It is true that it failed to detect the motion of the earth through the ether. Michelson and the physics establishment tried to save the ether in light of this failure by the Fitzgerald-Lorentz transformations. However, some physicists began to suspect that the ether did not exist at all. That is, the Michelson-Morley experiment failed to detect the ether because the ether did not exist.

There is a mythology in science as in all social institutions. One pervasive myth is that Albert Einstein read the Michelson-Morley paper and then formulated the Theory of Relativity to explain the failure. That should have happened, but it did not. Einstein claimed that he had never heard of the Michelson-Morley experiment when he developed Special Relativity. He already had a hunch that the ether was not needed. The real value of the Michelson-Morley experiment is that it allowed for the rejection of the luminiferous ether and prepared the community of physicists to look for other explanations.

Considering this so-called failure and the change in view that it prepared physicists for, I think that it is fair to ask, "Does science really progress?" Well, yes. We know much more about light now than we did 2,000 years ago or even 100 years ago. However, science does not progress by adding more and more data. It changes and progresses when new ideas that better fit the data are proposed and accepted by the scientific community. That is, science progresses as its ability to explain phenomena increases.

Light once was explained as an extension of our sense of touch. It then became a particle, and then a wave. While a wave, it was united with the phenomena of electricity and magnetism. In 1905, Albert Einstein proposed a solution to the photoelectric effect. He said that light came in packets of energy that he called photons, which had wave-like properties. The ether was no longer needed.

- 1996, revised 2004

References:

Billington, David P. 1996. *The Innovators, The Engineering Pioneers Who Made America Modern.* John Wiley and Sons, Inc. New York.

Boorstin, Daniel J. 1983. *The Discoverers, A History of Man's Search to Know his World and Himself.* Vintage Books, A Division of Random House. New York.

Burke, James. 1985. *The Day the Universe Changed.* Little, Brown and Company. Boston.

Einstein, Albert and Leopold Infeld. 1938. *The Evolution of Physics, The Growth of Ideas From Early Concepts to Relativity and Quanta.* Simon and Schuster. New York.

Gribben, John. 2002. *The Scientists.* Random House. New York.

Halliday, David and Robert Resnick. 1970. *Fundamentals of Physics.* John Wiley and Sons, Inc. New York.

Hann, Judith. 1991. *How Science Works, 100 Ways Parents and Kids Can Share the Secrets of Science.* Reader's Digest Association, Inc. Pleasantville, New York.

Harre, Rom. 1981. *Great Scientific Experiments, 20 Experiments that Changed Our View of the World.* Phaidon Press, Ltd. Oxford.

Mason, Stephen F. 1962. *A History of the Sciences.* Collier Books. New York.

Michelson, Albert A. and Edward W. Morley. 1887. *On the Relative Motion of the Earth and the Luminiferous Ether.* The American Journal of Science Third Series. 34 (203):333-345

Questions to Think About

1. What are the steps to the experimental method?

   [handwritten notes] · Observe   · Control
   · Hypothesize   · Differences
   · Manipulate variable

2. What is the Law of Reflection? Refraction?

   [handwritten notes] ↳ Angle in = Angle Out
   ⌐ Light bends on enters medias on characteristics ways

3. What role did the Islamic Empire play in the development of Western science?

   [handwritten notes] · Optics, book, challenge & Greeks
   · Brought to Europe

4. How do lenses work?

   [handwritten notes] · Continuous curvature causes light to bend. Such that it converges

5. Newton's theory of light used both particles and waves. How were they related?

   [handwritten notes] Particles move through ether & get of vibrations
   — pique & particles

6. How did the experiments of Thomas Young demonstrate the wave-like property of light?

   [handwritten notes] Corpuscles would ?? ??

7. What is meant by wavelength and amplitude?

   [handwritten notes] distance between crests — height

8. Who were Michelson and Morley, and what did their experiment seek to do?

   [handwritten notes] Ether - not observed

9. Did their experiment fail? How might experiments really fail?

   [handwritten notes] No, faulty reasoning

10. What does this story about the change in understanding about the nature of light illustrate how science changes?

    [handwritten notes] Progress comes from new ideas

BOYLE, BOLTZMANN, AND BANYA

BANYA

Баня парит, баня правит. (*Banya steams, banya cures.*) -Russian Proverb

I recall an especially hot day in central Russia. I had been studying the lake at Galich, a town north of the Volga River and about 6 hours NE of Moscow. On that day (the 21st of June) we took a hike to a village called Bykee to visit the home where my wife's father had been born and raised. The village was a small collection of log homes, each with its own garden and bath house or banya. On that day I had not had a good hot bath for several weeks. The central hot water delivery system was being cleaned in Yaroslavl (where I had my apartment) and in Galich. What hot baths I had taken were from water that I had heated on the stove. The day was especially miserable because the temperature had risen to the mid 30's centigrade, and we were beset by mosquitoes and horseflies. So, when I arrived in Bykee, being even hotter was the farthest thing from my mind. Somehow, I allowed the current owner of the home to convince me that this would make me very clean and cure my ills. For some reason, I relented.

The woman of the house said that she would have to have several hours to prepare the fire and heat it up. In the mean time, my student and I studied the glacial geology of the area.

Hers was a typical Russian banya. It was a small building with a low ceiling and made of spruce logs (see Figure 4-27). In the center of the small building was a large, brick stove with chambers for heating water and a place on top where stones were heated. Steam was generated when water was tossed onto the heated stones. The owner showed us the rudiments of what we had to do and left the rest to my student and me.

Anyway, I stepped into the log building and a wall of hot, dry air hit my face and made its way deep into my lungs. Immediately, I began to sweat. The sweat quickly evaporated and my body's cooling system began to work. I was given a place of honor, a shelf about a meter or more off of the floor (and less than a meter from the ceiling). As water was poured onto the hot stones on the top of the wood stove, a cloud of steam poured out into the small room. Steam carried more of the heat into the air and the room became very hot.

FIGURE 4-27. The log banya in the village of Bykee near Galich, Russia.

We relaxed in the steam, tried our hand at massaging each other with a venik, a bundle of birch twigs dipped in hot water. Secretly, I think that Greg got a kick out of beating his professor with a bundle of twigs. Then, we bathed in metal tubs of hot water. I recall looking up at the thermometer mounted on the wall. I was astounded to see that it read 98°C, nearly the boiling point of water! Suddenly the steam felt very powerful.

THE STRENGTH OF STEAM

Steam is no stronger now that it was a hundred years ago, but it is put to better use.   -Ralph Waldo Emerson

The power of steam was a real question in 18th Century Europe. Although devices that operated by steam power had been produced as far back as the Alexandrian Greeks, the first true steam-powered engine appeared around 1698 and was built by Thomas Savery (1650-1715). This was a very simple machine with a single large chamber that was filled with steam. The chamber then was cooled by water from the outside which caused the steam to condense and produce a vacuum. Water from a mine then was pulled into the evacuated chamber. This was a very simple design that fellow Englishman, Thomas Newcomen (1663-1729) improved upon by converting the chamber into a piston (see Figure 4-28). Like that of Savery, the Newcomen atmospheric engine employed the expansion of steam and the contraction of its condensation. The Newcomen engine caused the piston to rise when steam entered the chamber. Then, cold water flowed into the chamber and the steam condensed causing the piston to fall. The first Newcomen engine appeared in 1712 and was the engine of choice for the next 60 years.

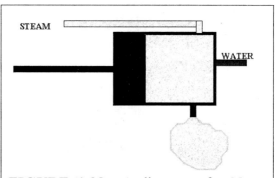

FIGURE 4-28. A diagram of a Newcomen engine. Steam enters and causes the piston to rise. Then cold water is introduced, the steam condenses, and the piston falls.

Despite its popularity, the Newcomen atmospheric engine was very inefficient. It generated than about 5.5 horsepower and was only about 1% efficient. James Watt (1736-1819, United Kingdom), instrument maker for the University of Glasgow, repaired a model of the Newcomen engine and realized that he could improve on the design by adding a second cylinder that was cooled by a jacket of cold water (Figure 4-29). Thus, the steam would condense and cause the piston to fall without cooling the chamber and have to waste coal on heating the chamber again. He produced his first improved steam engine in 1778. Then, in 1782, he made a major improvement by allowing the main piston to be pushed both ways. This new double-acting steam engine was just what the industrial revolution needed. hysicists were trying to understand just why it worked. This was more than a game. If they could understand why it worked, then they might be able to build a better, more efficient steam engine.

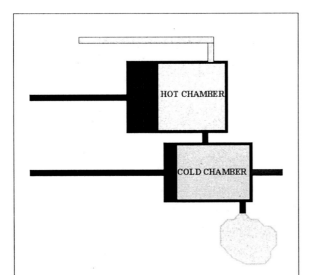

FIGURE 4-29. A diagram of the Watt steam engine. Steam enters the hot chamber, which has a jacket of steam to keep it hot. The steam then rushes into and condenses in the cold chamber which has a jacket of cold water.

The steam engine and its development outstripped the science of its day. Science really did not have a good explanation for how it worked. But the steam engine had become such an important technological tool by the dawn of the 19th Century that a theoretical understanding of how it worked became necessary for economic and strategic reasons. By understanding, maybe a better steam engine could be designed.

A SCIENCE OF HEAT BEGINS

Not withstanding work of all kinds done by steam-engines, notwithstanding the satisfactory condition to which they have been brought today, their theory is very little understood, and the attempts to improve them are still directed almost by chance.- Sadi Carnot

The systematic study of heat had been undertaken only sporadically prior to the invention of the steam engine. Perhaps, the most relevant research in that direction was that of Robert Boyle (1637-1691;

United Kingdom) and Robert Hooke (1635-1703, United Kingdom). Prevailing views of material and heat in the 17th Century were that substances were continuous and were not divided into discrete particles. Heat was viewed as a kind of fluid called caloric that filled substances. After all, when things heated up, they usually began to swell as if something were being added to them. Boyle began to consider a mechanical definition of heat. He did this by considering gasses.

Suppose that you have a volume of a gas in a chamber with a piston on the top. As the piston compresses the gas, the pressure and temperature both rise. If you keep the piston constant and increase the temperature, the pressure rises as well. Thus, temperature, pressure and volume are all related. Boyle reasoned that the pressure rose when the gas was heated because the gas was divided into atoms. These atoms moved relative to their temperature. So, the hotter they were, the faster they moved and the harder they hit the side of the chamber (see Figure 4-30).

His contemporaries like Rene Descartes (1596-1650) did not believe in atoms. After all, if atoms existed, then a vacuum must exist between the atoms. The vacuum was even harder to believe in than atoms were. Still, the idea of a mechanical universe began to catch on. Isaac Newton (1642-1727) formulated laws of motion and described the universe as a clock that worked with mathematical precision.

The struggle to understand the nature of heat led to a modern understanding of chemistry and to a new area of physics called thermodynamics. In particular, thermodynamics is the study of the relationships between the various forms of energy. In fluid theory of heat, friction liberated heat trapped in an object. The atomic view, however, said that friction caused an increase in atomic motion, which then was detected as heat.

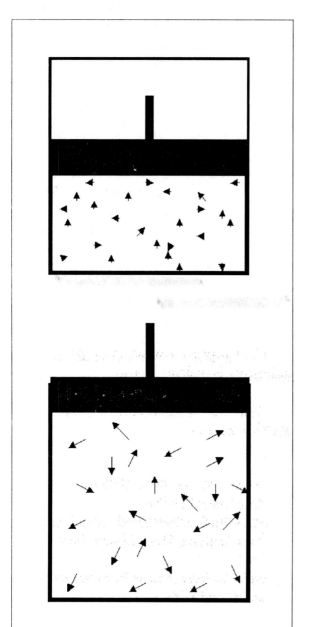

FIGURE 4-30. An illustration of Boyle's argument. Both pistons hold the same amount of air (number of atoms, each represented by an arrow). The piston on the top has a lower pressure because the atoms are not moving as fast or are cooler than those in the lower piston.

Insight into the caloric controversy came with another technological innovation. Earlier, cannons were cast with the hole in the barrel. Later, it was found that cannon barrels could be made more precisely if the hole were cut into the cannon after it was made. The process of cutting cannon barrels generated an enormous amount of heat. According to the fluid theory, a sharp cutting tool should release more heat than a blunt cutting tool because the sharp tool cut through more metal in a given amount of time. However, Count Rumford (1753-1814) noticed that blunt cutting tools generated much more heat than did sharp ones. As a consequence of this compelling evidence, heat began to be viewed as a form of mechanical (vibrations of atoms) energy.

In France, engineers and physicists alike were trying to determine just how the thermal energy was translated to the mechanical energy of the steam engine. Chief among them was Sadi Carnot (1796-1832; France) who in his short life did much to set the foundation of a new science, that of thermodynamics despite his adherence to the Caloric fluid theory. He examined steam engines and observed that the efficiency inherent in the steam engine or any heat engine was determined by the difference in temperature between the hot and cold chambers or how steep the temperature gradient could be be made between the working parts of the engine. He determined the greater the difference, the greater the efficiency. Carnot used this concept to pioneer the scientific explanation for the conversion of heat to mechanical energy.

LAWS OF THERMODYNAMICS

Available energy is the main object at stake in the struggle for existence and the evolution of the world.

-Ludwig Boltzmann

James P. Joule (1818-1889, England) became interested in whether or not energy was destroyed or just changed forms in conversions like those of steam becoming mechanical energy. At first he looked at the amounts that wires heated up as electric current flowed through them. Then, he performed a very famous and simple experiment. He had a set of paddles in a container of water. The paddles were driven by the force of weights falling (Figure 4-31). The energy of the weights could be calculated and the change in temperature of the water could be measured. He found that the churning paddles caused a repeatable rise in the temperature of the water.

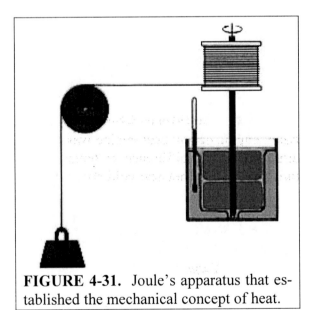

FIGURE 4-31. Joule's apparatus that established the mechanical concept of heat.

Later, William Thomson, Lord Kelvin (1824-1907) noticed Joule's work and was able to repeat it. Kelvin and the German, Rudolph Clausius (1822-1888), together formulated the First Law of Thermodynamics in 1851. That is, *energy is neither created nor destroyed but can be converted from one form to another.*

Clausius recognized that the interconversion would never be 100% efficient and that some of the energy would be lost in other forms, particularly as heat. This explained why machines constantly needed a supply of energy.

Why, when set into motion, does a wagon stop rolling? Friction with the wheels and axles of the cart cause molecular motion to increase thus causing the temperature of the tires and bearings of the axles to rise. The heat generated is dispersed to cooler parts of the wagon and to the air. Thus, motion (kinetic energy) is translated into heat that is lost. The same explanation can be used for why balls stop bouncing and machines grind to a halt. The dispersion of heat is irreversible and explains why perpetual motion machines are impossible.

This tendency toward disorder and dissipation is called entropy. Simply put, the second law of thermodynamics says *that in a closed system, entropy or disorder increases.* Trefil and Hazen (1995) define the second law with three statements:

1. Heat will not flow spontaneously from a cold to a hot body.
2. You cannot construct an engine that does nothing but convert heat to useful work.
3. Every isolated system becomes more disordered with time.

An Austrian physicist, Ludwig Boltzmann (1844-1906) defined the second law mathematically and based his definition on the idea that the energies of the components of a system would tend to become evenly distributed.

While writing this essay I made myself a cup of Jasmine tea. When I put it on the table, the mug was hot, and the water was near boiling. I took a few sips and burned my tongue; so, I set it aside while I worked on the essay. About 35 minutes later, I picked up the mug. It felt cold to the touch and the tea was luke warm. What happened? Well, the tea and mug were warmer than their surroundings causing heat to be conducted to the table and surrounding air. The mug, the tea, and the air eventually came to the same temperature. The story of the tea was explainable by employing the second law of thermodynamics.

So, heat moves as a consequence of the second law of thermodynamics. Because heat moves, engines such as steam and gasoline motors work by causing energy to move. Similarly, living things take the energy stored in substances called food (fats, carbohydrates, nucleic acids, and proteins) and convert that energy to the ordered structure and chemistry of life.

A more profound message can be found in my mug of Jasmine tea.. Why didn't the mug stay warm? Why didn't the tea pull extra heat from the air and become hotter? Newton's physics allows such things to happen. However, Boltzmann and others showed that some events have a greater probability than other events. Lord Kelvin, in his recognition of how events seem to move in particular directions, said that entropy defines the directionality of the universe. We discern that direction as time.

Boltzmann believed that entropy was a confirmation of the molecular or atomic nature of matter. In Austria, his views were not generally accepted. Despondent over his lack of appreciation and in ill health, he committed suicide in 1906, within a year of the confirmation of the existence of atoms by Albert Einstein.

By the beginning of the 20th Century, the understanding of thermodynamics was

References:

on a firm footing and lent support to emerging technologies as well as to the emerging sciences of quantum mechanics and relativity. More recently, a third law has been proposed. This states that because molecular motion is manifest as heat, a point at which there is no molecular motion is absolute zero.

BANYA AND THERMODYNAMICS
С лёгким паром! (*With a light steam!*)
  -A greeting for someone emerging from banya

Discussions of heat and entropy bring me back to my first time in banya. Although I have had banya many times since then and am planning to build one of my own, that experience was the most memorable one. It was like being in a great thermodynamics experiment. Heat was conducted to the water on the hot stones where water molecules began to vibrate faster and faster until they became a gas (steam). The steam began to spread throughout the room by convection and become dispersed throughout the room according to the second law of thermodynamics. Soon, it felt as though I was in a steam engine as the steam condensed on my skin and conducted its heat into me. I jumped from the shelf and hugged the floor after the third ladle of water was thrown onto the stove. I soaped up and enjoyed dumping buckets of hot water over my head. Thanks to the first and second laws of thermodynamics, I left the banya very clean, somewhat lighter and quite cool on a very hot day.

-1996, revised 2004

Adkins, C.J. 1987. *Thermal Physics.* Cambridge University Press. Cambridge, UK.

Billington, David P. 1996. *The Innovators, The Engineering Pioneers Who Made America Modern.* John Wiley and Sons, Inc. New York

Carnot, Sadi. 1824. *Reflections on the Motive Power of Fire and on Machines Fitted to Develop that Power.* Memoir Translated by R. H. Thurston. Paris.

Coveny, Peter and Roger Highfield. *The Arrow of Time, A Voyage Through Science to Solve Time's Greatest Mystery.* Fawcett Columbine. New York.

Feynman, Richard P. 1995. *Six Easy Pieces.* Helix Books. Addison-Wesley Publishing Co. New York.

Goodsell, David S. 1996. *Our Molecular Nature, The Body's Motors, Machines and Messages.* Copernicus, Springer-Verlag New York, Inc. New York

Halliday, David and Robert Resnick. 1970. *Fundamentals of Physics.* John Wiley and Sons, Inc. New York.

Hann, Judith. 1991. *How Science Works, 100 Ways Parents and Kids Can Share the Secrets of Science.* Reader's Digest Association, Inc. Pleasantville, New York.

Lambert, Frank. 2003-2004. *A Student's Approach to the Second Law and Entropy.* http://www.entropysite.com/students_approach.html

Lynds, Beverly T. 1995-2004. *About Temperature.* http://my.unidata.ucar.edu/content/staff/blynds/tmp.html

Mason, Stephen F. 1962. *A History of the Sciences.* Collier Books, New York.

Pidwinny, Michael. 1999-2004. *Laws of Thermodynamics.* http://www.physicalgeography.net/fundamentals/6e.html

Trefil, James and Robert Hazen. 1995 & 1998. *The Sciences, An Intergrated Approach.* John Wiley & Sons, Inc. New York.

Questions to Think About

1. Why does the air in banya get so hot?

   Steam

2. What gives the steam engine its power?

   Pressure of the vapor

3. What is the importance of the steam engine to the science of heat?

   How it works is based on heat

4. How did James Watt improve the steam engine?

   Double-acting steam piston, cooling chamber

5. What is the difference between the Caloric Theory and Mechanical Theory of heat?

1) Heat was a fluid that filled things

2) T°, P, V are all related

6. How did Robert Boyle and Sadi Carnot provide the foundation for Thermodynamics?

Carnot importance is difference in temp

Boyle - T°, P, V are related, mechanical

7. In what way did James Joule disprove the Caloric Theory?

water paddle exp

8. What is the First Law of Thermodynamics? Who defined it?

Energy is neither created or destroyed - Kelvin & Clausius

9. What is the Second Law of Thermodynamics? Why was Ludwig Boltzmann despondent about his theory?

· In a closed system, entropy / disorder decreases

· People wouldn't accept it

10. What are some consequences of entropy?

Cold tea

11. In what way is the so-called Third Law of Thermodynamics a special case of the Second Law?

Abs 0 = no motion

12. What aspects of the theory of heat will I have to consider as I build and operate my own banya?

H

QUESTIONING REALITY

MY FATHER'S SUNGLASSES

I was led into such perplexity by the unbelievability of the thing that I began to doubt the faith of my own eyes.

-Tycho Brahe

My father was no scientist nor did he aspire to be one. However, he was a good storyteller, and, therefore, he possessed the air of authority that storytellers have for the naive listener. He owned a carpet cleaning franchise, and I worked for him. I remember his attempts to tell me about the polarity of water and why it was such a good universal solvent for cleaning carpets. Now I know that although his conclusion was valid, his explanation was gibberish.

His attempts at science usually were like that, but frozen in my memory is a scientific demonstration that he gave me one time. He almost always wore sunglasses, polarized sunglasses, and one pair broke in half. He showed me that when light passes through two polarized lenses, the amount of light that passes through the two lenses changes as the one lens is turned relative to the other one. I don't remember his explanation, but in this case, the demonstration was worth a thousand words. Still, what I remembered most vividly was when he interposed a third lens between the two that were turned so that no light came through. As he twisted the middle lens, a faint, but visible amount of light appeared. However, when he put the third lens behind the two, there was no change See Figure 4-32). This was a mystery that he did not even try to explain, but I did not forget it.

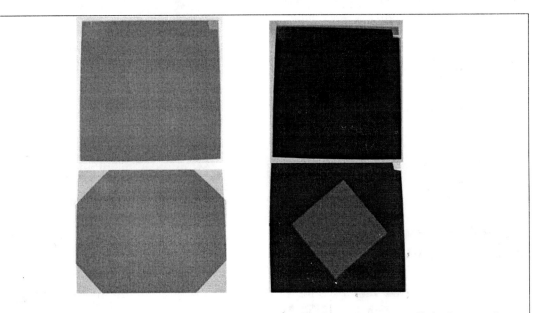

FIGURE 4-32. These are polarizing films in different orientations on a light box and simulate my father's demonstration with the sunglasses. Upper left, two films with the same orientation showing the maximum light transmission with two Polaroid films; upper right, two films with perpendicular orientation; lower left, two films at 45° angle to each other; lower right, three films two of which are perpendicular with a smaller third sandwiched between them and at 45° angle to the larger films.

Similar strange behaviors of light led to a new way of understanding the fundamental nature of nature. At the end of the 19th Century, the laws of mechanics, thermodynamics, and electromagnetism had been formulated. Collectively, these represented a triumph of science and painted a picture of the world that was continuous, logical, and predictable. The general belief was that if the momentum and position of all particles in the universe could be known, the entire future of the universe itself could be known. This mechanical, deterministic, clockwork view of nature was comfortable, and the end of the exploration of the physical structure of reality seemed to be at hand. There were just a few pesky things left to understand: radioactivity, blackbody radiation, the photoelectric effect, the orbit of Mercury, etc. Answers to these problems led to revolutions in thought requiring that we give up our comfortable notions of space, time, and a deterministic, mechanical Newtonian universe.

PLANCK'S CONSTANT

...the whole procedure was an act of despair because a theoretical interpretation had to be found at any price, no matter how high that might be.

-Max Planck

One of the first holes in the theoretical edifice of the 19th Century came with the attempt to explain how bodies glow as they are heated. To study the phenomenon, physicists invented a theoretical entity called a blackbody (see Figure 4-33). This was an item that absorbed all external energy, including light energy; so, it appeared black. Thus, all of the energy that came from it was emitted as a consequence of its heating through energy absorption. In 1859 Gustav

Kirchhoff derived a proof that a blackbody, a sphere of material that absorbed all energy, with a hole in its side to receive energy that would hit and be re-emitted within the sphere until it exited the hole, would emit energy that was determined by the temperature and the frequency of the emitted light. This flew in the face of the electromagnetic theory of James Clerk Maxwell, which predicted that the intensity (brightness) of the light, not the frequency, should determine the energy. Experimental evidence suggested that Kirchhoff was right. However, what did it mean?

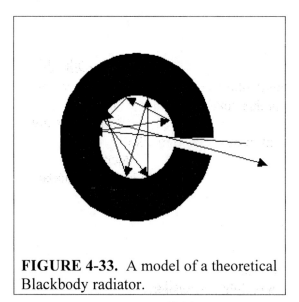

FIGURE 4-33. A model of a theoretical Blackbody radiator.

A number of attempts to model the blackbody problem mathematically through the end of the 19th Century failed. The formulas that had been generated described the phenomenon well at low frequencies or high frequencies, but not at both ends of the electromagnetic spectrum. Finally, in 1900, Max Planck (1858-1947, Germany), who serendipitously held the chair at Heidelburg University that Kirchhoff had left when he went to Berlin, produced a formula that agreed with measurements of emissions. The formula, known as Planck's Radiation Formula derived a constant from existing constants (like Boltzmann's constant and the speed of light) now known as Planck's Constant (*h*; see Figure 4-34). Although he had solved the energy emission problem, Planck's formula opened a whole new set of problems for physics.

$$\Delta E = h \nu$$

where:

$$h = 6.626196 \times 10^{-34} \text{ joule-sec.}$$

ν = Wavelength

FIGURE 4-34. Max Planck's Radiation Formula with *h*, Planck's Constant.

The problem or the "high price" that Planck paid was that the formula dictated the energy increases by whole number multiples of the constant. In other words, the energy emitted was not continuous, but stepwise. Planck interpreted it to mean that energy was not continuous, but came in units or quanta. However, he still considered light to be a wave.

A problem similar to that of blackbody radiation was called the Photoelectric Effect (see Figure 4-35). That is, when light strikes a metal plate, a current can be detected. Experimental measurements indicated that the energy of the electrons emitted from the metal plate was related to the frequency of the light and not its intensity. Albert Einstein (1879-1955, Germany & US) considered this problem and solved it by assuming that light energy traveled in localized bundles that he called photons and whose energy was defined by the Planck formula. Thus, light had properties that seemed more like a particle. This unexpected solution to the Photoelectric Effect, that light moves through space like a particle, also seemed to fly in the face

of all the experimental evidence that confirmed the wave-nature of light. Robert A. Millikan (1868-1953,) in his oil drop experiments to determine the charge of individual electrons, seemed to confirm Einstein's photon theory.

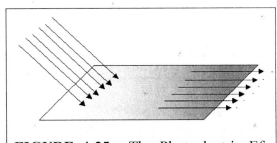

FIGURE 4-35. The Photoelectric Effect. When light of a high enough frequency strikes certain metal plates, a movement of electrons or weak current can be detected.

Unambiguous confirmation of the Photon Theory was provided by A.H. Compton (1892-1962; US) in 1923 when he aimed high energy x-rays at a graphite block. The way in which they scattered suggested that light was particulate, or more precisely, both a particle and a wave. Both Millikan and Compton independently derived Planck's Constant. The importance of this cannot be overstated. Planck's Constant is very small, but it is not zero. In a universe with no Planck's Constant, energy would not come in quanta, and the laws of classical physics would be equally valid at all scales. There would be no quantum physics. This was the high price that Max Planck referred to.

BOHR'S ATOM
Anyone who is not shocked by quantum theory has not understood it. Niels Bohr

At the turn of the 20th Century other problems began to loom with classical physics. Radioactivity had been observed and demonstrated as a phenomenon of certain elements. It appeared that the constituent atoms of certain elements like Radium were unstable and would spontaneously break off parts of themselves. This suggested that matter really consisted of complex parts. J.J. Thomson (1856-1940; United Kingdom) discovered the electron. Thomson surmised that the atom, which is neutrally-charged, must have a balance of positive and negative charges. Thus, he assumed that the atom must be like a plum pudding, a sphere of positive charge with enough electrons embedded in it to balance the charge. Ernest Rutherford (1871-1937; New Zealand, Canada, and United Kingdom) who would eventually be Thompson's successor at the Cavendish Laboratory in Cambridge, tested that theory at Victoria University (now called the University of Manchester in Canada) fired alpha particles (particles with a +2 charge) at a very thin gold leaf. Most of them sliced right through as if they were going through a plum pudding. However, he detected that a few bounced back. By the deflection of the alpha particles and lack of recoil by the gold leaf, calculated that the bulk of the mass of an element resided in a tiny positively-charged nucleus surrounded by negatively-charged electrons. His interpretations of experiment seemed clear. However, in a strict Newtonian interpretation, it could not be true. In the classical view, an electron would tend to spiral into the nucleus and accelerate as it did. An accelerating charge would then radiate increasingly higher frequencies of light and then crash into the nucleus. Thus, all of the atoms in the universe should have collapsed in on themselves almost as soon as they were formed. Obviously they did not.

Niels Henrik David Bohr (1885-1962, Denmark) began to work with Thomson but almost immediately conflicts between the two caused Bohr to look elsewhere. He went to work with Ernest Rutherford at Manchester in 1912. Bohr considered the problem of the Rutherford atom and applied the quantum theory of Planck and Einstein to the construction of a new kind of model. He supposed that electrons could exist only in discrete orbits around the nucleus (Figure 4-36). They were stable and would not radiate energy in such orbits. If they received energy in quanta defined by the Planck equation, the more energetic electron would occupy the next larger stable orbit. If it radiated energy, then it lost a similar quantum of energy. Bohr's atom helped to explain the stability of the atom and why each element showed certain spectral lines when heated.

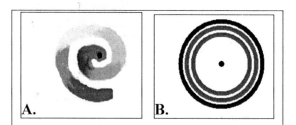

FIGURE 4-36. Models of the hydrogen atom. A. is the Rutherford atom with its electron in an accelerating fall into the nucleus. It radiates increasingly energetic light as it accelerates. B. is the Bohr atom with only discrete orbits allowed, each with different energy levels.

Louis de Broglie (1892-1987; France) wrote his doctoral thesis in 1924 on electron waves, which he based on the works of Planck and Einstein. He showed how electrons, entities that clearly seemed particulate, had properties as waves, and, therefore were similar to photons. This particle-wave duality theory formalized the concept that matter itself had wavelike properties. He showed that the allowed orbits of the Bohr model of the atom had distances that allowed a resonating, whole wavelength or whole number multiples of whole wavelengths. Thus, the lowest allowed orbit of an electron was a single electron wave. The next orbit was 2 wavelengths, etc. De Broglie's theory was confirmed by experiment in 1929. Clearly, light, electrons, and nuclear components had properties of waves and particles. How did they know when to behave as particles and when to behave as waves?

Erwin Schroedinger (1887-1961; Austria) built on the work of de Broglie and produced equations to describe the wave mechanics of electrons in the hydrogen atom. In this case, the allowed orbitals were regions of space within which the probabilities of the occurrences of electrons were determined. Thus, the electrons were not localized, but spread through space as probability waves.

MEASURING UNCERTAINTY

I think that modern physics has definitely decided in favor of Plato. In fact the smallest units of matter are not physical objects in the ordinary sense, they are forms, ideas which can be expressed unambiguously only in mathematical language.   Werner Heisenberg

The probabilistic nature of small entities in the quantum realm can be seen when photons, electrons, or other small entities are measured. Consider light. It seems to propagate as a wave function but collapses to a real point or particle when measured. Consider the diffraction of light waves as they encounter a double slit. The waves that propagate through the slits support or interfere with each other such that a characteristic bright-dark banded pattern appears on the detector, which in this case is black and white film (Figure 4-37). The reaction of the silver atoms (turning black) is with the quantum energy imparted by particular photons, not by waves. Thus, the propagating light waves collapse as individual photons on the film. What happens if we send photons through the device one at a time? Well, the photons react with individual silver atoms as before. However, the pattern, given enough time, appears as the bright-dark banded pattern of diffraction (Figure 4-38). But if they went through one at a time, how did they know about the interference? The interpretation is that an individual photon propagates as a wave and interferes with itself as it encounters the double slit. Then, it collapses as a photon when it reacts with a silver molecule in a pattern governed by probabilities. Similar results have been obtained for electrons and other subatomic constituents. Indeed, individual atoms would propagate and interfere in the same way.

Thus, we have to try to understand the quantum-level of reality as a scale that is governed by probabilities that interact as waves. The difficulty arises when the measurement is taken. A black silver grain on photographic film is not a probability. It is either black or white. Einstein was very uncomfortable with this concept and assumed that the probability and measurement problems represented a theory that was incomplete. He once asked in reference to the measurement problem, "Does the moon still exist if you do not look at it?"

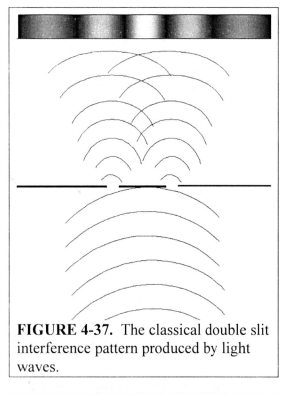

FIGURE 4-37. The classical double slit interference pattern produced by light waves.

FIGURE 4-38. Individual photons emitted through a double slit apparatus also shows a diffraction pattern. Above is a pattern at the 32-photon level. After millions of photons, the expected classical pattern appears on the photographic film.

Werner Heisenberg (1901-1976; Germany) considered the implications of the measurement problem and produced his Uncertainty Principle in 1927 (see Figure 4-39). In essence, the uncertainty principle states that the error (error in measurement) in defining an object has to be greater than h-bar, also known as the reduced Planck's Constant. Since that number is very small, uncertainty at the scale of the visible is far less than the error of our instruments to take measurements. However, for objects like electrons, whose size is in the realm of

Planck's Constant, the uncertainty is enormous. Thus, at the quantum scale, uncertainty is a law of nature.

Well, if the quantum world is so fraught with error and unreality, why is it such an important part of physics? The predictions of quantum physics and agreements between theory and observations are just too persuasive to be ignored. A very short list of the value of quantum mechanics would include: how chemicals react, how stars work, radioactivity and nuclear energy, the nature of minerals, and CAT scans.

$$\Delta x \times \Delta p > h/2\pi = \hbar$$

FIGURE 4-39. Werner Heisenberg's Uncertainty Principle. With this equation, he raised uncertainty in the physical worls to the level of a law. In words it states, the uncertainty in position times the uncertainty of momentum is greater than Planck's Constant divided by 2 pi, which equals h bar (also called the Reduced Planck's Constant).

If quantum strangeness underlies all reality that we experience, then why does Newtonian physics work so well at our scale? Where does the uncertainty of the quantum world disappear into the certainty of the visible scale? To deal with this problem, Bohr defined the Correspondence Principle which said that the differences between quantum calculations and classical calculations gradually disappears at an object approaches the realm of the visible. For example, the difference between the classical prediction and quantum prediction of the wavelength of light emitted when an electron drops from orbit 2 to orbit 1 in a hydrogen atom (diameter of the atom is 5.3×10^{-11} meters) is 67%. However, if the electron is excited to the 25,000[th] allowed orbit and drops to the 24,999[th] orbit (the diameter of this hydrogen atom is 3.3×10^{-2} meters), the difference between classical and quantum predictions is only 0.007%. Thus, the weirdness goes away at our scale where the difference between Planck's Constant and the object becomes greater and greater.

POLARIZERS REVISITED

One can understand the spirit and character of quantum electrodynamics without including this technical detail of polarization. But I am sure that you will all feel uncomfortable unless I say something about what I have been leaving out. -Richard Feynman

That brings us back to the polarizer problem of Figure 4-32. Later in high school and college I learned that light was a wave and the frequency (or wavelength) determined the color. Well, the wave property of light also explained the polarizing films and how they worked. The physics text described a polarizing film as a picket fence or parallel rows of molecules that excluded all light that did not wave or vibrate parallel to them. For example, in Figure 4-40, light wave A, a wave that vibrates side to side, will not pass through the polarizing film with the molecules or grating arranged up and down. On the other hand, light wave B will pass through. Thus, it is clear that when two polarizing films are arranged perpendicularly to each other, no light gets through. I discovered that the problem actually had a name in physics called the Three-Polarizer Paradox. It demonstrates the weird logic that operates at the level of the light wave or electron.

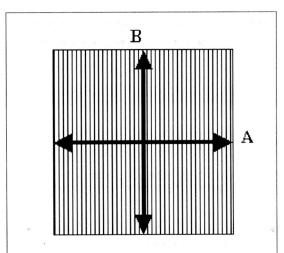

FIGURE 4-40. A polarizing film with light wave A and wave B. A is perpendicular to the orientation of the "picket fence" structure of the polarizer, so it does not get through. Wave A is parallel to them and does get through.

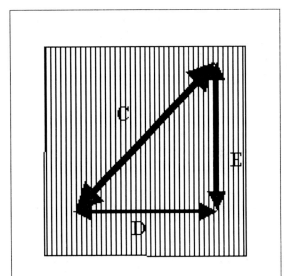

FIGURE 4-41. A polarizing film with light wave C. This can be constructed of vectors D and E. Because E is parallel to the polarizer, it gets through.

The problem is more complex when considering light waves that are orientated at some other angle to the polarizing film as in Figure 4-41. The classical explanation is that light wave C has component vectors D and E. With this orientation, E gets through the polarizing film. Does that answer the Three-Polarizer Paradox? Not really. Classical physics assumes that the polarized orientation of the light waves striking the polarizing film was determined. Thus, the vector necessary to go through the third film must have already been filtered out. Obviously, it was not.

Quantum theory has an explanation of the Three-Polarizer Paradox, though. Photon waves that strike the polarizing film have a certain probability of having the appropriate orientation and going through. That "decision" is made when they encounter the film. This is another example of the measurement problem that I discussed earlier. In a strict sense, the encounter with polarizing film is a measurement. The "decision" is made again when the photons encounter the middle film at an angle, which allows some to get through to encounter the last film.

Quantum physics is strange and operates by logic, which is foreign to the physics at our scale. Yet, it works and explains phenomena that defy explanation by classical means. However, both Einstein and Planck were disturbed by the implications of the theory that they helped to create. In reference to the probabilistic nature of the quantum theory Einstein lamented that he did not believe that God played dice with the universe. To which Bohr replied, "Albert, stop telling God what to do."   -2004

References:

Baggott, Jim. 1995. *The Meaning of Quantum Theory.* Oxford University Press. Oxford.

Casti, John L. 1989. *Paradigms Lost.* Avon Books. New York.

Chandrasekhar, B.S. 1998. *Why Things Are the Way They Are.* Cambridge University Press. Cambridge, UK.

Feynman, Richard P. 1985. *QED, The Strange Theory of Light and Matter.* Princeton University Press. Princeton, NJ.

Feynman, Richard P. 1995. *Six Easy Pieces.* Helix Books. Addison-Wesley Publishing Co. New York.

Feynman, Richard P. 1997. *Six Not-So-Easy Pieces.* Helix Books. Addison-Wesley Publishing Co. New York.

Halliday, David and Robert Resnick. 1970. *Fundamentals of Physics.* John Wiley and Sons, Inc. New York.

Hann, Judith. 1991. *How Science Works, 100 Ways Parents and Kids Can Share the Secrets of Science.* Reader's Digest Association, Inc. Pleasantville, New York.

Mason, Stephen F. 1962. *A History of the Sciences.* Collier Books, New York.

Schweber, S.S. 1994. *QED and the Men Who made It.* Princeton University Press, Princeton, NJ.

Trefil, James and Robert Hazen. 1995 & 1998. *The Sciences, An Intergrated Approach.* John Wiley & Sons, Inc. New York.

Questions to Think About

1. What is mysterious about the Three-Polarizer Paradox?

   Two lens can block all the light. If a 3rd is added, it makes no difference and some light can get through

2. What is a Blackbody Radiator?

   A blackbody radiator absorbs all external energy, including light energy, including light energy, making it appear black
   – Gustav Kirchoff

3. Why did Max Planck say that the formulation of his Radiation Formula was "an act of desperation" and "a high price to pay"?

   Energy would not come in quanta, laws of classical physics would be valid at all scales.

4. What was Einstein's contribution to Quantum Theory? What was the support for his theory? Light energy travels in localized bundles called photons where energy is defined by the Planck formula, –light had properties of a particle
   –Robert Millikan– Oil Drop Experiment

5. How did the model of the atom produced by Neils Bohr differ from the models of Thomson and Rutherford?

   • T&R Electron in an accelerating fell towards the nucleus.

   • Discrete orbits allowed, each with different energy levels.

6. What is the Particle-Wave Duality?

   Broglie – electrons, which clearly seemed particle-like, had properties as waves. Matter has wavelike properties.

7. What is the "Measurement Problem" at the quantum level?

   At the quantum level, there are certain errors in measurements that cannot be accounted for.

8. What is the meaning of the Heisenberg Uncertainty Principle?

   Uncertainty at the scale of the visible is very small. However, at the quantum level, it can be huge. Uncertainty is the law. As it approaches the realm of the visible, it gets smaller

9. Why did Einstein reject the theory that he helped to create?

   Took uncertainty as an error in measurements

   Does not feel God played dice with the universe

10. What is the quantum theory explanation for the Three-Polarizer Paradox? Why does classical theory fail to explain it?

    Photon waves that strike the polarizing film have a certain probability of having the appropriate orientation and going through. Decision is made again as encounters happen

SWORDS AND PLOWSHARES

IN THE PRESENCE OF MINE ENEMIES

Thou preparest a table before me in the presence of mine enemies. Psalms 23:4

Last summer I visited Andrei, a friend of mine in Kostroma, Russia. As always, when friends meet in Russia, whether there is time or not, we had tea. My companions and I had been traveling much of the day, and all of us enjoyed the chance to sit and hide for a time from the mid-day sun. We brought out kolbasa, candy, and cake to go with the tea. Most importantly, we talked, for tea in Russia is a medium for communication.

Andrei showed me some of the items that he had in the small museum in his office. Then, he showed me an abstract sculpture that he had made of old computer memory devices, a sculpture that he called the Evolution of Memory. I recognized most of the components, but in the middle there was a square dark brown piece that I had never seen before. I asked what it was, and Andrei grinned. He responded cryptically, "It is 2 megabytes from 1974…to target your cities." Slowly, it dawned on me that he was showing me a component of a nuclear missile's guidance device. He went on to say that he once worked on the computer components of nuclear missiles. I stood amazed to see that this same person who had shown me such extraordinary kindness many times over was once my enemy.

The subtle, pervasive terror that I experienced while growing up during the Cold War with its constant threat of nuclear annihilation swelled back upon me momentarily. Weakly, I snapped a photograph of the sculpture (Figure 4-42). Then, he laughed, poured me another cup of tea, and we began to make plans for the day.

The specter of radioactivity and its potential for destruction plays on the minds of all who were alive between 1950 and 1990. You can see it in literature and film from the second half of the 20th Century. Although tensions between the superpowers have abated somewhat, nuclear proliferation has seen to it that this world is only a little safer now.

FIGURE 4-42. The evolution of memory, a sculpture by Andrei Pinchikov. The missile guidance chip is indicated by the arrow.

Given its importance politically and technologically, it is hard to realize that the science and technology of nuclear radiation began only a little more than 100 years ago. In the early years, physicists probed the secrets of the atom and major discoveries were made with a series of elegant experiments. However, the whole area of nuclear physics began with the accidental exposure of photographic film in a drawer.

DECIPHERING THE NUCLEUS

(The feeling is one of catching) an elephant by its tail...without meaning to...and now I don't know what to do with it.   -Otto Frisch

Henri Becquerel (1852-1908, France) was studying the phosphorescence of a uranium salt in 1896 when he noticed that unexposed film kept near the uranium compound was exposed as a ghostly image. He tried it with whole series of uranium salts, all with the same results. He understood that the uranium must have been emitting something similar to x-rays that that had recently been discovered by Wilhelm Konrad von Roentgen (1845-1923, Germany). He assumed that the emissions, like x-rays, were able to penetrate the protective covering of the film and expose it. This demonstration of natural radioactivity excited the interest of a physics student named Marie Curie (1867-1934, Poland & France). She had married a shy physicist named Pierre Cuire (1859-1906, France) only one year earlier. Together they set out to understand Becquerel radiation and found that Thorium exhibited it too. From tons of pitchblende they isolated minute quantities of new radioactive elements that they called Polonium and Radium. Their work demonstrated that radiation, a term coined by the Curies, was a characteristic of the particular elements and not characteristic chemical reactions. Thus, radiation had something to do with the atoms of which the elements were constructed. Henri Becquerel, Marie Curie, and Pierre Curie were jointly awarded the Nobel Prize in physics for their work on radioactivity. Marie received numerous other awards including a second Nobel Prize in Chemistry for her work on radioactive elements.

The work of Becquerel and the Curies ushered in a golden age of atomic research. Much of that research occurred at the Cavendish Laboratory of Cambridge University, the research institute that James Clerk Maxwell designed and staffed before his death in 1879. His successor, J.J. Thomson (1856-1940, UK) discovered the electron and his successor, Ernest Rutherford (1871-1937, NZ, UK) gave us our first modern concept of the atom. In a series of brilliant experiments, Rutherford identified three kinds of nuclear radiation that he called alpha (α), beta (β), and gamma (γ). Alpha rays were made of particles that were large, positively charged, and quickly attenuated in air or by a piece of paper. Beta rays were made of negatively charged particles that he suspected were electrons from the nucleus. Beta particles had greater energy than alpha particles did and had greater range. They would pass through paper but could be stopped by metal foil. The third category of radiation, the gamma ray, was made of high-energy photons, like x-rays. Gamma rays could pass through most small obstacles and were stopped only by heavy metals like lead or by thick concrete. Rutherford used sources of alpha particles to probe the atom. With one such probe he determined that most of the mass of an atom resided in a very small positively charged nucleus. He reasoned that that the nucleus was made of positively charged protons, the number of which determined the elemental properties. He also assumed that if a nucleus emitted an alpha particle, it must have changed from one element to another one that was lighter. Conversely, if he could unite alpha particles with a naturally occurring nucleus, he could make a heavier element. In 1919 Rutherford bombarded nitrogen with alpha particles and generated oxygen with the release of free protons. This proved that elements could be changed or transmuted by adding or subtracting the complement of protons in the nucleus. James Chadwick (1891-1974, UK) studied under Rutherford and was able to change other light elements as a consequence of alpha particle bombardment.

Other experiments using the methods of alpha particle bombardment caused certain elements, especially Beryllium, to emit a penetrating type of radiation unlike alpha, beta or gamma. Substances such as graphite or paraffin stopped these new rays. More importantly, they ejected high-energy protons from target nuclei. Chadwick calculated that the new radiation must be made of particles nearly the same mass as protons, but neutrally charged. Rutherford had proposed the existence of such particles years earlier and said that they were made of electrons joined to certain protons in the nucleus and were the sources of beta particles. Chadwick called these new elementary particles neutrons. Armed with neutrons, Chadwick was able to transmute elements, especially the larger ones, more easily than with alpha particles, which were large, positively charged, and repelled by the strong electropositive force in the vicinity of all atomic nuclei. Neutrons, because they were neutrally charged, did not experience electropositive repulsion, and were more easily incorporated into the target nuclei. This was especially important for work with larger atoms like uranium.

The existence of the neutron solved some other problems, especially the problem of the isotope. Elements had been studied well enough to determine the presence of atoms with slightly different masses, but identical chemical properties. Consider carbon for example. Most carbon is stable, but slightly heavier isotopes exist. One is highly radioactive. We now interpret these as isotopes, all with 6 protons. Stable carbon, carbon-12 has 6 protons and 6 neutrons. Radioactive carbon, carbon-14, has 6 protons and 8 neutrons.

The alpha particle, because it was charged, could be accelerated in an electromagnetic field. The first such accelerator was made by John Cockroft (1897-1967, UK) and E. T. S. Walton (1903-1995, UK), also at the Cavendish. In 1932 they accelerated protons to such an extent that they were able to split atoms of Lithium (3 protons) into 2 atoms of Helium (2 protons each) plus the release of measurable amounts of energy. During the same year in the USA, a team of scientists headed by Ernest O. Lawrence (1901-1958), operated another type of accelerator called a cyclotron, which duplicated and confirmed the results of Cockroft and Walton. In addition, that cyclotron and other more powerful particle accelerators were able to generate very energetic electron beams that eventually produced the first transuranic (above uranium) elements and radioactive isotopes.

Frederic Joliot (1900-1958, France) and his wife (who also was the daughter of Marie and Pierre Curie), Irene Joliot-Curie (1897-1956, France) both of France were investigating the nature of the atom. They did some of the important experiments that led to the discovery of the neutron. However, they received the Nobel Prize for the first production and recognition of artificially induced radioactivity in 1934. The new isotopes of nitrogen, phosphorous, silicon, and aluminum were unstable and released both positive (positrons) and negative electrons during their decay.

Enrico Fermi (1901-1954, Italy & USA) began to consider the theoretical and experimental work first of electrons and then of the atomic nucleus itself. In 1934 he worked out the theory of Beta decay. He said that the neutron is not made of a proton combined with an electron as suggested by Rutherford, but instead the neutron changed to a proton with the release of an electron and a recently discovered, nearly massless neutrally charged particle called a neutrino. Also, he was stimulated by the artificial radioactivity reported by the Joliot-Curies. He began to bombard many different elements with neutrons and discovered that neutrons, slowed by passing them through paraffin or water, worked best to incorporate into the target nuclei. He concluded that nuclear transmutation happened in all nuclei, which combined with neutrons. After receiving the Nobel Prize for his work on neutrons in 1938, Fermi immigrated to the USA where he continued his work at Columbia University in New York City.

In the mean time, two Germans, Otto Hahn (1879-1968, Germany) and Fritz Strassmann (1902-1980, Germany) targeted uranium with slow neutrons and were startled to discover Barium isotopes among the reactant nuclei. Barium had about half the number of protons as uranium. That meant the uranium nucleus did not just chip, but actually broke in half. Hahn was very cautious, but soon his results were confirmed by Otto Frisch (1904-1979, Austria & UK), a colleague of Niels Bohr (1885-1962, Denmark) and Frisch's aunt and former colleague of Otto Hahn, Lise Meitner (1878-1968, Austria & Sweden). The community of physicists immediately understood the implications of the Hahn-Strassmann results. In particular the nucleus of uranium could be split to release immense amounts of energy.

Consider the fundamental conflicting forces acting on the nucleus. It is composed of a tight association of protons, all of which have positive charges. The electrostatic repulsion should cause all nuclei to fly apart, but they do not. Thus, there must be an even stronger gluing force with very short range that holds the protons together. In part, it is the release of such energy that Einstein's famous $E=mc^2$ refers to. Because the uranium atom split apart, many more of the potential gluing forces were broken and released as energy expressed in the electrostatic repulsion (about 200,000,000 volts) of the two fragments. Bohr and others calculated that such a fission of the nucleus would yield more than 20 million times the energy of an equivalent mass of TNT.

DEATH UNLIMITED
I am become death, the destroyer of worlds.   -The Rig-Veda

By the time of the Hahn-Strassman results, much of Europe was falling under the cloud of fascism with severe restrictions placed on Jews including their wholesale dismissals from academia in Germany, Austria, and Italy. Such actions led to the hemorrhage of academic talent from those countries to Britain and the US. Thus, almost overnight the US became preeminent in nuclear physics.

Fermi and his team repeated the Hahn-Strassmann experiment in 1940, but this time noticed that in the fission process, the products released more neutrons than were used. Thus, if enough of the fissionable material were available, the release of extra neutrons would trigger a chain reaction of nuclear fission. Such an idea had already occurred to a recent Jewish immigrant from Hungary named Leo Szilard (1898-1964, Hungary & USA) who, in 1934, took out a patent on nuclear fission, specifically the concept of a chain reaction that could yield energy or even a bomb.

Leo Szilard and other physicists, particularly those from the Fermi group wished to communicate to the US government the dangerous possibility of a nuclear weapon being produced by Nazi Germany. To that end, they approached Albert Einstein, who then was at the Princeton Institute for Advanced Study. After Einstein understood the implications of a chain reaction, he quickly grasped its possible consequences. Later, a letter drafted by the Fermi group was signed by Einstein and then sent to Franklin Delano Roosevelt. This was Einstein's only involvement in the production of an atomic weapon.

An immediate outcome of the letter was the creation of The Uranium Committee, to study the practical issues in procuring and purifying uranium ore as well as the possibility of using uranium in a nuclear weapon. In 1940 Fermi received a grant to search for moderators or ways to slow neutrons to achieve a chain reaction with uranium. This was the time at which he confirmed the Hahn-Strassmann experiment and attempted to achieve a limited chain reaction. Fermi discovered that only the Uranium-235 supported the neutron chain reaction. However, U-235 was a very rare isotope and the much more abundant U-238 simply absorbed the neutron without splitting, but slow or moderated neutrons were absorbed much more readily by U-235.

About the same time Edwin McMillan and Philip Abelson of UC Berkeley identified that U-238 changed to element 93 (called Neptunium). However, that was unstable and short-lived, but through an additional beta decay event produced element 94, Plutonium. This was more stable and did undergo fission upon the absorption of slow neutrons.

Work and money ramped up after the bombing of Pearl Harbor and the US entrance into World War II. Fermi became part of the team to investigate the use of Plutonium for a bomb. This group was centered at the University of Chicago, where Fermi proposed building a nuclear reactor which would put the concept of a sustained, controlled chain reaction to the test and at the same time provide a mechanism to produce or breed plutonium from U-238. On December 2, 1942 Fermi stood before the reactor made of uranium pellets surrounded by graphite blocks to serve as moderators. As the control rods were withdrawn, the Geiger counter began to rattle, and a controlled reaction was on its way.

Earlier in 1942 General Leslie Groves (1896-1970) who had overseen the construction of the Pentagon, was appointed to direct the construction of a nuclear weapon, a project code named The Manhattan Engineering Project. His immediate problems were where to build the plutonium breeder reactors, and how to isolate the fissionable U-235 from the more abundant U-238. Also, he had to assemble teams of scientists to pursue aspects of the problem and appoint a scientist who would coordinate the production of a working atomic bomb.

He chose Hanford, Washington as the site of the nuclear reactors for producing plutonium. The science and technology of isolating U-235 was much more complex. He considered the technology of several methods, but settled on two: the cyclotron and gaseous diffusion. Lawrence, who had built the first cyclotron, proposed separating the two isotopes by accelerating them in the ring of a cyclotron. The theory was that U-235, being smaller would form a tighter circle and ultimately allow for the separation of the isotopes. The gaseous diffusion method converted uranium to a gas and then allowed it to diffuse through miles of pipe. U-235, because it was slightly lighter, should arrive at the end a little earlier than U-238. Thus, by either method, U-235 would be collected one atom at a time. The focus of the uranium isolation was at Oak Ridge, Tennessee.

His more challenging decision was who to select as leader of the bomb team. He chose J. Robert Oppenheimer (1904-1967, USA), a physicist of unusual talents ranging from theoretical physics to poetry to language. He was supposed to have taught himself Sanskrit one summer just for fun. He was viewed as a "wunderkind" by the Germans with whom he had studied and earned a doctorate. One of Oppenheimer's early decisions was to bring all of the scientists together in a research facility to be based at Los Alamos, New Mexico rather than scattered across the country in academic labs.

The technical problems of creating an atomic weapon were legion. First, there was no room for mistakes. The fissionable material, once produced, was so rare that it could not be wasted. Thus, much of the work was done by taking some measurements and then producing appropriate mathematical models to understand them in the context of a bomb. One of the earliest issues to determine was the critical mass of the fissionable material necessary to produce a run-away chain reaction, which would lead to an explosion.

The critical mass is that amount of fissionable material that would be large enough to capture enough emitted neutrons to produce uncontrolled nuclear fission. For uranium that was calculated to be about 35lbs of pure U-235 shaped into a sphere. Such a mass was necessary to produce the explosion, however, it would spontaneously detonate; so, the solution seemed to be to bring two subcritical masses together at the time of detonation. The easiest way to do that was to create a kind of cannon with a subcritical U-235 bullet fired into a subcritical ring (Figure 4-43). The Los Alamos scientists were so confident of this design that it was not tested before it was dropped on Hiroshima.

FIGURE 4-43. This is the design of the Uranium-235 cannon bomb. A subcritical bullet (B) is fired into a subcritical ring (R) producing a spontaneous explosion.

Calculations indicated that Plutonium, because it was contaminated with a super-reactive isotope would explode before the subcritical masses came together. In such a case, a cannon-type plutonium bomb would be an expensive dud. Seth Neddermeyer (1908-1988; USA) came up with the idea that a hollow sphere of plutonium if surrounded by shaped explosive charges would implode or squeeze a subcritical mass into supercriticality. The idea, though brilliant as a solution, was technically very difficult. Finally, Neddermeyer sold the implosion concept and work began perfecting the explosives and detonators to make it happen. The solution was a mixture of fast and slow explosive charges surrounding a hollow sphere of plutonium (Figure 4-44). To insure that there would be enough ambient neutrons to begin the chain reaction at the right time, they designed a component out of beryllium and polonium that would send a spray of neutrons at the critical moment of implosion.

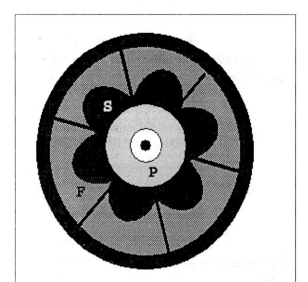

FIGURE 4-44. The design of the implosion bomb with its array of fast (F) and slow (S) shaped charges surrounding a hollow plutonium sphere with the beryllium-polonium initiator in the center.

There was much less confidence in the implosion design and much more available plutonium than uranium-235; so, the decision was made to test the implosion bomb at a site in the Alamogordo Desert. The test was carried out on July 16, 1945 at 5:30 A.M. The pessimistic expectations for this complex design were laid to rest as a flash of light filled the predawn sky and a fireball rose to the heavens followed by the now familiar mushroom cloud. The observers, awed by the sight, were surprised by the powerful shockwave that arrived 30 seconds later and then by a deafening roar. Estimates of the bomb's yield ranged between 15,000 and 20,000 tons of TNT, much higher than the expected range of 500 to 5,000 tons. Oppenheimer later said that as he watched the fireball rise, he thought of the ancient Hindu text, "I am become death, the destroyer of worlds."

By the time that the atomic weapons could be deployed, Germany had been defeated, and many of the scientists who had worked on the project questioned the need for the bombs. Nevertheless, the political decision was to use them until Japan surrendered unconditionally. The first to be deployed was the uranium-235 cannon-type bomb on August 6, 1945. This was slimmer than the implosion device, and, therefore, referred to as Little Boy. Aboard a B-29 named The Enola Gay the bomb was flown from the island base on Tinian to Hiroshima where it detonated at 8:16 AM, 19,000 feet above the city with a yield of 12,500 tons of TNT. Destruction was nearly total with very few structures left standing. The human toll was astounding and included 140,000 casualties as the immediate result of the explosion with another 60,000 from wounds or radiation exposure by the end of 1945. In all, more than 54% of all of Hiroshima's people had died as a direct consequence of a single bomb.

Three days later another B-29 named Bockscar carried a Fat Man implosion bomb to Nagasaki on August 9. As the bomber approached its target, the city was completely clouded over. Low on fuel, they had to decide whether to find the target by radar or abort and dump Fat Man into the sea. Suddenly, a small break opened in the clouds and Fat Man slid into it at 11:02AM and detonated 1,650 feet above the ground. The yield of the more effective implosion design generated a destructive force of 22,000 tons of TNT. The loss of life was comparable to that of Hiroshima, and one week later Japan surrendered unconditionally.

As the news of success spread through the physics community, reaction was mixed. Some were elated; others were appalled. Leo Szilard, the man who had the patent on the atomic bomb, was one of the strongest voices against its future use and advocated that nuclear weapons technology be surrendered to a world government. Einstein and Bohr warned of an arms race that would be economically debilitating and threaten the end of civilization.

Others like Edward Teller (1908-, Hungary & USA) advocated the continued development of nuclear weapons. He proposed, even before the atomic bomb had been created, that a fission bomb would produce enough heat and pressure to force heavy isotopes of hydrogen to fuse and release energy by the same mechanism that drives the sun. The advantage was that the resulting explosion would be limited only by the amount of fusionable material. Teller referred to it as the Super.

Driven by the test of a Soviet fission bomb in 1949, the US began work on thermonuclear fusion bomb technology. The first fusion bomb was detonated in a test on Eniwetok atoll in the Marshall Islands and yielded a destructive force in excess of 10 million tons of TNT. The race was on.

COLORS AND FLAVORS

Those of us who helped put together the standard model are naturally rather proud of it, since it brought a good deal of simplicity out of a bewildering variety of phenomena.   -Murray Gell-Mann

The focus of nuclear weapons research during World War II was more than a distraction for physicists. Enrico Fermi pointed out that the research also was good physics. It provided methods and instruments that allowed for a deeper understanding of the material universe. Prior to World War II the nucleus was made of protons and neutrons. Then, in the 1950's using high-energy accelerators and cyclotrons, the atoms of nuclei were bombarded to reveal a chaotic assemblage of smaller particles and their antiparticles that eventually numbered about 100. What did it mean? They seemed to form families in arrangements that suggested that protons and neutrons were composed of more fundamental particles, that Murray Gell-Mann (1929- , USA), who worked with Fermi at Chicago, called quarks in 1963. Independently, George Zweig (1937- , Russia & USA) came up with the same theory based on his work at CERN, the European nuclear research center.

Quark theory says that each particle like the proton or neutron is made of three smaller elementary particles of two types (Gell-Mann called them flavors) with regard to charge: the up quark with a charge of +2/3 and the down quark with a charge of –1/3. Thus the formula for a neutron is 1 up and two down (+2/3 –1/3 –1/3 = 0 net charge); and that of a proton is 2 up and 1 down (+2/3 +2/3 – 1/3 = +1 net charge). They are held together by a strong force, which has the unusual property of having a stronger hold as the quarks move apart, almost as though a spring were holding the quarks together. Gell-Mann noted that quarks in triplets are confined and inseparable. He used the metaphor of primary colors to communicate the quark relationships as they are confined within a proton or neutron. He said that each of the three quarks could be likened to a primary color such that a proton is a "white particle" composed of a red, blue, and green quark (Figure 4-45). Also, flavor was independent of color. The seeming complexity seemed unlikely and untestable since they could not be seen alone. However, experimental evidence suggested that they were real. For example, electrons fired at a neutron scattered as though there were three subparticles with partial charges.

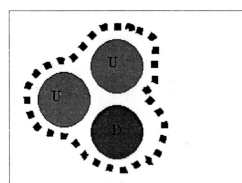

FIGURE 4-45. A proton, a white particle, with its three colored quarks that are confined within the color force barrier. The flavors (U & D) are independent of the colors.

Theoretical physicists had assumed that the behavior of quarks and the strong force that held them together was symmetrical and related to the electromagnetic force in its form. George Zweig's thesis advisor, Richard Feynman (1918-1988, USA) earned his PhD in physics in 1942 and went to work on the Manhattan Project where he was made head of the computing division (at that time, computers were people). After the war he went to Cornell where with another Los Alamos alumnus Hans Bethe (1906-, Germany & USA) he worked on quantum electrodynamics, the interactions between electromagnetic force and particles like electrons. Feynman created a pictorial means of depicting electromagnetic interactions called Feynman Diagrams.

Consider a simple interaction (Figure 4-46), the electromagnetic force transmitted from one electron to another by a photon. In this case, the photon is virtual and communicates the electromagnetic force from one electron to another. Any particle that communicates force is called a gauge

particle, and the photon is the gauge particle for all electromagnetic interactions.

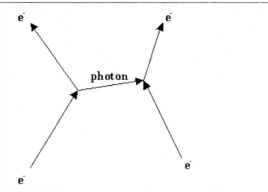

FIGURE 4-46. A Feynman Diagram that illustrates a simple interaction between electrons with the electromagnetic force transmitted by a virtual photon.

The gauge particle for quarks and the interaction called the strong force is called the gluon, which transmits the color force that holds the quarks in confinement. As quarks exchange gluons, they change color, but the full complement remains constant. Protons and neutrons always remain white particles. Consider Figure 4-47 (top), which shows the quarks of a neutron. They change color as they exchange gluons, but up quarks remain up quarks no matter their color. That is illustrated on a Feynman Diagram (Figure 4-47, bottom).

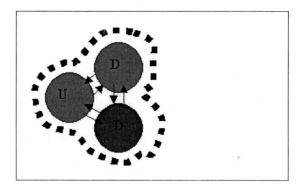

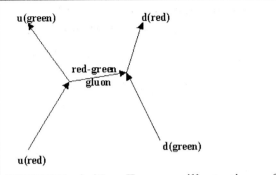

FIGURE 4-47. Top: an illustration of colored quarks confined within a neutron as they exchange gluons. Bottom: a Feynman diagram of a gluon-mediated exchange of the strong force.

The theory of quarks is not adequate to explain what happens during beta decay in which a neutron spontaneously changes to a proton and generates an electron and a neutrino, a reaction necessary for the creation of plutonium from U-238. This is a consequence of another force that acts within the nucleus called the weak force. This force is a kind of bridge between the electromagnetic force and the strong force and acts on particles characteristic of each of them.

The weak force, however, is more complex in that it has three possible gauge particles called bosons that can transmit positive, negative, or zero charge (W^+, W^-, and Z^0, respectively). Weak force bosons are very large particles with short range, less than the diameter of a nucleus. When a W^+ boson or W^- boson interacts with a quark, it can change the flavor of that quark. That is, if a down quark (-1/3) releases a W^- boson, it transforms into an up quark (+2/3). The upshot is that a neutron changes to a proton. It can pass that charge to a neutrino that converts to an electron (as in Figure 4-48 top), or the gauge particle can decay into a neutrino and electron (Figure 4-48 bottom).

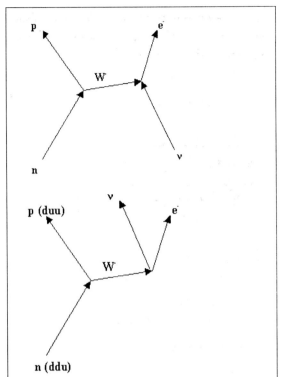

FIGURE 4-48. Two types of Weak interactions. Top: a neutron changes to a proton as it releases a W^- boson that gives its negative charge to an electron neutrino converting it to an electron. The bottom illustration shows more precisely a down quark releasing a W^- boson that decays into an electron and an electron neutrino.

High-energy collisions in cyclotrons and other types of accelerators revealed more massive flavors of quarks and their related electrons and neutrinos (collectively called leptons). The most massive quark, called the top quark has only recently been observed, though from the standpoint of symmetry, physicists knew that it had to exist. Thus, the strong force, the weak force, and the electromagnetic force are similar and symmetrical with one another. This is the outline of what has become the Standard Model that was developed in the 1970's (see Table 4-2). The fourth fundamental force, gravity, still eludes description in the way of the other three. If symmetry prevails, then the gravitational force would be carried by gauge particles (called gravitons) with unlimited range (like photons) and exchanged between matter particles (leptons and quarks).

SWORDS INTO PLOWSHARES

They shall beat their swords into plowshares, and their spears into pruninghooks; nation shall not lift up sword against nation, neither shall they learn war any more. -Isaiah 2:4

Certainly the triumph of particle physics was the Standard Model, which was developed by those who were trained in war. It reached the present form in the 1970's and has been confirmed numerous times. That was the direction of pure science. Particle physicists wanted to know how the material world was constructed in a fundamental way.

TABLE 4-2. A table of elementary particles as given by the Standard Model. Quarks and Leptons make up the particles of matter. More massive particle families are in columns II and III. The mass (given as energy in electron volts calculated from $E=mc^2$) and charge are given for each of the leptons and quarks. The full standard model would have the quarks and leptons reflected by their anti-particles. Thus, there are 24 matter particles and 4 force carriers. The force carriers also list the mass and range of the particle. The strength of each of the forces relative to the Strong Force also is given. If gravity were united with this model, the force carriers would include gravitons with 0 mass, infinite range, and a relative strength of 6×10^{-39}.

Quarks	u (up) ~5MeV +2/3	c (charm) ~1.5GeV +2/3	t (top) ~178GeV +2/3	γ (photon) mass = 0 infinite range strength =1/137	**Force Carriers**
	d (down) ~10MeV -1/3	s (strange) ~100MeV -1/3	b (bottom) ~4.7GeV -1/3	g (gluon) mass > 0.1 GeV range = 10^{-15} strength = 1	
Leptons	ν_e (electron neutrino) <50eV 0	ν_μ (muon neutrino) <0.5MeV 0	ν_τ (tau neutrino) <70MeV 0	Z (Z boson) mass =91.1GeV range = 10^{-17} strength = 10^{-5}	
	e (electron) 0.511MeV -1	μ (muon) 105.6MeV -1	τ (tau) 1.784GeV -1	W (W boson) 80.4GeV range = 10^{-17} strength = 10^{-5}	
	I	II	III		

The technology of the atom moved along, too. Not only were very small thermonuclear warheads that could be carried by missiles developed, but also methods for the peaceful use of atoms were proposed. Project Plowshare was

developed to see how nuclear devices could be used for large-scale excavations. Fortunately, that idea was shelved.

The most obvious peaceful use of the atom has been in the generation of electrical power by reactors that are not much more sophisticated than Fermi's first one under the squash court at the University of Chicago. Some countries like France and Russia generate the lion's share of their electrical output by nuclear means. I remember the promise of nuclear energy here. The politicians said that with nuclear power electricity would be so cheap that it would not be metered. That did not happen. Rising costs of materials and public disillusionment made nuclear energy in the US a political hot potato, especially in the wake of the near disaster at Three Mile Island and the catastrophe at Chernobyl.

I grew up during a time when atomic war seemed immanent. I remember air raid drills, bomb shelters, and civil defense caches of food and water. Those actions spoke more of the naïveté of politicians who allowed their belief systems to overshadow the messages from science. Fortunately, no power was willing to try a nuclear strike. In fact, the paradox was that the fear of mutual destruction prevented another world war even though tensions ran very high during the time of the Cold War.

Wasn't the cause of all that terror what science had wrought? Indeed, given the chance to relive the Manhattan Project era, most of the physicists would have done it all over again. They were like kids in a candy shop with unlimited resources. More frightening to me, though, was that those who made the decision to use the weapon did not understand it. Ignorance never is a source of security, but it is a source of unreasoned certainty. We are made safer in a democracy only if the public at large seeks to understand the complexity of the issues, some of which are uncovered by science.

The prediction of Isaiah has not come to pass. The sword of nuclear energy stands side by side with the plowshare, and it has given us new ways of learning war. I think of that as I contemplate Andrei's smile. He was a former enemy, and now a fast friend. The threat of mutual destruction is not the enduring solution to the success of humankind, but understanding is. Through acquaintance and understanding Andrei, along with many other former soviets, and I have gained deep mutual respect. Similarly, the deep understanding of the material universe that science provides will be a source of solutions to energy generation and the fundamental causes of human suffering that make wars inevitable.

-December 2004

References:

Blow, Michael. 1968. *The History of the Atomic Bomb.* American Heritage Publishing Co., Harper & Row. New York.

Curie, Eve. 1939. *Madame Curie.* Translated by Vincent Sheehan. Doubleday, Doran & Co., Inc. New York.

Curie, Pierre. 1903. *Radioactive Substances.* Nobel Prize in Physics Address. IN: Ferris, Timothy, ed. 1991. *The World Treasury of Physics, Astronomy, and Mathematics.* Little, Brown, & Co. Boston.

Einstein, Albert. 1946. *Out of My Later Years.* Carol Publishing Group.

Fermi, Laura. 1954. *Atoms in the Family, My Life with Enrico Fermi.* The University of Chicago Press. Chicago.

Ferris, Timothy. 1988. *Coming of Age in the Milky Way.* Anchor Books, Doubleday. New York.

Gell-Mann, Murray. 1994. *The Quark and the Jaguar.* W.H. Freeman & Co. New York.

Gribben, John. 2002. *The Scientists, A History of Science told through the Lives of its Greatest Inventors.* Random House. New York.

Hahn, Otto and Fritz Strassmann. 1939. *Proof of the Formation of Active Isotopes of Barium from Uranium and Thorium Irradiated with Neutrons; Proof of the Existence of More Active Fragments Produced by Uranium Fission.* Die Naturwissenschaften 27(6):89-95. Translation in 1989 Journal of Chemical Education May: 363-369.

McKay, Alwyn. 1984. *The Making of the Atomic Age.* Oxford University Press. Oxford.

Peake, Barrie. 1989. *The Discovery of the Electron, Proton, and Neutron.* Journal of Chemical Education. 66(9): 738.

Plokinghorne, John. 1981. *The Particle Play.* W.H. Freeman & Co. Oxford.

Rhodes, Richard. 1986. *The Making of the Atomic Bomb.* A Touchstone Book, Simon & Schuster, Inc. New York.

Rhodes, Richard. 1995. *Dark Sun, The Making of the Hydrogen Bomb.* A Touchstone Book, Simon & Schuster, Inc. New York.

Trefil, James. 1973. *From Atoms to Quarks.* Charles Scribner's Sons. New York.

Questions to Think About

1. Who first detected and explained what nuclear radiation was? What were the contributions of Pierre and Marie Curie?

   Henri Becquerel
   - Radiation was a result of elements - looked for along

2. What were the elegant experiments that detected the presence and types of nuclear radiation? *Alpha - +, attenuated in air*

   Gold Foil   Beta - neg stopped by foil
   Gamma - stopped by lead

3. How was the new knowledge of nuclear radiation used to probe the nature of the atom? *- mass in nucleus*
   - # of protons determine properties

4. What was the Hahn-Strassman experiment? What were its implications?

   - hit uranium w/ slow neutrons   - split nucleus = lots of energy
   - uranium broke in 1/2,

241

5. What is the evidence for the gluing force within the atomic nucleus? Why must it be stronger than the electromagnetic force?

electrostatic repulsion should cause protons to fly apart, - stronger strong force w/ short range

6. How did Enrico Fermi first demonstrate the concept of a chain reaction?

products released more neutrons they received

7. What was the Manhattan Project? What was the initial compelling impetus to produce a fission bomb? What two types of bombs were produced? Which type was used on Hirosima? On Nagasaki? What were the responses of some of the scientists?

flooded by Ger, bund rules for us, -build one before others
Fatman - Implosion - Nag
Littleboy - Canon - Hiroshima
mixed

8. Was the Manhattan Project science, technology, or both?

Both

9. What is the evidence for the existence of quarks?

-nuclear ctirons were bombarded
- Chaotic assemblage of smaller particles
Murray Gell-Mann

10. What is the Standard Model? How do quarks and other fundamental particles fit within it?

11. Be able to distinguish between leptons, quarks, and force carriers.

ONE STONE

A BIG STONE

Only two things are infinite, the universe and human stupidity, and I'm not sure about the former. -Albert Einstein

Not long after I got my driver's license in Oklahoma, some friends and I decided to go camping at a place about 80 miles to the east of Tulsa on the Illinois River. The weeklong trip was a series of adventures that now make interesting telling (but I would not want to relive most of them). Anyway, we were camped on a gravel bar in the river (realize that this "river" was about the size of Penns Creek in central Pennsylvania) when a thunderstorm began. We retreated to the shelter of a large overhang of rock on the side of a nearby mountain. We watched the rain pour over the rock shelf and felt the wonderful cool, damp air as we sat safe from the rain, wind and lightening. Near us was a large box-shaped block of stone that had fallen from the ceiling of the rock ledge many years ago. Anyway, there were four of us and a large stone on a mountainside. I don't know who of us first had the idea to roll it off the side of the mountain, but soon we were obsessed with seeing what kind of wonderful splash this rock might make when it hit the water. The stone was very large and even four obsessed teenage boys would not have been able to move it except that it sat at a precarious angle on the edge of the cliff. Still, after much struggle, the stone finally moved, slowly and then lurched over the side. It flew down the mountain taking saplings and smaller stones with it. Just as it approached the water, it took to the air and hit the center of a calm backwater. The large stone made a memorable splash with waves pouring up over the shore. The waves finally calmed to a complex of ripples. Finally, the water was calm again with the changing patterns of raindrops.

The owner of the camp heard the sound through the storm and recognized that a large rock had come loose from the mountain. He found us and gave us a tongue-lashing. Even after that, we had grander plans for larger stones, but fortunately we became sidetracked. This was not my first "experiment with gravity", but it was one of my most memorable.

EDDINGTON AND EINSTEIN

Relativity teaches us the connection between the different descriptions of one and the same reality. -Albert Einstein

Concerning gravity, Albert Einstein[2] (1879-1955) made a much greater splash when in 1919 the physicist, Arthur Eddington (1882-1944), led an expedition to an island in the south Atlantic off the coast of Africa. There he and his team made measurements of stars around the disk of the sun during a total solar eclipse. The results of his observations were astonishing. Stars very close to the sun were not where they were supposed to be. Their positions had moved as though the light propagating from them had bent. That is, the sun behaved almost like a lens.

Remarkably, Eddington's measurements agreed with values that were predicted by the General Theory of Relativity, a new theory of gravity that had been proposed by Albert Einstein only a year earlier. The results of Eddington and the confirmation of the General Theory of

---

[2] You can find more information about Albert Einstein in *Evidence and Einstein's Brain*.

243

Relativity propelled Einstein into the public eye almost over night.

Why? Was the reading public so familiar with the General Theory that it just had to know? That is unlikely. Years later, after he wrote a book about relativity, a reporter asked Eddington if he was one of the three people who understood the theory. Eddington paused until the reporter explained that he was just joking. Eddington responded that he paused because he couldn't think of the third person.

Einstein became a celebrity because relativity was and is counterintuitive. In addition, the astronomical observations of Eddington were risky tests of Einstein's counterintuitive theory. That Einstein was able to discover a physical law that was so much against everyday experience meant that Einstein must be a genius.

YOUNG ALBERT
The only thing that interferes with my learning is my education.-*Albert Einstein*

Einstein's schooling was in the late 19th century German system. Although he was quiet and uncomplaining as a child, young Albert chafed under the rigid system and identified it later in his life as the time in which he developed a suspicion of authority, particularly authority in education.

His family moved from Germany to Milan. Finally, Albert went to Zurich to study. He was very young (16) when he took his entrance exams in 1895, and he failed to score high enough marks to be admitted to the Swiss Federal Polytechnic School. He did manage to be admitted to a school in Aarau. There, he seemed to open up a little and enjoy his education. The next year, he again applied to the Polytechnic School and was admitted at last. His early years there were happy

enough. He enjoyed mathematics and physics. However, later in his education he began to question the authorities in physics.

He received his doctorate in 1905. In that same year he published three very important papers. One paper explained Brownian movement as proof for the existence of molecules, another explained the photoelectric effect and was significant in the development of quantum physics. The third set the background for the Special Theory of Relativity, a new way of looking at light and other electromagnetic phenomena. Through the 19th century a deep understanding of electromagnetism began to develop. Michael Faraday (1791-1867) described light as a combination of electrical and magnetic phenomena that propagate through a field or lines of force, the strength of which decrease according to the inverse square of the distance. James Clerk Maxwell (1831-1879) took Faraday's mechanical views and set down a set of equations that define the phenomena of electromagnetism, as well as atoms, the fundamental nature of matter. Similar strides had been made in mechanics and thermodynamics so that near the end of the 19th century, some physicists thought that they could see the end of physics.

Later in life, Einstein claimed that he came to the principle of relativity when he was 16, the year he began to study at Aarau because he failed to gain entrance to the Swiss Federal Polytechnic School. He was on a walk one day and asked himself the question, "What would the world look like if I traveled on a beam of light?" In this thought experiment Einstein understood that a Newtonian universe of absolute space would allow him to travel at the speed of light and the light itself would appear to stand still. However, Einstein was bothered by the Newtonian Universe in that it required an absolute state of rest, and the motions of all objects could be measured against that absolute state of rest. As natural as that might seem, it ultimately meant that the laws of physics must be different for those in motion relative to those at rest. Einstein could not accept this paradox and embraced a principle of relativity.

As defined by Galileo[3] (1564-1642), being at rest is the same as being in constant (no acceleration) motion. Therefore, the laws of physics do not change from one frame of motion to the next. Maxwell's equations of electromagnetism also predicted that the speed of light was constant, regardless of the frame of reference. Thus, electromagnetic theory proposed that light could never appear to be at rest for any observer. Put another way, no observer (or any other object of mass) could travel at the speed of light. Einstein adopted the constancy of the laws of physics and the constancy of the speed of light (see Figure 4-49) as the two postulates on which he based relativity. Einstein realized that if these postulates were accepted, then ideas of the constancy of space and time must change. He recognized that the logical consequences of relativity were:
1. Time slows for objects as they go faster.
2. Distance contracts in the direction of motion.
3. Mass increases for objects in motion.
This was Einstein's theory of uniform motion, and it was called the Special Theory of Relativity.

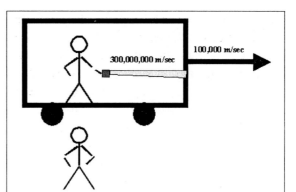

FIGURE 4-49. An illustration of Einstein's second postulate, that the speed of light is constant for all observers in all frames of reference. That is, the speed of light is not additive. The train is speeding along at 100,000 m/sec. However, both the rider and outside observer measure the velocity of light from the flashlight at 300,000,000m/sec.

By the time he received his doctorate, Einstein had angered most of his professors to the extent that they would not give him good letters of recommendation. They viewed his bothersome questions as irritating, particularly because by raising the questions, Einstein challenged their authority in physics. Thus, he could not find a teaching position and became a patent clerk in Switzerland.

NEWTON'S LAWS
Watch the stars, and from them learn.
To the Master's honor all must turn,
Each in its track, without a sound,
Forever tracing Newton's ground.
                                    -Albert Einstein

Isaac Newton (1642-1727) had formulated a Universal Law of Gravitation[4] (see Figure 4-50). In his law, the force of

---

[3] Discover more about Galileo in *A Man with a Telescope* and *Principia Mathematica: The Foundation of Modern Physics.*

[4] Find more information about this and Newton's Laws of Motion in *Principia Mathematica: the Foundation of Modern Physics* and *A Trinity: Invention, Science and Dreams in the Development of Rocket Technology..*

gravity was related to the masses of objects and their distance. Like light, gravity obeyed the inverse square law. That is, both light and gravity decrease according to the square of the distance between the centers of the two masses. For example if the large mass (M) is the sun and the smaller mass (m) is the earth, the force of attraction at 2 times the earth orbit (2r) would be $1/4^{th}$ that of 1 earth orbit. (Similarly, at twice the orbital distance, the earth would receive $1/4^{th}$ the light from the sun). G, the Universal Gravitational constant, is the same for any two bodies of mass (Its value is very small, but significant. $G=6.67 \times 10^{-11} N\text{-}m^2/kg^2$.)

With his law of gravitation, Newton could predict the orbits of planets and estimate the mass of the moon (among other things). The Law of Gravity also serves to explain the orbit of The International Space station and the trajectories of interplanetary vehicles. So, what's wrong with it? Why did Einstein formulate something different?

Although Newton's Law of Gravity was powerful in that it could describe and predict the forces involved, it could not describe the phenomenon itself. It did not answer the question, "What is gravity?" Indeed, Newton's law had one serious flaw in that it required action-at-a-distance. That is, it implied that gravity acted on objects without their actually coming into contact. Einstein attempted to solve that problem and to save a modified mechanical universe by the formulation of the General Theory of Relativity, a theory about gravity. The General Theory grew from Einstein's insight that the force of gravity and acceleration are equivalent. In fact, he called this The Principle of Equivalence.

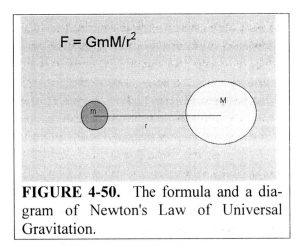

$$F = GmM/r^2$$

FIGURE 4-50. The formula and a diagram of Newton's Law of Universal Gravitation.

He illustrated the Principle of Equivalence by the following thought experiment. Suppose that an observer were in an enclosed room. If that room were accelerating at 9.8m/sec/sec, the observer would not be able to tell the difference between being on earth and accelerating through space. Such "artificial" gravity would be as real to the observer as the familiar tug of the earth's gravitational field.

WAVES IN SPACETIME

My intellectual development was retarded, as a result of which I began to wonder about space and time only when I had already grown up.

-Albert Einstein

Einstein said that mass distorts the three dimensions of space and the fourth dimension that we call time. Together, he called this spacetime. Since objects of mass are just highly concentrated bodies of energy (that is the meaning of $E=mc^2$), massive bodies distort spacetime. They create waves or curves in spacetime, just as my large stone created waves in the Illinois River.

Thus, Eddington's observations can be interpreted in this way. Particles of light that propagated from stars move through spacetime. As they encounter space that is curved by massive objects like the sun, the light path also curves. The orbital motion of the earth around the sun can be explained in a similar way. The gravity well created by the sun encounters the smaller well created by the earth. The orbital motion of the earth is an interaction of the two spacetime curves. The orbit of Mercury (much closer and more influenced by the gravity well of the sun) can only be understood and predicted by the General Theory of Relativity.

An interesting consequence of the General Theory is the possibility of stars with sufficient mass to collapse in on themselves becoming so massive that light cannot escape from them. (Today, we refer to such objects as black holes[5]. Einstein was reluctant to accept the existence of black holes.) Another (and I believe more important) consequence of the General Theory is that because all bodies of mass are mutually attractive, the universe could not be static. Either massive bodies are flying apart or flying together. Einstein considered this and introduced a cosmological constant to balance the tendency of the universe to collapse in on itself.

Shortly after the first publication of the General Theory, Edwin Hubble's (1889-1953) observations of the heavens showed that light from distant galaxies was shifted toward the red end of the spectrum. That is it was less energetic than it should have been. It was as though the waves of the normal light that emanated from distant objects had been stretched out.

Because the speed of light is constant, objects that move away from us at nearly the speed of light will tend to stretch out the vibrations or frequencies of light, making the light appear to be more and

more red. This change in frequency relative to speed is called the Doppler Effect. It occurs in sound as well as light and can be detected as a drop in frequency as a car or ambulance moves past. The drop in frequency or pitch is related to the speed of the vehicle (see Figures 4-51 and 4-52).

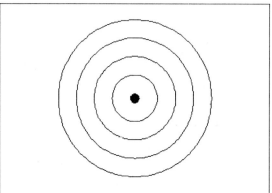

FIGURE 4-51. Sound or light waves propagating from a stationary source.

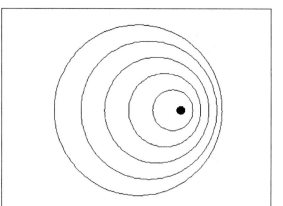

FIGURE 4-52. Shorter wavelengths pile up ahead of a moving object while longer wavelengths stretch out behind. The degree of distortion is related to the speed of the object. This doppler effect can occur in light as well as in sound.

However, the implications of his observations were even more astounding. Everywhere he looked Hubble saw that galaxies were moving away. Also, the farther the galaxy, the greater its red shift. Because light has a finite speed, the more

---

[5] See *Stars and the Beauty of Science* for more about black holes.

distant galaxies were more distant from us in time as well. Thus, he realized that not only is the universe expanding, but its expansion was slowing down. The red shift remains the most compelling confirmation to date that the universe is expanding. When Einstein looked back over his career, he claimed that the Cosmological Constant was his greatest mistake.

QUEST FOR THE T.O.E.

...not only to see how nature is and see how her transactions are carried through, but also to reach as far as possible the utopian and seemingly arrogant aim of knowing why nature is thus and not otherwise.   -Albert Einstein

Stephen Hawking[6] (1942-) and others have taken the expanding universe and considered what it must be expanding from. That is, if objects in the cosmos are going farther apart, then there must have been a time in the past when they were closer together. In fact, the theory suggests that there was a time (or I should say a time before time) when all of the cosmos was a singularity (like a giant black hole). The universe began to expand in a big bang when spacetime and the laws of physics appeared.

Will the expanding universe continue to expand or will it begin to slow down? Is there enough matter in the universe for the mutual gravitational attraction to cause the universe to deflate and ultimately to return to a singularity in a big crunch? These and other questions are now being explored by cosmologists with the goal of finding a fundamental TOE (Theory of Everything) or Unified Field

Theory in which all of the fundamental forces could be unified by the same set of equations.

More than 60 years earlier, after a period of wandering following his self-imposed exile from Germany after the Nazi's took over (because he was a pacifist and a Jew, the feeling was mutual), Einstein came to Princeton's Institute for Advanced Studies. There, he spent most of his time in search of a theory that united gravity with the forces of electromagnetism and other short-range forces that occur within the atom. This was viewed as an almost hopeless task by many physicists of the day because, in part, Einstein did not believe in the ultimate precepts of quantum physics, the physics of the very small, atom-level interactions. His main problem with quantum physics was that it was based on probabilities and seemed to require an almost mystical action-at-a-distance. Einstein worked on the problem of uniting the fundamental forces in almost professional isolation until his death in 1955.

Now, again physicists like Hawking are in search of a unified theory. Hawking is confident that a unified theory is very near. Whatever form the TOE takes, it must be consistent with the General Theory of Relativity. An interesting development from the search for a TOE has been the explanation of why matter even began to come together into stars and galaxies. Particularly, if the big bang occurred as an even expansion, how did matter accrete? Now, it appears that galaxies form larger structures in the cosmos as almost wave-like patterns. Mathematical descriptions of this require a return of a cosmological constant. Maybe Einstein didn't blunder so badly after all.

Like a great stone landing on the calm waters of science, Einstein's view of the universe shattered the 19th century con-

---

[6] Stephen Hawking, one of the finest minds in cosmology, holds the Lucasian chair of Mathematics at Cambridge. This is the same position that was held by Isaac Newton.

cept of fixed time and space. Even now waves from the General Theory of Relativity continue to stir up the water of physics as it struggles to find a theory of everything. It is perhaps appropriate that he was named ein stein, a German phrase that literally means *one stone.*

-1997, revised 2004

References:

Clark, R.W. 1971. *Einstein, The Life and Times.* The World Publishing Co. New York.

Einstein, A. 1961. *Relativity, the Special and the General Theory.* Crown Publishers, Inc. New York.

Ferris, T. 1997. *The Whole Shebang, A State-Of-The-Universe(s) Report.* Simon and Schuster. New York.

Feynman, R.P. 1997. *Six Not-So-Easy Pieces, Einstein's Relativity, Symmetry, and Space-Time.* 3rd edition. Addison-Wesley Publishing Co., Inc. New York.

Frank, Philipp. 1953. *Einstein, His Life and Times.* Alfred Knopf. New York.

Hawking, S.W. 1988. *A Brief History of Time.* Bantam Books. New York.

Hawking, S.W. and R. Penrose. 1996. *The Nature of Space and Time.* Princeton University Press. Princeton, NJ.

Horgan, J. 1996. *The End of Science.* Broadway Books. New York.

Peebles, P.J.E. 1993. *Principles of Physical Cosmology.* Princeton University Press. Princeton, NJ.

Ridley, B.K. 1994. *Time, Space and Things.* 3rd edition. Cambridge University Press. New York.

Smoot, George and Keay Davidson. 1993. *Wrinkles in Time* .Little, Brown, & Co. London.

Thorne, K.S. 1994. *Black Holes and Time Warps, Einstein's Outrageous Legacy.* W.W. Norton & Co. New York.

Zee, A. 1989. *An Old Man's Toy, Gravity at Work and Play in Einstein's Universe.* Macmillan Publishing Co. New York.

Questions to Think About

1. What observation catapulted Albert Einstein to international fame?

2. Who first proposed the concept of relativity?

3. What are the two postulates of relativity and what are their logical consequences?

4. What are the differences between the Special Theory and the General Theory of Relativity?

5. What is the Principle of Equivalence?

6. What is meant by spacetime?

7. How does the Doppler Effect confirm the Theory of Relativity?

8. What are the implications of Edwin Hubble's observations?

9. How did Einstein eliminate the problem of action at a distance from the theory about gravity?

10. What is the goal of a T.O.E.?

THE PLANETS

HOLST

And this shall be for music when no one else is near.   -Robert Louis Stevenson

For the past few weeks I have been immersed in spackle, paint, and varnish at home. The old horsehair plaster and 150-year-old molding needed another makeover. The particular cracks and holes made by my children had lost their charm, the uniform use of antique white had made the leap from utilitarian to depressing. Thus, I found myself late one evening with lavender paint in my hair and spackle dust in my beard with only the radio for company. Finally, even the radio with its frenetic DJ's or the drone of presidential debates had become depressing, too. I turned on the stereo and set the CD player at any selection. As I walked back into my purgatory of paint fumes, I heard the slow, deep opening to Mars, the Bringer of War, the first movement of Gustav Holst's symphonic suite called The Planets. The martial staccato of Mars (movement 1) and the dance-like Jupiter (movement 4) almost matched my brush strokes. Soon the music lifted me from the mundane to the ethereal much more effectively than an additional cup of coffee would have.

Holst had composed the Planets at the beginning of the 20th Century. Influenced by the Greek concepts of celestial harmony and music of the spheres, he composed a suite of tone poems that had seven movements (the number of planets that the ancient Greeks recognized). However, they placed the Earth in the center of the universe with the seven planets (Moon, Sun, Mercury, Venus, Mars, Jupiter, and Saturn) moving around the fixed Earth. Holst adopted the modern cosmology with the sun in the center of the solar system. He added Uranus and Neptune, both discovered since the advent of the telescope. Also, he ignored Earth. Thus, Holst's suite contained the same number of planets as the ancient Greek cosmology. Since the composition and first performance of The Planets in the autumn of 1918, the planet Pluto has been added to the pantheon of celestial bodies in orbit about the sun.

STRUCTURE OF THE SOLAR SYSTEM

The Planets in their stations list'ning stood.   -John Milton, *Paradise Lost*

The sun dominates the solar system with 99% of its mass. Thus, either directly or indirectly, the sun influences the motions of all other celestial bodies in the solar system. This is most obvious when considering the motions of the nine planets that orbit the sun. Although the planets differ from one another with their distinctive attributes, they do share some interesting characteristics. Most obviously, all planets move around the sun in the same direction (counter clockwise as seen from above) and they have nearly circular orbits. Also, most planets lie in the same plane, called the ecliptic. Only Pluto deviates significantly from this pattern with an orbit that inclines 17° from the plane of the ecliptic. Also, almost all of the planets rotate the same direction (counter-clockwise as viewed from above) on axes that incline no more than 30° from celestial north. Other exceptions include the slow clockwise rotation of Venus and the extreme tilts of Neptune and Pluto which lie nearly on their sides.

TABLE 4-3. Mean density, diameter and mass of the nine planets of the solar system. Density is g/ml with water equal to 1.00. In this table, diameter is expressed as multiples of the diameter of the Earth. Similarly, mass is expressed as multiples of the mass of earth.

Planet	Density	Diameter (relative to Earth)	Mass (relative to Earth)
Mercury	5.4	0.39	0.05
Venus	5.2	0.95	0.82
Earth	5.5	1.00	1.00
Mars	3.9	0.52	0.11
Jupiter	1.3	10.98	317.00
Saturn	0.7	9.03	95.00
Uranus	1.3	4.04	15.00
Neptune	1.8	3.91	17.00
Pluto	2.1	0.18	0.0021

The four inner or terrestrial planets have relatively high densities but small volumes (see Table 4-3). The four outer giant planets, however, have large volumes and smaller densities. Indeed, the giant planet called Saturn would float on water if there were a sea large enough.

BODE'S LAW

...just a couple of clods in the sky.
-Karl Friedrich Gauss

Titius von Wittenburg (1729-1796) noticed the regularity of the orbits of the known planets and produced an empirical relationship that fit them quite well. Later, Johann Bode (1747-1826), did much to popularize the empirical rela-tionship. He was so successful that the numerical sequence became known as Bode's Law.

The algorithm for the sequence is:
1. Write the planets in order.
2. Beneath each planet write a 4.
3. Then create a sequence of 0 (Mercury), 3 (Venus), 6 (Earth), etc. After Venus, the number doubles for each succeeding planet.
4. Add 4 to the appropriate number in 3) and divide by 10 to get the number in Earth orbits or astronomical units (A.U.).

TABLE 4-4. A comparison between actual orbital distances and those predicted by Bode's Law. The numbers in parentheses correspond to steps in the Bode's Law algorithm.

1) Planet	2) 4	3)	4)	Observed value
Mercury	4	0	0.4	0.4
Venus	4	3	0.7	0.7
Earth	4	6	1.0	1.0
Mars	4	12	1.6	1.5
?	4	24	2.8	?
Jupiter	4	48	5.2	5.2
Saturn	4	96	10.0	9.5

Although somewhat arcane, the sequence worked well in approximating the orbits of planets if the position between between Mars and Jupiter were skipped (See Table 4-4). The agreement between predicted orbits and observed orbits was just too good and begged for the existence of an undiscovered planet at 2.8a.u. Bode himself predicted that a planet would be found there.

In the mean time, William Herschel (1738-1822) discovered a new planet beyond Saturn in 1781. This one occurred at 19.2a.u. (Bode's Law predicted 19.6a.u.). He wanted to name it after George III, an action that earned him the rank of court astronomer and a new state-of-the-art telescope. In the end, he continued the tradition of naming planets after Roman gods. Nevertheless, this discovery confirmed the validity of Bode's Law and served to intensify the search for the predicted planet between Mars and Jupiter.

At the end of the 18th Century Franz von Zach organized a celestial police force to scan the skies in a systematic way to find the missing planet between Mars and Jupiter. In 1801 an Italian astronomer named Giuseppe Piazzi (1746-1826) followed a small object that moved relative to the stars. With almost infinite patience using a poor quality telescope in the days before photography, Piazzi watched the new tiny planet through the winter until it disappeared behind the disk of the sun. The mathematician Karl Friedrich Gauss calculated the time and location of the new planet when it would emerge from behind the sun. His calculation was so close that Piazzi found it again and named it Ceres. Of course, it resided at 2.8a.u. where Bode's law predicted it would. Soon, astronomers discovered other small objects at 2.8a.u. Clearly, they were not planets; they represented a new class of celestial objects that Herschel named asteroids (star-like). Disappointed that they were nothing special, Gauss sneered that the asteroids were "just a couple of clods in the sky."

In the latter part of the 19th Century, Uranus began to be studied with greater intensity. It became clear that the new planet had small but perceptible deviations in its orbit. That could be explained if a new planet orbited the sun outside of the orbit of Uranus. According to Bode's Law, such a planet must be about 388a.u.

Two mathematicians took on the task to calculate the mass and position of a new planet. John Couch Adams from England worked five years to complete his calculations and took them to Sir George Airy, the Royal Astronomer, and Reverend J. Challis of the Cambridge Observatory to look for the new planet. However, they were slow in searching because they had questions about the accuracy of the young man's results. In the mean time, Urbain Jean Leverrier from France worked out the problem in two year's time but later than Adams. Leverrier took his results to J. G. Galle of the Berlin Observatory. Galle found the new planet almost immediately in 1846 and suggested the name Janus, but Leverrier preferred the name Neptune.

Then, Adams made his calculations known and the controversy ensued. The French claimed plagiarism on the part of Adams. Quickly, John Herschel, son of the discoverer of Uranus, came to Adam's defense, but clearly the problem came about as a consequence of the hesitation that Airy and Challis had regarding the solvability of the problem. Indeed, Neptune did not obey Bode's Law very well. Neptune was located at 300.7a.u. and Bode's Law predicted that it would be around 388a.u. Fortunately, Leverrier and Adams happened to make their calculations during a short time in which this discrepancy (from the perspective of the Earth) did not matter.

By the beginning of the 20th Century, at the time that Gustav Holst wrote The Planets, the solar system had grown to eight planets and many asteroids. Moons had been observed around Mars and all of the giant planets. An expanding list of comets continued to be cataloged.

PLANET 'X'

That was the eighteenth of February, 1930, about four o'clock in the afternoon, I'd realized in a few seconds flat that I'd made a great discovery, that I'd become famous, and I didn't know what would happen after that.

-Clyde Tombaugh
(from an interview in 1991)

By 1846, careful observations of the planets and their movements in the solar system suggested that another planet lay undiscovered beyond Neptune. However, no serious search began until 1905. At that time, Percival Lowell[7] (1855-1916; USA), who had built a state of the art observatory near Flagstaff, Arizona in 1894, did a rough calculation of the orbital perturbation of Uranus, which he believed could be caused only by an undiscovered outer planet. He called the undiscovered body Planet X and dedicated himself to a search for it from 1905 until his death in 1916. At first, he calculated the likely position of the unknown planet and studied the skies for two years search with a 5-inch telescope. He compared photographic plates by overlying them and looking for the anomalous movement relative to the background stars characteristic of orbiting bodies. In 1911, Lowell stepped up the search with a more powerful 40-inch telescope. Later, he added a 9-inch camera and began to compare the plates that it generated with a blink comparator, a device that projects of plates rapidly so that visual comparisons can be made rapidly. His search was cut short by a stroke in 1916.

Lowell's death not only ended the search for Planet X but also caused turmoil for the

---

[7] Percival Lowell is best known for his search for evidence of intelligent life on Mars. Please see *Inferno and Purgatorio* for more about him.

Lowell Observatory. Finally, Roger Lowell Putnam, one of Lowell's nephews, emerged as the observatory's director and trustee in 1927 with the financial backing of others in his family. Putnam upgraded the equipment, particularly a new telescope.

In 1928, a self-taught amateur astronomer named Clyde Tombaugh (1906-1997, USA) sent drawings of Mars and Jupiter that he had made from observations with a reflecting telescope that he had built to the Lowell Observatory for comment. Soon after that, he was hired as one of the operators of the new telescope and given the task of finding Planet X. Tombaugh solved some of the technical problems associated with the new telescope and set about generating detailed photographic plated that he, too, examined using the blink comparator. On the afternoon of February 30, 1930, Tombaugh found Planet X.

The new planet then had to be named. Lowell's widow ultimately suggested Constance. Suggestions also came from across the globe. However, the Lowell observatory settled on Pluto, the god of the underworld, as a fitting name. Also, its abbreviation (PL) was made of the same letters as Percival Lowell's initials.

Pluto, an odd planet, more closely resembles a moon than one of the outer gas giants. It likely escaped from its orbit around Neptune by an interaction with Triton, a large moon of Neptune.

Certainly, the solar system was revealing itself as a beautiful and wonderful place. Where had this wondrous system come from? Was it unique?

NEBULOUS ORIGINS

It can have no place in my system and is plainly errorous.   -Isaac Newton

Rene Descartes (1644) had suggested that the solar system grew from a collection of gas that developed comet-generating vortices. In turn, the comets accreted into planets. Others contemplating the origin of the solar system built on the Cartesian Hypothesis. In particular, the philosopher Immanuel Kant (1724-1804) and later Pierre-Simon LaPlace (1749-1827) refined the notion of the nebular origin of the solar system.

LaPlace (1796) developed the concept of a cloud of gas that began to rotate as it condensed into rings that became the planets and a central mass that became the sun. The rings and their positions in the Kant-LaPlace Hypothesis could explain the regular intervals of the planets, the ecliptic, the uniformity of axes and rotations. In short, the nebular hypothesis held great explanatory power.

By and large, the nebular hypothesis remains today one of the strongest theories regarding the origin of the solar system. Current views are that a cloud of dust and gas left by the explosion of an earlier star began to accrete. As it condensed, it began to spin and flatten into a disk (Figure 4-53).

The developing disk condensed most of the matter (>99%) in the center through gravitational attraction. Smaller rings and vortices developed within the disk (Figure 4-54) as the protosun began to ignite through nuclear fusion supported by the great heat of compression.

Protoplanets developed from the accretion of dust and gasses. As the masses of the protoplanets increased, their gravitational fields also increased and caused them to enlarge into planets. During this time, the sun ignited producing a solar wind that drove lighter elements from the inner solar system and produced the density and size differences between the inner terrestrial planets and the outer gas giants (Figures 4-55 & 4-56).

FIGURE 4-53. The initial nebula beginning to accrete and spin.

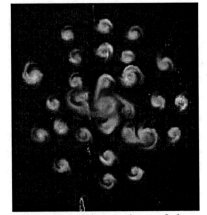

FIGURE 4-54. Illustration of the protosun surrounded by unconsolidated vortices of gas and dust.

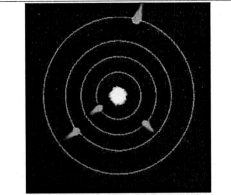

FIGURE 4-55. Protoplanets orbit the young sun.

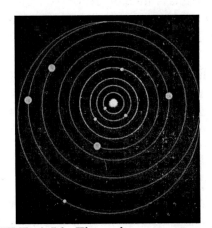

FIGURE 4-56. The solar system as it appears today, though the orbital distances are not drawn to scale. Note the distinctly eccentric orbit of Pluto.

In the nebular hypothesis, moons were protoplanets that began to orbit their respective planets instead of falling into them. Some pieces of the early nebular accretion remain in the solar system as comets. Also, the asteroids remain as planetesimals that were unable to consolidate through the gravitational influence of the giant Jupiter.

Strong confirmation of the Nebular Hypothesis comes from observations of young stars, many of which lie in the centers of rotating disks of material. Still, this does not demonstrate the mechanism of planetary formation directly and could just show a stage in the accretion process that forms stars.

The most serious challenge to the nebular hypothesis came from the Capture Theory of James Hopwood Jeans (1877-1946), a British astronomer. He proposed that a star passed the sun and drew out a strand of stellar material that settled into orbits. The material then came together through accretion and became planets. Thus, the planetary origins would be similar to those of the nebular hypothesis after the rings of stellar material appeared. However, because such close stellar encounters should be exceedingly rare, a solar system such as ours might be unique.

A test of this Capture Theory and its prediction of the unique nature of our solar system would be to search for other planets orbiting other stars. Indeed, in recent years very large Jupiter-like planets have been "observed" circling other suns by detecting the perturbations on the motions of their respective stars. As of August of 2001 about 50 extra-solar planets have been discovered.

Recently, however, large free-floating planets have been observed in Orion. If such planets exist outside of the influence of stars, how did they form? Clearly, the Nebular Hypothesis might be correct but incomplete.

PLANETS AND POETRY

...our time will be remembered as the historic moment when we first learned what the rest of the Solar System is like.
                                                    -Carl Sagan

I finished cleaning my paintbrushes as the last haunting cords of movement 7 of The Planets faded into silence. Of course, Holst did not write this work as a scientific treatise or as an exploration of the physics of the harmony of the cosmos. Indeed, his influences came mainly from astrology and mythology. His view of the planets was simple and primitive.

Equally simple, Bode's Law might just be a coincidental sequence of numbers that happen to conform to the orbital distances of most planets. Still, it caused astronomers to begin the search for a planet when they located the asteroids. The Nebular Hypothesis might be incomplete or a special case of a more general theory of planetary origins.

The Planets remain objects of great beauty and interest. Indeed, the true beauty and joy of science can be seen in the great period of discovery and exploration during the last 50 years of the 20th Century. During that time robotic probes visited all of the major planets (except Pluto), moons, asteroids, and at least one comet. We have visited our moon and have taken the first steps to a human presence on Mars.

I finished my work on the house that evening, turned off the CD player, and walked outside into a brisk October night. The sky was clear with a waxing moon. Inspired by the music of Holst, I looked up to see the two bright lights of Jupiter and Saturn. The allure was too great. I brought out my telescope and spent the next hour enjoying the visual poetry of the two planets.

                                                    -2000, revised 2006

References:

Halliday, David and Robert Resnick. 1970. *Fundamentals of Physics.*. John Wiley and Sons, Inc. New York.

Hoyle, Fred. 1972. *Astronomy.* Crescent Books, Inc. London.

Lee, Wayne. *To Rise From Earth.* Facts On File, Inc. New York.

Moore, Patrick and Gary Hunt. 1990. *The Atlas of the Solar System.* Crescent Books. New York.

Sagan, Carl. 1995. *The Voyage Out.* In: Scientific American. 1995. *Triumph of Discovery, A Chronicle of Great Adventures in Science.* Henry Holt Reference Book. Henry Holt and Co. New York.

Swimme, Brian and Thomas Berry. 1992. *The Universe Story.* HarperCollins Publishers. New York.

Questions to Think About

1. Who was Gustav Holst?

2. Where is most of the mass of the solar system concentrated?

3. What is Bode's Law?

4. How were Uranus and Neptune discovered?

5. Who was Karl Friedrich von Gauss and how did he figure in the discovery of the asteroids?

6. How did Tombaugh discover Pluto?

7. What is the nebular hypothesis of Kant and LaPlace? How does it help to explain the origin of the solar system? How does it explain the ecliptic?

8. What were some of the challenges to the Kant-LaPlace theory? What is a confirmation of the K-L theory?

9. Why did I suggest that the nebular theory might be incomplete?

10. What is an extra-solar planet? What is the significance of such planets?

MOON STORIES,
ORIGINS OF THE EARTH-MOON SYSTEM

A LUNACY

Though this be madness, yet there's method in't.

-William Shakespeare, Hamlet Act II.

I recall a particular warm autumn night when I was a graduate student A group of us were trying to come up with ways to keep from studying; so, we went to the local park to play on the swings, jungle-jim, etc. We played around for a while and finally ended up on the merry-go-round. A guy with us suggested that we could turn very fast if we leaned out while we were being pushed, and then simultaneously fell to the center. Wow! The outcome was better than I could have imagined. We spent much of the evening trying to get the most out of that merry-go-round until all of us were thoroughly dizzy and some visibly ill.

Before we left the park, most of us tumbled to the ground and looked at the great bowl of the sky on that nearly cloudless night. Just as the merry-go-round experience left an impression on me, so did the shining full moon. We joked that we were driven to such lunacy by the full moon. Ironically, the conservation of momentum, a fundamental law of physics that was the basis for our merry-go-round experience was also central to the explanation for the origin of the moon, the tides, and the fate of the earth-moon system.

Momentum is product of the mass of a body times its velocity. You can see the law at work in many of the ways that we play. A baseball bat imparts momentum to a baseball. Similarly, a cue stick transmits momentum to the white ball that gives it up to the target ball. In all, momentum is conserved. That is, the whole momentum of the system remains constant. However, the total energy is dissipated through friction and gravity. If we return to the baseball example, the ball flies from the bat with momentum that comes from the swing of the baseball bat. The ball flies off at some angle relative to the ground. It returns to the ground because the gravity of the earth exerts a constant downward force on the ball. Its linear velocity from the batter slows down because of the constant friction with the air during its flight.

Now, consider a ball attached to a string (see Figure 4-57). Let's say that you swing it over your head so that the string is parallel to the ground. Swing the ball so that it turns about one turn per second at radius 2. Then pull the string through the tube so that the ball is at radius 1. The ball will go much faster (represented by the magnitude of the arrows on the diagram). That is because the total momentum of the system is conserved. Put another way, the momentum of the ball at radius 1 equals the momentum of the ball at radius 2. Because the mass does not change, the velocity must change. Thus, the ball at radius 2 must travel half as fast as the ball at radius 1. This is what happens when a figure skater pulls in her arms when she is turning. What does this mean? Well, the momentum depends on the center of mass in a system and its distance from the center of the system. When a skater begins to spin with her arms extended, the center of gravity is removed from the centerline of her body because the extended arms also have mass. When she pulls her arms in, the center of mass moves almost to the center of the system, and her turning speed increases.

That is exactly what happened to us on the merry-go-round.

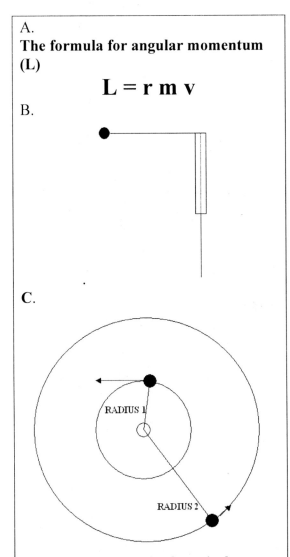

A.
The formula for angular momentum (L)

$$L = r\,m\,v$$

B.

C.

RADIUS 1

RADIUS 2

FIGURE 4-57.A. The formula for angular momentum. L (angular momentum), r (radius from the center of the system to the center of gravity), m (mass of the system), velocity. B. a tube seen from the side with a string and a ball in circular motion. C. The system of Figure 4-57B In motion from above at two different radii (RADIUS 1 & RADIUS 2) The arrows represent the magnitudes of the velocities if the angular momentum remains constant.

ORIGIN OF THE MOON?

The study of the Moon is particularly important in planetary science because it is directly related to the origin and evolution of the Earth and other terrestrial planets. —A. Gusev et al. (2003)

The earth-moon system, too, has an angular momentum. That, too, must have been conserved throughout its history. In this case, however, the moon is smaller than the earth and less dense; so, the center of mass of the whole system still lies within the sphere of the earth. Also, the moon is tied to the earth by gravity rather than a string, and that is what makes this problem much more complex.

Although far apart (240,000 miles), the earth and moon are still close enough so that different parts of them exert different gravitational tugs on one another. The differential gravitational tugs produced by relatively close bodies of mass are called tidal forces (see Figure 4-58). Thus, the differential pull distorts both bodies in the system. This concept is fundamental to our understanding of the earth-moon system.

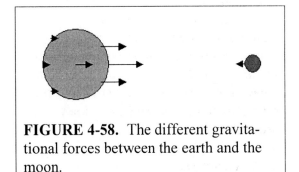

FIGURE 4-58. The different gravitational forces between the earth and the moon.

Ocean tides are among the most visible effects of the dual tug. The global oceans are distorted by the pull of the moon and, to a lesser extent, by the pull of the sun. The highest tides called spring tides occur during times of new moon or full moon when the moon and sun pull together on the ocean (see Figure 4-59A). Tides of the least magnitude, called neap tides occur when the tug of the sun and the tug of the moon are at right angles to each other (see Figure 4-59B).

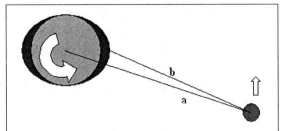

FIGURE 4-60. Diagram of the earth-moon system with the relative positions of the earth, moon, and ocean tide maxima. Line a represents the gravitational pull from the earth's center of mass. Line b represents a weaker tidal gravitational force from the high tide peak. The peak of the high tide is pushed ahead of the moon by the rotation of the earth.

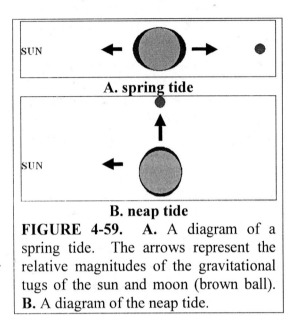

A. spring tide

B. neap tide

FIGURE 4-59. A. A diagram of a spring tide. The arrows represent the relative magnitudes of the gravitational tugs of the sun and moon (brown ball). B. A diagram of the neap tide.

The connection of the moon to the tides came with the realization that the high tides arrived an hour later each day, just like the moon. George Darwin (1845-1912, England), second son of Charles and Emma Darwin, was a mathematician and astrophysicist who became interested in tidal forces and set out to explore them mathematically. He considered a simple system like that of Figure 4-60. Even the most casual observers of the moon and tides knew the following:

- The earth turns on its axis once each day, but the moon takes about 28 days to make the same circuit about the earth.
- The peak of the high tide does not lie beneath the moon, but precedes it.

Darwin recognized that the tides were pushed ahead by the friction of the "solid" earth with the liquid oceans. Thus, the earth would lose energy and slow down. However, the tidal gravitational force produced by the tidal bulge (Figure 4-60, line b) would pull the moon along even faster. As the moon accelerated, it should get even farther from the earth. Based on those assumptions, George Darwin calculated that the moon should be receding from the earth at about 3-5 cm per year. He then used his results to determine that the earth and moon separated about 4 billion years ago. He also knew that the conservation of momentum would mean that the earth-moon system turned much faster as the center of mass approached the center of the system. He imagined that the earth may have been spinning so fast 4 billion years ago that a tidal tug from the sun might have been enough to cause a large distortion wave to break away from the early molten earth. The piece of the earth that escaped became spherical and settled into orbit around the earth. Through tidal acceleration, the moon receded to its present position. This "fission theory" for the origin of the moon was the first such theory that grew from a mathematical treatment. It seemed to be able to explain what was known about the earth-moon system at the time. Furthermore, Darwin suggested that the scar of separation could still be seen as the Pacific Ocean basin.

Darwin's was not the only theory floating around. The nearly circular orbit of the moon suggested that it must have been formed in place. There are few ways in which that could happen. The most likely would be that as the earth condensed out of the accretion disk that surrounded the sun, a stray planetoid or other nearby protoplanet kept the entire disk from accreting; so, it formed as a double planet. This was in line with the Kant-LaPlace hypothesis for the origin of the solar system that had been accepted by the scientific community since the beginning of the 19th Century[8].

A third competing theory was that the moon formed in another part of the solar system and was captured by the gravitational well of the earth. Such a capture would have to take into account the near perfect circular orbit of the moon. This capture model was the least likely of all of those proposed. It assumed that a planet in an unstable solar orbit came close to the earth at just the right angle and slow enough speed to be caught in earth's orbit without smashing into the earth.

These three theories for the origin of the moon were on the table in the 1960's. That they could not be resolved without taking samples from the moon itself served as an argument for the Apollo Program. Consequently, the Apollo astronauts brought back a treasure trove of 382 kilograms of rocks from the moon's surface (see Figure 4-61)

---

[8] See *The Planets* for further explanation.

from six sites, but they did not serve to answer the question. Indeed, they only made the whole matter more difficult to understand.

FIGURE 4-61. Moon rocks in storage at Johnson Space Center.

GIANT IMPACT THEORIES
Our thinking of the solar system as a plodding and predictable place has [given way] to the notion of planet-size objects careening into one another in wild, stochastic ways. -Robin Canup

The evidence that evolved from the moon exploration revealed a planet that was depleted in heavy or dense elements like iron. In keeping with that, the residual magnetism in the rocks suggested that the moon had once had a small core, but that it no longer had an active one that could generate a magnetic field. Furthermore, the isotopic signatures of the moon rocks were the same as those of the earth. These results posed particular problems for each of the theories.

The fission theory could account for low iron because the moon was supposed to have broken away from the outer part of the molten earth. The denser elements would have sunk into the sphere so that iron and other metals would have been rarified on the surface from which the moon was born. In fact, the fission theory could account for many of the problems except one important one. For the earth to have spun fast enough to eject a moon-sized chunk into orbit, it would have had to have spun much faster than the current angular momentum suggests that it did. Thus, the conservation of angular momentum negates this view.

The double planet view of LaPlace would explain the identical isotopic signatures and the nearly circular orbit of the moon. However, nearly one-third of the volume of the earth is an iron core. The moon has an iron core than might be less that 10% of that. How could two bodies accrete in the same part of the solar system and be so different in their relative proportions of iron?

The captured planet theory was just too improbable to begin with, but made much less likely by the identical isotopic signatures of the moon and earth. If a planetary body had been formed in a different part of the solar system, it would have had very different rations of oxygen isotopes, for example. Thus each theory had its problems and support. However, the problems were not so great that any one was rejected outright. Nor were any supported well.

Then, a new idea emerged in the early 1970's when William Ward and Al Cameron at Harvard University proposed that the moon was created by a single large collision between between the protoearth and a smaller planet about the size of Mars. The giant impact would have vaporized part of the mantle and set a spray of material into space around the earth.

Almost simultaneously and independently, William Hartman and Donald Davis from the Planetary Science Institute in Arizona considered the conditions of the early solar system, place of much more debris than now. The earth and all of the planets formed during a period we call the Great Bombardment. At this time planetary bodies were accreting or growing by drawing smaller bodies to

them in the Kant-LaPlace mode. Likely there were many more planetary-sized bodies during this period, and there must have been some spectacular collisions between them. Hartman and Davis supposed that the collision of a near-by but smaller planet collided with the earth and the collision ejected enough of the earth's mantle material to form the moon.

The two groups discovered that they had independently arrived at the same conclusion about the moon at a planetary science meeting in 1974. The collision theory had the advantage of providing explanations for the low lunar density, its near absence of iron, its circular orbit, and its angular momentum. Hartman and Davis were the first to publish the idea in 1975 in the journal *Icarus.* They were met by silence. Even though the collision theory could explain much, it relied upon a catastrophic mechanism, a very unpopular concept through the history of modern geology. Then, the theory gained new life at another conference in 1984. Interest grew as the explanatory power of this new theory became apparent. Then, with the advent of ever more powerful computers through the 1990's, sophisticated simulations of such collisions began to narrow the parameters of the model to match what we observe today.

The current and generally-accepted scenario is that near the end of the Great Bombardment, about 4.5 billion years ago, a planet between 1 and 2 times the mass of Mars struck the protoearth at between 10 and 15 kilometers per second (see Figure 4-62 A&B). The collision occurred at a shallow angle, which served to mix the mantles of the two planets and spray the mantle material into space around the earth while much of the impactor's core remained in the earth. The cloud of material began to separate into a ring as the matter within the Roche limit fell back to the earth (Figure 4-62 C). Far beyond that, the material escaped into interplanetary space. The remaining band began to accrete material rather quickly and the moon assembled itself through gravitational attraction in that ring. Models suggest that the assembly might have occurred in only 100-1000 orbital periods. Also, the models indicate that the newly-formed moon would have been no farther from earth than about 16,000 miles, 15 times closer than it is now (Figure 4-62 D).

As researchers attempted to reconcile computer models to observations, they learned much about the dynamics of collisions and planetary formation. Thus, they could give plausible scenarios for a large moon. The earth has the largest moon, relative to its size, of any other planet in the solar system except Pluto-Charon. Our sister planet, Venus, has no moon at all. Certainly, being a planet of our size is not guarantee that we would have any kind of moon.

Furthermore, the collision could help to understand why the rocks of the moon have the same isotopic composition as the earth, while it has a very different distribution of elements, particularly dense metallic elements. The circular orbit came about as a natural consequence of the accretion in a ring of ejected material. The momentum of the system was a consequence of the initial spin of the protoearth and the extra momentum added by the collision. This theory is not without its problems, but almost all current views are variations on the collision theory.

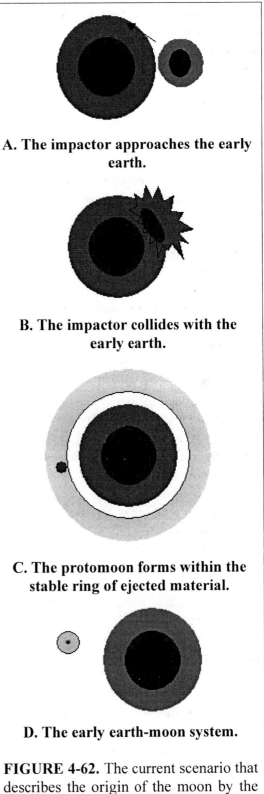

A. The impactor approaches the early earth.

B. The impactor collides with the early earth.

C. The protomoon forms within the stable ring of ejected material.

D. The early earth-moon system.

FIGURE 4-62. The current scenario that describes the origin of the moon by the collision theory. a and b illustrate the collision. c and d illustrate the assembly. Black indicates the iron core.

NEW THEORIES &VESTIGES OF OLD ONES

(E)ven mistaken hypotheses and theories are of use in leading to discoveries. This remark is true in all of the sciences.

—Claude Bernard

On the surface this has been a story about the determination of the origin of the moon or, more-appropriately, the origin of the earth-moon system. A simple view of it would be that most of the 20th Century saw three competing theories. We went to the moon, and a fourth theory emerged. Although this is an adequate outline of what happened, it does help to support a common and very incorrect view of how science works. Think of science as a community of scientists in communication with each other through their publications, conferences, symposia, and meetings. Theories are strongly-held views by members of the scientific community. Their views are informed by constant communication, and, therefore, always subject to change. Yet even in that changed view vestiges of old ideas usually can be found. Consider the theories of the origin of the moon. Within the collision theory, traces of its three predecessors can be found. The fission theory can be seen in the primary need for the ejection of mantle material. The Kant-LaPlace accretion model can be seen in the way that the moon forms out of the coalescence of the ejecta in orbit about the earth. The capture theory provides the impactor.

Thus, the theories in science are malleable. They change in response to observations and better ideas as to how those observations might be explained. Ultimately, that is what the methods of science aim for, to provide better explanations of nature. Unfortunately, this mode of self-correction in science is sometimes viewed as its weakness. I suggest that the introspective, self-examination is the greatest strength of science. Indeed, our understanding of nature is still very much in its waxing phase. Certainly, as good as it sounds, the story of the earth-moon system is not over yet.

- 2004

References:

Canup, R.M. and E. Asphaug. 2001. *Origin of the Moon in a Giant Impact Near the End of the Earth's Formation.* Nature. 412:708-712.

Cameron, A.G.W. 1997. *The Origin of the Moon and the Single Impact Hypothesis V.* Icarus. 129: 126-137.

Dreifus, G. and H. Wanke. 2002. *Comment on: Comparative Geochemistry of Basalts From the Moon, HED Asteroid, and Mars: Implication for the Origin of the Moon.* Geochim. Cosmochim Acta. 66(14): 2631-2632.

Gusev, A., N. Kawano, and N. Petrova. 2003. *Gravitational Investigations on the Selene Mission (Japan) and the Existence of a Lunar Core.* Astronomical and Astrophysical Transactions. 22(4-5):579-584.

Halliday, A. and M. Drake. 1999. *Colliding Theories.* Science. 283(5409):1861-1864.

Jayawardhana, Jay. 1998. *Deconstructing the Moon.* Astronomy. 26(9): 40-46.

Lee, D. and A. Halliday. 1997. *The Age and Origin of the Moon.* Science. 278(5340):1098-1104.

Melosh, Jay. 2001. *A New Model Moon.* Nature. 412: 694-695.

Righter, Kevin. 2002. *Does the Moon Have a Metallic Core?* Icarus. 158: 1-13.

Ruzica, A., G.A. Snyder, and L.A. Taylor. 2002. Response to the *Comment by G. Dreifus and H. Wanke on: Comparative Geochemistry of Basalts From the Moon, HED Asteroid, and Mars: Implication for the Origin of the Moon.* Geochim. Cosmochim. Acta. 66(14): 2633-2635.

Shore, S. 2000. *Time and Tide II.* Mercury. 29(4): 11.

Spudis, P. 2001. *What is the Moon Made Of?* Science. 293(5536):1779-1781.

Ward, W. and R.M. Canup. 2000. *Origin of the Moon's Orbital Inclination from Resonant Disk Interactions.* Nature. 403:741-743.

Wright, Karen. 2003. *Where did the Moon Come From?* Discover. 24(2):60-68.

Questions to Think About

1. What does the conservation of momentum mean?

2. What is meant by tidal force? What is an earthly consequence of the tidal forces between the earth, moon, and the sun?

3. Why does the moon separate from the earth about 3-5 cm per year?

4. How did George Darwin use the recession of the moon to calculate the age of the earth-moon system?

5. Before 1970 there were three competing theories for the origin of the Earth-Moon system. Can you think of a strength and a weakness of each one?

6. In general, what is the giant impact theory? Why did it replace the other three theories?

7. What does the phrase "science is self-correcting" mean?

8. Where is the center of mass of the earth-moon system?

9. Why are the solar eclipses always during times of the new moon?

10. You have seen the Kant-LaPlace accretion model in the essay, *The Planets*. How does the model serve to explain both the origin and formation of the solar system and the origin of the earth-moon system?

INFERNO AND PURGATORIO

DANTE'S TRILOGY

I look'd aloft, and saw his shoulders broad
Already vested with that planet's beam,
Who leads all wanderers safe through every way.

-Dante. Inferno, *Canto I.*

I recall a friend whose grandfather had died and left his family a library. I was young, but I had learned the value of books, especially books as beautiful as these. My strongest memory was of the old copies of Dante's Trilogy, *Inferno, Purgatorio, and Paradiso.* I got lost in the poetry, but I struggled to read it just the same. I loved trying to match the Doré prints to the story. Later, I was required to read it in college, and even that did not ruin its fascination for me. Three epic poems are about the transit of Dante through hell and purgatory (the place where souls are purged before they can go the heaven) escorted by the Roman poet, Virgil (who had written a similar account in his epic poem, the Aeneid). Then, Dante's guide changed to Beatrice, a secret love, who helped him to ascend the spheres of heaven.

In those days, as now, many things fascinated me. The space program had landed its first men on the moon just the summer before college began, and I followed successive missions. As information began to be collected from the less spectacular, but very informative robotic missions, a picture of our closest planetary neighbors began to emerge. As with Dante's trilogy, Venus, Mars and the Earth began to be described almost as an inferno, a purgatory, and a paradise.

VENUS, THE INFERNO

Leave all hope, ye that enter.
-Dante.*The Inferno,* Canto III.

Venus, the bright morning (and evening) star, known also as Lucifer (Latin for light bringer), remained shrouded in mystery until some of the first space missions of exploration began to unlock its secrets. A planet that seemed to be a benign, cloud-shrouded sister to earth revealed herself as very different and quite appropriate to the name, Lucifer.

By the end of the 1950's we already knew that Venus had a nearly circular orbit and that it was slightly smaller and less massive than the earth. Furthermore, the US, using the great radio telescopes like the one at Arecibo bounced radio waves off the planet and built up a low-resolution picture of the surface. Also, they discovered that Venus rotated at a snail's pace (one full rotation every 243 Earth days).

The first missions to Venus occurred in 1961 (Soviet Venera 1, contact was lost, but it did fly by Venus) and 1962 (the US Mariner 2, Mariner 1 failed to launch). These were flyby missions and relied on telemetry from a great distance (35,000-100,000 km). Still, they were able to measure surface temperatures in excess of 400C and atmospheric pressures of more than 90 bars. Although earthlike in its appearance, the surface of Venus was an oven with temperatures high enough to melt lead and atmospheric pressure high enough to crush a submarine.

TABLE 4-5. A chronology of the exploration of Venus. The name of the spacecraft, the year launched (Y), the country of origin (C), the type of mission (M), and its success (S/F) are given for each exploration vehicle. FB=flyby; P=probe; O=orbiter; L=lander. F=failure; S=success, PS=partial success. Spacecraft names in bold indicate successful or partly successful missions.

NAME	Y	C	M	S/F
SPUTNIK 7	1961	USSR	FB	F
VENERA 1	1961	USSR	FB	PF
MARINER 1	1962	US	FB	F
SPUTNIK 19	1962	USSR	FB	F
MARINER 2	1962	US	FB	S
SPUTNIK 20	1962	USSR	FB	F
SPUTNIK 21	1962	USSR	FB	F
COSMOS 21	1963	USSR	?	F
VENERA 1964A	1964	USSR	FB	F
VENERA 1964B	1964	USSR	FB	F
COSMOS 27	1964	USSR	FB	F
ZOND 1	1964	USSR	FB	F
VENERA 2	1965	USSR	FB	F
VENERA 3	1965	USSR	L	F
VENERA 1965A	1965	USSR	FB	F
VENERA 4	1967	USSR	P	S
MARINER 5	1967	US	FB	S
COSMOS 167	1967	USSR	P	F
VENERA 5	1969	USSR	P	S
VENERA 6	1969	USSR	P	S
VENERA 7	1970	USSR	P/L	S
COSMOS 359	1970	USSR	P	F
VENERA 8	1972	USSR	O/L	S
COSMOS 482	1972	USSR	O	F
MARINER 10	1973	US	FB	S
VENERA 9	1975	USSR	O/L	S
VENERA 10	1975	USSR	O/L	S
PIONEER VENUS 1	1978	US	O	S
PIONEER VENUS 2	1978	US	P	S
VENERA 11	1978	USSR	O/L	S
VENERA 12	1978	USSR	O/L	S
VENERA 13	1981	USSR	O/L	S
VENERA 14	1981	USSR	O/L	S
VENERA 15	1983	USSR	O	S
VENERA 16	1983	USSR	O	S
VEGA 1	1984	USSR	L/P	S
VEGA 2	1984	USSR	L/P	S
MAGELLAN	1989	US	O	S
GALILEO	1989	US	FB	S
CASSINI	1997	US	FB	S
MESSENGER	2004	US	FB	
VENUS EXPRESS	2005	ESA	O	
PLANET-C	2007	ISAS	O	

As Table 4-5 illustrates, the exploration of Venus went through several phases. The initial vehicles were designed for simple flyby telemetry. Those were followed by probes, designed to descend into the atmosphere of Venus; orbiters, satellites of Venus; and landers, spacecraft designed to land on the surface of the planet. Each type of mission faced different kinds of problems; however, all had to leave earth, survive interplanetary space, and then work to gather and send information on arrival. Most of the initial failures were due to problems during launch. However, some were to due to failures in the ability to complete their missions. For example, Venera 1 had a near flawless launch on 12 February 1961, but radio contact was lost and could not be reestablished. Thus, technically, Venera 1 was the first space vehicle to visit the vicinity of another planet (within 100,000 km), but it did not return any information. Mariner 2, also a flyby mission, was launched in 1962 and flew within 35,000km of Venus. It radioed back telemetry of the planet during the rendezvous and ended its life in orbit around the sun.

The subsequent history of exploration of Venus is marked by a near continuous stream of failures from 1962 to 1967 (see Table 4-5). Then, the Soviet Venera 4 arrived safely on October 18, 1967. The transportation vehicle (called a bus) released a probe that entered the venutian atmosphere. It radioed back measurements of pressure, temperature, atmospheric composition, atmospheric density, and wind speed as it descended to within 25km above the surface by special parachute. The bus relayed the information to earth while it also looked for a magnetic field, and cosmic rays, among other things. The flawless performance and successful relay of information to earth established our understanding of Venus as a Hadean world. It also established the primacy of Soviet planetary exploration, particularly of Venus. That superiority seemed to be supported by a series of spectacular successes punctuated by several spectacular failures. Notable achievements included Venera 7, which operated as an atmospheric probe, but landed and continued to relay information for 23 minutes while on the surface. Thus, Venera 7 became the first spacecraft to return data from the surface of another planet.

The success of Venera 7 paled to that of Venera 9, which on October 20, 1975 landed on the surface of Venus, opened its lens cover and began to relay television pictures back to earth. The pictures showed a rocky landscape with shadows and an ambient midday brightness comparable to that of the earth on a cloudy day. Venera 9 had made a soft landing and its cooling systems allowed for operation for nearly an hour on the surface. Whereas Venera 9 sent back video of a landscape of blocky and little-weathered rocks, Venera 10 only 3 days later landed on a site that was worn smooth and showed considerable evidence of weathering.

Through the next 15 years the US and Soviet Union orbiters and probes. The orbiters equipped with radar developed a detailed image of the surface beneath the clouds. Only the Soviet Union deployed landers. The picture of Venus as a tortured world dotted by numerous, almost randomly arranged volcanoes began to emerge. The surface appeared young with relatively few meteor impact craters, thus erosion and/or deposition of volcanic rock must have been quite active until recently.

MARS, THE PURGATORIO

Meanwhile we lingered by the water's brink,

Like men who, musing on their road, in thought

Journey, while motionless the body rests.

When lo! As, near upon the hour of dawn,

Through the thick vapours Mars with fiery beam

Glares down in west, over the ocean floor.

-Dante. *Purgatorio,* Canto II

Mars, a planet about the size of our moon, had been studied by astronomers for some time by telescope. Intriguing surface features could be seen at the limit of resolution. Percival Lowell[9] (1855-1916) interpreted the dark lines on the planet as canals. He was influenced by the observations and description of an Italian astronomer, Giovanni Schiaparelli, who in 1877 referred to the lines on Mars as *canali*, Italian for channels. Lowell transliterated the term and incorrectly assumed that Schiaparelli had meant canals, engineering projects of an advanced, intelligent race. This misunderstanding led to an explosion of suspect science mainly because Lowell saw what he wanted to see. He produced maps of the planet that clearly showed an elaborate network of canals. For good or ill, that also spawned a mound of science fiction.

As with Venus, much information had been gathered from the time of the ancients through the modern period. Details of its orbit, size, mass, and general composition of the atmosphere and surface could be determined from earth-bound observations. More careful telescopic examination allowed for the dismissal of the large surface features as engineered structures. Still, its lure was very great, and generated a record of ex-ploration comparable to, and in some ways more elaborate, than that of Venus (see Table 4-6).

Like the exploration of Venus, the earliest attempts to send interplanetary robotic observers were failures. The first partial success came with Mars 1, a Soviet flyby vehicle that had lost contact prior to arrival in 1963. From 1964-1969, the US achieved success with its Mariner 4-7 series of flyby missions. Mariner 4 during its encounter with Mars on July 14-15, 1965 was the first spacecraft to photograph the Martian surface and relay data back to the earth. The images of around 1% of the planet's surface showed an almost moon-like cratered landscape. Sensors detected an atmosphere with a barometric pressure between 4 and 7.5 mb (that of the earth is around 1,000 mb and Venus is more than 90,000mb). Mariner 4 detected no magnetic field. Thus, it appeared that Mars was a cold and dead world.

The Soviet success first came with the Mars 2 and 3 missions. They were launched in May of 1971, just days apart and planned as duplicate identical missions to decrease the odds of complete failure (as they had done with Venera 9 and 10). These were ambitious in scope. They were each made of an orbiter and a lander component. The lander of Mars 2 failed, but the lander of Mars 3 did enjoy a partial success. Unfortunately, its achievement was short-lived, and the lander's instruments shut down after only 20 seconds on the surface. The explanation was that a dust storm, which was raging at the time, interfered with its operation. Other successes came with two orbiters, the US Mariner 9 (1971) the Soviet Mars 5 (1973).

---

[9] See *The Planets* for more information about Percival Lowell and the discovery of Pluto

TABLE 4-6. A chronology of the exploration of Mars. The name of the spacecraft, the year launched, the country of origin, the type of mission, and its success are given for each exploration vehicle. FB=flyby; P=probe; O=orbiter; L=lander; R=rover. F=failure; S=success, PS=partial success. Spacecraft names in bold indicate successful or partly successful missions.

NAME	Y	C	M	S/F
MARSNIK 1	1960	USSR	FB	F
MARSNIK 2	1960	USSR	FB	F
SPUTNIK 22	1962	USSR	FB	F
MARS 1	1962	USSR	FB	PS
SPUTNIK 24	1962	USSR	L	F
MARINER 3	1964	US	FB	F
MARINER 4	1964	US	FB	S
ZOND 2	1964	USSR	FB	F
MARINER 6	1969	US	FB	S
MARINER 7	1969	US	FB	S
MARS 1969A	1969	USSR	O	F
MARS 1979B	1969	USSR	O	F
MARINER 8	1971	US	FB	F
COSMOS 419	1971	USSR	O/L	F
MARS 2	1971	USSR	O/L	OS
MARS 3	1971	USSR	O/L	S
MARINER 9	1971	US	O	S
MARS 4	1973	USSR	O	PS
MARS 5	1973	USSR	O	S
MARS 6	1973	USSR	L	F
MARS 7	1973	USSR	L	PS
VIKING 1	1975	US	O/L	S
VIKING 2	1975	US	O/L	S
PHOBOS 1	1988	USSR	O/L	F
PHOBOS 2	1988	USSR	O/L	PS
MARS OBSERVER	1992	US	O	F
MARS GLOBAL SURVEYOR	1996	US	O	S
MARS 96	1996	RUSS	O/L	F
MARS PATHFINDER	1996	US	L/R	S
NOZOMI	1998	JAPA	O	S
MARS CLIMATE ORBITER	1998	US	O	F
MARS POLAR LANDER	1999	US	L	F
DEEP SPACE 2	1999	US	L	F
2001 MARS ODYSSEY	2001	US	O	S
MARS EXPRESS	2003	ESA	O/L	PS
SPIRIT (MER-A)	2003	US	R	S
OPPORTUNITY (MER-B)	2003	US	R	S
MARS RECON ORBITER	2005	US	O	
PHOENIX	2007	US	L	
NETLANDERS	2007	FRA		
MARS 2009	2009	US	R	
MARS 2011	2011	US		

Then, in 1976, the US achieved a spectacular pair of successful missions, comparable to that of Venera 9 and 10. The US deployed two orbiter-landers called Viking 1&2. Viking 1 arrived at Mars and entered into orbit on June 19. Over the next month the orbiter surveyed the planet to find an appropriate landing site for its lander. Finally, the lander separated and touched down safely at Chryse Planetia. Viking 2 entered a Martian orbit on August 7 and deployed its lander on September 3. The second Viking landed at the Utopia Planetia.

The landers carried out a whole string of experiments and measurements to search for life and for conditions that might support life and future missions to Mars. They dug into the soil, sniffed the air, and measured seismic activity. They operated for years during which they experienced extremes in Martian temperature (-123C to –23C), windstorms, and dust storms. The orbiters continued to observe and map the red planet from above.

The orbiters produced the most complete picture of the planet up to that time, certainly a very different picture from that developed by Percival Lowell. Mars seemed to be divided into a geologically young northern hemisphere that had a large, low plain with very few impact craters. The southern hemisphere, on the other hand, had features that made it seem very old, with broken highlands and many impact craters. More surprisingly, they detected regions of extinct volcanoes, some of which were enormous mountains. In fact, Olympus Mons is the largest volcano known in the entire solar system.

Perhaps the most interesting features were valleys like the Vallis Marineris, a huge system of canyons which seemed to have been produced by tectonic activity. However, other smaller valleys and surface features seemed to bear the marks of flowing water and wind. If wa-ter had been plentiful enough for it to flow on the surface of Mars, it might have been plentiful enough to support life (and might be plentiful enough to support a future human presence on the red planet). The orbiters circled the planet for years (Viking 2; 706 orbits until July 25, 1978; and Viking 1, more than 1400 orbits until August 17, 1980). The landers continued to operate and return data until April 11, 1980 (Viking 2) and November 13, 1982 (Viking 1). The combined data from the Viking landers and orbiters began to assemble a picture of a planet that was nearly earth-like with a surface carved by water and wind, a dead purgatory of a world on which life might once have managed to take hold.

RED ROVERS

And thence we issued out, again to see the stars. -Dante. *Inferno,* Canto XXXIV

Sadly, the further exploration of Mars languished for nearly two decades. Then, after seven months in space, the Pathfinder lander entered the atmosphere of Mars and deployed its large parachute on July 4, 1997. Just seconds before impact with the ground, it inflated a battery of air bags and bounced on the surface of the red planet like a great ball. After the air bags deflated, the base platform, named after the late Carl Sagan, opened up like the petals of a great flower. It was refreshing to see scientists so ecstatic over this technological achievement. Press conferences after the landing were filled with cautious optimism about the rest of the mission.

This marked a return to Mars since the landing of Mariner 4 in 1965 and the Viking series probes in the mid 1970's. For more than 20 years other priorities occupied NASA. However, the relatively low cost of this robotic mission and increased interest in Mars after the discovery of life-like "fossils" on a Martian meteorite (see *Red Planets and Microbes*) made this a logical next step in the exploration of the solar system.

In particular, the objectives of this and other missions to Mars included:

1. The search for past life on Mars
2. Martian climate and its lessons for the past and future of Earth's climate
3. Geology and resources that could be used to support future human missions to Mars.

After some minor problems with the deployment of the Sojourner vehicle, it rolled down the ramp and on to the Martian soil two days (sols; a Martian day is called a sol) after landing. The rover, hardly larger than a milk crate, maneuvered very slowly (about 1cm per hour) over the rocky terrain powered by solar cells (and a backup supply of D batteries). Although small, Sojourner carried an instrument that could analyze the elemental composition of rock.

Rocks examined by Sojourner were given nicknames like Barnacle Bill and Yogi. Results of the analyses showed that the two rocks were different enough to have had different origins. That and the orientations of the rocks suggest that the area once had flowing water. Even more exciting was the great diversity of rocks in the landscape which landscape appeared to have been shaped by water over a long period of time, or at least by many successive flood events. Where there was water, there could have been life. Also, some of that water might remain trapped and usable by human colonists on Mars. Sojourner continued to operate until contact was lost on September 27.

While Sojourner crawled on the surface, Mars Global Surveyor joined her in orbit above on 12 September 1997. The mission of the surveyor was to produce high resolution images of the Martian surface, and among many other directives, search for water. It also was to produce very precise topographic images of the surface.

The Global Surveyor succeeded in all of its tasks. The high-resolution images coupled with laser measurements for topographic mapping produced some of the most spectacular images of Mars. The outcome of the mission was the examination of surface features that had indicated the action of water by the lower resolution images of the Viking orbiters.

The successes of the Pathfinder-Sojourner-Surveyor missions were followed by a string of heartbreaking failures. One, the Mars Climate Orbiter made it safely to Mars, but because of the continued use of the archaic English system of measures used by some members of the team, the orbiter misunderstood a command and plunged into the Martian atmosphere. Then, on October 21, 2001, Mars Odyssey, another orbiter, joined Mars Global Surveyor. This new orbiter had equipment aboard that allowed it to analyze for elemental composition from a distance. In particular, it was looking for the element hydrogen, which should indicate large amounts of water. Almost immediately, Odyssey found the signature of water ice beneath the surface of many areas of the planet. Planetary scientists already knew that water ice occurred near the poles; however, they became very excited when the signature of water began to appear near the equator, a place where liquid water could exist on a seasonal basis.

Toward the end of 2003 three spacecraft approached Mars, the European Space Agency Mars Express, and the US Mars Exploration Rovers (MER), Spirit and Opportunity. The Mars Express released its lander, Beagle 2, on December 19, 2003. The lander then entered the atmosphere on December 25 but that was followed by silence. The Mars Express orbiter is working and has the task to map the geology, mineralogy, and atmospheric movements.

On the heels of Mars Express came the US rovers. The first, MER-A also called Spirit, landed on January 3, 2004 in Gusev Crater. This site was chosen because orbital reconnaissance suggested that the crater had been a drainage basin, with meandering streams and evidence of sedimentation. The lander, similar to that of Pioneer-Sojourner, opened up its petaloid cover and deployed Spirit. After a period of checks, Spirit rolled off the lander on January 15. At first, Spirit experienced software problems, but they were taken care of and the mission is proceeding.

The second Mars Express Rover (MER-B), Opportunity, landed in a small crater on January 24. This site in Merandi Planum is on the opposite side of Mars from Spirit. It is a site that Odyssey suggested might be rich in hematite, an iron ore that usually requires water in its formation. Two rovers, their landers and three orbiters now study Mars in a coordinated attempt to learn as much as we can before humans attempt their ascendance into the heavens.

PARADISO

His glory, by whose might all things are moved,
Pierces the universe, and in one part
Sheds more resplendence, elsewhere less.
   -Dante *Paradiso,* Canto I

Dante continues his epic poem with the Paradiso in which he visits heaven. He rises from Earth and visits levels of paradise. Curiously, Venus is the third level of Heaven and Mars is the fifth level of Heaven in Dante's vision.

However, we have visited these worlds vicariously through our robotic emissaries. On Venus, we have found a tortured world, a fitting image of anyone's hell. Mars, though habitable with considerable technological support, still is a barren, desert world with a thin atmosphere of carbon dioxide and temperatures that plunge to well below Arctic extremes. The study of these worlds, our sister worlds, teaches us even more about how planets work. They give us examples what happens on a planet with a run-away greenhouse effect (Venus), and a planet that is too small to have the gravity to hold onto its atmosphere (Mars). Still, they have features in common. Both planets have volcanoes and other evidences of tectonic activity. Curiously, even though their atmospheric densities are very different, the relative composition of carbon dioxide 95-98% is quite similar[10].

Is such knowledge worth it? Is it just an extravagance? The whole Mars Pathfinder mission cost $260 million. That seems like a lot, but it is less than 20% of the cost of a single B-2 bomber (I have a habit of measuring large projects in terms of B-2 bombers, ~$1.5 billion apiece). The spin-off technologies from such enterprises can feed directly into Earth orbiting weather satellites, prospecting, communications, and robotics (and this is a very short list).

The observations of other worlds therefore return much to us through our global infrastructure. More importantly, though, they teach us much about our own world, as a planet among others in a solar system. However, this planet is blessed with life. It is our home, our paradise. Earth is the only place that we have found in the universe on which more resplendence is shed.

   -2004

References:
Caidin, Martin and Jay Barbree. 1997. *Destination Mars.* Penguin Studio. New York.

---

[10] See *Gaia: Science, Pseudoscience, or Fruitful* ⌐‗‗‗ ⌐or an elaboration on this.

McNab, David and James Younger. 1999. *The Planets.* Yale University Press. New Haven.

Moore, Patrick. 1998. *On Mars.* Cassell. London.

Zubrin, Robert. 1996. *The Case For Mars.* The Free Press. New York.

Most of the information and all data that I used about missions to Mars and Venus came from the Goddard Spaceflight Center website:
http://nssdc.gsfc.nasa.gov/

Questions to Think About

1. What country was the first to visit Venus?

2. What are the differences between flyby missions, probes, orbiters, landers, and rovers?

3. What was the first lander on Venus? What did it tell us about that planet?

4. What did the first video images of Venus indicate?

5. Considering the environment of Venus, why did the first landers survive no longer than an hour?

6. What did the first successful missions to Mars tell us about that world?

7. What did we learn from the Viking missions? Why were they so successful?

8. How was the Pathfinder mission different from the Viking missions?

9. What have we learned from the Global Surveyor and Mars Odyssey missions?

10. What is the current mission on Mars? What are they looking for?

11. What lesson did we learn from the Mars Climate Orbiter?

12. What do we know about the Earth's two sister worlds as a consequence of our exploration? What are some of the important questions that we need to answer about those planets?

13. Why did I compare the three planets to Dante's trilogy?

IMPACTS

THUNDER FROM THE NORTH

...then there was a roar of thunder from the north.

-A witness to the Tunguska fireball.

Around 7 in the morning on June 30, 1908, a flash of light as bright as the sun shattered the peace of northern Siberia. The fireball grew over the Siberian forest into an expanding mushroom cloud. The shock wave that followed had enough power to knock a witness off of his porch 50km away and destroy vegetation for a radius of 44km. The ensuing fire consumed more than 2,150km^2 of Taiga forest.

Cities as far away as Irkutsk, Tblisi, and Jena recorded seismic waves. Meteorologists in Britain recorded fluctuations in barometric pressure around the same time, which indicated that the pressure wave circled the Earth twice. The explosion even created a local geomagnetic storm that persisted for more than four hours.

It triggered an array of atmospheric anomalies that could be observed as far away as the Antarctic. One of the most interesting stories came from a letter to the Times of London on July 1, 1908. The author described the northern sky growing brighter with a salmon-pink tinge through the evening until 2:30 a.m. He even claimed to be able to read by the light until clouds obscured it. Almost certainly, he was describing the glow of the forest fires.

Despite its global attention, the phenomenon was not studied directly for another 19 years. The Tungus region in Siberia was so remote (and still is) that an expedition could not be mounted until 1927. Political instability of the last years of Nicholas II, World War I, and the Russian Revolution coupled with the remoteness of the Tungus region all caused the project to be delayed.

L. A. Kulik, the expedition leader, was beset by problems from the start. The soggy, peaty soils, short summers, legions of mosquitoes, and temperatures that plunged to 40 below made work miserable. Most importantly, even though the trees fell in a pattern that indicated a center to the explosion, there was no crater. He assumed the peat absorbed the impact and spent many days digging at the epicenter of the explosion in a vain attempt to find the impacting object.

An explanation of the Tunguska Event became as elusive as the explosion was spectacular. Clearly, the pattern of devastation, eyewitness accounts, and absence of an impact crater indicated an aerial explosion. What could have caused such a thing? Some of the more far-out explanations include the explosion of a UFO, a collision with a black hole, and an accident with a powerful secret weapon. More rational explanations include the collision of a small piece of Comet Encke or a stony meteorite.

KINETIC ENERGY

We call this form of energy heat energy, but we know that it is not really a new form, it is just kinetic energy.

-Richard Feynman

That the Tunguska Event was an explosion is clear. The magnitude of the explosion has been estimated in several ways. Changes in barometric pressure that were recorded in London indicate a blast of at least 10 megatons (1,000 times more powerful than the Hiroshima bomb). Damage to the forest suggests a force of more than 20 and perhaps up to 40 megatons.

The force (I use this term very loosely here) of the explosion is due to the kinetic energy, or energy due to an object's motion. Kinetic energy can be calculated by the following formula:

$$KE = 1/2 \; [Mass \; X \; (Velocity)^2]$$

Thus, the motion of an object has a much larger effect on the energy than does the mass. Put another way, a bullet with the mass of 1gram and traveling with the velocity of 1,400 meters per second has the same kinetic energy as a 1 kilogram brick that has fallen 200 meters!

If the object struck the Earth at 20 kilometers per second, and had an explosive energy of 20 megatons of TNT, then the diameter would have been about 0.08 kilometers. The dirty snowball structure of a comet would allow for the break-up necessary to produce an airburst upon collision with the atmosphere. The sudden slowing would cause the comet's motion to be changed to the energy of gas molecular motion (this would be observed as heat and the expanding pressure wave of the explosion).

A stony meteor could produce the same effect. Unlike metallic meteors, stony meteors are aggregate structures that can fly apart upon collision with the atmosphere. If the stones are small enough, they will fly apart and scatter as debris also without producing a crater.

A COMET BURNED

On the other side,
Incensed with indignation, Satan stood
Unterrified; and like a comet burned.

-Milton's *Paradise Lost*

A dramatic example of the power of a cometary impact came in 1994 following the discovery of Comet Shoemaker-Levy 9. The team of Carolyn and Gene Shoemaker and David Levy discovered a fragmented stream of comets on March 18, 1993. Their observations indicated that the comet was in orbit around Jupiter with an orbital period of about 2 years. Their calculations of its orbit indicated that a single comet came very close to Jupiter on an earlier pass and the gravitational forces (called tidal forces) pulled it into at least 21 observable pieces, the largest of which had a diameter of about 2 kilometers (see Figure 4-63). Further, they predicted that the "string of pearls" would impact Jupiter on its next pass.

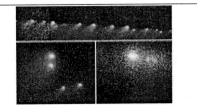

FIGURE 4-63. Some of the first images of Comet Shoemaker-Levy 9. from: http://nssdc.gsfc.nasa.gov/planetary/comet_body.html

FIGURE 4-64. Images of impacts on the Jovian atmosphere. From: http://nssdc.gsfc.nasa.gov/planetary/comet.html

The scientific community had a little more than a year to prepare and train instruments on Jupiter. The fragmentary stream began to strike Jupiter on July 16 and collisions continued until July 22, 1994 (see Figure 4-64). The fragments hit the Jovian atmosphere at about 60 kilometers per second with an explosive energy of about 5 *million* megatons. That is, its explosion was 500,000 times more powerful than the Tunguska fragment. Imagine the destruction to earth if a similar impact were to occur on our planet. The energy generated would be sufficient to disrupt ecosystems, cause short-term changes in climate, massive loss of life, and local extinctions. Now try to imagine the destructive force 20 times that of Shoemaker-Levy 9.

LAST DAY OF THE CRETACEOUS
And there were flashes of lightning, loud noises, peals of thunder, and a great earthquake... Revelation 16:18

There is clear evidence that such a collision occurred on the Earth around 65 million years ago. This was the culmination of an investigation begun by Walter Alvarez in the mid 1970's. However, it was the first satisfying answer to a 150-year-old question, "What happened to the dinosaurs?"

A solution to the last major objection to the theory came in 1992 when a large crater on the northern Yucatan peninsula was dated to 65 million years by geochronologist Carl C. Swisher (see Figure 4-65). The crater at Chicxulub was 170-200 kilometers in diameter and began to pull together other observations that indicated an impact in the Gulf of Mexico area. More than that, the crater and related evidence began to tell a story of immense destruction.

It appears that a 10-20 kilometer asteroid struck the Earth at 25 kilometers per second with the force of 100 *million* megatons (10 million times the explosive energy of the Tunguska fragment). It hit an area rich in carbonates, sulfur compounds and straddled land and sea.

Barely slowed by the atmosphere, the asteroid plunged deep into the rocks of Chicxulub. As it did, the immense kinetic energy turned the asteroid and 100,000 cubic kilometers of the surrounding rock to vapor that expanded explosively. Vaporized rock or ejecta shot back up out of the crater and sprayed glassy tektites over the Gulf of Mexico and Caribbean Seas. Much of the rest went well out of the atmosphere, solidified into varying sized ejecta particles (sand to boulder sized) on ballistic trajectories that caused them to reenter all over the Earth. Individually, their impacts on the atmosphere and ground would have been negligible. However, so many objects reentering the atmosphere and burning up at about the same time would have quickly radiated an enormous amount of heat onto the ground. In some places the temperature at ground level could have risen to as high as 1000C. This would have caused as much as 90% of all terrestrial plants to ignite quickly. All of this was in addition to the more "local effects" of the impact fireball and destruction caused by tidal waves.

Very fine dust and smoke that had been injected into the upper atmosphere remained suspended and scattered incoming light, reducing or completely halting photosynthesis for months. In addition, the blanket of dust caused Earth to plunge into a planet-wide winter with temperatures dropping by more than 40C for 6 months to a year.

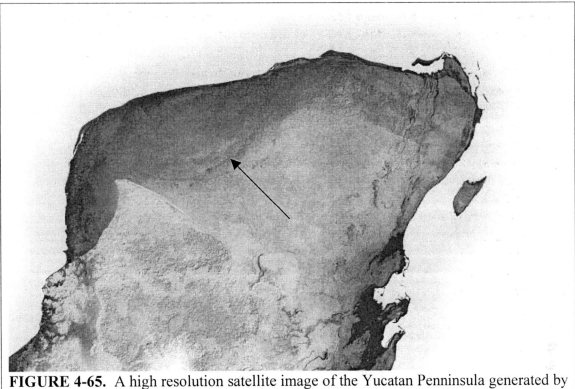

FIGURE 4-65. A high resolution satellite image of the Yucatan Penninsula generated by the JPL NASA Center. The image clearly shows the margin of the Chicxulub impact crater (at the arrow). From http://www.jpl.nasa.gov

The formation of nitrogen oxides (a combination of the two most common elements in the atmosphere during the explosion), caused strong acid rain events by the formation of nitric and nitrous acids in the lower atmosphere. However, the nitrogen oxides in the upper atmosphere combined with ozone and led to the rapid and prolonged depletion of the ozone layer. This effect could have lasted for decades.

The cooling was then followed by a very long general rise in temperature as the high altitude dust settled. Because the impactor hit carbonate-rich rock, enormous amounts of CO_2 were released immediately. In addition, the rise in CO_2 from fires and general depression of photosynthesis caused atmospheric carbon dioxide levels to rise producing a greenhouse warming for 10,000 to 500,000 years.

Many other effects of the planet killer meteors have been postulated, including the triggering of extended volcanic activity just from the jolt of the impact. Indeed, there is evidence of extended volcanic activity following the Chicxulub impact.

Clearly, even if only some of the effects occurred following the impact, widespread ecological collapse would have followed. Large terrestrial animals would have died quickly. Plants, because their seeds and spores were more resistant to cold and dark, would have fared better. A similar ecological collapse would have occurred in the oceans. Thus, the boundary between the Cretaceous and Tertiary periods was a very sharp one in which global biodiversity suddenly dropped by 70-80%.

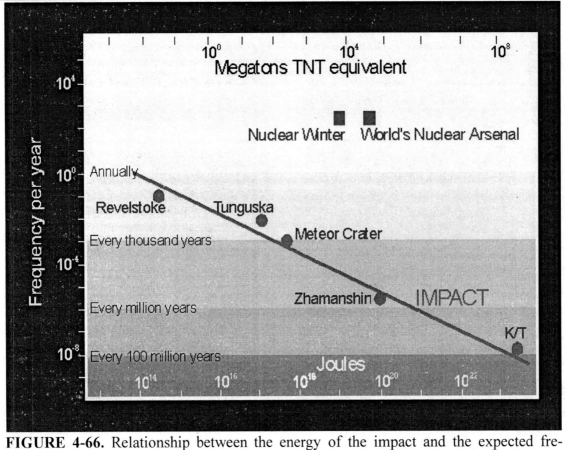

FIGURE 4-66. Relationship between the energy of the impact and the expected frequency of such a collision. From: http://impact.arc.nasa.gov/reports/spaceguard/sg-2.html

The history of this planet seemed to be punctuated by extinction events like that of the Cretaceous-Tertiary boundary. Indeed, the extinction at the end of the Permian Period (the boundary between the Paleozoic and Eras) was even more severe, and it was not triggered by an impactor. Either way, the loss of species was not permanent and recovery was rather quick by the measure of geological time. Of course that was good for the Earth, but not for the 70-80% of species that became extinct at the time of the catastrophe.

RISK

We are being told that the dangers are involuntary, irreversible, and hidden.
-Mary Douglas & Aaron Wildavsky

Fortunately, the occurrence of a Chicxulub (or K/T) sized asteroid impact is exceedingly rare, on the order of one per 100 million years (see Figure 4-66). However, this is an average. Such objects (10-20 kilometer asteroids) exist. Even smaller ones impacting the Earth could cause widespread destruction. In March 1989, a 0.5 kilometer wide asteroid passed within 700,000 miles of the Earth. Although that was beyond the moon, it was a near miss when considering that it takes Earth only a few hours to travel that distance in its orbit. An asteroid that size could have produced damage on the order of the Tunguska event or greater. More frightening to me is that the asteroid was not detected *until it had passed Earth.*

Risk assessment is a matter of weighing the likelihood of an event against its potential for harm. For example, a rare event that has very limited potential for damage can be ignored safely. However, rare events that have very damaging or devastating consequences cannot be ignored. It is to mitigate the financial blows of such events that people carry car, house, and life insurance.

Similarly, it would be prudent to carry a kind of global insurance by attempting to identify as many Near Earth Objects as possible and project the likelihood that they might impact our planet. With sufficient lead-time (on the order of 10-100 years), we could deflect the course of such objects with current technologies. However, if we observe a potential impactor a year before a collision, there is very little that could be done to prevent catastrophe. There are programs designed to identify and track these NEOs. Examples include NASA's Near Earth Asteroid Tracking System (NEAT); Spacewatch (University of Arizona); and Lowell Observatory NEO Survey (LONEOS); and Project Spaceguard. Such programs could be our global life insurance policy.

TUNGUSKA REVISITED

We know of no one that has died from an asteroid impact. That's true, but then who has ever died from a thermonuclear explosion? -Arthur C. Clarke

The Tunguska Event has caused a stir because it is difficult to explain. The damage is clear. The cause is becoming more clear, but still controversial.

We were very lucky that the Tunguska comet or rocky meteor struck Earth in such a remote location. However, if it had arrived just four hours later, it would have hit St Petersburg. That would have been a disaster of far greater magnitude. More frightening, what if the Tunguska comet/meteor had struck the Earth during the height of the cold war, say during the Cuban Missile Crisis? What would have been the global impact of a full retaliatory response?

1999, revised 2005

References:

Alvarez, Walter. 1997. *T. rex and the Crater of Doom.* Princeton University Press. Princeton, NJ.

Douglas, Mary and Aaron Wildavsky. 1982. *Risk and Culture.* University of California Press. Berkeley.

Monastersky, Richard. 1992. *Giant crater Linked to mass Extinction.* Science News 142:100.

Newman, James R. 1963. *Science and Sensibility.* Anchor Books. Doubleday & Co., Inc. Garden City.

Raup, David M. 1986. *The Nemesis Affair.* W.W. Norton & Co. New York.

Raup, David M. 1991. *Extinction, Bad Genes or Bad Luck?* W.W. Norton & Co. New York.

Sagan, Carl and Ann Druyan. 1997. *Comet.* Headline Book Publishing. London.

Steel, Duncan. 1995. *Rogue Asteroids and Doomsday Comets.* John Wiley and Sons, Inc. New York.

Sutton, Ann and Myron Sutton. 1962. *Nature on the Rampage.* J.B. Lippencott Co. New York.

Questions to Think About

1. What was the Tunguska event? Where did it occur?

    Huge explosion, fire in Tunguska Russia

2. Why was the expedition to the Tungus region delayed?

    Cold, WWI, Czarist revolution, Bolsheviks

3. Why do you suppose did the expedition spend so much time digging?

    Naturally to look for a crater

4. How was the Tunguska event similar to the Shoemaker-Levy-9 impact with Jupiter?

    Huge explosion little crater

5. How does the crater at Chicxulub satisfy the requirements for the impact site of a planet killer bolide?

    Size, location rock size

6. What cascade of events followed the impact of the Chicxulub bolide?

    Fires, CO_2, Ice age, heating, depletion of ozone, acid rain

7. Why did plants make the transition better than large dinosaurs?

    Seeds and spores need to eat, "breathe" CO_2

8. How likely is another such planet killer bolide impact?

    highly, lit possible

9. How does that relate to the concept of risk? What is being done to mitigate the risk?

    Still want to prepare, NASA

10. What could have happened if the Tunguska comet/meteor hit 4-5 hours later?

    Hit St. Petersburg

BURNING QUESTIONS AND REVOLUTIONS IN CHEMISTRY

A BURNING DESIRE

Scholars have speculated that gunpowder - a mixture of saltpetre, charcoal, and sulfur - was discovered during attempts to prepare an elixir of immortality. -William H. Brock, 1992.

When I was in Junior High School, I became very interested in how to make a big bang - not the cosmic but the pyrotechnic type. I knew that black gunpowder was made of sulfur, saltpeter, and charcoal. However, I discovered very quickly that knowing the components was not sufficient to make black gunpowder. Real gunpowder had to be made to exacting proportions; so, I experimented with the three ingredients (really, this dignifies the trial and error process that I actually used). I found the most effective proportions, but still I was not satisfied with the performance of the mixture.

I tried to grind the three constituents into a very fine powder in order to provide the most complete mixture. Then, it occurred to me that if I could dissolve the components together, I could get the most even mixture possible. Unfortunately, however, saltpeter was soluble in water, but sulfur was notoriously insoluble. After consulting some old chemistry texts, I found that sulfur would dissolve in carbon disulfide - a very smelly liquid. Anyway, I made a paste of the components and allowed the black cake to dry. Then, I broke it up and filtered out the large chunks with aluminum window screen. Still, it did not burn to my satisfaction.

I cast about for another idea, and then it came to me. I knew from previous experience that sulfur would melt if heated gently. Therefore, I heated the mixture in an old jar lid over the flame of an alcohol lamp. The sulfur began to melt as I had hoped that it would. Then, a bubble began to form in the middle of the lid. Quickly, I removed it from the flame, and the bubble deflated. BAM! It exploded. I ran up the basement steps and met my mother who had come down to investigate. There I stood in a sulfurous cloud with singed hair and a burned face. Later, my mother said that despite that despite the apparent trauma, all I did was shout, "It worked!"

LAVOISIER, A REVOLUTIONARY

The body of chemistry is prepared for its soul, and Lavoisier is born.
- George Eliot, 1872

I was not the only person to have trouble with gunpowder. In fact, the substance had always been somewhat capricious from its creation in China through the 18th Century in Europe. Not only was it hard to make, but it suffered from problems of consistency and quality control.

Antoine Lavoisier (1743-1794), a member of the lesser nobility in France, used his training in law, the sciences and a keen business sense particularly with regard to accounting, to oversee the gunpowder works at the National Arsenal. This was more than just a trivial government post. The quality of gunpowder in 1775 was a matter of national security for the French who were at war with the British and about to enter the American Revolution. Lavoisier brought all of his skill to bear on the problem and soon the Arsenal was producing the highest quality gunpowder in the world.

Lavoisier had used a large portion of his inheritance to purchase the finest chemical instruments in the world and had made significant contributions to the field of chemistry before his appointment to the Gunpowder Commission. His position and experience at the Arsenal spurred his interest in combustion. His methods confirmed for him that the total amount of matter that entered a reaction also ended up as its products. Thus, there was not net change in weight when considering all of the reactants. This Law of the Conservation of Matter was not new with Lavoisier. Indeed, the ancient Greeks had formulated the law. However, Lavoisier's adherence to the law of the conservation of matter caused him to stress the experimental method, the method of equation, and the methods of analysis and synthesis. His work led him to reject the prevailing views of the day, and in 1789 (the same year as the French Revolution) to produce a revolutionary document of his own, *Elements of Chemistry, in a New Systematic Order, Containing all the Modern Discoveries.* With this book, Lavoisier outlined the foundation and nature of what chemistry was to become in the 19th century.

What was so revolutionary about his book? What views did it help to supplant? How did it create a new discipline? Answers to these questions have to involve a return to the philosophies of the ancient Greeks.

ARISTOTLE, AGAIN

Sir Toby: Does not our lives consist of the four elements?
Sir Andrew: Faith, so they say; but I think it rather consists of eating and drinking.
Sir Toby: Th'art a scholar; let us therefore eat and drink.
Shakespeare, *Twelfth Night* II,iii

The earliest views of Thales of Miletus (c.625-c.550 B.C.) and his followers were that the material world was made of a single underlying substance. Thus, the apparent diversity of materials and their properties were illusions in a way. Thales said that all things were made of water; other Monists (those who believed in a single underlying material reality) gave it other names such as eperion, and fire. Pythagoras carried the concept to its most esoteric conclusion with his assertion that the underlying reality was number. All of the monist theories addressed both the material and how it combined to produce its sensible properties.

Later, a more elaborate concept that involved four elements supplanted the theories of the Monists. Aristotelian Four Element Theory was a formalization of the theories of Empedocles (ca. 450 B.C.) from Acragas in Sicily who said that four "elements" or principles each with a variable set of properties could explain the diversity of the material world.

Consider Figure 4-67. Fire and Water are elemental principles that are opposites and do not share properties. However, Water and Air share the property of moisture with a gradient from water to air. Similarly, adjacent elements share related properties. Thus, the four elements are not set as distinct entities but as variable entities with variable properties. Those variations coupled with the infinite range of possible proportions certainly could produce the variety that we sense in the material world.

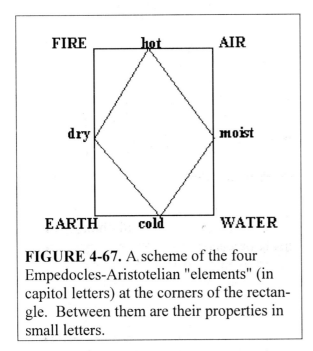

FIGURE 4-67. A scheme of the four Empedocles-Aristotelian "elements" (in capitol letters) at the corners of the rectangle. Between them are their properties in small letters.

Aristotle of Stagira (384-322 B.C.), a former student of Plato, left Athens following a dispute after Plato's death. He went north and became a tutor to the young prince, Alexander of Macedon. Following the conquests of Athens and of much of the known world by Alexander, Aristotle returned to Athens to teach. In the mean time, Alexander set up cities after the style of the Greeks throughout his empire, many of which were named for him (each one was called Alexandria). One such Alexandria on the Nile delta in Egypt became a Mecca for philosophers throughout the Greek world. The particular attraction was the library (also known as the Museum, a building and collection of manuscripts dedicated to the Muses). Within a generation, the seat of Greek Natural Philosophy moved from Athens to Alexandria. (Aristotle himself did not fare well after the death of Alexander. Forced to flee Athens, he died in exile in the north of Greece).

ALEXANDRIA AND ALCHEMY

Alchemy is a cosmic art by which parts of that cosmos -the mineral and animal parts- can be liberated from their temporal existence and attain states of perfection.   - Harry Sheppard, 1970

In Egypt, Greek Natural Philosophy came into contact with a very old material religion called Khemeia, meaning black. Adherents to the Black Art, later called Alchemy, dedicated themselves to the perfection of material things. Initially, the practitioners were those involved in the art of embalming but branched into other areas such as textile dyes, glass, and metallurgy. Their early work had allowed them to identify seven elements (gold, silver, copper, iron, tin, lead, and mercury). Because there were seven known planets, early alchemists had assumed that they had discovered one of the great secrets of nature and assigned attributes of the particular elements to the planets. As they embraced Aristotelian Natural Philosophy, particularly his Four Element Theory, they abandoned the old concept of element and adopted the concept of the element as principle. In this case, because the Aristotelian elements were variable, alchemists assumed that they had found a theoretical basis for the transmutation of materials, and they began to concentrate on the perfection of base metals to the highest form, gold.

This aspect of science was quite different from physics or biology. Little was written under the aegis of Alchemy whose terms and the symbols were deliberately cryptic and meant only for adepts. Similarly, methods of Alchemy employed very careful and precise procedures like distillation for purification and isolation of substances. These methods used instruments and glassware designed for particular purposes, which, too, remained hidden in the jargon of the practice.

After the fall of Rome and the decline of Natural Philosophy in the west, the Arab Empire rescued much of the learning of the Greeks. They did not just collect and house the knowledge but completed much original work in optics, astronomy, and medicine. Like Greek Natural Philosophy, Alchemy itself did not seem to spread west of Egypt until the advent of the Islamic Empire where, too, followers of the black art continued to practice.

Because the Islamic Empire stretched across Northern Africa, the straits of Gibraltar and into what is now Spain, Greek Natural Philosophy as well as Alchemy gained a foothold in Europe. After the fall of Toledo to Alfanzo VI of Castile in 1085, the great library there became available to the west. After centuries of translation and study, the western church incorporated Greek Natural Philosophy, particularly that of Aristotle into its orthodoxy.

At the same time, the west discovered the medicine of Hippocrates (c.460-370 B.C.), also a physician-philosopher from the early years of Alexandria. The Hippocratic Corpus defined a theory of health that mirrored the four-element theory of material. In particular, the body was healthy when its four fluids or humors (blood, phlegm, yellow bile, and black bile) were in balance. If one or more became too abundant, the body manifested a disease. For example, if a person had a fever, the face flushed, and felt warm. Therefore, the person had too much blood; so, the humors came back into balance by bleeding. In Hippocrates' view the humors tended to remain in equilibrium until

forced out of balance by the weather. (Even today, we speak of the flu season, etc.). Together with the works of Galen (129-199), a Roman Physician who wrote about physiology and anatomy, the Hippocratic Corpus formed the foundation of medical training in the tradition of Natural Philosophy.

IATROCHEMISTRY

A physician must seek for his knowledge and power within the divine spirit; if he seeks it in external things, he will be a pseudo-medicus and an ignoramus.
> -Paracelsus, ca. 1526

Physicians, however, were some of the staunchest adherents to the mystical philosophy of Alchemy. The secret preparation of elixirs and health potions fell right in line with the central purpose of the attainment of perfection. Around 1500 the conflict between Alchemy and Natural Philosophy heightened when Philippus Theophrastus, Bombast of Hohenheim, also known simply as Paracelsus (1493-1541) openly rejected the Hippocratic theory of disease.

The son of a physician, Paracelsus adopted the same profession, but never really settled down. He practiced throughout Europe as he wandered town to town. Later in life he was permitted to lecture at the University of Basel, but he did not have an official appointment there. During his practice, he openly scorned the Hippocrates-Galen tradition of medical training. Indeed, Paracelsus, the name that he gave himself, was a direct reference to a Greek medical author named Celsus. Paracelsus meant greater than Celsus.

He rejected the four humors theory of health and began to treat diseases with chemicals. He claimed that the poison was the cure (the same claim made by

Homeopathy today) and that health was a product of three principles: sulfur, mercury, and salt. The lack of harmony between the principles brought about disease. Thus, he claimed that each disease should have a separate, carefully prepared cure. This became the foundation of his form of Iatrochemistry, or medical chemistry.

Paracelsus, a practicing alchemist, was successful because his methods worked. In the tradition of the Renaissance, he rejected the hierarchy of Aristotle and gave a boost to an understanding that the life and non-life must obey some or all of the same laws of nature; otherwise, chemicals alone would not work as a cure for disease.

Paracelsus came into conflict with almost everyone who encountered him, friend and foe alike. He was driven out of many of the cities that he visited and died at 48 in Salzburg while treating the Bishop there. Still, he left behind many writings and had numerous followers. Indeed, he was seen as a medical counterpart to Luther's stand against orthodoxy, and the next 100 years saw the development of the chemistry of Paracelsus.

In Britain, Robert Boyle (1627-1691) attempted to explain the findings of chemistry in terms of mechanical philosophy (see *Old Books and Atoms* for a more indepth description of Boyle's experimental work, especially with regard to gasses). Boyle began to describe chemical elements as "elementary substances like sulfur". Further, he studied combustion and noticed that a flame in a container absorbed part of the air. Similarly, a mouse in a jar absorbed some of the air. Thus, he speculated that some part of the air was vital for both respiration and combustion. He knew that gunpowder, a highly flammable substance, contained a nitrogenous substance (saltpeter). Likewise, air contained another nitrogenous substance.

Thus, the nitrous spirit was responsible for both.

PHLOGISTON

In the course of my inquiries, I was, however, soon satisfied that that atmospherical air is not an unalterable thing; for that the phlogiston with which it becomes loaded...depraves it, as to render it altogether unfit for inflammation...
                                    -Joseph Priestley, 1784

By the end of the 17th Century, the German Iatrochemical School had developed the three principles of Paracelsus to explain combustion as well. Sulfur represented the principle of inflammability. Mercury was the principle of volatility and salt was the principle of fixity. Again, these were not elemental substances but properties or states of matter.

Joachim Becher (1635-1682) of Mainz (in present-day Germany) extended the theory of German Iatrochemistry by addressing the nature of chemical change, something that the Aristotelian four-element theory could not do. He said that solids (or earths) contain each of the three Paracelsan principles: salt, mercury, and sulfur. Combustion was the separation of the sulfur principle from a solid.

Georg Ernst Stahl (1660-1734) called the sulfur principle phlogiston, a name derived from the Greek word for burning. Stahl said that the light and heat in a fire was phlogiston, and the ash left behind after burning a substance like charcoal was devoid of phlogiston and, therefore, could not burn. Similarly, metals could burn if ground finely enough. Thus, iron filings burned and gave off phlogiston. The residue of rust (also called a calx) was the metal minus phlogiston; so, the calx was the more elementary substance (see Figure 4-68).

Metal ⟶ Calx + Phlogiston
FIGURE 4-68. The relationship between a calx, phlogiston, and the metal.

This explanation served in a variety of ways. It provided a universal explanation for the phenomenon of combustion. Secondly, it explained why combustion could not occur in a vacuum and why combustion ceased in a closed container. The vacuum had no air to absorb the phlogiston, and the air in a closed container became so filled with phlogiston that no more could leave the combustible object.

Soon, adherents to the phlogiston theory began to find it a useful explanation for their studies of gasses. In Britain Joseph Black (1728-1799) prepared a new kind of air (we call it carbon dioxide) by heating limestone. He collected this air and found that it would not support combustion. In fact, he made the same air by burning charcoal. In addition, respiration and fermentation produced it. Thus, this new gas, which he called fixed air, seemed to be phlogiston itself.

Henry Cavendish (1731-1810) also studied a variety of gasses. He took inflammable air (hydrogen), a substance that Robert Boyle had studied, and exploded it with a spark. He found that the product of his experiments was pure water. Further, he used methods that he had developed for weighing gasses to show that the inflammable air (and the mass of the atmospheric air) accounted for the mass of the water produced. Thus, water could not be an element.

Perhaps one of the most interesting chemists of his day was Joseph Priestley (1733-1804), also from Britain. He was a non-conformist or Unitarian minister with an interest in almost everything who developed a fascination for the sciences through his contact with Benjamin Franklin (1706-1790). At first, the phenomenon of electricity occupied his attention. Then he turned to the study of gasses.

Like Robert Hooke, Priestley was a superb experimentalist. One of his earliest investigations involved an examination of fixed air (carbon dioxide) and its solubility in water. He went to a nearby brewery and poured a glass of water back and forth above the vat. Soon, he had developed soda water.

He experimented with a variety of other gasses, some of which were soluble in water. Thus, he made a trough filled with mercury and collected the gas over that (see Figure 4-69). In addition, he used a large lens (he called it a burning glass) to generate clean heat to separate components of calcinated substances.

In his most famous set of experiments, Priestley used *mercurius calcinus*, a red oxide of mercury as a source of gas. He heated the red oxide until the calx turned to the quicksilver of mercury and a gas collected in his trough. The air that accumulated had some interesting properties. It was colorless and poorly soluble in water. The most interesting aspect was that the air supported a burning candle with a very bright flame. He put mice in it and kept them alive much longer than in regular air. He even tried breathing it himself and recommended it as a medical treatment.

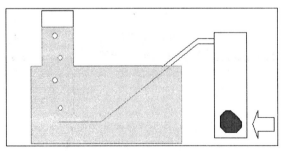

The degree that this new air supported combustion convinced Priestley that he had isolated a kind of air that had no phlogiston in it. It supported combustion so vigorously because it pulled phlogiston out of combustible substances. Thus, Priestley called his new gas "dephlogisticated air".

In 1774, Priestley visited Lavoisier in Paris and described the methods by which he had collected dephlogisticated air. Lavoisier saw the importance of the discovery almost immediately and repeated the experiments that Priestley had performed. He noticed that as the red *mercurius calcinatus* weighed more than the mercury that it produced upon heating. In addition, as the air recombined with the hot mercury, the resulting calx weighed more than the original mercury did by the weight of the collected gas. Lavoisier, who wished to save the law of the conservation of matter leapt at the explanation that the mercury and the dephlogisticated air were different elements and they combined to form the calx of mercury. He called the element oxygen or acid maker.

ELEMENTS OF CHEMISTRY

We think only through the medium of words. Languages are true analytical methods. -Antoine Lavoisier

Lavoisier soon developed a general theory of combustion that abandoned the need for phlogiston. He said that as objects burn or become calcinated they combine with oxygen. He explained Cavendish's results with inflammable air (Lavoisier called it hydrogen or water maker) as a combination of the elements hydrogen and oxygen.

Elements of Chemistry (see Figure 4-70 for the title page) introduced his new concept of chemical element, which he defined as "the last point that analysis can reach". This he borrowed from Boyle, but Lavoisier actually demonstrated it. He listed 33 elements in the text, but some like light and heat (he called it caloric) were not material and others were compounds.

With new elements, he had to come up with a new precise way to standardize chemical names. He developed the same method that we still use today. Thus, after *Elements* chemistry looked modern and waited only for the advent of Dalton's atomic theory to make the transition complete.

Lavoisier wrote *Elements of Chemistry* in a very clear style. His wife, Marie, helped him with the text, the experiments, and illustrations. Although the book itself presented no new discoveries, Lavoisier had skillfully compiled a set of laws and methods in a way that was consonant and formed the foundation of a completely new science.

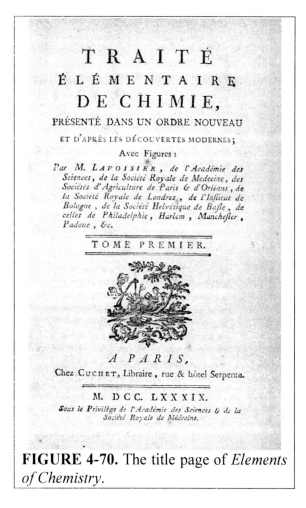

FIGURE 4-70. The title page of *Elements of Chemistry*.

ENDINGS AND BEGINNINGS

It required only a moment to sever his head, and probably 100 years will not produce another like it. Lagrange, 1794

Priestley continued his experimental work but was forced out of Britain for his opposition to the armed intervention in the American War of Independence and for his support for the French Revolution. Indeed, a local mob burned his house to the ground. After that, he moved his family to London, but did not find peace until he came to the United States to live out his last days up the Susquehanna River, just a few miles from my home.

Black converted to the antiphlogiston science of Lavoisier. However, neither Cavendish nor Priestley ever gave up the theory of phlogiston. The Germans were equally slow in accepting the chemistry of Lavoisier but came around about a generation later.

Lavoisier did not live to see the triumph of his book. On May 8, 1794 Marat, his political enemy, denounced Lavoisier who was then charged with treason and sentenced to the guillotine. Perhaps the only true charge in the list of indictments was that he had been a tax collector under the old regime. Thus, the revolutionary died in a revolution, but his words lived on. The logic of Lavoisier's argument as a simpler explanation for combustion and the formation of compounds brought about the demise of the phlogiston theory. Thus the quest for elements began, and the *Elements of Chemistry* set the agenda for the science of chemistry through much of the coming century.

-October 2001, revised 2005

References:

Brock, William H. 1992. *The Norton History of Chemistry.* W.W. Norton & Co. New York.

Brown, Ira., ed. 1962. *Joseph Priestley, Selections from his Writings.* The Pennsylvania University Press. University Park, PA

Dunbar, Robin. 1995. *The Trouble with Science.* Harvard University Press. Cambridge.

Harre, Rom. 1981. *Great Scientific Experiments.* Phaidon. Oxford.

Holt, Jack R. and Patricia Nelson. 2001. *Paths of Science.* Kendall/Hunt Publishing Co. Dubuque..

Jaffe, Bernard. 1931. *Crucibles, The Lives and Achievements of the Great Chemists.* Jarrolds Publishers. London.

Lavoisier. Antoine; trans. Robert Kerr. 1965 (originally 1789). *Elements of Chemistry.* Dover Publications, Inc. New York.

Mason, Stephen F.1962. *A History of the Sciences.* Collier Books. New York.

Schofield, Robert E. 2004. *The Enlightened Joseph Priestley, A Study of his Life and*

Work from 1773 to 1804. The Pennsylvania State University Press. University Park, PA.

Strathern, Paul. 2000. *Mendeleyev's Dream,* *The Quest for the Elements.* Thomas Dunne Books, St. Martin's Press. New York.

Questions to Think About

1. How did Lavoisier's study of gunpowder cause him to consider elements in a different way? Why was the post that Lavoisier held so critical to France in the latter half of the 18th century? *This post was a matter of national security as quality of gun powder is vital.*

2. What was the Monist theory of material? In what important way was Pythagoras different from the other Monists? *Material world is made of one single-underlying substance. Pythagoras - underlying reality was number.*

3. How was the theory of Empedocles and Aristotle different from that of the Monists? How was it different from the theory of material of today? *Four elements each with changeable set of properties can explain the diversity of the material world. (Fire, Water, Air, Earth), Material made of many more elements*

4. What was the origin of Alchemy? How did its basic theory fit well into the concept of health and disease? *- Alchemy - Chinese, Egyptian - Greek natural philosophy, Black; perfection of material things, 7 elements. Body is healthy when fluids are in balance*

5. Who was Paracelsus and how did he change chemistry and medicine? *rejected hippocratic theory of disease, each disease has its own separate cure treated diseases with chemicals*

6. What is phlogiston? How did the phlogiston theory of combustion differ from that of today? *Phlogiston is what makes objects burn. Must be in the item to burn. Released after burning.*

7. Who was Joseph Priestley? To what fields of science did Priestley contribute? To what other fields besides science did Priestley contribute? *Unitarian Minister. Isolated air which had no phlogiston in it. Medicine.*

8. Why did Priestley leave Britain and settle in the US? *Opposed Armed intervention in the US and supported the French Revolution.*

9. The essay indicates that Priestley and Lavoisier together brought about the great revolution in thought that led to modern chemistry. What contributions did each one make?

10. What was the importance of *Elements of Chemistry*? *Elements chemistry*

IN HOT WATER

IN COLD WATER

There are many who...recite their writings while bathing.... -Horace

During the semester break the house was busy with guests. The ambiance of the house, which usually resembled a quiet library, changed to that of a train station. Anyway, the increased activity brought about problems in unexpected ways. Most importantly, we began to notice that the hot water never seemed to be available or nearly enough. Finally, around the New Year (major appliances always seem to self-destruct on a holiday) I turned on the hot water faucet and let the water run...and run...and run. The water did not warm up. I went into the basement and fiddled with the electric water heater and discovered that it had blown a fuse. No problem. I just removed the old fuse, and put in a fresh 30amp fuse. I listened for the reassuring squeals, groans, and pops that told me the elements were heating water. Within 15 minutes the water was warm enough to take a very quick shower.

I assured myself that the fuse had blown because of heavy usage. Anyway I satisfied myself that I had fixed the problem. Imagine my surprise when I returned home that evening to discover that the water was cold...again. This led me through a series of steps to narrow the cause of the problem. Finally, after I had exhausted all possibilities (and had blown 16 more fuses), I resigned myself to the reality that an element had shorted out and had to be replaced. By this time, I had read enough about replacing a heating element to know that I did not want to try it myself. So, I called a plumber. My concern was borne out when a quick and easy 15-minute job turned into a messy 2-hour chore. The

element was not just bad, but it was embedded in a slurry of freshwater limestone or calcium carbonate. The plumber scraped and muttered. Finally he lectured me about how to maintain the hot water heater as he handed me the bill.

FIGURE 4-71. My hot water heater with a pile of calcium carbonate that had been scraped from the inside.

The fundamental problem with the hot water heater is the water, which in Freeburg Borough comes from groundwater which has been in contact with limestone or calcium carbonate ($CaCO_3$). Small amounts of weakly soluble limestone dissolve into water as a salt (much less soluble than common table salt). In fact, my drinking water has just about as much $CaCO_3$ as it can hold. That is, it is saturated in calcium carbonate. That's O.K. as far as drinking goes. However, when water is heated, the dissolved $CaCO_3$ salt acts very strangely. It begins to come out of solution and coat heating elements and the insides of pipes, a kind of hardening of the house arteries. Calcium and to a lesser extent Magnesium salts behave this way, and water that contains significant concentrations of one or both of these elements is called hard water.

Hard water can be a nuisance in other ways, too. Calcium ions interfere with the solubility of soap and make it hard to remove. Thus, slick skin and soapy hair can be another consequence of hard water. Unfortunately, this situation means that the bather must use more hot water to eliminate the soap.

PH AND POWERS OF 10

The value of the hydrogen ion concentration...will have the form of a negative power of 10.   -Soren Sorenson

Now, rain is just about the least hard of all water. Neither calcium nor magnesium occurs in the air, but there are other substances that commonly do occur and dissolve into water. Their presence can change water and make it acidic. Indeed, the acidity or pH of a solution is based on the tendency of pure water (H_2O) to separate into charged H^+ and OH^-. This tendency is very slight such that at neutrality ($H^+ = OH^-$), the amount of H^+ is only 0.0000001g per liter.

Soren Sorenson (1868-1939), a Danish chemist, recognized that the strengths of acids depend on the concentration of H^+ and set about to create a scale that defined "actual degrees of acidity" in 1909. Because he found it cumbersome to deal with such small numbers, he produced the pH scale that uses the negative exponent of the hydrogen ion concentration (That is, negative power of 10 or negative log). Thus, 0.0000001 can be written as 10^{-7}g hydrogen ions per liter, and its pH is -(-7) or pH 7. In this way, pH 3 is $10^{-3} gH^+/L$. Note that this means for each change in pH unit, there is a 10-fold change in H^+. For example, pH 6 has 10 times more H^+

than pH 7. A drop from pH 7 to pH 3 means a 10^4 increase (7-3) in H^+.

By far, the most common acid maker is simple carbon dioxide (CO_2). When it dissolves in water, the combination makes carbonic acid (H_2CO_3). In fact, CO_2 is so soluble (about 200 times more so than oxygen) that it makes all natural rainwater somewhat acidic.

The normal amount of CO_2 that dissolves into water makes rain water about pH 5.6. This is about 25 times more acidic than neutrality. Slightly acidic rain then can percolate into the ground where it picks up more CO_2 from decomposition in the soil. This weak carbonic acid reacts with minerals in the soil and bedrock. The resulting process dissolves minerals, including calcium carbonate, deep underground. Therefore, dissolved limestone in groundwater is the major contributor to hard water.

The dissolution of limestone, if given enough time can leave cavities or caves in otherwise solid rock. I can see an example of that phenomenon right outside my back door. The ridge behind my house, which consists primarily of limestone, is riddled with caves. In fact, the underlying bedrock of the whole valley is mainly limestone. It should not be surprising that groundwater in that valley has high levels of calcium carbonate, therefore, such water is somewhat hard.

I explained how limestone got into the hot water heater. However, I did not explain why it came out of solution and caused the problem. Simply put, calcium carbonate was a salt, but it was not very soluble. That is, it occurred only in very low concentrations in water. Anything that reduced the solubility, then, could cause additional calcium carbonate to come out of solution as a precipitate.

In part, the explanation for this behavior has to do with the nature of carbonic acid, H_2CO_3. This can dissociate into water and carbon dioxide. Depending on the pH, it can dissociate into H^+ and HCO_3^-, or $2H^+$ and CO_3^{--}. Both carbonate (CO_3^{--}) and bicarbonate (HCO_3^-) require large amounts of dissolved CO_2 to remain in solution. Although carbonate and bicarbonate are ions, CO_2 is a gas and gasses are driven out of water as the temperature rises. The relationship between different forms of inorganic carbon in water can be seen in Figure 4-72. At pH 8.3, almost all of the inorganic carbon exists as bicarbonate (HCO_3^-). However, water at pH 7 has a mixture of free CO_2 and HCO_3^- in equilibrium.

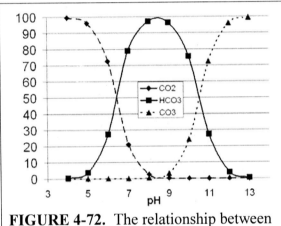

FIGURE 4-72. The relationship between different forms of carbonate (also called inorganic carbon) relative to pH. From Wetzel, 1983.

So how can that explain what happened in my hot water heater? Well, the heating elements heated the water and drove its CO_2 out of solution, which caused the pH necessarily to rise. Carbonate (CO_3^-), a form of inorganic carbon that is relatively insoluble, especially when it combines with calcium, appears. If the shift produces enough carbonate, the excess fell out as a precipitate.

This effect can be seen in places other than hot water heaters. I have visited very hard water sites in Oklahoma and Pennsylvania. Freshwater limestone or travertine forms around actively growing algae and plants. What happens in that

case? Instead of heat, the photosynthetic organism removes CO_2 from the boundary layer around it and the calcium carbonate falls out of solution. Coral uses the photosynthesis of its symbiotic algae in a similar way to extract calcium carbonate from seawater in the construction of great coral reefs. In fact, the strange chemistry of inorganic carbon, particularly that of calcium carbonate, led to the precipitation and formation of the vast limestone deposits through which my drinking water percolates.

A RAIN STORM

The sky is changed,-and such a change!
O night
And storm, and Darkness! -Lord Byron

Rain is the ultimate source of that percolating groundwater, and it determines the success (and failure) of agriculture that is so pervasive in my area. Still, water in rain has its own chemistry that influences that of surface and groundwater. In order to understand that influence, I have followed the courses of a number of rainstorms through the years that I have lived in central Pennsylvania.

I recall one storm in particular that lasted from February 11-12, 1998 (see Table 4-7). Rain began to fall by 6:30 p.m. In anticipation of the event, I had set up a simple collection device to estimate the volume of the rainfall and its pH (see Figure 4-73).

Rain fell steadily, and I collected 25ml of rain during the first hour. [That converted to 317milliliters per square meter per hour ($ml/m^2/hr$)]. Also, instead of 5.5, the pH of this rainwater was 4.5. That is, it was ten times more acidic than I had expected *if the only dissolved substance that contributed to pH were CO_2.* Obviously, something else was in the rainwater.

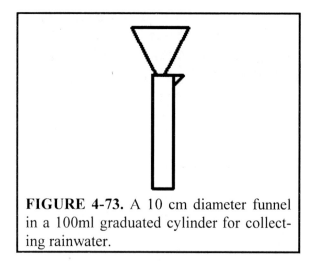

FIGURE 4-73. A 10 cm diameter funnel in a 100ml graduated cylinder for collecting rainwater.

After an hour, I put the collector outside again. Rain fell at the same rate as during the first hour (317 ml/m^2/hr). However, this time pH fell to 3.4, another ten-fold increase in acidity. What was happening?

Air can contain strong acids such as sulfuric and nitric acids. Sulfuric acid (H_2SO_4) is produced naturally and released by volcanic activity. Also, burning coal, particularly soft or high sulfur coal can produce it. Similarly, nitric acid (HNO_3) is made by the action of lightning in an atmosphere made of nitrogen and oxygen gasses. Humans produce. nitric acid by reactions that occur within the internal combustion engine.

The distribution of pH in rainfall over the U.S. shows a distinct plume over central Pennsylvania that falls in the pH 4-5 range. Most of that excess acid is due to the release of sulfates from coal-fired power plants and heavy industries in the Ohio valley. Curiously, some claim that we worry too much about acid sulfate deposition because natural sources such as volcanoes produce so much. Still, no one can deny the regional influence of burning coal. That is, there are no volcanoes in Ohio.

What happens when such acid rain strikes the ground? Well, soil buffers or absorbs the acid very well, so there is little or no impact. Although statues

markers, and similar limestone or marble structures can be damaged by chemical dissolution.

The pH of surface water like ponds, lakes, rivers, and creeks might be influenced depending on the amount of carbonate in the system. That is, the more carbonate, the more acid it can absorb before its pH begins to change.

This carbonate buffer system is particularly good at resisting changes in pH down to about 4.5. Below that, all inorganic carbon occurs as free CO_2 or carbonic acid. How well a carbonate system can buffer water is determined by the amount of inorganic carbon present, particularly in the bicarbonate and carbonate forms. I measure this by adding a standard sulfuric acid solution to 250 ml of water. The resulting calculation is called the Acid Neutralizing Capacity or ANC and is expressed in μ equivalents H^+ that can be absorbed per liter of lake water. For hydrogen ions 1 μg/L = 1 μeq/L[11].

I study two small lakes in western Union County, Pennsylvania. They are only about a mile apart, but one is on sandstone (no carbonate) and the other is on limestone (calcium carbonate). Typically, 250 ml of water from the sandstone basin can absorb about 1 ml of standard acid before its pH reaches 4.5. That translates to an ANC of about 100μeq/L. So, each liter of water can absorb about 10^{-4}g H^+/L (note that this is the same amount of H^+ as in pH 4).

The limestone pond (see Figure 4-74), however, can absorb up to 20 ml of the same acid before the buffer system is broken. Thus, the well-buffered pond has an ANC of 1,600μeq/L which means

---

[11] 1 μg/L is a millionth of a gram in a liter. 1 μeq/L is a millionth of an equivalent per liter. An equivalent in the case of hydrogen ions is equal to the gram mass of the ions that react. Because the atomic weight of hydrogen is very

l, 1 μg/L = 1 μeq/L.

that each liter of lake water can absorb H^+ equal *to less than pH 3*. Clearly, only waters that occur in poorly buffered basins are at risk from acid rain. Unfortunately, such areas are not rare in the northeastern U.S. Parts of the ridge and valley province in Pennsylvania, the Poconos, and Adirondacks, just to name a few, are areas that continue to be damaged by acid rain.

FIGURE 4-74. A photograph of the well-buffered pond that I study in Union County, PA. Note the outcrop of limestone in the center of the photo.

I continued to monitor the storm. By the fifth hour, the rain had begun to taper off. Finally, from midnight on to the end of the rain at nine the next morning, the "rain" was just a continuous drizzle. Still, the drizzle-fog through the night had a pH of about 3.4 (this is about 160 times more H^+ than natural rainwater at pH 5.6).

TABLE 4-7. History of a rainstorm on February 11-12, 1998 in Selinsgrove, PA. Water was collected by the apparatus shown in Figure 4-73 for at least one hour (8 hours for the last reading). Rate of rainfall is given as $ml/m^2/hr$.

Hour	pH	rate of rainfall
1	4.5	317
3	3.4	317
5	4.0	203
7-15	3.4	18

The surprising result of this observation was the pH throughout the storm. The textbook explanation of acid precipitation suggests that the pH should be quite low at the beginning of the storm as rainwater washes out gaseous and particulate sulfates and nitrates. After that, the pH should rebound to near normal levels. Obviously, this did not happen. The pH began low, went lower (more acidic), and stayed very low until the end of the storm.

Ecological problems often defy simple answers because they are complex systems with many interacting parameters. Still, regardless of the trajectory of pH values during the storm, a pH range of 3.4-4.5 is unusually low. Distant volcanoes or lightning strikes cannot explain that range. The only good explanation is an anthropogenic (human-produced) cause.

AN ACID HELL
Between us and heaven or hell there is nothing but life, which of all things is the frailest.   -Blaise Pascal

As bad as northeastern U.S. looks, there are areas in the U.S. that have been reduced to moonscapes by the local ravages of acidic air pollution. Still, there is a place in our solar system that makes even these places look like paradise.

Venus[12], with its run-away greenhouse warming, has a thick atmosphere of CO_2 and a surface temperature that approaches 460C. The planet is always shrouded in clouds, however, these clouds are not made of water but of concentrated sulfuric acid. On Venus, there is unrelenting acid rain.

Fortunately, our planet was saved from that horrible fate by the occurrence of life. Carbon dioxide became incorporated into the carbon of living things. Life augmented (perhaps led to) the precipitation of dissolved CO_2 as limestone that served to trap most of the inorganic carbon on earth. Some of which forms the great beds of limestone through which groundwater percolates beneath my hometown.

This morning, after my shower, I went to the basement to check on the hot water heater and see that the timer, to which it was attached, still allowed it to come on only about four hours a day. Then, I checked the water softener to make sure that it operated properly to trap calcium ions before they went into the water heater.

Complex problems like acid rain, global warming, water pollution, and broken hot water heaters do not have universal answers. However, my guiding principle must be to think globally, but act locally.

-1998; revised 2005

References:

Fishbein, Seymour L., ed. 1976. *Our Continent, A Natural History of North America.* National Geographic Society. Washington, D.C.

Gallant, Roy A. 1986. *National Geographic Picture Atlas of Our Universe.* National Geographic Society. Washington, D.C.

Goody, Richard. 1995. *Principles of Atmospheric Physics and Chemistry.* Oxford University Press. New York.

Huggett, Richard John. 1997. *Environmental Change, The Evolving Ecosphere.* Routledge. New York.

Hutchinson, G. Evelyn. 1957. *A Treatise on Limnology. Volume 1. Geography, Physics and Chemistry.* John Wiley & Sons, Inc. New York.

Shriner, David S., Chester R. Richmond, and Steven E. Lindberg, eds. 1980. *Atmospheric Sulfur Deposition, Environmental Impact and Health Effects.* Ann Arbor Science Publishers, Inc. Ann Arbor, MI.

Wetzel, Robert G. 1983. *Limnology.* 2nd ed. Saunders College Publishing. New York.

Wilson, Edward O. 1994. *Naturalist.* Island Press/ Shearwater Books. Washington, D.C.

Information used in writing this essay also came from:
http://www.epa.gov/
http://www.nasa.gov/

---

[12] See my essay *Inferno and Purgatorio* for further information about Venus and its atmosphe

Questions to Think About

1. What is hard water? What causes water to become hard?

   Water that contain significant amounts of Calcium, and sometimes, magnesium. Limestone dissolving in water

2. What is pH? What does it mean?

   Measure of acidity in a solution - based on tendency of H_2O to separate into charged H^+ and OH^- Scale that defines actual degrees of acidity

3. What is special about pH 7?

   Mixture of free CO_2 & HCO_3^- in equilibrium Neither Acidic nor basic.

4. What does calcium carbonate precipitate out of solution when water is heated? What else can cause it to come out of solution?

   Heating elements drive the CO_2 out of the solution, which caused pH to rise. CO_3 is relatively insoluble, especially when mixed with Calcium. -photosynthetic organisms can remove CO_2

5. Why is all rainwater slightly acidic?

   CO_2 in the air mixes w/ the rain causing the slight acidity. Also, Sulfuric and nitric acids help.

6. What are the primary acidifying agents found in acid rain? What are their anthropogenic sources?

   Nitric Acid - combustion engines. CO_2 - Breathing engine Sulfuric Acid - Burning Coal

7. Why is the northeastern US so prone to acidic precipitation? Is all of it harmful?

   . Coal-fueled powerplants and heavy industry in OHIO . No, but it depends on where it lands

8. What happened during the storm? What could explain the difference in acidity?

   . pH got lower and lower during the storm

9. What is the concept of Acid Neutralizing Capacity? What is its implication in the determination of acid-sensitive water?

   ANC is H+ that can be absorbed per unit of lake water. Amount of buffering needed, what is the Shows how much buffering is needed.

10. Describe the conditions on Venus. How could they be explained relative to carbon dioxide.

    Rough - CO_2 atmosphere, 460°C. Greenhouse

OLD BOOKS AND ATOMS

AN OLD BOOK

I love everything that's old, - old friends, old times, old manners, old books, old wine...and old friends are best!

-Goldsmith (1773)

When I was an undergraduate student, I stumbled into a small-town used bookstore in central Arkansas. The store was not large, but I remember that it had a dimly-lit back room with a rickety book case. I scanned the bookcase in the darkness and happened upon an old manual of Chemistry, published in 1821 (see Figure 4-75 for an image of the title page). I recall that the book sold for $25.00, an amount that I never carried with me. Amazed at the age and condition of the book, I showed it to my companion. Immediately, he wanted to buy it, too. Of course, he did not carry enough money with him, either. So, we raced each other back to campus to beg and borrow the amount necessary to purchase the book. Somehow, I managed to gather the funds first and rushed back to buy it. I began to have second thoughts as I handed the collection of bills and change to the shop owner, but I bought the book anyway.

I carried the "treasure" back to campus and began to read it. The book did not have an index, so I read excerpts as I searched for archaic or alchemical references. Instead, I found a rather modern view of chemistry couched in antiquated phrases and very tiny type. By the time I finished my first perusal of the book, the sky had darkened and the old leather of the cover had stained my jeans and hands.

On Monday morning I took the book to my General Chemistry teacher. As fate would have it, the friend whom I had beaten in getting the book was there, too. I showed the book to the chemistry teacher and we began to relate the details of our race. How-

ever, he clearly was not listening to us. As he looked at the book, he became more and more excited, and flipped through the pages so rapidly that the covers came off in his hands. Then, he began to show me the "subtleties" that I had missed. First, there were no chemical formulas through the whole 338 pages of text. The author made only vague references to an atomic theory that had been amended by an American chemist. He kept the book for most of the remainder of the semester under the pretext of reattaching the covers, which he did not do. I did get it back before I left school for the summer break. As he handed it to me, he asked if I planned to be a teacher. I responded that I didn't know. Anyway, he said that this book would be a very interesting addition to a science course because it shows some of the ferment that occurred when modern chemistry was just getting started.

In particular, the ferment involved the search for elements and confirmation of the atomic theory of matter. Chemistry did this as it quickly shed itself of the vestments of alchemy, a view that clung to the belief that matter was made of four elements (earth, air, fire, and water) that were continuous and not packaged into discrete, indivisible units. This preatomic view had appeal because it seemed simpler than the notion that atoms might exist, or worse, that there might be a void between them. Rejection of the concept of the void was almost universal among the Greeks, a view that influenced science well into the 19th century. One of the earliest challenges to Alchemical-Aristotelian chemistry came in the 17th Century.

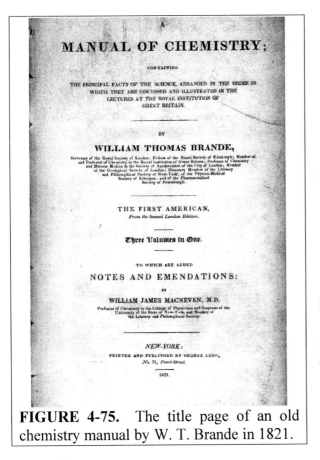

FIGURE 4-75. The title page of an old chemistry manual by W. T. Brande in 1821.

THE SCEPTICAL CHYMIST

For some learned men have been rather content to believe what they so boldly affirm, than be at the trouble and charge, to try whether or not it be true.

-Robert Boyle (1661)

Robert Boyle (1627-1691) was the 14th child of the Earl of Cork in Ireland. He was educated at Eton, and then spent much of his youth in Geneva. While there, he traveled to Italy where he became acquainted with the experimental work of Galileo. By the time he returned to England in 1644, he had become a staunch believer in the experimental method and joined the so-called Invisible College at Oxford where anti-Aristotelian sentiment ran high.

Boyle's talent as a theoretician required an equally talented experimentalist to explore his ideas. He found such a man in Robert Hooke (1635-1703), and as a team, they began to investigate concepts of chemistry based on the mechanistic philosophy of experiment and mathematics. Much of their experimental work involved the study of air and the relationships between temperature, volume, and pressure. In particular, their research demonstrated a clear mathematical relationship between those attributes of "air" (today we would use the more general term, gas).

Hooke improved the design of a vacuum pump and assisted Boyle in experimental work that became known as Boyle's Law, the first empirical law of chemistry. In a way, this served as a significant challenge to the Aristotelian view that a vacuum was not necessary as an explanation for the elemental composition of material things. After all, the vacuum pump could draw down a vacuum, and, more importantly, the results of Boyle's gas experiments suggested that air was made of small spring-like particles (he called them corpuscles) that moved about in the void. The speed with which they moved depended upon their temperatures.

Suppose that we have a closed container with a given volume of gas. As the gas warms up (and the volume does not change), the pressure rises. Boyle reasoned that the gas contains a given number of spring-like corpuscles. As they absorb heat, they move faster and strike the walls of the container with more force. This manifests itself at our scale by an increase in pressure. Aristotelians responded that the pressure should increase because more of the element heat (or fire) entered the container.

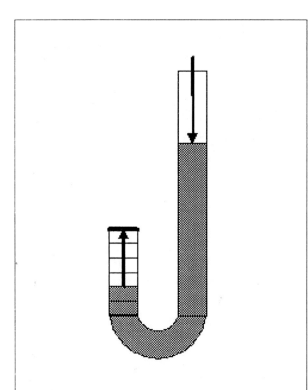

FIGURE 4-76. A diagram of the device used by Hooke and Boyle to investigate the relationship between pressure and volume. They increased pressure by pouring mercury into the top of the j-tube with the shorter arm sealed. The scale on the short arm allowed them to measure volume while the height of the mercury column determined pressure. Redrawn from Conant (1951).

The relationship between volume and pressure could not easily be explained by invoking the Aristotelian dogma. That is, if a sealed volume of gas doubles in size (a plunger rises in a cylinder) and the temperature remains constant, the pressure drops. Boyle reasoned that this result could be explained *only* if the gas were made of separate springy particles moving through a larger vacuum when the volume increased.

Hooke was talented at making and using particular experimental equipment. For example, the device in Figure 4-76 served to increase the pressure of a gas that was trapped in the shorter leg of the J-tube. The

pressure (inferred as inches of mercury) increased while the gas followed a predictable and repeatable decrease in volume.

Boyle further theorized that the number of elements might be much greater than the four (or three) required by Aristotle. He inferred this from examinations of the products of combustion, particularly the multiple compounds produced when wood burns. The mechanistic philosophy of Boyle had a great influence on Isaac Newton (1642-1727), who likewise adopted the corpuscular view of nature.

ELEMENTS AND ELECTRICITY

In the present state of our knowledge, it would be useless to attempt to speculate on the remote cause of the electrical energy...; its relation to chemical affinity is, however, sufficiently evident. May it not be identical with it, and an essential property of matter? -Humphry Davy

For more than a century, the Aristotelian-Alchemical continued to hold sway. However, the experimental approach to the investigation of chemical phenomena had led to much knowledge about gasses, metals, alkalis, acids, etc. The old explanations had become more forced and unsatisfactory

Antoine-Laurent Lavoisier (1743-1794) compiled the existing chemical knowledge with the new view that nature consisted of many elements[13]. He defined element as a substance that could not be decomposed into simpler substances. He compiled these ideas in his *Treatise on the Elements of Chemistry* in 1789, the same year as the French Revolution. The treatise took a modern ap-

---

[13] See *Burning Questions* for a more complete explanation of Lavoisier as the founder of modern chemistry.

proach and defined 33 different elements (he treated heat and light as elements among the 33).

Unfortunately for Lavoisier and science, he supported the establishment of a constitutional monarchy in France. Thereby, for that and older personal reasons, he became a bitter political enemy of Marat[14]. Lavoisier was taken during the Reign of Terror and condemned to death on trumped-up charges for his participation in collecting taxes for the old regime. At his trial, Judge Coffinhal declared, *"The Republic has no need of scientists"*. Lavoisier died by the guillotine on May 8, 1794.

Ten years later, The Republic of France under Napoleon reversed the sentiment of Coffinhal and honored an Italian scientist for his shocking invention. That man, Alessandro Guiseppe Antonio Anastasio Volta (1745-1827) received the Legion of Honor for his creation of the battery. Such a device allowed the continuous and reliable flow of electricity for the first time.

Volta got the idea from the work of a fellow countryman named Luigi Galvani (1737-1798) who studied physiology and anatomy. Galvani dissected a frog during a thunderstorm and noticed that the muscles of the frog twitched when he touched the nerve with his scissors. He did some experiments that led him to believe that the electricity came from the tissue of the frog. He confirmed that by collecting fluid from a dissected frog and immersing two electrodes in the fluid from which he made electrical sparks.

Galvani's experiment later impressed Mary Shelly and other Romantics, but Volta, a physicist, did not believe that Galvani had tapped "animal electricity"; so, he set about making a battery out of inanimate parts. He stacked alternating disks of different metals with felt in between the metal disks. Electricity began to flow when he saturated the pile of metal and felt with a weak acid. In fact, he referred to his contraption as a pile, a term that the French still use for battery.

Initially the battery saw little practical use. However, scientists began to employ the device almost immediately in their studies of chemical elements and compounds. In Britain, Humphry Davy (1778-1829) became apprenticed to a surgeon-apothecary in an effort to help his family after the death of his father. While an apprentice, he read Lavoisier's *Elements* and developed an interest in chemistry and its new direction. His earliest experiments had to do with the physiological effects of nitrogenous gasses, particularly nitrous oxide (laughing gas).

By 1800 Nicholson and Carlisle used the voltaic pile to generate current that they use to decompose water into its constituents of hydrogen and oxygen. In the same year, Davy began to perform similar experiments in which he decomposed a variety of compounds by putting an electrical current through different solutions, a process that he called electrolysis (see Figure 4-77). He found that decomposition followed predictable patterns. For example, when water separated into its constituent elements by means of electrolysis, hydrogen always came off at the negative pole while oxygen came off at the positive pole. Davy reasoned that hydrogen must be positive and oxygen negative. Also, electrical charges appeared to be the means by which the constituent elements of a compound stayed together.

Davy continued his work to separate compounds and ores in an effort to find

---

[14] Marat, a journalist and would-be scientist, had applied for membership into the French Academy of Science before the revolution Lavoisier was most vocal in leading the attack that resulted in denying Marat admission, an insult that he never forgave.

new elements. By the means of electrolysis, he isolated potassium, sodium, magnesium, calcium, strontium, and barium. He worked on chlorine, silica, iodine. Perhaps, his greatest claim to fame was that he discovered and mentored Michael Faraday (1791-1867), one of the greatest physicists of the 19th Century.

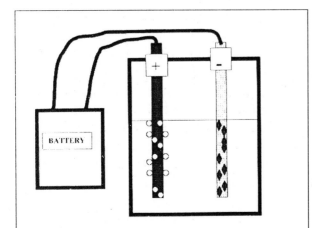

FIGURE 4-77. A general diagram of electrolysis. The elements of a compound move to appropriate poles according to the charge of each constituent element. The clear circles are negative while the black diamonds are positive.

A NEW SYSTEM

We might as well attempt to introduce a new planet into the solar system, or to annihilate one already in existence, as to create or destroy a particle of hydrogen.
                                 -John Dalton (1808)

When Davy conducted his electrolysis experiments, John Dalton (1766-1844), a British Quaker, speculated about the constituents of air. In particular, he wondered how the gasses of air could mingle and not layer out. Likewise, he became intrigued with the problem of the evaporation of water. How did water mix with the air? Finally, he concluded that gasses could mix and water could evaporate only if they came in discrete parts or atoms.

The concept of the atom had appeared here and there throughout the history of science. First proposed by the Greek, Democritus of Abdera (c.470-c.400 B.C.E.), the atom concept remained obscure because it required a vacuum between the atomic particles. Boyle and later Newton did speculate about the existence of atom-like corpuscles. Indeed, Newton's explanations of the gas laws used atom-like particles in his reasoning. Nevertheless, Dalton pulled together and codified atomic theory to make it a fundamental tenet of chemistry.

Dalton concluded that atoms, tiny indestructible and unchangeable particles, existed. Also, the size and mass of an atom varied according to the element. Thus, when elements reacted, they combined in simple whole number ratios. These postulates formed underlying explanations for the laws of chemistry that had been formulated up to that point:

- Law of Equivalent Weights. The combined weights of the reactants must equal the combined weights of the products.

- Law of Constant Composition. A particular compound is made of the same constituents, regardless of how it was made (this distinguished mixtures from compounds).
- Laws of Simple and Multiple Proportions. Elements combine in simple, whole number ratios according to weight.

Dalton took it upon himself to determine the relative weights of the known elements. He drew up a table of atomic weights based on hydrogen = 1 in 1803. He continued to work on the problem of atomic weights through the first decades of the 19th Century, but his work was too sloppy to yield accurate or repeatable results.

Jons Jacob Berzelius (1779-1848) was a Swedish chemist who took the philosophy of Dalton and the methods of Davy to lay the empirical foundation for atomic theory. Berzelius was exacting in his laboratory methods and published a table of the atomic weights of the elements in 1826 that agree quite well with modern values. He arbitrarily established the weight of oxygen at 100 and determined the weights of 42 other elements relative to that of oxygen.

Berzelius' careful work helped to establish atomic theory as outlined by Dalton. In particular, his results showed that atomic weights were not simple multiples of hydrogen. That observation was important and helped to still the last viable protest against the notion of multiple elements (That is, the elements could just be multiple atoms of hydrogen, the only true element).

Berzelius established that hydrogen, metals and alkalis tended to have a positive charge when combined in a compound. Oxygen, nonmetals and acids tended to have a negative charge. These charged elements

or ions combined according to the strengths of their charges. For example, Calcium ionized with a charge of +2 while Chlorine ionized with a charge of -1. Thus, when they combined to form a salt, two Chlorides united with one Calcium to make a neutral compound. Berzelius worked out the elemental compositions of many such compounds and established the meticulous laboratory methods for quantitative analysis.

In 1811 Berzelius introduced symbols for chemical notation. By and large, these symbols gave rise to those in use today (see Figure 4-78). Dalton attempted to introduce a cumbersome and cryptic pictographic system. Fortunately, Dalton's chemical symbols did not become popular. By the time Berzelius died in 1848, chemistry had become modern in form and method.

$$H_2O \quad H^2O$$

$$\bigcirc\bigcirc$$

FIGURE 4-78. Chemical Symbols for water. Top left is the modern symbol, top right Berzelius' symbol; bottom, Dalton's symbol.

My old book from 1821 illustrates the shift. It has a general discussion of atomic theory, but all elements and compounds are written out. However, I have another old book of chemistry that was published in 1857. This one looks much more modern. It has chemical formulas (though some are wrong) and modern-type chemical equations (see Figure 4-79).

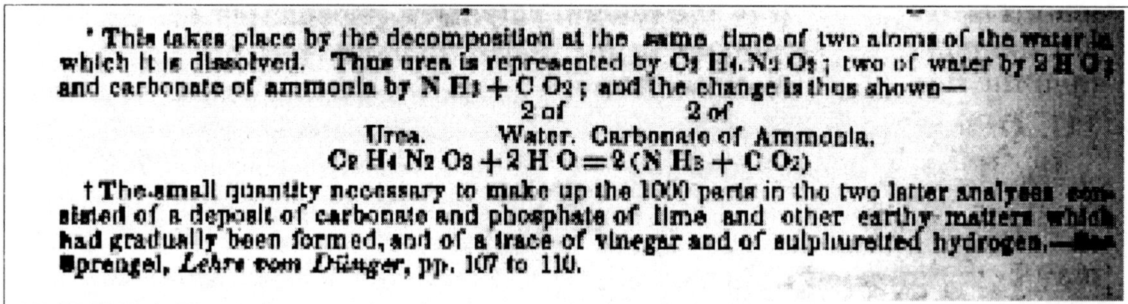

* This takes place by the decomposition at the same time of two atoms of the water in which it is dissolved. Thus urea is represented by $C_2 H_4 N_2 O_2$; two of water by $2 H O$; and carbonate of ammonia by $N H_3 + C O_2$; and the change is thus shown—

Urea.		2 of Water.		2 of Carbonate of Ammonia.

$$C_2 H_4 N_2 O_2 + 2 H O = 2 (N H_3 + C O_2)$$

† The small quantity necessary to make up the 1000 parts in the two latter analyses consisted of a deposit of carbonate and phosphate of lime and other earthy matters which had gradually been formed, and of a trace of vinegar and of sulphuretted hydrogen.—See Sprengel, *Lehre vom Dünger*, pp. 107 to 110.

FIGURE 4-79. A footnote in a book on agricultural chemistry by Johnston (1857). Note that the notation is modern with a modern chemical equation. Some of the particulars are wrong, however. Most notable is the formula for water. Here it is given as HO.

LAWS AND THEORIES

Innovation is not the product of logical thought, even though the final product is tied to logical structure. -Albert Einstein

In this story about old books, chemical laws and theories, I want you to focus on what happened at the turn of the 19th Century. The gas laws had been formulated more than a hundred years earlier. These and the other laws that followed them (e.g. Law of Constant Composition, Law of Equivalent Weights, etc.) are empirical or experimental relationships that are expressed mathematically. For that reason, good empirical laws must be based on data that have been gathered by careful and exacting methods.

Boyle's Law, a law based upon the detailed experiments and observations of Robert Boyle and Robert Hooke, shows a clear mathematical relationship between the volume of a gas and its pressure. It allows us to predict how pressure might change if the volume of a gas changes. However, it does not explain how that relationship comes about.

In the end, the purpose of science is to explain nature, and the essence of explanation can be found through the application scientific theories, all of which must be consistent with the laws of science. The explanatory power of the Element Theory of Lavoisier and the Atomic Theory of Dalton is enormous. They help to make sense of why the laws of chemistry are as they are. Thus, theories, statements that can be rejected and overthrown, are more important to science than unchanging laws. This is a curious paradox. Atoms, theoretical structures that cannot be seen, provide the explanatory power for a science whose methods are based upon observation. Scientists do not wring their hands over questions like, "Are atoms real?" For two hundred years, atoms have been useful.

- 2001, revised 2005

References::

Boyle, Robert. 1895 (first published 1661). *The Sceptical Chymist with an introduction.by M. M.Patterson Muir.* In: Everyman's Library series. J. M. Dent & Sons, Ltd. London.

Brande, William Thomas. 1821. *A Manual of Chemistry to which are added Notes and Emendations by William James MacNeven.* Printed and Published by George Long. New York.

Brock, William H. 1992. *The Norton History of Chemistry.* W. W. Norton & Co. New York.

Clarke, Donald, ed. 1978. *The How it Works Encyclopedia of Great Inventors and Discoveries.* Marshall Cavendish Books, Ltd. London.

Cobb, Cathy & Goldwhite. 1995. *Creations of Fire*. Plenum Press. New York.

Conant, James B. 1951. *Science and Common Sense*. Yale University Press. New Haven.

Harre, Rom. 1981. *Great Scientific Experiments*. Phaedon Press, Ltd. Oxford.

Hudson, John. 1992. *The History of Chemistry*. Chapman & Hall. New York.

Jaffe, Bernard. 1931. *Crucibles, The Lives and Achievements of the Great Chemists*. Jarrolds Publishers. London.

Johnston, James F. W. 1857. *Lectures on the Applications of Chemistry and Geology to Agriculture*. C. M. Saxton & Co. New York.

Lavoisier, Antoine Laurent. 1789 *Elements of Chemistry*. In: Hutchins, Robert Maynard, ed-in-chief. 1952. *Great Books of the Western World*. Vol 45. Encyclopedia Britannica, Inc. Chicago.

Leicester, Henry M. 1956. *The Historical Background of Chemistry*. John Wiley & Sons, Inc. New York.

Simmons, John. 1996. *The Scientific 100, A Ranking of the Most Influential Scientists, Past and Present*. Citadel Press. New York.

Questions to Think About

1. Why was the concept of atoms abhorrent to the ancient Greek natural philosophers?

   Felt that the world was only comprised on 4 elements.
   Disagreed w/ current situation.

2. How did Robert Boyle and Robert Hooke work together to produce Boyles Law?

   Boyle theorized, Hooke designed experiments.
   Hooke improved the design of the vacuum pump

3. What does Boyle's Law mean? How did it undermine the Aristotelian theory of material?

   Relationship btwn temperature, volume, and pressure. Gas heats up, pressure rises, particles move quicker. Aristotle → more fire in container

4. Who was Antoine Lavoisier? How did he change chemistry?

   Made more of many elements → Substance that cannot be broken down further
   Modern Approach

5. What is a battery? How did Volta get the idea for it? *← using Galvani's animal electricity*

   Attraction of metals in a weak acid.
   generates an electrical charge

6. Who was Humphry Davy? How did he use the battery? How did chemistry change through similar experiments?

   Bright, used battery to break down solutions into various elements

7. What led John Dalton to the idea that matter was made of atoms? How did Dalton's atom differ from our current view of the atom? *How can water evaporate*

   Size & mass depend on elements

8. What are the laws of chemistry mentioned in this essay and how do they support the existence of atoms? *Equivalent weights → reactant product*

   Constant Composition - compound made of same components
   Simple & Multiple proportions - elements combine in whole # ratios

9. In what ways did Jakob Berzelius help to make chemistry modern in form?

   Organization of elements into different categories

10. What is the concept of atomic weight?

    Each element has its own unique weight

11. How did the two old books mentioned in this essay [the manuals by Brande (1821) and Johnston (1857)] illustrate the changes in chemistry during the first half of the 19th century?

    Switch to elements

12. What is the value to science of atoms and similar theoretical entities?

    Empirical
    Laws based on data

CHANCE AND THE PREPARED MIND

A WAKING DREAM

To catch a bird, sprinkle salt on its tail to prevent it from flying away. -Anon.

I remember my grandfather as a weak, sickly man. By the time I was old enough to interact with him, he had suffered several heart attacks and struggled with emphysema (The family stories about him almost seemed to be about someone else). During that time we lived on the same lot as my grandparents; so I spent most of my time there. My grandfather didn't talk to me or carry on conversations. Usually, he put up with me or told me what to do. On a particular spring day, he had had enough of children's roughhousing and bickering. He singled me out as the instigator (likely that was true) and called me into his room, a place dominated by a large bed and TV. He didn't tell me to be quiet this time. Instead, he gave me a penny salt shaker and told me to go outside and catch a bird. He didn't explain why I should catch one, he just sent me on a mission, and I went.

He did not have to tell me how to catch the bird, I had heard the story before. I just had to pour salt on its tail...but how? I stood in front of the large yellow stucco house that had been built on the site of Washington Irving's encampment during his tour of the prairie in the early 19th Century. The City of Tulsa even erected a monument to him in front of the house (see Figure 4-80). Motionless, I stared at that monument trying to figure out how I was going to catch a bird with salt. I don't know how much time elapsed. Suddenly, a flutter and thud broke my waking dream. A baby Robin had flown out of a nearby Juniper and landed at my feet. Quickly, I fumbled with the salt shaker and dumped as much salt as I could all over the poor thing. Then, I scooped it up and returned triumphantly to the house with my prize.

My grandfather had a good laugh, and the bird amazed my siblings. I continued the triumphal procession into the kitchen where my mother and grandmother heard the story with disbelief. Then, they tried to talk me into giving up my prize. Ultimately, they were successful, but not without lots of persuasion.

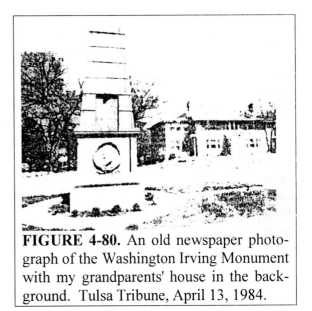

FIGURE 4-80. An old newspaper photograph of the Washington Irving Monument with my grandparents' house in the background. Tulsa Tribune, April 13, 1984.

I went outside with my mother. The Robin squirmed in my hand especially when its parents began to call and show their displeasure with me. I walked into the back yard and peered up into a large elm where the adults were calling. I remember looking up into that tree and wondering if the bird would be able to make it all the way to the first branch. I opened my hand, and the bird did not move. I then gave it a small toss. It fluttered until it managed to land on a branch near the parents.

My memory of that chance event is that I was surrounded by life. At that point, I was no longer dreaming. Even now, everything seems so vivid that I have trouble believing (except rationally) that the event occurred 40 years ago. I stood there on the flagstone path with the wind in my face and the sounds of birds calling and leaves rustling. The sights, sounds, odors all told of life, that enigmatic process that defies strict definition.

THINGS THAT BURN

All the forms of matter which present themselves to our view, whether in the solid crust of the globe on which we live, in the air which forms the atmosphere by which we are surrounded, or in the bodies of animals and plants - all are capable of being divided into the two great groups of organic and inorganic matter.
-James Johnston, 1857

Living things like Robins and Elms have particular properties that make them different from stones in the path and wind on my face. In 1807 Jon Jacob Berzelius coined the terms "organic" and "inorganic" to recognize the distinctions between the products of life and all other material substances, respectively. Indeed, these distinctions have been debated in science since the Golden Age and continue in the debate about life in extreme environments on earth and elsewhere.

Natural philosophers like Georg Ernst Stahl (1660-1734) solved the problem of the organic-inorganic dichotomy by suggesting that the complexity of life (and its products) could be explained only by the existence of a vital force that provided the organizing principle and animating spark. (Recall that Galvani

thought that he had discovered proof of that "spark"[15].)

Although some inorganic substances such as hydrogen could burn, most did not. On the other hand, almost all organic compounds could undergo combustion, and, when they did, they would release fixed air (or carbon dioxide) and water among their byproducts. Lavoisier had concluded that the materials of life must contain the elements carbon, hydrogen, and oxygen in varying proportions. He determined that by heating materials such as wood or fat and collecting their constituent parts. This determination procedure remained the standard method for organic compounds through the middle of the 19th Century. Nevertheless, the accumulated results suggested that organic compounds were quite bizarre when compared with their inorganic counterparts. For example, iron combined with oxygen in a limited number of ways in the production of compounds, while carbon combined with oxygen (and hydrogen) in a bewildering number of ratios.

A substance like iron oxide could be heated, separated into its constituent elements, and recombined to make iron oxide again. Sugar, a common organic compound, when heated would smoke or char even if it did not burn. It could be converted to its constituent elements (carbon-hydrogen-oxygen) by burning, but those elements could not be recombined outside of a living body to form sugar again.

The behavior of inorganic substances like iron oxide could be explained. Berzelius[16] had established that compounds are constructed of components (atoms) that have particular charges. Thus, molecules like iron oxide are made of positively and negatively charged ions. For example, iron can have a charge of +3 while oxygen has a charge of -2; so, hematite, an ore of

---

[15] See *Old Books and Atoms*
[16] See *Old Books and Atoms*

iron oxide has an empirical formula of Fe_2O_3 (with a net charge of 0). Berzelius referred to this electrical bonding as the Dualistic Theory. Soon, he saw that clusters of atoms sometimes stay together as a charged unit or radical. Recall that calcium carbonate ($CaCO_3$) had such a radical[17]. The carbonate unit was made of one part carbon and three parts oxygen with an overall charge of -1.

Simple carbon compounds could be interpreted in the Dualistic Theory. For example methane was made of one part carbon and four parts hydrogen. Since hydrogen had a positive charge, carbon must have had a charge of -4. Carbon dioxide (one part carbon and two parts oxygen), however, required that carbon have a charge of +4 because each oxygen had to have a -2 charge. These problems seemed minor compared to those posed by myriad other organic compounds. Again, the vitalist principle provided the justification for the strange behavior of life's molecules.

AN ACCIDENTAL SCIENCE

It was like a dark forest with few or no pathways.　　　　　　-Woehler

The clear distinction and explanation that separated organic from inorganic compounds changed dramatically following a simple set of experiments by Friedrich Woehler (1800-1882). He had been an undistinguished student at the University of Heidleberg from which he graduated with a degree in medicine. Later he said that he spent much of his spare time working on his own experiments in chemistry. With the blessing and advice of his mentor, Leopold Gmelin, Woehler went to Sweden to study in the laboratory of Berzelius with whom he struck up a life-long friendship. He learned the habits of precision

and careful measurement that so characterized the work of the Swedish chemist. After a year, Woehler returned to Germany and ended up on the faculty of a technical institute in Berlin. There, he began a very productive period during which his accomplishments included the isolation of aluminum in the metallic state.

Woehler's most lasting contribution came in 1828 when he attempted to prepare a pure solution of ammonium cyanate (NH_4CNO) from a mixture of silver cyanate (AgCNO) and ammonium chloride (NH_4Cl). (Some sources say that he mixed potassium cyanate and ammonium sulfate). He heated the preparation and allowed it to dry. As it did, long, white crystals began to grow. Woehler recognized the crystals (after some testing) as urea, a substance common in the urine of mammals (for example, an adult human typically excretes about 25g of urea per day). Urea had been isolated and characterized by H. M. Rouelle in 1773.

Woehler tested the "artificial urea" and pronounced, "it coincides perfectly with that of urea from urine." He had synthesized an organic molecule from inorganic precursors. He had found the chink in the armor of vitalism. He wrote to Berzelius: "I can no longer, so to speak, hold my chemical water and must tell you that I can make urea without needing a kidney, whether of man or dog; the ammonium salt of cyanic acid is urea."

In 1836 Woehler obtained a teaching post at the University of Gottingen. Students flocked to study under him there where he is said to have trained around 8,000 before he died in 1882. Also, at Gottingen he continued his collaboration with his friend Justus von Liebig (1803-1873).

A FORTUNATE CHEMIST

God has ordered all his creation by Weight and Measure.

---

[17] See *In Hot Water*.

-sign above the door to Liebig's lab

Liebig, like Woehler, was a tinkerer. His father was a dealer in paints and common chemicals, so he had a perfect laboratory in which to play. Later, he claimed that his experiments with fulminates (or other explosives) terminated several of his educational experiences (This seems to be apocryphal, though). He did obtain a grant from the Hessian government to attend the University of Bonn in 1820. There, he began to study under Karl Wilhelm Kastner and followed him to Ehrlangen the next year. Liebig became caught up in the political unrest of the university and spent three days in jail following a demonstration. That, coupled with his disappointment in Kastner as a chemist caused him to petition the government (with the help of Kastner) for a grant to study in Paris. While there, with the support of Alexander von Humboldt, he studied under some of the greatest chemists of the day (Gay-Lussac and Thenard). Liebig continued his study of fulminates. He published his work on silver fulminate with Gay-Lussac in 1824. That same year Woehler analyzed silver cyanate in Berselius' laboratory. Both came up with the same empirical formulas for the compounds (AgCNO). The problem was that they had very different properties. In particular, silver fulminate was explosive and silver cyanate was not. The pugnacious Liebig assumed that Woehler was incompetent. However, when both men met in 1826 and did joint analyses, they recognized that two different compounds could have the same formula. Berzelius coined the term isomer (meaning equal parts) for such compounds. This encounter began a lasting collaboration and enduring friendship between the two men.

Before Liebig's return to Germany, Kastner managed to secure a teaching post at Erlangen (and an honorary doctorate) for him. This was supported by von Humboldt in a letter to the Grand Duke who saw chemistry as a door to a brighter economic future. Thus, he moved the chemistry instruction out of the medical school and encouraged Liebig to move to Giessen in 1824. There with state patronage Liebig began to create a well-equipped research teaching laboratory. His state support allowed for a large laboratory budget and for qualified technicians who could create and maintain the equipment. Liebig argued that proper practical education in the methods of chemistry required that the state had to underwrite the education of its students. The state bought his argument and students began to flock to Giessen not just from Germany, but from the rest of Europe, and from overseas.

TABLE 4-8. Liebig's salary and laboratory budget (in florins) from 1824-1843 at Giessen. Adapted from Brock (1992).

Year	Salary	Lab Budget
1824	300	100
1825	500; 800	400
1833	880	619
1835	1250	714
1837	1650	714
1840	3200	1500
1843	3200	1900

Liebig also succeeded because he had something of value to teach. His research program was focused and successful. During this period, Liebig concentrated on the determination and analysis of organic compounds for which he developed rapid and accurate methods.

With Woehler, Liebig published a report about a group of organic compounds that seemed to have a common group, called the benzoyl group (C_7H_5O). This unit behaved like an inorganic radical in that it moved unchanged from compound to compound (benzaldehyde, benzoic acid, benzoyl chloride, etc). They published this as an example of an organic radical, a concept that Berzelius embraced, at least for a time.

At the same time in Paris, Jean Baptiste Andre Dumas (1800-1884) had been asked to solve a particular problem that occurred during a reception given in the Tuileries by Charles X. The candles used there during the reception gave off irritating fumes when burned. Dumas studied them and learned that they had been made of wax bleached with chlorine. Thus, the burning candles gave off HCl gas (hydrochloric acid). The puzzle was how the chlorine stayed in the wax. Dumas realized that the element had replaced some of the hydrogen in the carbon-hydrogen chemistry of the wax itself. According to prevailing dogma (especially that of Berzelius), this was impossible. Chlorine had a negative charge while hydrogen had a positive charge. How could components with opposite charges substitute for each other? At first Woehler and Liebig sided with Berzelius in the argument, but Dumas met with Liebig the next year and demonstrated the substitution. After this, Berzelius' dualism view fell into disfavor especially regarding organic compounds.

Dumas, Liebig, and other chemists through Europe began to see that organic molecules fell into families. There were alcohols, organic acids, esters, etc. Substitution reactions further began to shed light on the nature of these classes of compounds. However, the greatest mystery of organic chemistry remained unsolved. That is, what determined the particular properties of organic molecules anyway? Some isomers melted at very different temperatures. Some were soluble while their counterparts were not. How was this possible?

After 1843 Liebig left the study of organic chemistry (and Giessen) for physiology and biochemistry. Woehler returned to the investigation of his beloved minerals. Berzelius tried to accommodate his Dualistic Theory to substitution but made no significant contribution to organic chemistry after that. Although many others continued the study of organic chemistry, it had reached a plateau with the realization that the properties of organic compounds had to be related to their most important element, carbon. A new view of carbon though required a new vision, and the visionary was Friedrich August Kekule (1829-1896).

A DREAMER

Let us learn to dream...then perhaps we shall find the truth.
                    -Friedrich Kekule (1890)

Kekule went to the University of Giessen to study architecture. However, he began to attend Liebig's lectures and with some encouragement decided to devote himself to the study of chemistry. Liebig suggested that Kekule should go to Paris and study under Dumas. Kekule followed Liebig's advice and then went to England (1854-1855). While there claimed to have had a waking dream while riding atop a London bus. During his dream he saw atoms dancing in the streets. A pair joined then another joined the pair. Lines joined lines at the ends while "all kept whirling in a giddy dance." The conductor woke him from his vision. He claimed years later that this was the start of the Structural Theory of organic chemistry.

In 1858 Kekule adopted the current idea of valence, that is atoms combine with a certain number of others in making compounds. Kekule assumed that carbon must have a valence of 4 and that carbon atoms (unlike most other elements) could link with themselves to make long, complex, and stable carbon molecules. Thus, the structures (more than the component elements) determined the properties of organic compounds.

Archibald Scott Crouper (1831-1892) independently came up with a similar Structural Theory. In fact, his was more modern in its form than that of Kekule. For example, Crouper assumed that carbon could have a variable valence (how else to explain carbon monoxide and carbon dioxide as stable molecules). Anyway, Kekule beat him into publication and into the history books.

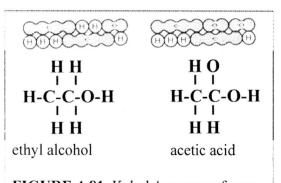

H H
| |
H-C-C-O-H
| |
H H
ethyl alcohol

H O
| |
H-C-C-O-H
| |
H H
acetic acid

FIGURE 4-81. Kekule's sausage formulas and Crouper-Brown graphic formulas for ethyl alcohol and acetic acid, respectively.

A fellow Scotsman and colleague of Crouper, Alexander Crum Brown (1838-1922), took the stick or graphic formulas that Crouper had generated for organic molecules and began to popularize their use. The graphic formulas saw popularity among those writing text books in Britain and Germany, so they were the forms in which the new generations of students learned organic chemistry. That was fortunate because Kekule represented molecules as cryptic sausage-like horizontal structures (see Figure 4-81).

One of the first great triumphs of the Structural Theory came from Kekule

himself when he determined the nature of benzene, a compound that had been isolated from coal tar. Analysis of the molecule confirmed that it had 6 carbons and 6 hydrogens. However, it did not have the properties that one would expect for a 6-carbon molecule. In particular, how could carbon have a valency of 4 and still connect to only an equal number of hydrogens? Chemists assumed that it must be unstable and able to take on more hydrogens, but the molecule resisted their attempts to saturate it. Kekule pondered the problem and came upon the answer in a dream. He related the event of the discover years later:

I was sitting writing on my textbook, but the work did not progress; my thoughts were elsewhere. I turned my chair to the fire and dozed. Again the atoms were gamboling before my eyes. This time the smaller groups kept in the background. My mental eye rendered more acute by repeated visions of the kind, could now distinguish larger structures of manifold conformation: long rows sometimes more closely fitted together all twining and twisting in snake-like motion. But look! What was that? One of the snakes had seized hold of its own tail, and the form whirled mockingly before my eyes. As if by a flash of lightning I awoke; and this time also I spent the rest of the night in working out the consequences of the hypothesis.

The hypothesis that he had stumbled on was that the 6-carbon chain doubled back on itself in a ring with alternating single and double bonds between the carbons (Figure 4-82). This kind of structure could make a stable 6-carbon and 6-hydrogen molecule. Kekule had deduced the structure based on the chemical description of the properties of benzene and the valency of carbon. It was a remarkably elegant solution and quickly accepted by the scientific community.

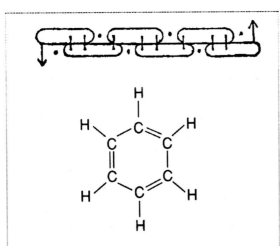

FIGURE 4-82. Top, Kekule's sausage diagram of benzene. Bottom, the modern structural formula for benzene.

SERENDIPITY

In the field of observation, chance favors only the prepared mind.
Louis Pasteur (1822-1895)

Horace Walpole created the term serendipity in 1754 to refer to accidental discoveries. However, discoveries in science really are not accidents. For example, organic chemistry developed by chance occurrences, dreams, and fortune, but the scientists all had minds prepared by study, opened by questions, and primed by curiosity. Still, the accidental discoveries, like my capture of the Robin, did not happen for a purpose. The bird did not fall at my feet because I had a mission or a waking dream (or a penny salt shaker). I just took advantage of the situation as it presented itself.

With the arrival of the Structural Theory, organic chemistry became modern in form, and, following 1860, it, like Hermann Hesse's Prince Dasa in *Magister Ludi*, "seemed to have been properly awakened and become ripe for setting out on the long journey." However, serendipity continued to play an important role in its development as a science and the endless technological advances in areas like plastics and other organic polymers, dyes, pharmaceuticals, food additives, etc. Ironically, the Structural Theory, which had become the death blow to the Vitalist Principle in chemistry, gave science one of the most powerful tools to probe the wonderful chemical complexities of life itself.

-March 2001

Resources:
Brock, William H. 1992. *The Norton History of Chemistry.* W. W. Norton & Co. New York.
Cobb, Cathy & Harold Goldwhite. 1995. *Creations of Fire.* Plenum Press. New York.
Fox, Marye Anne & James K. Whitesell. 1997. *Organic Chemistry,* 2nd ed. Jones and Bartlett Publishers. Boston.
Harre, Rom. 1981. *Great Scientific Experiments.* Phaedon Press, Ltd. Oxford.
Hudson, John. 1992. *The History of Chemistry.* Chapman & Hall. New York.
Jaffe, Bernard. 1931. *Crucibles, The Lives and Achievements of the Great Chemists.* Jarrolds Publishers. London.
Johnston, James F. W. 1857. *Lectures on the Applications of Chemistry and Geology to Agriculture.* C. M. Saxton & Co. New York.
Lavoisier, Antoine Laurent. 1789 *Elements of Chemistry.* In: Hutchins, Robert Maynard, ed-in-chief. 1952. *Great Books of the Western World.* Vol 45. Encyclopedia Britannica, Inc. Chicago.
Leicester, Henry M. 1956. *The Historical Background of Chemistry.* John Wiley & Sons, Inc. New York.
Lundgren, Anders & Bernadette Bensaude-Vincent, eds. 2000. *Communicating Chemistry; Textbooks and their*

Audiences, 1789-1939. Science History Publications. Canton, MA.

Roberts, Royston M. 1989. *Serendipity, Accidental Discoveries in Science.* John Wiley & Sons, Inc. New York.

Simmons, John. 1996. *The Scientific 100, A Ranking of the Most Influential Scientists, Past and Present.* Citadel Press. New York.

Trefil, James and Robert Hazen. 2000. *The Sciences, An Integrated Approach.* 2nd ed. John Wiley & Sons, Inc. New York.

Weisberg, Robert. 1992. *Creativity, Beyond the Myth of Genius.* W. H. Freeman. New York.

Questions to Think About

1. What were the distinctions between organic and inorganic? Why was combustion an inadequate way of distinguishing them?

   Products of life and all other material substance
   what could undergo combustion
   centers carbon.

2. How did the organic-inorganic dichotomy fit with the principle of vitalism?

   Vitalism -living things are different then non-living things -
   -no reason to question it.
   Organic Acid - Should be different in chemistry of life and chemistry of other things

3. How did Woehler demonstrate that those distinctions had to change?

   Created urine out of inorganic substances

4. What is the concept of isomer? Where did it come from?

   isomer- equal parts
   - Different compounds can have the same formula.   *Liebig and Wöchler disagreed*
   on their methods

5. Why was Justus von Leibig so successful?

   Huge findings and state support

6. What was the Dualistic Theory of Berzalius?

7. What were Kekule's "waking dreams"? How did they influence chemistry?

   Atoms dancing in the streets - lines dancing together

8. What is the Structural Theory of Organic Chemistry? What theoretical problems did it solve?

   Atoms combine with others to make compounds
   Structures determine determined the properties of organic compounds

9. Why was the structure of benzene such a problem? How did Kekule solve the problem of benzene?

   6 carbons & hydrogens. How did carbon with a valency of 4
   connect to equal hydrogens.
   Carbon ring

10. Compare serendipity with Pasteur's statement about the prepared mind. How do they come together to describe advances in science?

    Discovery is science create accidents. mind gives opportunity

318

SEEKING PATTERNS

A SEMINAR SPEAKER

Thou cunning'st pattern of excelling nature...

    -Shakespeare, *Othello* act IV, sc 2

Sometimes a teacher has the thrill of having a student return as a teacher. I had such an experience at the beginning of this month when David Seaborn returned to give a seminar about his research on algal ecology in Virginia. In the introduction to his presentation, Dave said that scientists seek patterns in nature. The statement struck me, and I became lost in thought over it for a short time.

At first, I considered whether all areas of science met that criterion. Maybe a search for patterns was just characteristic of ecology, but did it apply to most other areas of science? I considered those ideas for a time and searched my mind for examples. I returned from that limbo when Dave changed to the next slide and began to present patterns that he had discovered in his research. Of course I had forgotten a pad to take down notes and spied a loose piece of paper under my desk. As I checked to see if it would be an appropriate piece of scratch paper, I turned it over and saw the characteristic rows and columns of the Periodic Table of the Elements (see Figure 4-83). There in my hand was confirmation of the generality of Dave's assertion. The patterns of boxes on that table illustrated fundamental relationships between elements and provided the framework to understand and predict deeper, subtler patterns of the ultimate constituents of matter.

A WATERSHED

Chemistry has reached a state of development when...a meeting of a great number of chemists...be held so that a unification of a few important points shall be approached.

-Carl Welzein (1860; excerpt from invitation letter to Karlsruhe International Chemical Congress)

The origin of the Periodic Table can be traced back to Lavoisier and before. However, several critical events occurred around 1860 that make it a watershed year in the history of chemistry. Recall that terms, symbols, atomic weights, etc. had not been standardized. Communication from one laboratory to the next was a mess. Textbooks attempted to standardize communication but general agreement about terminology was hotly contested. Kekule[18] (1826-1896) suggested that a general conference of chemists might come to some agreement. Carl Welzein (1813-1870) sent out a call for an International Chemical Congress to convene in Karlsruhe, Germany. The meeting drew 127 of Europe's leading chemists to discuss these issues. The purpose of the meeting was to create a "unification of a few important points" in organic as well as inorganic chemistry. Most of all, the group sought to standardize the way in which atomic weights were calculated and expressed.

Recall that the concept of atomic weights was as old as Dalton's Atomic Theory[19]. The atoms of each element seemed to have a number of unique and consistent properties and atomic weight

---

[18] See *Chance and the Prepared Mind.*
[19] See *Old Books and Atoms.*

was among them. Atoms were too small to measure, but techniques of measuring the mass of one element relative to another had become established with Dalton and perfected with Berzelius. Still, there were problems. Atomic weights had to be determined by the combining weights of simple compounds. For example, water when separated by electrolysis, yielded two volumes of hydrogen to one volume of oxygen. The same ratio applied when combining oxygen and hydrogen to make water. Thus, water seemed to be one atom of oxygen and two atoms of hydrogen. The oxygen per unit volume weighed 16X that of each unit volume of hydrogen. Therefore, assuming that equal volumes of gas contained equal numbers of particles, an atom of oxygen was 16X more massive than an atom of hydrogen. The combining weights of other elements relative to known atomic weights gradually allowed chemists to fill in the list of known elements, a list that had grown to 54 by 1859. Particular problems arose, however, when calculating some relative weights because gasses like hydrogen seemed somewhat capricious.

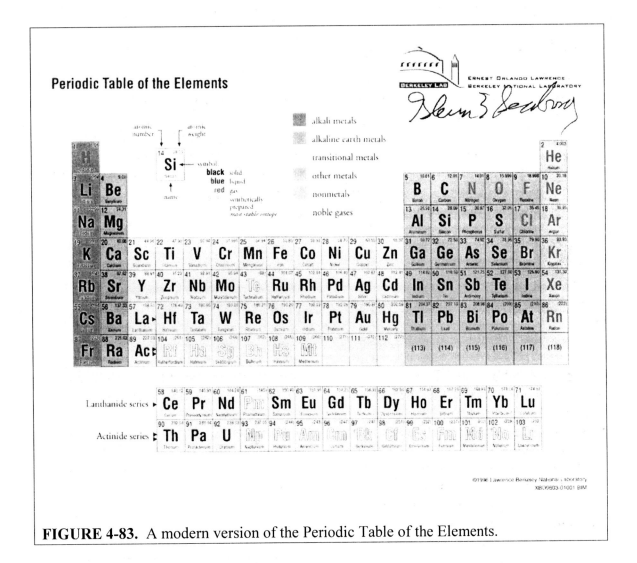

FIGURE 4-83. A modern version of the Periodic Table of the Elements.

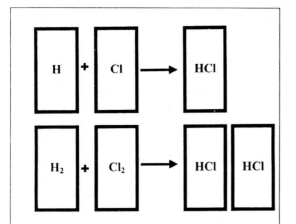

FIGURE 4-84. Two explanations for the formation of HCl. The top equation follows prevailing pre-1860's theory. The bottom equation follows Avagadro's hypothesis and experimental observation.

Consider the simple gasses, hydrogen and chlorine. When combined, they make another gas, hydrogen chloride (recall that we used HCl dissolved in water to make out iron and zinc salts). The odd thing is that one volume of hydrogen combined with one volume of chlorine makes two volumes of hydrogen chloride. How is that possible if each equal volume of gas has equal numbers of particles?

In 1811 an Italian chemist named Amadeo Avagadro (1776-1856) proposed that the gaseous elements combine as diatomic molecules. Thus, hydrogen gas existed as H_2, a diatomic molecule. That would explain the HCl problem. More importantly, if most atomic weights had been calculated relative to a gas like hydrogen, then relative weights would be half the size of atomic weights. Nevertheless, the influence of Berzelius[20] was considerable, and, in his view, diatomics were impossible.

Several of the attendees held the diatomic theory as key to a true system of molecular weights. None spoke as pas-

sionately or as convincingly as fellow Italian Stanislao Cannizzaro (1826-1910). He addressed the congress and demonstrated with logic and data how Avagadro's assumption simplified the problem. Although there was no general agreement at Karlsruhe, Cannizzaro brought copies of his papers and passed them out. As a consequence, the Avagadro assumption of diatomic molecules became generally accepted with a concomitant standardization of atomic weights.

OBSERVATION OF SPECTRA

Spectrum analysis...offers a wonderfully simple means for discovering the smallest traces of certain elements in terrestrial substances...and even of the solar system. - Kirchhoff & Bunsen (1860)

The year 1860 also saw the development of the spectroscope as a tool for the investigation and discovery of elements. Gustav Robert Kirchhoff (1824-1887) and Robert Wilhelm Bunsen (1811-1899) began to study how different elements glow when heated in a flame. Kirchhoff decided to spread the spectrum of light with a prism. Then, he and Bunsen discovered that bright lines in the spectra of glowing elements seemed to be characteristic of each element. So, they documented patterns of spectral lines in sodium, lithium, potassium, strontium, calcium, and barium. By 1863, Bunsen, Kirchhoff and others identified cesium, rubidium, thallium, and indium as new elements by using the spectroscopic method.

The spectroscope required a relatively invisible flame to work well. Bunsen designed such a gas burner, and even now, the Bunsen Burner has remained a common piece of equipment in most laboratories. Through the decade of the 1860's, standard tables of atomic weights and new tools such as the spectroscope led to the identification of more elements and the creation of more confusion. Finally the chaos began to clear as chemists started to order the elements ac-

---

[20] See *Old Books and Atoms*.

cording to standard atomic weights and look for patterns.

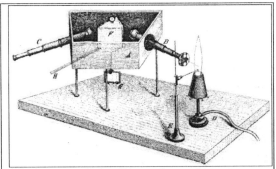

FIGURE 4-85. Illustration of a spectroscope from the paper by Kirchhoff and Bunsen (1860).

THE PERIODIC LAW

If all the elements be arranged in order of their atomic weights, a periodic repetition of properties is obtained.

-Dmitri I. Mendeleev (1869)

Dmitri Ivanovich Mendeleev (1834-1907, Russia), through the efforts of his mother, made his way from Siberia to St. Petersburg where was taught by von Liebig's student, Alexander Woskressensky (1809-1880). Thus, Mendeleev began his career in science following the footsteps of von Liebig[21] with original work in organic chemistry. Soon, however, he turned to a group of similar elements: tungsten, osmium, vanadium, and iridium.

On the recommendation of chemist and composer Alexander Borodin, Mendeleev was sent by the Tsar to Germany for advanced study. While there, he attended the Karlsruhe Congress and began to consider how elements might be ordered according to their atomic weights. On his return to Russia, Mendeleev wrote a textbook of organic chemistry in only 7 months. During that time he speculated about the relationship between atomic weight and elemental properties.

By 1867 he began to write Osnovy Khimi (Foundations of Chemistry). Then, he struggled with ways to present the elements in related groupings. After he published his first edition of Foundations, he noticed that the pattern of elemental properties repeated according to the series of atomic weights.

He was not the first to notice that some elements seemed to occur in families. For example, chlorine, bromine and iodine all tended to ionize with a charge of -1. They formed similar kinds of acids and similar salts. They made up the halogen family. On the other hand, lithium, sodium, and potassium comprised a group that tended to make ions of +1 charge. They made similar bases and similar salts. Other families suggested themselves as well.

He published his first periodic table in 1869. I have reproduced a modification of that table as Table 4-9. Nevertheless, it was his first attempt and illustrated in a very powerful way Mendeleev's Periodic Law. An important attribute to the table was that blank spaces (Mendeleev indicated them by question marks) appeared in the pattern. Thus, Mendeleev assumed that they represented undiscovered elements. However, because they were in families of elements, he could predict their properties and, thereby, systematize a search for them. Mendeleev predicted properties of some unknown elements that were uncanny in their accuracy, and, when those elements were finally discovered, helped to establish the Periodic Law.

TABLE 4-9. A modification of Mendeleev's first Periodic Table of the Elements. Note that the orientation of the periodic table is on its side relative to Figure 4-83. Mendeleev predicted particular properties for unknown elements indicated by **?.**

---

[21] See *Chance and the Prepared Mind.*

H=1			
Li=7	Na=23	K=39	Rb=85.4
Be=9.4	Mg=24	Ca=40	Sr=87.6
		?=45	?
		Ti=50	Zr=90
		V=51	Nb=94
		Cr=52	Mo=96
		Mn=55	Rh=104.4
		Fe=56	Ru=104.4
		Ni=Co=59	Pd=106.6
		Cu=63.4	Ag=108
		Zn=65.2	Cd=112
B=11	Al=27.4	**?=68**	*Ur=116*
C=12	Si=28	**?=70**	Sn=118
N=14	P=31	As=75	Sb=122
O=16	S=32	Se=79.4	Te=128?
F=19	Cl=35.5	Br=80	I=127

Lothar Meyer (1830-1895), a German and another attendee of the Karlsruhe Congress, began to write a general chemistry text in the late 1860's. Like Mendeleev, he attempted to order the elements and discovered that they exhibited patterns of periodicity in their properties. He ordered them according to atomic sizes (this can be estimated by dividing the atomic weight by the density of the element). He would have scooped Mendeleev if he had published right away, but Meyer delayed the release of his book by several years.

THE LAZY ELEMENTS

The unreactivity of the noble gas elements belongs to the surest of experimental results.

-Friedrich Paneth (1924)

That the elements exhibited a pattern of predictable properties was somewhat mysterious. Why should they behave that way? What did the spectral lines indicate? That elements showed such patterns in their spectra suggested to many that the atoms had simpler constituent parts and that the properties of elements just reflected the way that they were constructed. William Prout (1785-1850) had proposed such a hypothesis early in the 19th Century. He suggested that all elements were made of multiples of hydrogen, the simplest element. Berzelius ridiculed the idea and coined the phrase "Prout's Hypothesis" as a pejorative term. Still, the mystery of the periods could be allayed if some underlying building blocks could be discovered.

In the search for evidence to support Prout's Hypothesis or a modification of it, Lord Rayleigh (1842-1919) made ever more accurate determinations of the atomic weights of atmospheric gasses. By 1892, he had determined that oxygen was 15.882 times heavier than hydrogen. However, when he measured nitrogen, Rayleigh found that atmospheric nitrogen was denser than nitrogen generated from ammonia. This strange result suggested that nitrogen might exist in forms other than diatomics in the air. At this point, William Ramsay (1852-1916) took up the investigation and removed all nitrogen from the air. What was left seemed to have an atomic weight of 40 and had a spectroscopic signature of an unknown element. This new element refused to combine with anything and seemed to be monatomic. He called the new element Argon, Greek for lazy. It seemed to fall between Chlorine and Potassium-Calcium in the periodic table. He figured that it represented a whole new class of elements. Soon, Ramsay discovered helium (an element whose spectroscopic signature had been observed in the solar spectra). Mendeleev, at first was skeptical of the unreactive or Noble Gasses, but added them to his table in 1905, just two years before his death.

The end of the 19th Century saw revolutions in chemistry and physics. Discoveries of mysterious radioactive elements supported fundamental new insights as to the view that atoms had parts, a concept that Mendeleev never accepted.

ENTER THE PHYSICISTS

Now Rutherford has proved that the most important constituent of an atom is its central positively charged nucleus...

-Henry Moseley (1913)

Joseph John Thomson (1856-1940) succeeded Rayleigh at the Cavendish Laboratory, Cambridge. His investigations led to the discovery of negatively charged particles that emanated from an electrode in a vacuum. He measured the mass of the particles and estimated that they were 1000 times smaller than a hydrogen atom. He supposed that atoms could be made of such component parts. Later, the cathode ray particle was renamed the electron.

Ernest Rutherford (1871-1937) replaced Thomson at the Cavendish and continued research into the constituents of atoms. He discovered, through a series of brilliant experiments, that the atom's positive charge (and most of its mass) was concentrated into a very tiny volume in the center of the atom. Thus, he conceived of an atom as a small planetary system with a small massive positive nucleus at the center and the electrons in orbit around it.

A student of Rutherford, Henry Moseley (1887-1915) examined X-ray signatures of the elements. He noticed that the frequencies of emitted X-rays increased according to the placements of elements in the periodic table. He supposed that his results confirmed the stepwise increase in positive charge of the nucleus. Thus, he reckoned that atomic weight simply was a function of the positive charges. As a consequence, he created the concept of atomic number.

For example, hydrogen has an atomic number of 1. It has one positively charged particle or proton in its nucleus. Therefore, a neutral hydrogen atom has one proton and one electron. The electrons can vary, but the number of protons determines the nature of each element.

Moseley examined the X-ray signatures of most of the known elements before he joined the armed forces during World War I. Unfortunately for chemistry Moseley's life was cut short by a sniper's bullet at Gallipoli. However, during his brief existence, he fundamentally changed the periodic table and its meaning.

Other physicists like Niels Bohr[22] (1885-1962) considered the problem of spectroscopic lines and the planetary model of the Rutherford nucleus. Bohr was troubled by the problems posed by such a model. Particularly, what kept the electrons from crashing into the nucleus and staying there? He supposed that electrons could occupy only certain allowed orbits, and, as they gained energy, electrons occupied only orbits of particular higher energies farther from the nucleus and then dropped back down, thereby releasing that energy as light. The absorbed and released energies manifest themselves as colored lines in the spectrum of a heated element. Thus, he saw that this theory could explain the mysterious patterns of spectral lines and the stability of atomic structure.

Gilbert Newton Lewis (1875-1946) saw that the pattern of the periodic table itself reflected how electrons filled allowed shells around the nucleus. The innermost shell held up to 2 electrons. Thus, helium with atomic number 2 was neutral with a filled

---

[22] See *Questioning Reality.*

324

shell of electrons. Because atoms tended to give or accept electrons until they filled an outer shell, their reactive properties depended upon the relative number of electrons in the outer shell. Helium was full; so, it was unreactive.

Examine Figure 4-83. The elements of the first row have just a single shell that can take 2 electrons. The next row can have a shell outside of that with up to 8 more electrons (10 total in neon). Row 3 can take an additional 8 electrons outside of the 10 (18 total in argon), etc. Elements such as sodium (Na) with atomic number 11 have the shells characteristic of neon but a single electron in the next shell. Sodium (and all other elements in its family) give up the lone electron and ionize with a valence of +1 (that is, the ion has one more proton than electron). Chlorine (atomic number 17) has an almost full outer shell and accepts an extra electron to fill it. Thus chlorine tends to become charged as -1.

The problem of the inequality of atomic weights and atomic numbers was solved by James Chadwick (1891-1974), a colleague of Rutherford, in 1932 with his discovery of the neutron[23], an uncharged particle in the nucleus. Also, because the neutron was about as massive as the proton, it helped to explain why there could be variation in atomic weight within an element. This was the concept of isotopes and was the last piece necessary to understand the constituent parts of the atom and how they related to an understanding of the patterns of the periodic table.

The last major change to the periodic table came with a consideration of the so-called rare earth elements and where they might squeeze in the overall pattern. Glen Seaborg (1912-1999) solved that problem by pulling out the lantha-nide and actinide series and placing them as two rows at the bottom of the table. This has become known as the long form of the periodic table (see Figure 4-83). Also, Seaborg created transuranic (beyond uranium) elements like plutonium and showed that they, too, obeyed the periodic law with 15 elements in each of the rare earth rows.

The rare earths return to the main body of the table with element number 104. In theory, any number of elements can be created. However, most transuranics are so unstable that they can exist for only seconds or fractions of seconds before they break apart into smaller elements.

SEABORN AND SEABORG

The periodic classification of the elements is one of the most valuable generalizations in science.

-William H. Brock (1992)

In 1998 I stood in line at a meeting in Las Vegas to meet Glen Seaborg[24]. He was there to pass out signed copies of a periodic table of the elements that featured his modification (Figure 4-86). I remember that his hands were gnarled and he looked ill. I shook his crooked hand as I accepted a copy of the periodic table and engaged him briefly in conversation. I knew enough then to ask about his actinide modification. His eyes lit up, and he seemed younger as he talked about the periodic table. Then, he said pointing to the piece of paper that he handed me, "These aren't just colored boxes. They represent work by many people for many years, and what I did was small compared to them."

---

[23] See *Swords to Plowshares*.

[24] He died within a year of that conference.

FIGURE 4-86. Meeting Glen Seaborg in 1998.

Indeed, many contributed to a discovery and understanding of the patterns contained in the periodic table. But patterns in nature often reflect underlying structure and elucidation of the smallest part of that structure is difficult and important. Now it seems that the periodic law is a consequence of the deeper structure of quarks and other subatomic particles.

The story of the Periodic Table of the Elements illustrates very well David Seaborn's assertion that scientists seek patterns and attempt to explain them. Indeed, it is the need to explain the patterns that sets science apart from other human activities such as art. However, scientists have to be careful that they do not confuse the pattern for the explanation. At first, Mendeleev's table had no explanatory power, but it provided direction in the search for new elements. It provided a framework against which the patterns of spectroscopic analysis and other elemental properties had to make sense. Thus, the periodic law guided questions and helped to frame the answers about atoms, their constituent parts, and properties of elements.

-2001

References:

Brock, William H. 1992. *The Norton History of Chemistry.* W. W. Norton & Co. New York.

Cobb, Cathy & Harold Goldwhite. 1995. *Creations of Fire.* Plenum Press. New York.

Hudson, John. 1992. *The History of Chemistry.* Chapman & Hall. New York.

Jaffe, Bernard. 1931. *Crucibles, The Lives and Achievements of the Great Chemists.* Jarrolds Publishers. London.

Kirchhoff, Gustav & Robert Bunsen. 1860. *Chemical Analysis by Observation of Spectra.* Annalen der Physik der Chemie. 110: 161-189.

Leicester, Henry M. 1956. *The Historical Background of Chemistry.* John Wiley & Sons, Inc. New York.

Moseley, H.G.J. 1913. *The High Frequency Spectra of the Elements.* Phil. Mag. (1913): 1024.

Simmons, John. 1996. *The Scientific 100, A Ranking of the Most Influential Scientists, Past and Present.* Citadel Press. New York.

Trefil, James and Robert Hazen. 2000. *The Sciences, An Integrated Approach.* 2nd ed. John Wiley & Sons, Inc. New York.

Questions to Think About

1. What was the importance of the Chemical Congress at Karlsruhe?

2. How did the formation of HCl show problems with prevailing views? How were the problems solved?

3. What is a spectroscope? How did its use help in the discovery of atoms?

4. Ultimately, what did the spectroscopic signature mean?

5. What is the periodic law? How did it come to Mendeleev?

6. How did the periodic table help lead to the discovery of new elements?

7. Who, besides Mendeleev, discovered the periodic law?

8. What was Prout's Hypothesis?

9. What did I mean by the "lazy elements"?

10. How did Moseley change the meaning of the periodic table?

11. How did Lewis increase the explanatory ability of the periodic table?

12. Who was Seaborg and what was his modification to the periodic table?

STARS AND THE BEAUTY OF SCIENCE

AN ECLIPSE

My idea worked. I wanted to keep things as they were until the eclipse was total.
　　　-Mark Twain, *A Connecticut Yankee in King Arthur's Court*

In the summer of 1972 my uncle took me on a wonderful trip up through the center of the continent of North America and then westward toward Alaska. Although he asked if I would spell him while driving, his real reason for taking me was the company (he let me drive less than 200 miles on that 8,000 mile trip). I was still an undergraduate at the time of the trip, and I am certain that the overall summer experience convinced me (more than any academic experience) to apply to graduate school during the coming year.

In part, we went to Fairbanks to visit my cousin who had been stationed there by the U.S. Army as part of a meteorology unit. I rather enjoyed the routine of going out to Poker Flats missile range each morning to watch them collect telemetry from weather balloons and sounding rockets. The routine changed, however, on the morning of July 10. Then, an area north of Fairbanks was to experience a total solar eclipse. NASA had prepared a rocket to measure the flux in ozone during the eclipse. With all of the preparations for the telemetry, etc., no one remembered to bring colored glass or any other appropriate filters to view the eclipse. I quickly punched a small hole in a card and focused the image of the sun onto paper. The image, although imperfect because of the jagged edges of the hole, gave the few curious members of the meteorology team a look at what they were monitoring (Figure 4-87).

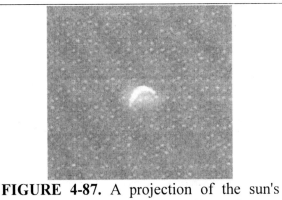

FIGURE 4-87. A projection of the sun's image near the peak of the eclipse close to Fairbanks, Alaska on July 10, 1972.

The pinhole camera was the same method that Galileo used to make his observations of the sun and its sun spots (a line of research that likely cost him his eyesight as well as his freedom). Galileo documented blemishes or spots on the sun and began to challenge the Aristotelian idea that the heavens were made of a different kind of substance that was uniformly bright and not subject to corruption. From that beginning, astronomers began to understand that the sun was another star around which the earth and other planets moved.

STELLAR TAXONOMY

Every fact is a valuable factor in the mighty whole.
　　　-Anne Jump Cannon, from Ferris (1988)

Stars had been categorized for thousands of years particularly their locations and associations within patterns of stars or constellations. Also, the brightness of stars began to be recorded. Brightness and location provided the first standard method of naming stars with a Greek letter denoting the relative brightness followed by the constellation within which it occurred. For example,

Vega, the fifth brightest star in the sky (excluding our sun) is the brightest star in the constellation Lyra. Thus, the proper "scientific name" for Vega is Alpha Lyrae.

With the advent of photography stars could be catalogued with much greater precision. That, coupled with advances in accurate measurements of stellar positions, allowed observers to estimate the distances to different stars. This was accomplished by the parallax method. That is, an estimate of distance based on a triangulation to the star based upon two different observations. The two observations lie at the base of a triangle with the star at the apex. The longer the baseline, the more accurate the distance estimate. In the case of stars, the observations can be made 6 months apart so that the base line is the full diameter of the earth's orbit around the sun. Distances were important because they could be used to determine the actual brightness of stars. For example, Altair and Deneb are two stars in the group called the "Summer Triangle" (the third one is Vega). Altair appears to be brighter than Deneb. However, that is because Altair is a relative neighbor to our sun. Its real brightness is about 13 times that of our sun. Deneb, on the other hand, is more than 100 times farther away than Altair. Thus, it is one of the brightest stars in the sky with a light output of 60,000 times that of our sun.

Anne Jump Cannon (1863-1941, USA) was a computer in the old sense. Banned because of her sex from serious scientific study, she worked to evaluate and record stars and their spectra as she viewed them on photographic plates. Cannon categorized thousands of stars and noticed that they tended to fall within certain types based on color (a consequence of surface temperature).

She created a spectral classification system that is still in use today (see Table 1). She arranged the stars from hottest (white to blue) to coolest (red) according to the letters: O-B-A-F-G-K-M.

TABLE 4-10. The spectral classification system created by Anne Jump Cannon.

SPECTRAL CLASS	TEMPERATURE (K)
O	400,000
B	28,000
A	10,000
F	7,500
G	6,000
K	5,000
M	3,500

Her system began to show that there was order in the seeming limitless number of stars. For her work, Cannon was the recipient of numerous awards, including two honorary doctorates. She worked until several weeks before her death. By that time, she had classified more than 300,000 stars.

Cannon's insight provided the foundation that led to the simultaneous discovery of the relationship between the temperatures of stars and their brightness. Ejnar Herzsprung (1873-1967), an amateur Danish astronomer, and Henry Norris Russell (1877-1957), a Princeton astronomer discovered the relationship called the Herzsprung-Russell Diagram (see Figure 4-88). The diagram took shape in the decade after 1911.

Stars like our sun (a category G star) fall along a gently curving line through the

Herzsprung-Russell Diagram. This is called the main sequence and more than 80% of all stars are found there. Other bright stars occupy the Giant and Supergiant portions of the diagram and another cluster in the dim but hot group called white dwarfs.

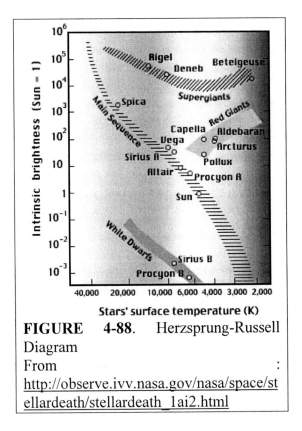

FIGURE   4-88.   Herzsprung-Russell Diagram
From   :
http://observe.ivv.nasa.gov/nasa/space/stellardeath/stellardeath_1ai2.html

The shape of the Herzsprung-Russell diagram suggested that there was some underlying uniformity between stars of the main sequence as well as among the categories of giants and dwarfs. Physicists assumed that the diagram was a clue as to how the stars worked. In addition, ample geological evidence from the 19th century suggested that the earth and the solar system were quite old, and during its history solar output must have been quite constant. However, sources of energy that would drive the sun simply were not known so physicists tended to present ages for the sun on the order of millions or hundreds of millions of years.

HOW DO THEY WORK?
What is possible in the Cavendish Laboratory may not be too difficult in the sun.
                    -Arthur Eddington

Arthur Eddington (1882-1944, UK) accepted that the sun must be quite old and suggested that the source of energy might be found in the atomic nucleus. Ernest Rutherford (1871-1937; New Zealand, Canada, & UK) had succeeded in showing that the atom must have most of its mass concentrated in a tiny positively-charged nucleus with its size determined by a cloud of tiny negatively-charged electrons. Radioactivity seemed to be a consequence of changes that occurred within the nucleus of certain atoms. When Rutherford, then director of the Cavendish Laboratory, bombarded certain elements with alpha particles (essentially helium nuclei), he managed to change some of the elements to different ones. Rutherford referred to this as "the new alchemy".

In 1926, Eddington proposed that the sun and all other stars operated by nuclear reactions in which Einstein's $E=mc^2$ came into play. He argued that the sun must be made mostly of hydrogen throughout and that the center of the sun was so hot that nuclei could fuse despite the mutual repulsion of the positively-charged protons. That is, if hydrogen fused to produce helium, a little of the total mass was converted to energy (He did not know how much would be converted at the time).

Hans Bethe (1906-), one of the most nimble scientific minds of the 20th century, tackled the problem of nuclear fusion. He immigrated to the United States in 1935 and began to consider the fundamental nuclear reactions that powered the sun. By 1938 he showed that the production of energy by the collision of protons (called the proton-proton reaction) was sufficient to explain the solar energy output. Also, he worked out a more energetic sequence of reactions called the carbon cycle that could explain the energies of the hotter stars on the main sequence.

The stars on the main sequence are hydrogen burners (in this sense I mean that they fuse hydrogen to make helium). Thus, four hydrogens ultimately combine to make one helium with a loss of only 0.6% of the total mass in the process. However, because the energy generated is mass times the velocity of light squared ($E=mc^2$), that small mass translated to a very large amount of energy.

By the 1930's, physicists understood that the nucleus was made of a collection of protons and neutrons. Protons had a charge of +1 and a mass of about 1 atomic mass unit (amu). Neutrons, whose existence had been proposed much earlier but whose discovery had occurred only in 1932, had a charge of 0 and a mass about the same as a proton. The mass values of protons and neutrons are not quite 1 when isolated. Protons have a mass of 1.00734 and neutrons have a mass of 1.00867 (0.5% more massive than the proton). However, the mass of the carbon-12 nucleus (6 protons and 6 neutrons) is 12.0000amu. Francis William Aston (1877-1945) measured the difference between the sum of the mass of individual particles and the mass of the carbon-12 nucleus (the so-called mass deficit) is 0.096amu. That is, he found a deficit of 0.008amu per particle (0.096/12). Aston multiplied the deficit times 10,000 to give a "packing fraction" of 80 for carbon-12. That number represented the relative amount of mass converted to energy in the fusion process. In general, the packing fraction of elements and their isotopes increased through the periodic table until iron-56, which had a packing fraction of 94. Curiously, pack-

ing fractions decline for elements more massive than iron.

Also, neutrons seem to be stable in nuclei in which the number of neutrons and protons are about equal in small elements (e.g. carbon-12 has 6 protons and 6 neutrons). Carbon-14 has 6 protons and 8 neutrons. This isotope of carbon is unstable and one neutron will undergo beta decay in which the neutron seems to decay into a proton, an electron, and a neutrino. The resulting nucleus of Nitrogen-14 has 7 protons and 7 neutrons and is stable. Fusion and beta-decay are the means by which small elements (smaller than iron) can change to other elements.

WHEN THEY DIE
Science is not everything, but science is very beautiful.   -J. Robert Oppenheimer

Our sun is a star on the main sequence and is made primarily of hydrogen (1 proton) that produces fusion energy in the production of helium-4 (2 protons and 2 neutrons). The mutual gravitational attraction of the enormous ball of gas is the source of the energy that drives the fusion reaction. Thus, the pressure of the gas increases toward the center or core of the sun where temperatures in the range of 15,000,000K provide the energy necessary for protons to overcome their electrostatic repulsion and come close enough for the strong nuclear force to glue them together. The released energy pushes against the crush of gravity and helps to maintain the sun at a constant temperature and pressure.

As the sun "burns" in this way, an "ash" of helium-4 accretes at the center of the star. In another 4-5 billion years the core will become a large ball of helium-4. The drop in energy output will cause the crush of gravity to ignite a shell of hydrogen around the core. When the energy produced can no longer push against the collapse, the temperature in the helium core will increase enough to allow for the fusion of helium nuclei to form carbon-12. This reaction will produce much more energy and consume fuel at a prodigious rate. The increased energy output will cause the outer gas ball to balloon outward, and for a time, our sun will become a red giant. In the end the accumulating ash of carbon in the core will not ignite under the pressure that the mass of the sun can generate. After about a billion years as a red giant, the sun will begin to collapse until the mutual repulsion of electrons (called electron degeneracy pressure) will take over and support the structure. By that time the sun will be very small, about the size of the earth, and very hot at first. It will become a white dwarf and gradually cool.

This general scenario had been deduced for our sun in the 1930's. The question was how massive could a star be and end as a white dwarf? A young Indian mathematician, Subrahmanyan Chandrasekhar (1910-1995, India & USA) on a boat to England in 1930 began to consider what he had read about white dwarfs. He calculated how massive stars would have to be to end as white dwarfs. To his surprise, his calculations predicted that a white dwarf star would develop only if the mass of the star is less than about 1.45 times the mass of our sun. That was a very surprising result. When Chandrasekhar presented it at a meeting of the Royal Astronomical Society in 1935, Arthur Eddington, who at first had supported the young Chandra, publicly ridiculed the idea. Chandra received support from physicists like Niels Bohr and ultimately left Britain to teach in the U.S. at the University of Chicago.

The Chandra limit of 1.45 times the mass of the sun was a mysterious barrier.

Eddington maintained that all stars end as white dwarfs. Massive stars just shed excess mass as they aged and died. Increasingly, observations of giant and supergiant stars suggested otherwise.

Physicists in the U.S. and Russia pondered this problem of the fate of massive stars. Fritz Zwicky (1898-1974) proposed that stars of high mass could squeeze their cores until the degeneracy pressure of electrons could no longer support them. Then, under enormous pressure, electrons and protons would fuse in a kind of reverse beta decay to form a ball of neutrons. The resulting neutron core would be thousands of times smaller than its predecessor and incredibly dense. Zwicky proposed that the neutron core could be the power behind massive stars. J. Robert Oppenheimer (1904-1967) considered his colleague Zwicky to be too flaky to be taken seriously. However, when he read a paper proposing a similar concept by the Soviet physicist, Lev Davidovich Landau (1908-1968), Oppenheimer paid attention to the idea. Indeed, he considered the concept of neutron stars and realized that this must be the fate of stars much more massive than the Chandra limit. His calculations also suggested that there was another limit at which the mass was so great that even the degeneracy pressure of neutrons could not support the star, and it would collapse into a black hole, an enigmatic phenomenon from which neither matter nor light could escape.

THE FORGE OF ELEMENTS
The stars are the crucibles in which the lighter atoms which abound in the nebulae are compounded into more complex elements.   -Arthur Eddington

Neutron stars remained theoretical entities until the observations of pulsars and their relationships with supernovae began to be investigated. For example, Chinese astronomers had recorded a supernova event on July 4, 1054. Then, a star became brighter than a billion suns and could be seen easily during the day. The star faded relatively quickly, and in its place today, we see the Crab Nebula with a tiny pulsar (pulsating neutron star) in its center. Many other supernova remnants have pulsars at their centers.

Supernovae seemed to be responsible for much more that just neutron stars. Calculations by George Gamow (1904-1968) suggested that the energy of the Big Bang was sufficient to make only the elements of hydrogen and helium. Thus, he and others deduced that all other elements must have been made after that event. The only candidate that could provide enough energy for the production of elements up through Uranium was the energy of a supernova. What could cause such an outburst of energy?

Current scenarios suggest that very massive stars burn their nuclear fuels at a high rate. As the ash of successive fusion reactions accumulates at the center, the star takes on the appearance of a "layered onion" (see Figure 4-89) with heavier nuclei concentrated at the center and shells of lighter elements around it. In this case, the ashes of one reaction become the fuel for the next until the fusion of silicon produces iron (see Figure 4-89). Recall that iron is the most tightly packed of all elements. Thus, fusion of iron does not release net energy. So, the iron core grows until it exceeds the Chandra limit. At that point, within a second, the electron degeneracy pressure fails and the core collapses to a ball of neutrons with a diameter of a few kilo-

meters. The outer layers fall into the contracted core. The shockwave thus produced is sufficient to provide the energy for new elements. The collapsing layers meet a spray of neutrons from the core. As the neutrons are incorporated into nuclei and beta-decay converts unstable neutrons to protons, elements higher that iron appear in the expanding nebula that the explosion produces.

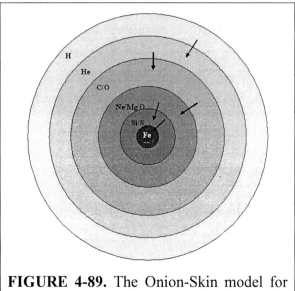

FIGURE 4-89. The Onion-Skin model for very massive stars.

Scientific iconoclast Fred Hoyle (1915-) outlined just such a scenario for supernovae and the production of heavy elements in the 1950's. Thus, the meaning of the Herzsprung-Russell Diagram became clear. Stars on the main sequence were hydrogen-burning stars. Stars beneath the Chandra limit spent a relatively brief time at the end of their lives as Giants and then collapsed to White Dwarfs. Very massive stars burned their fuels quickly (on the order of millions of years) and became Supergiants before they winked-out as Supernovae.

The Supernovae and the expanding nebulae are the sources of elements for stars (and their planets) of the next generation. Our sun is just such a second generation star. Consider the abundances of elements in our solar system (see Figure 4-90). Most of the matter is in the form of hydrogen and helium. Succeeding elements follow abundances predicted by the Onion Skin Model (note the peak at iron, element 26) and the production of heavier elements in a Supernova explosion (the decline in abundance from iron to Uranium, element 92).

Thus the theories of Eddington, Bethe, Chandraskhar, Oppenheimer, and Hoyle came together to explain the occurrences and abundances of all of the naturally occurring elements. Hydrogen and helium were made in the Big Bang. Succeeding elements up to iron were made in the regular fusion reactions within stars. Elements above iron came about in the explosions of supernovae.

A verification of that view came in 1987 when a Supernova flared up in a nearby galaxy. For a time SN1987A was as bright as the galaxy it occupied and confirmed the predictions of physicists through the 20th Century. They had used the laws of physics and deduced the scenario that SN1987A played out.

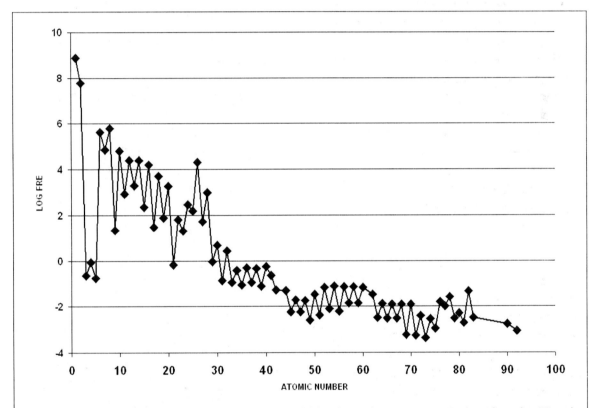

FIGURE 4-90. Abundances of elements within the solar system. Notice that the Y-axis is a logarithmic scale.

The universe is not a static entity. It expands and evolves with new elements being added through the normal operation of massive stars. Thus, almost all of the elements in our bodies and environment were formed in the bowels of stars long dead. I cannot help but look at a sunlit sky or stars winking in the blackness of night and feel a connection with the universe. As with most aspects of science, the explanation does not destroy the magnificence of nature, but serves to enhance the beauty.

-2001

References:

Arnett, David. 1996. *Supernovae and Nucleosynthesis, and Investigation* into the History of Matter From the Big Bang to the Present. Princeton University Press. Princeton.

Asimov, Isaac. 1991. *Atom.* Truman Talley Books. New York.

Bethe, Hans A. and Gerald Brown. *How a Supernova Explodes.* Scientific American Press.

Cannon, Annie J. 1929. *Classifying the Stars.* IN: Shapley, Harlow and Cecilia Payne. *The Universe of Stars.* Harvard College Observatory Press.

Chandrasekhar, S. 1990. *Truth and Beauty, Aesthetics and Motivations in Science.* The University of Chicago Press.

Ferris, Timothy. 1989. *Coming of Age in the Milky Way.* Doubleday. New York.

Gamow, George. 1952. *The Creation of the Universe.* The Viking Press. New York.

Gribben, John. 2002. *The Scientists, A History of Science Told Through the Lives of its Greatest Inventors.* Random House. New York.

Jastrow, Robert. 1967. *Red Giants and White Dwarfs.* Harper & Row, Publishers. New York.

Thorne, Kip S. 1994. *Black Holes and Time Warps, Einstein's Outrageous Legacy.* W.W. Norton & Co. New York.

Trefil, James and Robert Hazen. 2000. *The Sciences, An Integrated Approach.* 2nd ed. John Wiley & Sons, Inc. New York.

http://heasarc.gsfc.nasa.gov/docs/objects/heapow/archive/nebulae/sn1987a_acis.html

http://observe.ivv.nasa.gov/nasa/exhibits/sun/

http://observe.ivv.nasa.gov/nasa/space/stellardeath/

Questions to Think About

1. What are the differences between Astrology, Astronomy, and Cosmology?

2. What was the dominant cosmology until the time of Galileo?

3. Why did Claudius Ptolemy create an astronomy that used deferents?

4. Do you think that Copernicus created an astronomy or a cosmology?

5. Why did Galileo reject the Aristotelean cosmology?

6. Why was Galileo in trouble with Pope Urban VIII?

7. What are the two general types of telescopes? Which provides the image with least distortion?

8. Why is Astrology a pseudoscience?

9. What is meant by stellar taxonomy?

10. What were the contributions of Annie Jump Cannon?

11. The Herzsprung-Russell Diagram illustrates placements of main sequence stars, giant stars, and white dwarfs. How do the different stars get that way?

12. What is meant by packing fraction? What is its importance to stellar evolution?

13. What is the Chandra Limit, and what does it mean?

14. What triggers a supernova? What is produced in that explosion? What evidence do we have for that?

CHAPTER 5: CHANGING IDEAS IN GEOLOGY AND ENVIRONMENTAL SCIENCE

Therefore will we not fear, though the earth be moved, and though the mountains be carried into the midst of the sea.   Psalms 46:2

While an undergraduate student, I traveled up through southeastern Alaska where the sea and air form the most practical roadways. There, the forces of geology and the majesty of the environment envelop the traveler like few other places in the United States. In many ways, this experience was a confirmation for me that science and environmental study were what I would like to spend my life doing.

The essays in this chapter focus on the foundations of geology (Geology Through Lyell's Eyes, *Y2K, Deep Time, and Theory Choice in Geology, Reading the Earth, A Trip to Avalon*), paleontology (*Lost Worlds, A Trip To Avalon, Rivals, A Dinosaur With a Thumb on its Nose, Trilobite Tales*), and environmental science (*Ice Ages, Clouds, A Few Inches, A New Story to be Told Every Day, Found a Penny, The Children of Sir Gilbert Walker,* and *Nature's Storehouse*).

GEOLOGY THROUGH LYELL'S EYES

A RACE

To dig and delve in nice clean dirt
Can do a mortal little hurt.

-John Kendrick Bangs

I moved into my house in 1982. The old house had stood on its location since about the founding of Freeburg. In fact, the house had been built before there was electric wiring and indoor plumbing. More enigmatic anomalies occurred outside in the yard. There, I could trace evidence of a large Pennsylvania barn and a long low shed that housed a tannery. Still, the oddest feature was an old millrace that by 1982 had more closely resembled a terrace in the upper part of the yard near the house.

An old man down the road had identified the feature and even had a few stories about the race. A millrace is a canal into which water can be diverted to drive a millwheel. So, when in operation and good repair, it can resemble a creek. The story went that the outhouse had to be built across the race from the main house. The old man said one Halloween he went about the town "doing mischief" like knocking things over, particularly outhouses. Well, one outhouse happened to be the one at my house. He said that he pushed it over into the millrace. Then he heard shouting and splashing. He had pushed an occupied outhouse over and the owner could not get out because it had fallen over onto its door. Then, the boy faced a moral dilemma. Fortunately, he made the right choice, and the outhouse's occupant did not drown.

Aside from that story, he showed me the old millrace path as it wound through my yard, and my neighbor's yards from the creek down to the site of the old mill. I had forgotten that story when eight years later a friend of mine volunteered to help me build a greenhouse on the south side of my house. On an October morning the backhoe began to dig into the earth as the first step toward constructing the footing. The trench that came out from the corner of the house was particularly interesting. It dug through a jumble of rubble that was underlain by several layers of dressed stones. As I saw the cross section, I immediately recalled the old neighbor's tale of the race and realized that I was looking at its cross section (see Figure 5-1). Despite the story, I could see that the bed of the millrace was almost 2 meters across (distance that would certainly require a bridge to get to the outhouse) and nearly a meter deep. In addition, the back wall of my house was the north wall of the millrace. Also, the bed was filled with a mixed rubble of stones and soil. Clearly, the race had not filled with soil deposited by runoff but it had been filled mainly with field stones. I interpreted this to mean that the channel of the race had been filled deliberately and all at once (see Figure 5-1). The consequence of that structure was that the soil overlying the old race drains very well, in fact too well during drought years. Unfortunately, the opposite is true in the greenhouse itself. Because the footing of the greenhouse caps the race depression at both ends, the greenhouse tends to hold water and drain slowly.

338

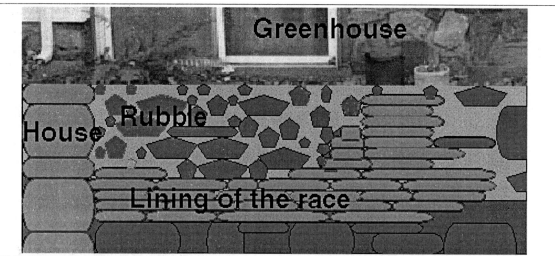

FIGURE 5-1. The existing house and greenhouse with a cutaway drawing of the placement of the millrace relative to the foundation of the greenhouse (light gray background) and the foundation of the house. Note the rubble layer within the original millrace.

FIGURE 5-2.. Horizontally-layered strata in Devonian outcrops in Snyder County, PA.

Things in the ground show their relative ages the same way that the components of the old millrace did. Similar relative positions can be seen in geological formations. Consider the strata in Figure 5-2. This is an outcrop from the lower Devonian of Snyder County. The layers on top are younger than those below. Thus, a relative age (younger to older) can be determined just on the basis of relative position. This is called the Law of Superposition, and it was one of the first laws of Geology.

STENO AND HOOKE

At the time when any given stratum was being formed, all the matter resting upon it was fluid, and, therefore, at the time when the lower stratum was being formed, none of the upper strata existed.

-Niels Steno (1669)

Most of the fundamental laws of geology were formulated very early. Even Leonardo da Vinci speculated about the origin of fossils in alpine rocks. The first clear law-like statements that dealt with the interpretation of strata were given by Nicholas Steno of Denmark (nee Niels Stenson; 1638-1686). He moved to Italy where, as a Catholic he felt much more comfortable than in Lutheran Denmark. Shortly after his move, the Duke of Tuscany asked him to dissect a large shark that had come into his possession. Steno was a skilled anatomist, and his dissection of the shark convinced him that fossils known as tongue stones (glossopetrae) really were the teeth of ancient sharks. This sparked his interest in the geology of the Tuscany region, which led to his publication of *De Solido Intra Solidium Naturaliter Contendo Dissertationis Prodromus (Forerunner of a Dissertation on a*

Solid Naturally Contained within a Solid), usually just called *The Prodromus.*

In the *Prodromus* Steno attempted to explain the landforms and particular geology of the Tuscany area by employing a set of general statements or laws:

1. Each rock layer (stratum) was laid down in an aqueous medium so that soft sediments layered onto hard sublayers. Fossils, the remains of living things, became incorporated into the strata in this initial soft stage.

2. The Law of Horizontality: Because the strata (rock layers) were laid down in a liquid medium, they originally formed in horizontal and laterally continuous layers.

3. The Law of Superposition: Because strata develop by the settling of particles in a liquid medium, newer strata must settle out onto older strata. Thus, younger strata overlie older strata.

4. Any departure from stacked horizontal layers resulted from later alteration by phenomena such as earthquakes and volcanoes.

Steno submitted his manuscript to the Catholic censors for publication. They delayed the approval for four months during 1668. Finally, he lost interest in geology altogether and the book (an abstract of a larger intended work) was published by one of the censors. The *Prodromus* had little impact on contemporary natural philosophers and had to wait for another century before his concepts of stratigraphy and the organic nature of fossils was accepted.

Robert Hooke (1635-1703), Newton's nemesis and contemporary of Steno, was born on the Isle of Wight, England. There, he made keen observations of the geology of the area as a young man. Later, he examined chalk from that area with a microscope and saw that that the rock was made of tiny remains of living things. He inferred that the Isle of Wight had been at the bottom of an ocean whose sediment received fossil remains and incorporated them into layers of the rock there. Then, violent and catastrophic actions of the earth (such as earthquakes) lifted the sediment up out of the ocean. He conceived of an earth whose land forms were made by sedimentation and uplift and wrote it up in a manuscript called *Discourse of Earthquakes* sometime in 1668. However, it was not published until 1705, two years after his death. The great departure of Hooke from contemporary natural philosophers was that the earth was made by a cycle of catastrophes rather than by a single great flood. This idea was not new even with Hooke. Avicenna, an Arabic natural philosopher around 1000, suggested that fossils were organic remains and that mountains were "the effects of upheavals of the crust of the earth, such as might occur during an earthquake, or they were the effect of water, which cutting for itself a new route, has denuded the valley."

Natural Philosophers could not help but speculate about the earth and its origin throughout the 18th Century. Unfortunately, most of the speculation was not based on interpretation of observations as Steno and Hooke had done. The authors did, by and large, see the need to provide a mechanical or non-mystical explanation for the earth particularly in the mechanical cosmos that Newton had bequeathed to science.

THE THEORY BUILDERS

If it is once settled that a theory of the earth ought to have no other aim but to discover the laws that regulate the changes on the surface, or in the interior of the globe...there is no reason to suppose, that man...shall ultimately prove unequal to this investigation. -Alfred Gottlob Werner.

As natural philosophers of the Enlightenment contemplated theories that explained the earth, they began to suppose, as Hooke had, that much more than just 6,000 years had passed since the origin of the Earth. Throughout the 18th Century, theory after theory was proposed to explain the earth and its features; most assumed that Noah's flood was not sufficient as an explanation. The theory that made the most notable departure from the Noachan Flood was that of George-Louis Leclerc, Comte de Buffon (1707-1788; see Figure 5-3) who had been made head of the Jardin de Roi (the King's Botanical Garden and Museum). There, while trying to make sense of the exhibits, he wrote a 44-volume treatise *Histoire naturelle* (1749-1767) as a means to bring order to the apparent chaos of nature.

FIGURE 5-3. Bust of George-Louis Leclerc, Comte de Buffon on the outside of the Natural History Museum in the Jardin des Plantes (formerly Jardin de Roi).

At the end of his life Buffon considered the origin and formation of the cosmos and the earth as having occurred in seven great epochs (rather that in seven days). He published the book *Les Epoques de la Nature* during the last year of his life (and one year before the French Revolution and Lavoisier's *Elements of Chemistry*). The most startling aspect of the book was that it required a long period of time. Buffon supposed that the earth was originally molten and took time to cool. Thus,

he based his estimate on how long a molten iron ball took to cool down and then extrapolated that to the scale of the earth to yield 75,000 years. Like Hooke and Avicenna, Buffon supposed that the actions of volcanoes and water had together been responsible for the features of the earth's surface.

Abraham Gottlob Werner (1749-1817) of Silesia (now Poland) spent most of his life as a teacher in Saxony. His knowledge of geology and his inference of geological process came from his observations of that region. He saw mountains with the oldest or primary rocks at the peaks with progressively younger rocks down their sides. He interpreted the geology and the formation of the mountains of the region to be consistent with a global ocean. He believed that the primary rocks like granite crystallized out of the sea followed by erosion and successive deposition layers as the ocean receded (see Figures 5-4 and 5-5).

Werner and his students interpreted the mountains themselves as proof of the early ocean and an indication of its original depth. The Wernerians or Neptunists, as they began to be called, became interested in discerning the order of strata and correlating those strata across Europe[1]. Thus, the Geological Column was a Neptunist concept. The organization of the Geological Time Table and many of the names of the periods within it came from the work of the Neptunists.

Werner refused to speculate about many of the details of the original ocean or about where the water went when it receded. However, he believed that the dissolved salts of the existing ocean became much more concentrated as the water left. Indeed, Werner saw the high salt level of the existing ocean as further proof of a much deeper primal ocean. Fossils, too, seemed to corroborate his view. The earliest strata contained fossils of marine invertebrates, then

---

[1] I expand on this in *Reading the Earth*.

fish, and later land-dwelling animals and plants.

FIGURE 5-4. A piece of granite from the Avalonian Terrane[2] in Maine. Note the crystalline appearance of its structure.

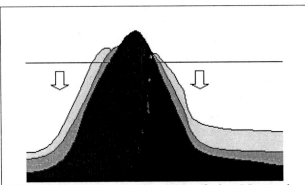

FIGURE 5-5. A diagram of the Neptunist view of the origin of mountains and strata. The primal rocks (in black) crystallized out of the global ocean. As the ocean receded other layers were laid down by erosion and further crystallization.

Baron Georges Cuvier (1769-1832), a follower of Werner and successor to Buffon as head of the Natural History Museum in the Jardin des Plants (the post-revolutionary name of the Jardin de Roi), saw the earth and the developing geological column as indicating a succession of catastrophes each followed by a new creation. Thus, Cuvier saw a direction in his study of earth's history as had the other followers of Werner.

The Neptunists were not, as sometimes presented, dedicated to explaining the surface geology of the earth based on the Noachan Flood. In fact, they too suffered attacks by the religious establishment for deviating from a literal interpretation of Genesis. Only in Britain did a handful of Neptunists attempt to reconcile the formation of the earth's features with the Biblical Flood. Generally, the followers of Werner began to think of long periods of time in which the agency of water was enough to explain the varieties of earth's features. Thus, the Neptunists tended to explain geology by a series of catastrophes with progress in a particular direction.

JAMES HUTTON

Dr. Hutton is obscure and perplexed from the multitude of facts which crowded on his mind.   -Humphrey Davy (1805)

James Hutton[3] (1726-1797) of Edinburgh, Scotland, a contemporary of Werner, was as chaotic in life as in his prose. He trained as a physician at Leiden but never practiced. He became interested in farming and studied farming practices in England and on the continent. After that he became a gentleman farmer and a fixture in the Scottish Enlightenment with Joseph Black (1728-1799), James Watt (17306-1819), and John Playfair (1748-1819).

Hutton came to the study of geology through his interests in chemistry, agriculture, and mineralogy, the same fundamental interests that drove Abraham Werner. In fact, his interests in chemistry and agriculture led him to develop a method with Joseph Black to extract ammonium for fertilizer from coal tar, an enterprise that made him independently wealthy. He gave up farming around 1768, and as a consequence, he gained the freedom to spend time in phi-

_____

[2] See *A Trip to Avalon.*

[3] See *Y2K, Deep Time, and Theory Choice in Geology.*

losophical speculation, experimentation, and extensive field work.

Hutton's field observations made him familiar with rock strata throughout Britain. Also, he knew of well-dated structures such as Hadrian's Wall and that almost no erosion could be detected on the 1500-year-old stones. Thus, he began to consider the possibility that the time required to wear down whole mountains would be immense. So, Hutton backed away from the question of the earth's origin and just said that the earth went through cycles of destruction and renewal as had been proposed by Hooke a century earlier. The primary difference between Hooke and Hutton, though was that Hutton proposed cycles that were not large, catastrophic events, but the uniform accumulation of everyday normal rates of mountain building and erosion. This concept of uniformitarianism coupled with time that was so great that it was without measure became the cornerstones on which Hutton built his theory.

Like Hooke, Hutton said that mountains were built by the upward push of molten material from within the earth. Thus, his Vulcanist or Plutonist theory described the earth as a great heat engine (see Figure 5-6). Within that theory sedimentary rock was laid down before it was pushed up from below. Thus, this theory did not require a global shrinking ocean, but it did require a very different way of thinking about the earth and the cosmos.

Hutton wrote his theory in an abstract, *System of the Earth* (1785), and later in a much larger book, *Theory of the Earth* (1788). After his initial writing, Hutton went out to the Scottish countryside and found confirmation of his theory. At a place called Glen Tilt, he found regular sedimentary rock with an intrusion of granite in it. He interpreted it to mean that the sedimentary rock had been in place when molten rock from below pushed up into it.

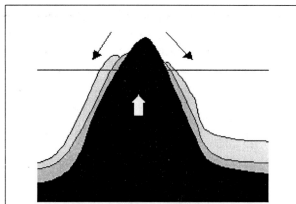

FIGURE 5-6. An illustration of the Hutton-Hooke Vulcanist explanation for the formation of mountains. Molten rock from the earth's interior pushes up and folds sedimentary rock. The action of erosion gives rise to new sedimentary rock.

Beyond his small circle, Hutton had almost no impact at the time. For one thing, his books were very hard to read. Also, the requirement of almost unlimited time seemed harder to accept than a global ocean. His ideas might have died away altogether if his uniformitarian principle had not been written down by John Playfair and published as *Illustrations of the Huttonian Theory of the Earth* in 1802. Even so, Hutton's theory languished in obscurity until a young revolutionary took the concepts of Hutton and melded them with extensive field data to bring about a fundamental change in Geology.

CHARLES LYELL
Geologists have been ever prone to represent Nature as having been prodigal of violence and parsimonious of time.
-Charles Lyell

Sir Charles Lyell (1797-1875) was that revolutionary but his life began almost with the same indecision as had marked the life of Hutton. He attended Oxford University where his interests varied from mathematics to the law and the classics. While there, he attended a lecture by the geologist William

Buckland (1784-1856) and developed a passion for geology. He took a degree in law and practiced for a time. While on a field study in France in 1828, Lyell decided to give up his law practice and continue his fieldwork in Italy rather than return to London.

While in Italy, he made several famous observations. First, he saw that many of the same shellfish in the coastal waters occurred as fossils in some of the uplifted strata. Also, he saw evidence for the fluctuation in water level as shown by marks left on coastal Roman ruins. The most famous of his observations, however, had to do with Mount Aetna, a large active volcano. He saw that the cone of the volcano had been built over many thousands of years by layers of ash from many successive eruptions. The cone, itself, therefore was quite old. However, it emerged from a sedimentary layer that had fossils indicating that it was geologically young. Thus, the "young strata" had been laid down, uplifted, and then punctured by the vent of the volcano (see Figure 5-7). If such structures were geologically young, how old must most other geological features be?

Fresh from his trips and geological observations, Lyell began to work on what would become a three-volume treatise that he meant to define the science of Geology. That was clear from his choice of the title, *Principles of Geology* (see Figure 5-8). This deliberate choice of title harkened back to Newton's *Principia*. Thus, Lyell meant his book to be the foundation of geology in the same way that Newton's *Principia* was the foundation of physics.

Lyell skillfully, and at times with a very heavy hand, began to present Hutton's concepts of uniformitarianism and cyclic renewal of the earth. Lyell removed the more mystical aspects that implied purposefulness on the part of the cycles and began to attack the positions of the Neptunists, especially the concepts of catastrophism and directionalism.

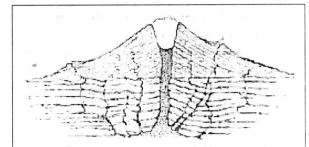

FIGURE 5-7. A diagram of Mount Aetna by T.H. Huxley (1881) based, in part, on work by C. Lyell.

The need for catastrophic explanation disappears if enormous amounts of time can be in play. Even the smallest agent of change can have a huge impact given enough time. He highlights this idea by the use of the subtitle: *An Attempt to Explain the Former Changes of the Earth's Surface by Reference to Causes Now in Operation.* Indeed, that is the whole foundation of uniformitarianism (or gradualism as Lyell called it) which is an "uninterrupted succession of physical events, governed by the laws now in operation."

Directionalism, however, seemed to be a more difficult argument to counter. The directionalist argument had two major bits of evidence to support it. First, the climate of the earth seemed to be gradually cooling. Following the arguments of Buffon and even those of earlier philosophers, the earth began as a molten ball and continued to cool gradually. At first Lyell argued that the earth only appeared to cool but actually cycled around a mean temperature. In later editions he abandoned this argument and admitted that the gradual climatic cooling seemed to be true. (Imagine that in a time when we are worried about global warming).

The second argument had to do with the apparent direction taken by life. He believed that the appearance of progressive change in life was just an illusion. He even stated that if the climatic requirements for the dinosaurs were to reappear, then *Ig-*

uanodon and its companions would return to the earth. Thus, he originally argued that the evolution of living things could not occur in the context of uniformitarianism. Finally, his friend Charles Darwin convinced him that a steady or apparent directional change could occur within a gradualist theory. So, over time and with later revisions, Lyell backed away from the strict gradualist position of a cyclic earth as proposed by Hutton.

Lyell was barely 30 when he published volume one of *Principles.* The book was written for professional geologists and for an educated general audience. It was well received because Lyell explained his arguments carefully and used example after example, some of which came from his own fieldwork. However, most of the examples came from the data collected by the Neptunists, themselves.

Volume one began with a history of geology up to 1830. In it he painted the catastrophists, neptunists, directionalists, and Biblical literalists in a very bad light. He then followed that with an extended analysis of gradual geological processes.

He intended to write only two volumes, but the second volume dragged on so that he shortened the second to describe the actions of living things as instruments of change. He also considered (and refuted in the early editions) existing theories of evolutionary change. This one he published in 1832. The third volume (1833) brought together both living and non-living forces as they acted in concert during the Tertiary Period.

Because Lyell was so young when he published the work, he managed to take it through 11 editions throughout his lifetime. Thus, he managed to guide thought of geology and geological process throughout the period of 1830 to 1875. Although his views evolved somewhat, Lyell never backed down from the concept of gradualism and the necessity of deep time. Thus, they became the central principles of the science of geology. His arguments were so well crafted and his presentation so compelling that within a generation only the most diehard geologists clung to the catastrophist view. The steady-state or cyclic theory of the earth that Lyell also borrowed from Hutton never did gain much of a following. Here the directionalist theories seemed to succeed in the long run with Lyell acceding to concepts of gradual warming and evolution in the end.

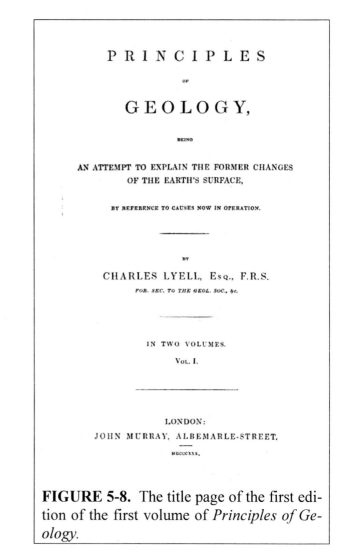

FIGURE 5-8. The title page of the first edition of the first volume of *Principles of Geology.*

CHANGES IN GEOLOGY
The vision of the mind authoritatively supplements the vision of the eye.

        -John Tyndall (1874)

How can one infer and interpret information from the past to reconstruct past events? In the case of the millrace I had an old neighbor to guide my observations and answer my questions. In a historical science like geology, the interpreter has to use the laws of sedimentology as defined by Steno with the principles of gradualism and deep time. They have to be applied in the same way in the interpretation of geological phenomena. Unlike physics and chemistry, which can be studied by experimentation, most of geology requires observation, description, and careful application of historical interpretation and reconstruction. Charles Lyell put together the pieces of the appropriate methods for investigation. It is the valid application of these methods that give rise to theories and allow them to be tested. Now geology explains phenomena under theories that would be quite foreign to Charles Lyell. Nevertheless, the fundamental methods and laws have not changed but have been augmented by modern technologies. Today, even catastrophic events like the meteor strike that eliminated the dinosaurs 65 million years ago can be examined by gradualist methods and explained by gradualist theories.

Lyell gave the purpose of his work at the end of the first chapter of the third volume:

These topics we regard as constituting the alphabet and grammar of geology; not that we expect from such studies to obtain a key to the interpretation of all geological phenomena, but because they form the groundwork from which we must rise to the contemplation of more general questions relating to the complicated results to which, in an indefinite lapse of ages, the existing causes of change may give rise.

At the time Lyell went through the revisions for his 11th edition, he was completely blind. Yet in his blindness, he continued to perfect the means by which we can see into the past. In that sense, we still look back in time through the eyes of Lyell.

-2001; revised 2005

References:

Blundell, D. J. and A. C. Scott. 1998. *Lyell: the Past is the Key to the Present.* Geological Society of London. London.

Boggs, Sam, Jr. 1987. *Principles of Sedimentology and Stratigraphy.* Merrill Publishing Co. Columbus.

Bowler, Peter J. 1992. *The Fontana History of the Environmental Sciences.* IN: Porter, Roy, ed. *Fontana History of Science.* Fontana Press. London.

Craig, G. Y. and J. H. Hull. 1998. *James Hutton - Present and Future.* Geological Society of London. London.

Drake, Ellen Tan. 1996. *Restless Genius, Robert Hooke and his Earthly Thoughts.* Oxford University Press. New York.

Hallam, A. 1984. *Great Geological Controversies.* Oxford University Press. Oxford.

Holland, C. H. 1999. *The Idea of Time.* John Wiley and Sons, Inc. New York.

Mason, Stephen F.1962. *A History of the Sciences.* Collier Books. New York.

Longwell, Chester R., Richard F. Flint, and John E. Sanders. 1969. *Physical Geology.* John Wiley and Sons, Inc. New York.

Lyell, Charles. 1990 (originally published 1830-33). *Principles of Geology.* Vol 1-3. University of Chicago Press. Chicago

Newton, Isaac. 1686. *Mathematical Principles of Natural Philosophy.* In: Hutchins, Robert Maynard, editor. 1952. Great Books of the Western World. Vol 34. Encyclopaedia Brittannica, Inc. Chicago.

Oldroyd, D. 1996. *Thinking About the Earth: A History of Ideas in Geology.* Athlone Press. New York.

Simmons, John. 2000. *The Scientific 100, A Ranking of the Most Influential Scientists, Past and Present.* Citadel Press. New York.

White, George W., ed. 1973. *James Hutton's System of the Earth, 1785; Theory of the*

Earth, 1788; Observations on Granite, 1794; and Playfair's Biography of Hutton. IN: Contributions to the History of Geology. Volume 5. Hafner Press. New York.

The present is the key to the past.

-Sir Archibald Geike (1835-1924)

Questions to Think About

1. What laws did Steno define? Why are such statements important to a science like geology?

2. What contributions did Robert Hooke make to an understanding of the nature of fossils? Was he the first to come up with this idea?

3. Who first proposed a theory that utilized long periods of time?

4. Who were the Neptunists? What was their theory of the earth?

5. Who were the Vulcanists (or Plutonists)? How did their theories differ from those of the Neptunists?

6. What was the primary contribution of James Hutton? What ideas did he borrow from others like Hooke? What ideas were original with him? Why did Hutton's theories make almost no immediate impact?

7. What convinced Hutton that the world was so old that it "had no beginning and no prospect for an end"?

8. I argued that Charles Lyell and his book began modern geology. How did he modify Hutton's theories to make a modern theory of the earth? What other reasons might have caused Lyell to have such an impact on the foundation of modern geology?

9. What is a directionalist theory?

10. How would you answer someone who makes the claim that the experimental method determines what is a science?

Y2K, DEEP TIME, AND THEORY CHOICE IN GEOLOGY

MILLENNIUM MADNESS

Madness is rare in individuals, but in groups, parties, nations, and ages, it is the rule.   -Friedrich Nietzsche

I recall the hoopla that surrounded the transition from 1999 to 2000, the dawn of the 3rd millennium. I considered the fuss important only because some pieces of equipment might have stopped working. Also, we were inconvenienced by the temporary loss of a few services.

Actually, the millennium, a thousand year period, is an accident of evolution (we have adopted a base ten number system because we have ten fingers), an accident of cosmology (a year has the particular period or length of time because of the earth's distance from the sun), an accident of biology (we have a life span that approaches 100 years, so ten times that length is just beyond the understanding of any one person but within the understanding of a culture), and an accident of history (numbering of the current era began at an arbitrary year 1). Thus, the particular year of 2000 (or 2001 if you are a purist) becomes trivial by almost any way of reckoning it.

Measured relative to the age of the earth, a 1000-year period is like a drop in the bucket. However, a serious consideration of the earth's age requires an understanding of the concept of Deep Time. That is, thinking of time in millions and billions of years. These periods of time are so much out of a human's everyday, lifetime or cultural experience that we can understand them only rationally. That is, we understand "billion" first as a word, secondly as a concept, and only dimly as a reality. It was the Geologists who, through their attempts to understand the formation of earth's landforms, brought the concept of deep time into science.

BY WATER

Werner had great antipathy to the mechanical labor of writing, and he could never be persuaded to pen more than a few brief memoirs.

-Sir Charles Lyell

Before the 18th century there was little speculation about the transformation of the earth's surface. Some troubling things like marine fossils on mountaintops appeared in the discussion but were explained away as failed creations of life or evidence of The Genesis Flood. That a single catastrophe like The Flood or series of flooding catastrophes could explain the earth's landforms gave way to a theory that assumed the earth originally was covered by water. Gradually, the waters receded, and as they did, landforms of the earth appeared above the waves and took shape. Adherents to this theoretical view were called the Neptunists after the classical god of the sea. An important aspect of this view is that it could explain the earth in the 5-10 thousand-year period assumed to have occurred since The Creation.

Neptunists explained crystalline rocks like granite and many other minerals as having grown as crystals in the waters of a younger earth. While covered with water, suspended rocks, sands, down to very fine particles differentially settled out and made the layers of sedimentary rocks.

German geologist, Abraham Werner (1750-1815), one of the principle Neptunist theorists supposed that the earth's landforms came about by the processes of precipitation and crystallization from a primordial sea. Therefore, older layers lay beneath younger layers. Werner even explained the occurrence of volcanoes as relatively new structures that were formed by subterranean coal fires.

BY FIRE[4]

With no vestige of a beginning and no prospect of an end.   -James Hutton

An alternative theory said that volcanoes were responsible for the origin of the earth's landforms. John Ray (1627-1705), a British scientist, believed that mountains were formed by volcanic action. Also, the layers of sedimentary rock recorded a series of volcanic eruptions. This view required much longer periods of time with the same mechanism repeating again and again. During the 18th century, the followers of Ray (called Vulcanists or Plutonists) explained the volcanic origin of continents, ocean basins, as well as mountains.

James Hutton (1726-1797), a contemporary of Abraham Werner, expanded on the Vulcanist theory. Through observations that he made in Edinburgh, Scotland and during his travels, he began to speculate that that the center of the earth is molten. Rocks like granite and basalt came from that molten center via volcanoes. Water then eroded the rocks of volcanic origin to produce sedimentary rocks.

Hutton assumed that the natural processes at work on the earth now are the same ones that shaped the surface of

---

[4] Please consult *Geology Through Lyell's Eyes* for an expansion on the contributions of Werner, Hutton, and Lyell.

the earth from the time it was a molten ball. This Uniformitarian Principle required immense amounts of time to wear down mountains, produce sedimentary rocks that then also erode away, etc. This principle became Hutton's major contribution to the sciences, and developed into the cornerstone of Geology.

Hutton's vision was quite grand. He saw the earth as a great heat engine with volcanoes producing the raw materials for the renewal of the surface landforms. The goal of this cycle of rocks and erosion was the production of soil.

MODERN GEOLOGY IS BORN

When we compare the result of observations in the last thirty years with those of the three preceding centuries, we cannot but look forward with the most sanguine expectations to the degree of excellence to which geology may be carried.

-Sir Charles Lyell

Hutton's vision was set down in a rambling 1000 page book called the *Theory of the Earth* in 1795. It was poorly written and his explanations were so ambiguous that arguments arose almost immediately as to what his conclusions really were.

Sir Charles Lyell, a fellow Scot with an interest in Geology, took parts of the Neptunist theory that explained sedimentation, the formation of sedimentary rocks, and the relative ages of sedimentary rock layers. Also, he retained the view that the earth had an origin and a history.

Lyell kept much of the Huttonian Vulcanist theory and expanded on the Uniformitarian Principle. He eliminated Hutton's view of an eternal earth, but retained the requirement of long periods of time. In short, his theory proposed that the earth's surface became more uneven by volcanic or igneous processes and became more even by erosion or aqueous processes.

Lyell's *Principles of Geology* (Volume 1 was first published in 1830) was well written and successfully integrated portions of the Vulcanist and Neptunist theories with the central theme of gradualism, based on the Uniformitarian Principle. The book grew to three volumes and went through 12 editions. It had a major impact on geologists and naturalists of the mid-19th century, including a young naturalist named Charles Darwin on his voyage of discovery.

The vestiges of the Neptunist Theory became manifest in a young earth view in which the earth was shaped by a series of catastrophes. Lyell would not budge on his requirement of a gradual, uniformitarian process of landform creation. By the end of the 19th century, Gradualism had won out in the community of Geologists and catastrophes were no longer allowed as explanations.

A PHYSICIST'S CHALLENGE

His impulse was to correlate phenomena and arrive at the principle underlying them, and this gave him a certain impatience with branches of science that were still in the observational stage...

-A Student of Lord Kelvin

Traditional disciplines within geology such as minerology and stratigraphy blossomed during the 19th century. Descriptions of minerals and the physical processes involved in the formation of rock layers seemed to be pretty well known. Strata had been classified into broad ages and correlated across the planet[5]. All could be explained within a gradualist theory.

_____

[5] I have expanded on this in *Reading the Earth.*

Geologists theorized that mountains, continents and ocean basins formed on the earth as a consequence of gradual cooling from a molten ball. As it cooled, it shrank slightly, thereby wrinkling the outer crust. It was in consideration of the cooling rate that a crisis arose in the sciences when physicists like William Thompson, Lord Kelvin chose to tackle the problem of the age of the earth using the principle of uniformitarian gradualism, the fundamental principle of geology itself. If the earth cooled from a molten ball to an earth with a molten interior and a crust of only 50 miles thick, then the earth could be no more than 100 million years old. Indeed, some of Kelvin's calculations seemed to say that the earth was as young as 24 million years. This new young earth theory was based on a physical calculation that was confirmed by other physicists.

Not until the discovery of radioactivity and the realization that the interior of the earth contains small amounts of radioactive elements did a source of heat appear to counter Kelvin's assertion. At the time, though, his argument had been so compelling that some geologists had begun to accommodate theory to agree with the new dates. They assumed that the Uniformitarian Principle must be modified to say that geological activity was much more intense during the early earth and then it slowed down in more recent times.

The discovery of radiation and the understanding of the half-lives of the products of radioactive decay led to the opposite problem. This indicated that the earth was immensely old, on the order of billions of years. Also, the cooling rate must have been so slow that ocean basins and mountains could not be explained that way. It was an intellectual Pyrrhic victory.

SLIDING CONTINENTS

It is probable that the complete solution to the problem of the forces will be a long time coming. The Newton of drift theory has not yet appeared.

-Alfred Wegener

The view at the turn of the 20th Century was that the earth was very old. Its continents and ocean basins had been altered by fluctuations in water level, mountain formation, and erosion. How were mountains formed? Volcanoes were easier to understand than the large mountain ranges of folded sedimentary rock. What could have generated enough force to cause large expanses of sedimentary rock to buckle and rise? Some postulated that rolling currents developed in the mantle, a hot zone between the molten core and the solid crust. As the mantle moved, parts of crust wrinkled above them. This served as an explanation for why there were mountains of very different ages and how mountains could have been formed in the absence of a cooling, shrinking earth.

Also, it was noted that although continents seem to be made of recycled materials, the core of the continents was made of granite, a kind of igneous rock. The ocean basins, on the other hand, were made of basalt, another kind of igneous rock. Curiously, the granite was less dense that basalt, so it appeared that the continents were higher because they "floated" on the denser mantle and ocean basin material.

Alfred Wegener (1880-1930) embraced the concept of floating continents at the turn of the 20th century. Although he had received a doctorate in astronomy in 1905, Wegener quickly turned his attention to the weather and made impor-

tant contributions to the study of meteorology. In the mean time, he became intrigued by the remarkable fit between the continents of South America and Africa. Although he was not the first to do so, Wegener gave the connection his full attention in 1914 as he lay in a hospital recovering from wounds suffered during the First World War. As he convalesced, Wegener began to collect evidence from stratigraphy and paleontology. He discovered that there are places that seem geologically continuous from one continent to another as if they were just torn apart. Also, the two continents shared particular plant and animal fossils that could not have made the transit across the Atlantic Ocean.

Wegener collected enough evidence to convince him that all of the earth's continents had once been connected into a supercontinent that he called Pangaea. He published his ideas in 1915 in *The Origin of Continents and Oceans* (see Figure 5-9). In Wegner's view, the continents then broke apart and drifted to their present positions as they floated or slid over the plastic mantle. He looked in vain for a force sufficient to overcome the enormous forces of friction. He speculated that lunar tidal forces or the centrifugal force exerted by the spinning earth would be enough to move the continents like great ships over the earth's surface. The community of geologists did not accept Wegener's ideas. His evidence was viewed as circumstantial and his explanations for the movement absurd. What is more, he was an outsider, a meteorologist meddling in geology.

Wegener spent his professional life working on meteorology and defending his theory of Continental Drift to no avail. He died during an expedition to Greenland at age 50, and his theory of Continental Drift was relegated to an interesting footnote in the history of geology.

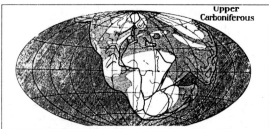

FIGURE 5-9. Alfred Wegener's illustration of Pangaea from *The Origin of Continents and Oceans.*

NEWTON OF DRIFT THEORY

One of the truly remarkable earth scientists of this century.

-National Academy of Sciences Memoir

Harry Hess (1906-1969) earned a Ph.D. from Princeton in 1932, two years after the death of Wegener. During World War II, Hess served in the U.S. Navy, ultimately rising to the rank of Rear Admiral. He developed a system to track German submarines and made thousands of depth soundings across the Pacific Ocean. Following this experience he continued his interest in ocean basins by forming and directing the Princeton Caribbean Research Project.

During this time, Hess considered some lines of evidence that were coming to light in sea floor research. First, examination of the sediments of the floor of the Atlantic Ocean showed that they were quite young and thin. Static Earth Theory required that the ocean basins had accumulated sediment continuously for the earth's long history. However, collected sediments were thicker and older nearer the continental margins and younger toward the middle of the Atlantic.

The center of the Atlantic Ocean had a ridge that ran the full length (north to south) and was equidistant from continents to the east and west. Hess and others recognized that the ridges were volcanic in origin and were sites of upwelling and spreading of material from the mantle. Hess suggested that the ridge overlay a rising convection current that was fueled by heat from radioactive decay. This explanation came together with evidence that ocean crust returned to the mantle at ocean trenches where the spreading seafloor forced oceanic crust to dive beneath the less dense continental crust. Furthermore, the subducted crustal material must melt when it dives into the mantle and rise again to form volcanoes. That continental volcanoes were associated with these areas of subduction confirmed the theory.

In 1962, Harry Hess put all of this together in his theory of Sea Floor Spreading (see Figure 5-10). In this view, the continents did not plow through sea floor, but rode on them as passengers. At last the obstacle to Wegener's Continental drift was overcome. A plausible mechanism for change had been offered. Hess became Wegener's much-needed Newton of drift theory.

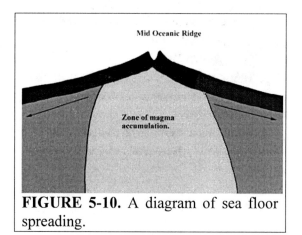

FIGURE 5-10. A diagram of sea floor spreading.

Sea Floor Spreading is the fundamental concept on which the Theory of Plate Tectonics is built. In this theory, the earth's surface is divided into a number of crustal plates like a cracked egg (see Figure 5-11). The plates move by spreading or slipping past each other. Sometimes they collide (the Indian and Eurasian Plates), and sometimes they slip beneath or subduct beneath another plate (the Nazca and South American Plates). This is a beautiful theory in that all landforms on the earth can be explained by these actions accompanied by erosion.

By 1967, the theory was defined and began to be tested. Now, the theory is useful in understanding landforms on Io, Venus, Europa and other planetary bodies. More direct measurements of the movement can now be made by satellite. The Atlantic Ocean spreads at about 5cm per year. Other plates move at different rates. The surface of the earth is anything but static.

THEORY CHOICE

What better criterion could there be than the decision of the scientific group? - Thomas Kuhn

Now return to the various theories that I have explored. The Neptunists said that a primary sea had covered the earth. From that sea, rocks and minerals began to crystallize. As the waters receded, more layers formed so that younger layers overlay older layers. This theory did not require a very old earth, but it did require a place for all of that water to go.

In the Vulcanist Theory, landforms were created gradually by successive volcanic events. Thus, long periods of time were necessary. Indeed, in the Vulcanist theory of Hutton, time became cyclic, without a beginning or an end, operating on the Uniformitarian Principle.

Charles Lyell then took parts of the Neptunist and Vulcanist Theories and wove them into a new way of explaining the earth. He kept the stratigraphy and minerology of the Neptunists and adopted the uniformitarian gradulaism of Hutton with the concept of an earth with a molten center. In this view of deep time, the earth was very old, but it did have a beginning. Lyell's theory did survive challenges by the catastrophists and physicists who said that the earth had to be much younger. Wegener's Continental Drift theory never entered the mainstream of the science of geology. It was interesting, but offered no mechanism to explain how the continents could move. Then following Hess' theory of Sea Floor Spreading, Wegener's Continental Drift transformed into Plate Tectonics, the central paradigm of geology.

Still, Plate Tectonics is not completely new. It has vestiges of Neptunism, Vulcanism, Static Earth, and Continental Drift. Above all, it is a fruitful theory allowing our explanations of landforms to go beyond the bounds of this earth and through immense periods of time.

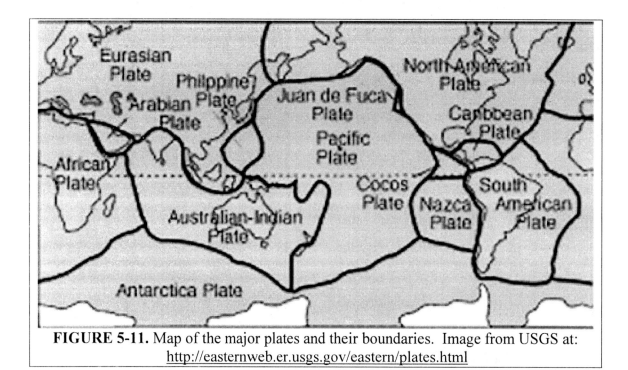

FIGURE 5-11. Map of the major plates and their boundaries. Image from USGS at: http://easternweb.er.usgs.gov/eastern/plates.html

Thus, the concept of deep time became part of Geology, and allowed for the development of subtle, more general theories to explain the nature of the earth. The fruitfulness of deep time as a principle caused it to weave itself into all disciplines of science. Thus, my rational understanding of deep time tempered my enthusiasm for celebrating the new millennium.

Y2K

Someday we'll all look back on this, laugh nervously, and change the subject.
                                    -A Bumper Sticker

The year 2000 came and went, and much ado was made of that "landmark" time. I was so tired of hearing about it that I welcomed the next week when our attention-deficit culture turned its eyes to something else. After all, during the past 2000 years the Atlantic widened by only 100 meters. The whole Atlantic Ocean began to form only 140 million years ago, a mere $1/30^{th}$ of the age of the

earth. On New Year's 2000, I sang and danced. I celebrated friendships and life. These things were far more important to me than a celebration of insignificance.
                                    -1999; revised 2004

References:

Bowler, Peter. 1992. *The Fontana History of the Environmental Sciences.* Fontana Press. London.

Gould, Stephen. 1987. *Time's Arrow, Time's Cycle.* Harvard University Press. Cambridge, Mass.

Gould, Stephen. 1997. *Questioning the Millenium.* Harmony Books. New York.

Kuhn, Thomas. 1977. *Objectivity, Value Judgement, and Theory Choice.* In: Curd & Cover, eds. 1998. *The Philosophy of Science, The Central Issues.* W.W. Norton & Co., Inc. New York. pp 102-118.

Lyell, Charles. 1990 (originally published 1830-33). *Principles of Geology With a new Introduction by Martin J. S. Rudwick. Vols. 1-2.* The

University of Chicago Press. Chicago.

Schuchert, Charles. 1928. *The Hypothesis of Continental Displacement.* Annual Report of the Board of Regents of the Smithsonian Institution. US Government Printing Office. Washington. pp 249-282.

Trefil, James and Robert Hazen. 1998. *The Sciences, An Integrated Approach.* John Wiley and Sons, Inc. New York.

Wegener, Alfred. 1966 (originally 1915). *The Origin of the Continents and Oceans.* Translated by John Biram. Dover Publications, Inc. New York.

Questions to Think About

1. What were the contributions of Werner, Hutton, and Lyell in the development of modern geology?

2. How did Lord Kelvin and other physicists present a significant challenge to one of the fundamental principles of geology?

3. How was that challenge resolved?

4. What was Alfred Wegener's theory of the earth? Why was it generally not accepted by geologists?

5. How could Harry Hess be described as *The Newton of Drift Theory*?

6. What is the theory of seafloor spreading? How does it help to explain the surface features of the earth?

7. How do continental volcanoes fit into the theory?

8. How is Plate Tectonics different from Continental Drift?

9. What do you think of the following comment by Thomas Kuhn: *What better criterion could there be than the decision of the scientific group?* To what was he referring?

10. Consider the history of geology. Did new theories ever really supplant those that preceded them? How does Plate Tectonics carry the vestiges of the Neptunists, Vulcanists, Hutton-Lyell, and Wegener.

READING THE EARTH

A MAP OF MY COLLEGIATE LIFE

Pilfered away, by what the Bard who
 sang
Of the Enchanter Indolence hath called
"Good-natured lounging," and behold a
 map
Of my collegiate life.
     -William Wordsworth

There are few maps that are as interesting as geological maps, multi-colored mosaics and sweeping lines. I found them to be beautiful; so, naturally, when I was a student I decorated my dorm room with a geological map of Oklahoma (Figure 5-12). Its "psychedelic" appearance complimented my roommate's nearly equal-sized poster of Jimi Hendrix on the other side of the room. I knew something of the geology of northeastern Oklahoma because I had grown up there and hunted for fossils almost everywhere I went. When I went to college on the southeastern side of the Ozarks in Arkansas, I discovered that some of the things that I had learned in Oklahoma would help me in Arkansas. Both areas were marine and mainly from the Carboniferous periods. Thus, I became interested in the geology of Arkansas. I admit that I was not so interested in mapping the geology; I just wanted to use an understanding of the distribution of rocks to help me to find fossils. In my search, I ranged over the northern half of Arkansas seeking trilobites and nearly complete crinoids. Truthfully, though, I was thrashing about blindly. The university had no geological maps (or geologists for that matter); so, I had to discover what I could. At first, I relied on word of mouth directions. Later, I learned to read the rock and stop at likely spots. This distraction made me something of a hazard as I drove. Also, I recognized likely fossil-bearing rocks in places where parking was not allowed. In the process, I had my car towed once, and the state police asked me to move my car many times. The outcome was that I wore out two used cars, accumulated quite a nice fossil collection, and learned something about stratigraphy in the process. The way that I learned the relationships between sedimentary rocks, the arcane names for the various systems, the relative ages, and the fossils that they contained was not very different from the methods employed during the 18th and early 19th centuries in the history of geology.

LEARNING TO READ[6]

Learn to read slow: all other graces
Will follow in their proper places.
     -William Walker

The dawn of understanding the sequence of rock began slowly. Nicolaus Steno (1638-1686), a Danish natural philosopher who went to live and work in Italy in the 17th Century, developed the first set of laws in geology while he studied the strata of rock around Rome. His Law of Superposition said that younger layers overlie older layers. The Law of Horizontality stated that all strata were originally laid down horizontally and any deviation from the horizontal came later during deformation of the rock. Although these laws seem today to be statements of the obvious, at the time that Steno wrote them, there was nothing obvious in geology at all. Indeed, even

---

[6] The information in this section is a condensation of *Geology Through Lyell's Eyes* and *Y2K, Deep Time, and Theory Choice in Geology.*

the understanding that fossils were the remains of once living organisms was not generally accepted. Robert Hooke (1635-1703) studied the strata on the Isle of Wight and concluded that the layers were unique and could be distinguished by the fossils that they contained. Such insights as those of Steno and Hooke languished because layers of rocks and their fossils could not easily be reconciled with the Biblical accounts of Creation and the Flood.

Abraham Gottlob Werner (1749-1817), one of the founders of the Neptunist school of geology, said that rocks precipitated out of the global ocean created by the Biblical Flood. Thus, he proposed a connection between the Biblical account and the observations of strata and fossils. He theorized that the first rocks to precipitate were granites (primary rocks). Then, a sequence of secondary rocks with an associated series of fossils formed the remaining lay-

ers. Although his explanation seemed compelling, it did not match well with observation.

The appreciation of sedimentary rocks increased throughout the 18th Century. Giovanni Arduino (1714-1795; Italy), a provincial director of mines defined the rocks of the Italian mountains as Primary (metal-containing strata, but no fossils), Secondary (well defined strata with fossils), and Tertiary (strata of low mountains that contain fossils, gravel, sand and clay). Similarly, Johann Gottlob Lehman (1719-1767), German professor of mineralogy defined a similar series of strata and declared that all geological strata were laid down in a sequence according to age. By the dawn of the 19th Century, the different ages of rocks fell into the categories: Primary, Transitional, Secondary, Tertiary, and Diluvial oldest to youngest, respectively.

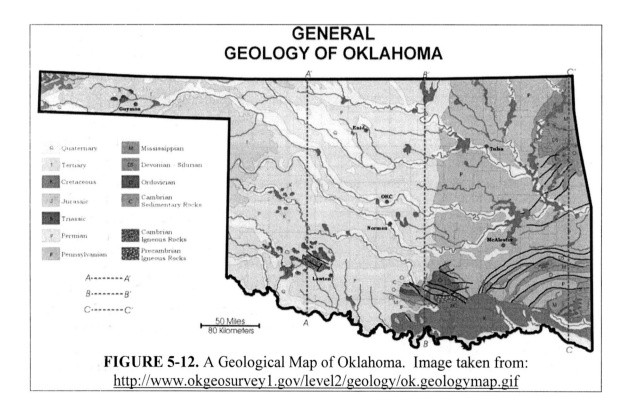

FIGURE 5-12. A Geological Map of Oklahoma. Image taken from: http://www.okgeosurvey1.gov/level2/geology/ok.geologymap.gif

By the beginning of the 19th Century, the study of geology also led to a growing understanding that the earth and its surface features were formed over long periods of time. James Hutton (1726-1797), a geologist in Edinburgh Scotland, presented the concept of a cycle of rock formation and erosion. This required immense amounts of time, and suggested that different strata are removed from each other by time.

The study of the sequence of rock in a modern sense began with Georges Leopold Chretien Frederic Dagobert Cuvier[7] (1769-1832) and Alexandre Brongniart (1770-1847) in Paris. They examined the Tertiary rocks in the Paris basin and correlated outcrops of strata according to the vertebrate fossils that they contained. The Paris Basin was particularly good for this because its strata occurred in a nearly unbroken sequence from the Secondary through the Tertiary periods. Cuvier and Brongniart studied the strata and read their contents like leaves of a great book. Thus, they were able to reconstruct the sequence of strata, and, thereby, map the basin. They published the map and their conclusions in 1802. In this case (and all cases of geological mapping), the construction of the map allowed a four dimensional description of the area (three dimensions of space and time). Thus, they concluded that the region around Paris had been inundated by alternating periods of marine water and freshwater.

Because the Paris Basin appeared to present a succession of vertebrate types that lived and were supplanted by other vertebrates in newer strata, Cuvier theorized that the earth was destroyed by a series of global floods, each followed by a new creation.

The geology of the Paris Basin extended across the English Channel into eastern and southern England. There, a man untrained in science and independently of Cuvier, also taught himself to read the rock strata. William Smith (1769-1839) became interested in interpreting rock strata while he was employed as a surveyor for a canal system around the city of Bath. He collected fossils and noted the strata in which each type was found. Smith realized that the strata could be correlated according to the fossils which they contained even if the types of rocks differed. He also pioneered methods of mapping the ways that strata dip and rise. Based on his extensive field work, Smith produced a geological map of the Bath area. Then, after he was fired[8], he traversed the country as a freelance surveyor with a dream to produce a geological map of England and Wales. Throughout that time, he lived at the edge of poverty, and was committed to debtor's prison for a while. Furthermore, the founder of the fledgling Geological Society of London attempted to steal the geological map from Smith and produce it independently. Finally, Smith did produce his beautiful map in 1815 (see Figure 5-13); however, he was so deep in debt that he had to sell his precious fossil collection at the time that he was fighting for priority. To add insult to injury, Smith was not allowed to join the Geological Society because he was not a member of the gentry. Only much later after suffering more personal and professional disappointment was his work finally recognized by the Geological Society in 1831 when it awarded him the first Wollason Medal, the society's highest award. At

---

[7] Find more about Cuvier in *Rivals*.

[8] In part, he was fired because he spent so much time on his mapping project.

which time, Smith was called "The Father of British Geology."

NAMING THE STRATA

Who hath not own'd, with rapture-smitten frame,
The power of grace, the magic of a name?

-Thomas Campbell

The stratigraphic methods of Cuvier and Smith pointed to the importance of fossils as more than geological curiosities. They served to connect concurrent strata, even if the types of rocks differed. The importance of fossils can be seen in the modern names for the Transitional Era, now called the Paleozoic (= ancient animals), and the Secondary Era, now called the Mesozoic (= middle animals). At the beginning of the 19th Century such empirical methods were necessary for the science of geology to become modern. With the ability to map strata over very large areas, there was a need to define particular stratigraphic sequences and develop a formal set of names for them.

Currently, the categories of the Geological Timeline are in hierarchical categories. Eons are divided into Eras, and Eras are divided into Periods. The formalization of the categories, after recognition of the Paleozoic, Mesozoic, and Cenozoic Eras was the definitions of the Periods or systems that they contained. See Table 5-1 for a list of the periods or systems of the Phanerozoic Eon, the eon that includes multicelluar life. It indicates the place of discovery, the author(s), the date proposed, and the origin of the name.

Particular stratigraphic sequences within the Mesozoic Era were developed first. Mainly, these were the strata examined by Smith and to a lesser extent by Cuvier. Jean Baptiste Julien d'Omalius d'Halloy (1783-1875) produced one of the earliest geological maps of France, and through his study, defined the uppermost sequence of Mesozoic strata as the Cretaceous Period. He derived the name from the chalk (Latin for chalk is Creta) which defined most of the strata in western Europe. The sequence just beneath the Cretaceous was defined on the basis of its marine fossils, particularly ammonites. Thus, even though the rock types were very different across France, Switzerland, and England, they were united on the basis of their fossils. his second sequence was defined by Alexander von Humboldt[9] (1769-1859) in 1795 and called the Jurassic Period after the Jura Mountains of Switzerland. The lower Mesozoic strata were grouped within the Triassic Period and defined in 1834 by Frederick von Alberti in southern Germany.

The geology of the Paleozoic Era was older and much more complex than that of the Mesozoic. However, one of the most distinctive and well-known systems contained the economically important coal-bearing strata. William Conybeare (1787-1857) and William Phillips (1775-1828) named it the Carboniferous System in 1822. In the United States the extensive Carboniferous has been separated into the younger Pennsylvanian and older Mississippian Periods.

---

[9] In this way, von Humboldt anticipated one of the primary methods of Cuvier and Smith.

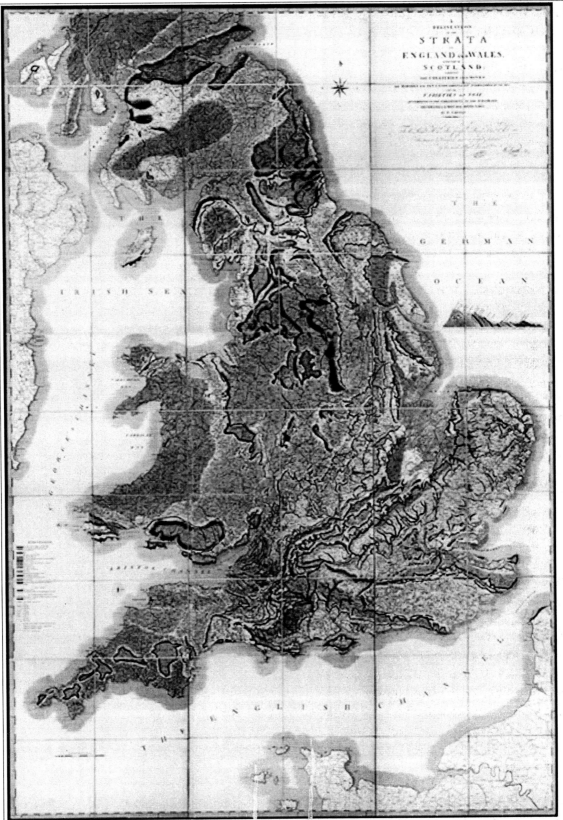

FIGURE 5-13. William Smith's Stratigraphic Map of England and Wales. The image is of a facsimile that hangs in the University of New Hampshire.

TABLE 5-1. The formal names of the geological systems of the Phanerozoic Eon. This includes the type locality, the author(s), date proposed and source of the name.

SYSTEM NAME	LOCALITY	AUTHOR(S)	DATE	SOURCE OF THE NAME
QUATERNARY	France	Jules Desnoyers	1829	Means the 4th period
TERTIARY	Italy	Giovanni Arduino	1760	Means the 3rd period
CRETACEOUS	Paris Basin	Omalius d'Halloy	1822	From Creta, the Latin word for chalk.
JURASSIC	Northern Switzerland	Alexander von Humboldt	1795	Named after the Jura Mountains
TRIASSIC	Southern Germany	Fredrick von Alberti	1843	Name reflects the occurrence of 3 distinctive strata in its type locality
PERMIAN	Perm, Russia	Roderick I. Murchison	1841	From Perm, the type locality
CARBONIFEROUS	Central England	William Conybeare & William Phillips	1822	Name reflects the abundance of coal in this system
DEVONIAN	Devonshire, England	Roderick I. Murchison & Adam Sedgwick	1840	From the type locality
SILURIAN	Western Wales	Roderick I. Murchison	1835	From the name of an ancient Welsh tribe
ORDOVICIAN	Scotland and Western Wales	Charles Lapworth	1879	From the name of an ancient Welsh tribe
CAMBRIAN	Western Wales	Adam Sedgwick	1835	From Cambria, the Latin name for Wales

In 1831 two very different men set out to unravel the lower Paleozoic geology of Wales. Adam Sedgwick (1785-1873) was trained as a mathematician, but became the Woodwardian Professor of Geology at Cambridge. Largely self-taught as a geologist, he dove into the subject with great enthusiasm. In fact, he took special interest in a young student named Charles Darwin who accompanied Sedgwick on one of his forays into the Welsh countryside.

Roderick Impy Murchison (1792-1871) came to geology in a very different way. A Scot, he joined the British army at 15 and served until after the Napoleonic Wars. Then, at home, he led an empty life with an interest only in fox-hunting. At 32, however, he struck up a friendship with the scientist, Humphry Davy, who introduced him to the natural sciences. Murchison became fascinated with geology and discovered that he had quite an aptitude for stratigraphic work. He threw all of his energies into geology from that point on.

Murchison attacked the stratigraphy of Wales from the south where he began mapping the lower "Old Red Sandstone", a series below the Carboniferous. He then worked into a system below that. He named it the Silurian after an ancient Welsh tribe and identified it on the basis of the rocks and fossils. During the same time, Sedgwick worked on a much older series that was deeply folded and so altered that fossils were not very much help. He called this the Cambrian after Cambria, the old Roman name for Wales. They published their descriptions of the Silurian and Cambrian systems in 1835.

Then, the two men began to study the sequence of strata around Devonshire in southern England. Eventually they recognized that the sequence of rock lay between the distinctive Carboniferous above and the Silurian below. The new system had distinctive fossil assemblage, and they named it the Devonian after Devonshire.

Murchison, who had made quite a name for himself, was enticed to travel to Russia and work on the geology there. While working in the Perm region of Russia, he identified a series above the Carboniferous, which he called the Permian in 1841. Murchison took advan-

tage of his travels in Russia and Scandinavia to map his beloved Silurian system everywhere he could. He became convinced that life appeared in the Silurian and any of the strata assigned to the Cambrian that had fossils had to be part of his Silurian. At first, the friends disagreed in a friendly way. After a time they began to fight over the boundary strata of their respective systems. Murchison especially viewed the Silurian as his empire and was loath to give up any territory to Sedgwick's Cambrian. The solution came much later (1879) when Charles Lapworth (1842-1920), a Scottish geologist studied the Cambrian-Silurian boundary strata in Scotland. There, the fossils and rocks were much clearer in defining an intervening series that he called the Ordovician after another ancient Welsh tribe and settled the Murchison-Sedgwick controversy, but it was after both men had died.

Thus, by the end of the 19th Century, all of the formal higher categories in the geological timeline from the abundant appearance animals to the present, an Eon called the Phanerozoic, had been defined. The eras and periods had been arranged in their relative positions, called relative chronology. With the discovery of radioactivity and the recognition that radioactive decay provided a reliable clock for timing events and periods, the relative chronologies could be given actual times before the present. Thus, geologists have been able to add ranges of time to the formal descriptions of eras and periods.

QUESTIONS, & ANSWERS

I keep six honest serving-men
(They taught me all I knew);
Their names are What and Why and
*   When*
And How and Where and Who.

                    -Rudyard Kipling

I wrote this essay as an answer to a student's question last spring semester. I had presented the geological timeline, and she asked where did all of whose names come from, and how do we know they are in that order? I love such questions. They allow me to connect the material that we are studying with the humanity of the science. Of course, I have received my share of less than good questions. Indeed, despite the prevailing educational adage that there is no such thing as a stupid question, I have received many stupid questions. To clarify my position, I might further define a stupid question as one whose intent is to gain advantage rather than to gain knowledge. Such questions might be applauded on the courtroom floor, but they have no place in a hall of learning. Unfortunately, my response to the student was not as inspired as her question, but it did lead me on a search for answers. The most inspired questions, though, are the ones that we ask ourselves. These are the ones that can lead to answers that don't exist in books. Cuvier and Smith asked the earth how strata were situated and then developed methods to answer those questions and in the process produced beautiful maps that answered even more questions. The earth beckoned to others who used the methods of Cuvier and Smith to define the periods of the geological timeline. Thus, slowly, geologists learned to read the earth's surface. Does that mean that there are no more questions if we have these answers? Of course not. Geological maps and ever more detailed geological timelines help to frame new questions as they guide answers in the forms of explanations. Indeed, that the earth is covered by strata that differ and is described by a history that can be divided into well-defined periods, points to many wonderful and subtle questions that are being asked now and will be asked in the future.

Scientists do more than ask questions, though. They seek to answer them. Often, the search for answers is lonely, and sometimes destructive as in the case of William Smith. More often than not, the search leads to a dead end because nature does not give up her secrets easily. Sometimes dumb luck intervenes. With all of the problems of the search, then, why do scientists bother? They do because there is a joy in the search itself. What appeared as indolence to others who watched me leave on my fossil forays when I was a student was for me a complex mixture of fun, adventure, discipline, work, and education. Although I am not a geologist, I do not regret a moment that I spent trying to read the earth.

                    -2004

The Geological Timeline

EON	ERA	PERIOD	MARGULIS & SCHWARTZ (1998)	BOLD, ET AL. (1987)
PHANEROZOIC	CENOZOIC	QUATERNARY	0-2.5	0-2.5
		TERTIARY	2.5-66	2.5-65
	MESOZOIC	CRETACEOUS	66-144	65-136
		JURASSIC	144-213	136-190
		TRIASSIC	213-238	190-225
	PALEOZOIC	PERMIAN	248-286	225-280
		PENNSYLVANIAN	286-360	280-325
		MISSISSIPPIAN		325-345
		DEVONIAN	360-408	345-395
		SILURIAN	408-438	395-430
		ORDOVICIAN	438-505	430-500
		CAMBRIAN	505-590	500-570
PROTEROZOIC	VENDIAN		520-700	570-3100
	RIPHEAN		700-1800	
	APHEBIAN		1800-2600	
ARCHEAN			2600-3900	
HADEAN			3900-5000	3100-4700

Geological Timeline and approximate dates for the respective time intervals as given in Margulis & Schwartz (1998) and Bold, et al. (1987). Dates are in millions of years.

References:

Adams, Frank D. 1938. *The Birth and Development of the Geological Sciences.* Dover Publications, Inc. New York.

Boggs, Sam. 1987. *Principles of Sedimentology and Stratigraphy.* Merrill Publishing Company. Columbus.

Bold,

Bowler, Peter. 1992. *The Fontana History of the Environmental Sciences.* Fontana Press. London.

Geikie, Andrew. *The Founders of Geology.* 2nd ed. Dover Publications, Inc. New York.

Lyell, Charles. 1990 (originally published 1830-33). *Principles of Geology With a new Introduction by Martin J. S. Rudwick. Vols. 1-2.* The University of Chicago Press. Chicago.

Margulis, Lynn and Karlene Schwartz. 1988. Five Kingdoms.

Mather, Kirtley F. and Shirley L. Mason. 1970. *A Source Book in Geology, 1400-1900.* Source Books in the History of the Sciences. Harvard University Press. Cambridge, Mass.

Rudwick, Martin J.S. 1997. *Georges Cuvier, Fossil Bones, and Geological Catastrophes.* The University of Chicago Press. Chicago.

Trefil, James and Robert Hazen. 1998. *The Sciences, An Integrated Approach.* John Wiley and Sons, Inc. New York.

White, John F., ed. 1962. *Study of the Earth, Readings in Geological Science.* Prentice-Hall, Inc. Englewood Cliffs, N.J.

Winchester, Simon. 2001. *The Map the Changed the World.* HarperCollins Publishers. New York.

Questions to Think About

1. I compared the development of our understanding of rock strata to learning to read. What do you think of that comparison?

2. What was the contribution of (at least as far as geological mapping goes) of Georges Cuvier and Alexandre Brongniart? What was their conclusion?

3. What did William Smith do?

4. Why are fossils important in stratigraphic mapping?

5. What are the three Eras of the Phanerozoic Eon?

6. What are the Periods or Systems of the Phanerozoic? How were they defined?

7. What were the contributions of Adam Sedgwick and Roderick Murchison? Why did they begin as friends and colleagues and end as enemies?

8. How was their disagreement resolved?

9. How have real times been applied to relative chronologies in the geological timeline?

10. In what way is the geological timeline a fruitful structure similar to the periodic table of the elements?

A TRIP TO AVALON

Old habit of mind is one of the toughest things to get away from in the world. It transmits itself like physical form and feature . . .

-Mark Twain (A Connecticut Yankee in King Arthur's Court)

In the summer of 1996[10] I stood on the shores of Avalon. Great waves sent spray over broken granite which glistened pink in the sun. The landscape was striped by black lines of ancient lava intrusions that seemed to wear away faster than the granite and leave great scars in the stone (Figure 5-14). Tidal pools of seaweeds, small shrimps and sea urchins waited for the ocean to return with the pulse of the tides. Although the place was almost legendary in its appearance, it was not the Avalon of Arthurian legend but a region in the northeastern U.S. that includes eastern Massachusetts, the eastern part of Maine north of Portland, Rhode Island, eastern Connecticut and part of southeastern Canada (Figure 5-15). It was named Avalonia after the Avalon Peninsula in Newfoundland.

Avalonia is now a part of the North American continent, but its geology is very different from that of regions inland to it. That is, the rocks are different from those just inland in a region called the Gander Terrane. Indeed, the whole of New England appears to be a geological patchwork of exotic terranes. Avalonia and the Gander Terrane are separated by a fault line named for Lake Chargoggagogoggmanchauggagoggchaubunagungamaugg (called the Lake Char fault, for short).

---

[10] I wrote this essay during the summer of 1996 when I was teaching at the Eagle Hill Field Station in Maine.

FIGURE 5-14. A view of the bare rock of Avalonia at Schoodic Point in Acadia National Park . The dark rock in the center is an intrusion of basalt.

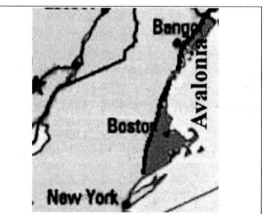

FIGURE 5-15. Approximate location of Avalonia in the northeastern US. I have indicated the southern portion of the Avalonia terrane that goes up into southeastern Canada. Image is modified from a freeware map taken from http://shareware.miningco.com/compute/shareware/library/education/bledmaps.htm

How can such a mysterious collection of terranes be explained? The current explanation in geology is a theory called Plate Tectonics[11]. In this view, the surface of the earth is broken into a number of crustal plates which move over the surface of the earth as a consequence of currents in the earth's mantle.

In some places currents rise in the mantle and create a spreading center on the surface. Such a spreading center occurs in the middle of the Atlantic Ocean where the mid-oceanic ridge continually creates more ocean floor between the Americas and the continents of Europe and Africa. Look at a map of the world and notice how the east coast of South America fits into the west coast of Africa. Thus, the Atlantic Ocean is getting bigger and pushing the plates of the Americas and Africa-Europe further apart.

The surface of the earth cannot expand. If some continents move apart, others must come together. Where currents in the mantle sink, they can carry crust beneath other crustal plates. In such places are found deep oceanic trenches, mountains, volcanoes and earthquakes. For example, today, the India Plate is ramming into the Eurasian plate, and the Himalayan Mountains have developed as a consequence of the collision. Furthermore, since the Indian plate continues to move northward, the Himalayas are growing.

There are other places where crustal plates are sliding past each other. This is the explanation of the action of the famous San Andreas Fault. The Pacific pate is sliding northward past the North American plate. As the plates catch and jerk past each other, the earth quakes.

This useful theory explains mountains, earthquakes, volcanoes, and the shapes of continents. In addition, it explains why mountains are of different ages and why some parts of the earth seem to have been

---

[11] See Y2K, Deep Time, and Theory Choice in Geology for an explanation of the development of Plate Tectonics.

tropical during some periods and frozen during other periods. The plates move about over the surface. Sometimes they are over the poles, sometimes they are in the tropics. This is the explanation for the distribution of many fossil plants and animals. For example, *Glossopteris*, a Permian plant, occurs in Antarctica. Further, it occurs in the same strata in South America, Africa, India, Madagascar, and Australia. Plate Tectonics suggests that those plates were once connected and have since split apart.

Evidence suggests that the continents were once connected in a large super-continent called Pangea, which, about 140 million years ago, began to break apart. North America and Eurasia together formed a continent called Laurasia while the southern continents formed another called Gondwanaland. The continents of Gondwanaland retained an association until fairly recently. Thus, the southern continental distribution of large flightless birds like ostriches (Africa), rheas (South America), emus (Australia), and moas (New Zealand) can be explained. The large flightless birds evolved before the continents split apart. Then, they evolved independently as populations became isolated while they rode their respective crustal plates across the southern hemisphere.

What does this have to do with Avalonia? In the examination of particular plates, geologists have determined that before Pangea, continental plates were separate. About 500 million years ago, Laurentia (the North American plate) lay across the equator. Africa was over the South Pole. Then, Avalonia, England and Northern Europe drifted northward toward Laurentia around 400 million years ago (Figure 5-16). In the great crunch that followed, Avalonia was caught between the North American

370

Plate and Africa (part of the Gondwana supercontinent) in the formation of Pangea. The Appalachian Mountains were raised in the collision. Later, when Africa and North America began to tear apart, breaks formed at the Lake Char Fault, but the ultimate break occurred off the coast of what is now North America. Thus, Avalonia remained attached to our continent. But the consequences of the collision and the subsequent tear can be seen in the pink granite of Avalonia. As the Avalonian terrane was squeezed and then torn, cracks developed which then filled with upwelling lava, which we see now as basaltic intrusions into the granite at places like Schoodic Point.

Legend says that King Arthur left England and traveled to Avalon to recover his strength after his last great battle. He waits to return to England as the "Once and Future King." Geology shows that Avalon itself was once part of England and traveled to North America to become part of another continent. Plate Tectonics suggests that the terrane of Avalonia might move once more. Thus, it is not out of the question that Avalon will once again be reunited with Europe on the changing face of the planet.

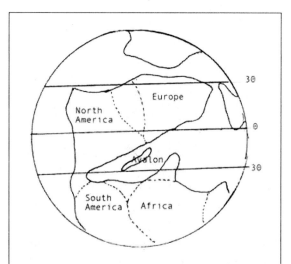

FIGURE 5-16. A map of the arrangements of plates around 400 million years ago (the Devonian Period). Avalonia is moving toward the North American Plate. The African and North American Plates are converging and trapping all smaller landmasses between them.

-1996, revised 2005

Sources that I used to write the essay:
Raymo, C. and M. Raymo. 1989. *Written in Stone, A Geological History of the Northeastern United States*. The Globe Pequot Press. Chester, Connecticut.

Questions to Think About

1. What is an exotic terrane?

2. What do Pangea, Gondwanaland, and Laurasia have to do with Plate Tectonics?

3. What is the significance of granite with intrusions of basalt as they appear at Schoodic Point?

LOST WORLDS

DANDELIONS

What is a weed? A plant whose virtues have not yet been discovered.

-Ralph Waldo Emerson (1878)

Now that final exams are nearly over, I have had some time to get outside and work in my garden. The preparation of the garden beds always begins with weeding. Although my daughter helped me with the chore, she was very vocal about how much she hated doing it and wanted to know why there are weeds. Well, simply put, weeds are plants that we don't want. Generally, we don't want them because they tend to be prolific, invasive, and a nuisance.

Take the dandelion, for example, it grows from a large taproot topped by a short stem with a rosette of leaves that lie close to the ground. The yellow flower head is made of more than 100 small flowers, each one of which has five petals that are fused to resemble a single petal. Thus, the flower head is yellow and covered with "petals". The fruits (a sunflower seed is really a fruit) are borne aloft by a parachute made of modified sepals. So, a single flower can make hundreds of fruits and a single plant can make nearly a hundred flowers! So, a single plant has the capacity to make more than 10,000 plants in a season[12].

Personally, I like dandelions. At least I prefer to see them in my lawn rather than a boring unbroken expanse of green grass. For the past 20 years, I have made no particular effort to eliminate the plants from my lawn. Why isn't my lawn covered with dandelions? In part, it is because dandelions require bare ground to germinate and grow successfully. That is why they do so well in gardens. It also explains why they don't cover the earth. They are in competition with other plants. So as other plants disappear from the earth, weeds like dandelions will find more opportunities.

FIGURE 5-17. A dandelion in fruit on the Susquehanna University lawn in April.

LAND PLANTS APPEAR

The continents of the whole world of that time were lifeless desert. But in the waters of the first ocean life developed and gradually increased on every side.

-Joseph Augusta (1963)

Now, try to imagine an earth without dandelions. Try to imagine an earth without obvious plants. Think of a landscape where the weeds are photosynthetic bacteria. This is what the Devonian Period looked like at its beginning. This period lasted about 50 million years

---

[12] The overabundance of offspring and limited immediate resources is the foundation of Natural Selection. For more on this see *The Mentor and the Heretic* and *Parasites and Darwin's Intellectual Triumph.*

(410-360 million years ago[13]), and the landscape changed completely through that time.

The landscape of the early Devonian Period was a bleak land with just a few small plants at the edge of the water. These plants were somewhat simple in form (see Figure 5-18). They had no roots or leaves, and they did not make seeds. Instead, they shed spores just as ferns and fern-allies do today. Although the plants were simple in form, the Paleobotanists gave them tongue-twister names like Rhyniophyta, Zosterophyllophyta, and Trimerophytophyta (no one was around to give them common names). Just before the beginning of the Devonian (in the upper Silurian Period) these types of plants appear in the fossil record.

Why? Why is it that land plants appeared at all? What advantage is imparted by living in the air? In fact, there are some definite disadvantages. The most important of which is that things living in the air must protect themselves from drying out. Land plants protect themselves with a waxy covering called cuticle. Also, since the cells are no longer in contact with water, plants that are taller than a few centimeters must conduct water from the ground to the upper parts. They do this with a special kind of tissue called xylem (the x is pronounced as a z). They conduct food with a type of tissue called phloem. Plants with such conducting tissues are called vascular plants.

The Silurian plants had features that we recognize in most of the familiar plants today. That is, they had special cells that conducted food and water. Sections of the stem show that the cells were organized to allow photosynthesis

to occur within the stem. In particular, they had openings called stomates through which carbon dioxide could move and allow the process of photosynthesis to occur.

Simply put, photosynthesis is the process by which light energy is used to change carbon dioxide into a usable form, a form that we call food. In the course of absorbing energy, the plant splits water into its component hydrogen and oxygen atoms. The hydrogen also is used in the food-making process. A waste product of the whole procedure is oxygen.

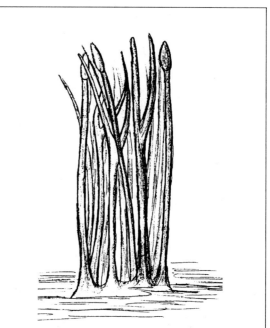

FIGURE 5-18. A common plant of the Lower Devonian that show features like plants we are familiar with today. These are in the Rhyniophyta group. Note spore cases terminate some of the branches. Redrawn from Bold et al. (1988).

Knowing something of the process of photosynthesis gives some insight into the advantages of living in the air. First, photosynthesis is driven by light energy. Far more light is available for photosynthesis in the air than in the wa-

---

[13] Please refer to the Geological Timeline in *Reading the Earth* for relative times of the various geological periods presented in this essay.

ter where light can be absorbed or re-flected. Also, carbon dioxide is far more accessible in air than in the water. Thus, the advantages for living in the air probably outweigh the disadvantages of potentially dehydrating.

Another very important advantage is that plants can disperse their spores much farther in air that in water. This is particularly true for species that might live in puddles and ponds. Usually spores of green algae, the undoubted an-cestors of plants, are very resistant to freezing and drying. So, in a way, they already had features that could be useful for aerial dispersal. However, the effec-tiveness of wind dispersal increases with the height from the ground. That is, the higher the spore is released, the farther it will go. So, having stems holding spore cases high in the air is an advantage. For that to work, the stems have to be sup-plied with water and be photosynthetic. An added bonus to all that is that spores could be made and shed over a long pe-riod of time.

The occurrences of waxy cuticle, supporting tissue (xylem), and resistant spores all had to occur in ancestors of the earliest land plants. If the algae were to live in ponds and other freshwater en-vironments that dry out periodically, such characteristics would have been advantageous. Once present, they were co-opted for use in a more permanent aerial existence.

Land plants began to appear in abun-dance during the Devonian period and then exploded in their diversity. By the upper Devonian, the landscape was filled with tree club mosses, giant horsetails, ferns, and precursors to the conifers (Figure 5-19). Also, the end of the De-vonian saw the advent of the seed, one of the great miracles of the plant king-dom. Thus, the pre-Devonian world was a lost world.

FIGURE 5-19. A fossil of an upper Devonian plant called *Archaeopteris*. This is a leafy branch from a tree that from a distance would have looked like a conifer.

INSECTS AND AMPHIBIANS
We look back through countless millions of years and see the great will to live struggling out of the intertidal slime, struggling from shape to shape and from power to power, crawling and then walking confidently upon the land...
-H. G. Wells (1902)

It was not long (in geological time) before arthropods began to appear among the fossils of land plants. Re-mains of crabs, centipedes, spiders and insects show that the abundant food source provided by land plants was quickly exploited. Although the Devo-nian forests and swamps were alive with flying insects, there would have been an eerie silence to our ears; there were no birds, mammals, or frogs to punctuate

374

the sounds of buzzing insects and plants rustling in the wind.

Perhaps most of us find the Devonian period interesting because that was when tetrapods (vertebrate animals with four legs) appeared. The earliest tetrapods have been found in greatest abundance in Greenland Devonian deposits. The first to be found was called *Ichthyostega.* It had a body that was slightly flattened with sprawling legs. It was clearly adapted for life in the water, but it had legs. More importantly, its skull had features that linked it directly to the lobe-finned fishes of the time. Not only did the lobe-fins have fleshy leg-like pectoral and pelvic fins, but they also had lungs in addition to gills (living relatives today, the Coelacanth and lungfishes, have fleshy fins and lungs, respectively). The bones in the legs looked like ours. For example, the forelegs had an upper arm bone, as well as a well-defined pair of lower arm bones, the radius and ulna. *Ichthyostega* also had six toes on its front feet and seven on its back feet. However, it was truly transitional. It had legs with the same general bones as its contemporary lobe-finned fishes as well as the tetrapods (like you and me) that followed it. An even more primitive tetrapod called *Acanthostega,* also found in Greenland, had a weaker leg with a radius and ulna of unequal length. In addition, it had eight toes (Figure 5-20). The most amazing thing about *Acanthostega* was the occurrence of gill arches and gill covers like those of most bony fish.

Early reconstructions of tetrapods like *Ichthyostega* show them walking over land on feet with five toes. However, more recent evidence suggests that the legs of *Ichthyostega* were like the flippers of a seal. It probably waddled clumsily on land. *Acanthostega*, on the other hand, could barely move on land

because its ulna was too short to help bear weight. Also, it had gills. Clearly, this animal was not adapted to a terrestrial existence. Why did it have legs? Could appendages like legs have other functions?

Since the discovery of *Ichthyostega* and *Acanthostega*, numerous other tetrapods from the upper Devonian have been found and described. They come from sites in Scotland, Quebec, Latvia, Estonia, Russia, and Pennsylvania in strata that cover about 15 million years (Controversial fossils have been found also in Australia). *Hynerpteon*, a tetraopod collected from an upper Devonian site near the village of Hyner in central Pennsylvania and a contemporary of *Ichthyostega*, had a more robust leg skeleton, and presumably, could move more effectively on land than *Ichthyostega.* Of the new discoveries, some have gills; some do not. Most deviate from the five-digit foot.

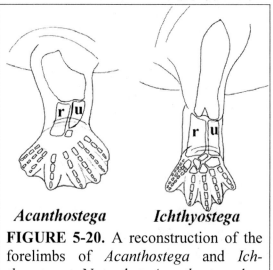

Acanthostega   *Ichthyostega*

FIGURE 5-20. A reconstruction of the forelimbs of *Acanthostega* and *Ichthyostega*. Note that *Acanthostega* has an ulna [u] that is 1/3 shorter than its radius [r]. Modified from Coates and Clack (1990).

It seems that legs did not evolve in order to stride confidently on land, but they evolved as jointed flippers for use in an aquatic environment. Then, these characteristics were co-opted to convert a jointed fin into a walking leg. That feature as well as an already functional lung allowed the tetrapods to leave the aqueous world and enter a new terrestrial world in which food was abundant.

THE DEVONIAN EARTH

I need give only one instance, namely the manner in which the Devonian system, when this system was first discovered, were at once recognized by paleontologists as intermediate in character between those of the overlying carboniferous, and underlying Silurian systems.

-Charles Darwin (1859)

How did amphibians appear in swamps that occurred in Greenland? Was the earth warmer then? Well, it may have been warmer, but Greenland was much closer to the equator then than it is now. Reconstructions of the earth based upon plate tectonic theory, paleomagnetism, and evidence of ancient glaciation indicate that the Northern supercontinent called the Old Red Sandstone continent straddled the equator during the Devonian period[14]. During the same time, the plates of Africa, India, Antarctica, Australia, and a piece of southern Europe were joined as a super continent called Gondwanaland. This land mass covered the south polar part of the earth and was moving in a collision course toward the Old Red Sandstone Continent. The seas (the Iapetus Ocean and Tethys Sea) that separated the northern and southern continents were very productive at this time. They were warm and surrounded by landmasses whose runoff made them fertile, somewhat like the Mediterranean Sea today.

---

[14] See Figure 5-16 in A Trip to Avalon for an illustration of the distribution of the landmasses on the Devonian Earth.

Trilobites[15], crinoids, brachiopods, and horn corals were particularly abundant. Squid-like nautiloids darted through the warm waters and played among coral reefs. Of the vertebrates, fishes were particularly abundant and diverse. Indeed, despite my apparent obsession with land-dwellers, the Devonian really was the Age of Fishes.

The sediments that washed into the Iapetus Ocean and Tethys Sea were ultimately caught in the merger of the northern and southern continents that made the great single land mass called Pangea. As the African plate rammed into the North American plate, sediments were raised and buckled by the force of the collision into the Appalachian Mountains along the eastern US.

THE EXTINCTION

In spite of the obvious importance of extinction, and in spite of the fact that hundreds of thousands of extinctions in the geologic past have been documented, we know surprisingly little about the process itself and surprisingly little about its actual role in evolution.

-David Raup (1984)

Toward the end of the Devonian, groups of brachiopods and corals disappeared. Marine plankton suffered loss of most species. This "event" occurred over an estimated 3-15 million year period. Curiously, most of the extinctions seem to have occurred in warm oceans. Freshwater taxa did not suffer such losses nor did cold-water marine species.

How can this event be explained? Some of the evidence indicates that global temperatures dropped over the period at the end of the Devonian. This would help to explain why warm water

---

[15] See *Trilobite Tales* for a description of these animals.

marine species suffered such losses (88% of acanthodian fishes died out in the warm seas while only 30% disappeared from fresh water). Almost 90% of the oceanic plankton (that leaves a fossil record) disappeared.

It would appear that a change in global temperature caused the extinction. However, the upper Devonian sediments indicate another cause. Iron is one of the most abundant elements on the earth's surface, and when it is incorporated into sediments, its color reflects the relative abundance of oxygen. Red or red-brown sedimentary rock is laid down in an environment with plenty of oxygen while rock that is gray or blue-gray indicates an environment in which oxygen was sparse. The upper Devonian sediments show frequent periods of anoxia or oxygen depletion. This phenomenon can be seen north of Selinsgrove on highway 11 between Northumberland and Danville (Figure 5-21). Most of the strata are red or reddish, and then change abruptly to gray then red, then gray.

The terrestrial ecosystems showed more gradual and continual changes throughout the Devonian Period. The Rhyniophytes, the earliest and simplest vascular plants, were supplanted by others that were better at water transport, more efficient at photosynthesis, and more effective at spore dispersal. This theme seemed to continue throughout the Devonian and suggests that the early extinction and evolution of plants was based on competitive displacement rather than a major spasm of extinction that occurred in the tropical seas.

There are other theories as to the extinction. One is that it was caused by the paleogeography of the continents or by the impact of a large meteor. There is no general agreement among paleontologists as to the ultimate cause because no scenario can adequately explain the differences in extinction rates on land and in the sea. Whatever the reason, the old Devonian world was lost forever as a new coal age world dawned.

FIGURE 5-21. Strata that indicate ambient oxygen fluctuations. Gray, oxygen-poor strata are sandwiched between red, oxygen-rich layers.

ILLUSIONS OF HISTORY

This quirky historical character of major evolutionary change in particular lineages – thoroughly explainable after the fact, however unpredictable in principle beforehand – constitutes the greatest fascination of the subject for many practitioners, myself included.

-Stephen J. Gould (2002)

Because we live at one end of a time line, we can fool ourselves into thinking that evolution has a purpose. As we look at plants and animals in the distant past, they look bizarre and exotic. Then, they look more and more familiar as they come closer to us in time. Land plants are the way that they are because of a series of accidents. If green algae could not make water-conducting tissue or if they could not make a waxy covering on the outside of their epidermis, they would not have been able to survive as anything but mosses and liverworts. Also, if the green algae had not already possessed a resistant spore, they would not be able to disperse themselves in the air. We might have forests that evolved from a line of kelps or red algae. On the other hand, the terrestrial environment might have remained relatively barren with a layer of photosynthetic bacteria still covering the land.

If a jointed fin or flipper had not evolved in a line of Devonian fishes, terrestrial vertebrates might move about by means other than four legs. Regardless, there would have been little to entice the early carnivorous animals if arthropods had not moved onto the land. The arthropods were there to take advantage of the abundant food produced by land plants. Indeed, vertebrates might have stayed in the "safety" of the water.

All of these scenarios are possible in the logic of evolution. Certain features like jointed flippers and resistant spores turn out to be very useful for something else in a new world. Sometimes the comfort of a world is shattered by a catastrophic disaster (like a meteorite) or by long, slow change (global cooling or warming) and organisms that are well adapted to the lost world disappear. That leaves the generalists to survive in time of adversity.

We see such a thing happening as we look back to the lost world that held the Passenger Pigeon and Carolina Parakeet, we see a new world in which "weedy" species such as Starlings and English Sparrows increase. The percentage of alien weedy land plants has risen to between 21-27% in Acadia National Park and 64% in Hawaii Volcanoes National Park.

Our world bears the legacy of the lost world of the Devonian. We live in a terrestrial world in which the land is dominated by vascular, seed-bearing plants and an astounding number of insects. Our bodies carry the limb archi-tecture that pulled *Ichthyostega* out of the water.

Life, in particular the diversity of life, is about our most precious resource, and it has been more than 3 billion years in the making. Will we continue to destroy the diversity of life on this world until it is completely changed into a new world dominated by weeds? If so, will that new world have a place for us or will we become part of a lost world?

-1997; revised 2002

References:

Augusta, J, and Z. Burian. 1963. *Prehistoric Animals.* Spring Books. London.

Bold, H.C., C.J. Alexopoulos, and T Delevoryas. 1987. *Morphology of Plants and Fungi.* 5th ed. HarperCollins Publishers, Inc. New York.

Carroll, R.L. 2002. *Early Land Vertebrates.* Nature 418:35-36.

Coates, M.I. and J.A. Clack. 1990. *Polydactyly in the Earliest Known Tetrapod Limbs.* Nature 347: 66-67.

Daeschler, E.B., N.H. Shubin, K.S. Thompson, and W.W. Amaral. 1994. *A Devonian Tetrapod from North America.* Science 265:639-642.

Daeschler, E.B.and N.H. Shubin. 1998. *Fish with Fingers?* Nature 391:133.

Gordon, M.S. and E.C. Olson.1995. *Invasions of the Land, The Transitions of Organisms from Aquatic to Terrestrial Life.* Columbia University Press. New York.

Gould, S.J. 1993. *Eight Little Piggies, Reflections in Natural History.* W.W. Norton & Co. New York.

Gould, S.J. 2002. *The Structure of Evolutionary Thought.* The Belknap Press of the Harvard University Press. Cambridge, Mass.

Knoll, Andrew H. 1984. *Pattern of Extinction in the Fossil Record of the Vascular Plants.* In: Nitecki, Matthew H., ed. *Extinctions.* The University of Chicago Press. Chicago. Pp. 21-68.

McGhee, G.R. 1989. *The Frasnian-Famennian Extinction Event.* In: Donovan, S.K., ed. 1989. *Mass Extinctions, Processes and Evidence.* Columbia University Press. New York. pp 133-149.

Osborne, R. and D. Tarling. 1996. *The Historical Atlas of the earth, A Visual Exploration of the Earth's Physical Past.* A Henry Holt reference Book. Henry Holt & Co. New York.

Raymo, C. and M. Raymo. 1989. *Written in Stone, A Geological History of the Northeastern United States.* The Globe Pequot Press. Chester, Connecticut.

Raup, David M. 1991. *Extinction, Bad Luck or Bad Genes?* W.W. Norton & Co. New York.

Stanley, Steven M. 1984. *Marine Mass Extinctions: A Dominant Role for Temperatures.* In: Nitecki, Matthew H., ed. *Extinctions.* The University of Chicago Press. Chicago. Pp 69-118.

Vitousek, P.M. 1988. *Diversity and Biological Invasions of Oceanic Islands.* In: Wilson, E.O., ed. 1988. *Biodiversity.* National Academy Press. Washington, D.C. pp 181-189.

Zimmer, C. 1995. *Coming Onto the Land.* Discover. 16(6):118-127.

Zimmer, C. 1998. *At the Water's Edge.* Touchstone Press.

Questions to Think About

1. What are the different types of fossils? How are they formed?

2. When was the Devonian period? What important geological events occurred during that time?

3. What are the advantages for a plant to grow on land versus the water? What are some disadvantages?

4. What might have allowed animals to invade and occupy terrestrial environments?

5. What structures were co-opted (evolutionarily) to allow tetrapods to take advantage of terrestrial environments?

6. What are some of the common animals in the Devonian seas?

7. What might have caused the mass extinctions at the end of the Devonian?

8. Why is purpose an illusion of the evolutionary history of life?

9. What are weeds? Give some examples of weeds.

RIVALS

HUNTING TREASURE

Trifles light as air are to the jealous confirmations strong as proofs of the holy writ. -Shakespeare

I worked my way up a gully near Huff Arkansas about 30 years ago. I had gone there with a fellow student named Mike to look for fossils in the Mississippian age deposits. The shale had been deposited when the area was at the bottom of a shallow, productive sea between 350 and 315 million years ago.

The fossils included brachiopods, crinoids, bryozoans, the occasional ammonoid, and the rare trilobite fragment. This provided me with a glimpse into the community structure of a marine environment long vanished. And I appreciated it that way years later in retrospect. At the time, however, I was hunting treasure.

Mike and I had gone there to hunt for fossils on that beautiful autumn day. We separated from each other and began to scan the shale. I could hear him scuffle over the loose rocks and the occasional soft thud as he examined and tossed aside a prospective rock.

The gully was one that Mike had walked just minutes earlier. There, I saw the intact top or calyx of a crinoid or sea lily (Figure 5-22). Although most of the fossils in the area were of crinoids, the tops with tentacles in tact were quite rare. Indeed, this was a treasure. I shouted and pointed to the calyx lying in place.

I was elated at my good fortune and taunted Mike for having missed it. Jealousy grew and we exchanged bitter words. We rode back to the college in silence. I clutched my treasure and stared out of the window. What was this thing that I cupped in my hand? How had it survived the assaults of time in such fine shape? How had it come to me?

FIGURE 5-22. The calyx and tentacles of the Huff crinoid (left) the circular disk on the right is a segment from the stem of a much larger animal. The scale is in cm.

FOSSILS

In endeavoring to discover the changes which have taken place on the earth in past geological times, the evidence furnished by fossils is of primary importance. -Henry Woods

Fossils are so called because they lie in the ground (fossorial). They occur as a conjunction of a series of unlikely events. First, the organism, suppose a crinoid in this case, must die and be covered with sediment quickly. Thus, it must occur in a place where sediment is being deposited. Because crinoids mainly are made of calcium carbonate, they can languish a little longer before being covered. Still, even with hard parts, they must be covered. Figure 5-23 illustrates the sequence of events that had to happen for a living animal to be changed into the fossil illustrated in Figure 5-22.

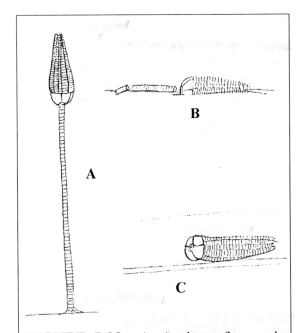

FIGURE 5-23. A. A view of my crinoid as it may have appeared in life. B. At death, it became disconnected from the stem and the upper part was covered quickly. C. About 300 million years later a slightly distorted crinoid calyx and tentacles eroded from the surrounding shales.

Within the sediment, oxygen concentration plummets thus reducing the efficiency of decomposition. Also, sediments tend to hold the organism together. If the chemical environment does not allow the calcium carbonate to dissolve, it will stay intact surrounded by the sediment that will become stone over time as more layers of sediment and geological processes create heat and pressure.

After the rock matrix solidifies, the fossil may dissolve thus forming a mold in which a replica or cast can form from dissolved minerals. Some fossils like petrified wood and vertebrate bones have been altered or petrified by the gradual replacement of compounds in the original fossil. Alteration by replacement can produce faithful reproductions on a large scale, but rarely reproduce the fine details. Fossils like crinoids usually show little or no alteration.

Still, fossils represent a distortion of the communities in which they occur. They over represent things with hard parts or structures that resist decay and pressure. Also, hard parts usually are not very informative as to the biology of the particular organisms.

The discovery of the fossil is the most unlikely event of all. The object has to weather out of rock or be exposed at the time when there is someone present to notice it. Significant finds then have to be brought to the attention of someone trained to interpret them.

The history of paleontology is filled with cases of jealousy, pride, and foolishness. It also illustrates the highest of rational human attributes to examine fragmentary evidence and make sense of a world long vanished. Fossils provide that window on the past and paleontology is the science devoted to deciphering their evidences.

IDEAS AND RIDICULE

Ridicule is the weapon most feared by enthusiasts of every description; from its predominance over such minds it often checks what is absurd, but fully as often smothers that which is noble.
                                            -Walter Scott

From the beginning, fossils became a source of speculation. Greek natural philosophers like Pythagoras assumed that they derived from once living things. They explained the occurrence of seashells on mountains as evidence that the mountains had once been under water. Leonardo da Vinci made the same assumption.

The Neptunists[16] used marine fossils as evidence of a Biblical flood or catastrophe by water. The biggest problem came when trying to interpret fossils as the remains of living things that did not resemble anything alive in the present. What could it mean? The Natural Philosophy of the Enlightenment dictated that all life was interconnected. Thus, extinction could not occur without unraveling the domain of living things. Indeed, Thomas Jefferson, a man steeped in the philosophy of the enlightenment, had charged Lewis and Clark to look for Mastodons in their trek across North America. That relatives of elephants were alive was not outlandish. Where else might they be hiding? The great explorations of the 18th and early 19th centuries had uncovered most of the elephants' hiding places; however, the earth began to yield much more bizarre creatures.

Expeditions of discovery sent plants, animals and natural curiosities back to conservatories, menageries, and museums in Europe. One of these, the Jardin des Roi, housed an encyclopedic garden of plants, a menagerie, and museums. George-Louis Leclerc, Comte de Buffon (1707-1788) began to organize the gardens and collections in a systematic way. He hired a young man named Jean-Baptiste Pierre Antoine de Monet, Chevalier de Lamarck (1744-1829) as an assistant curator of the gardens because he had written an impressive work on

the plants of France (*Flore Française*) in 1778.

Lamarck persisted as an underpaid assistant until after the French Revolution when he called for the Jardin des Roi (renamed the Jardin des Plantes; see Figure 5-24) and the Musee National d'Histoire Naturelle (the National Museum of Natural History) to be reorganized into 12 areas of natural history under 12 different professorships. His idea caught the attention of the National Assembly, a dangerous thing in 1793, the year that Louis XVI and Marie Antoinette died on the guillotine. However, the assembly agreed with his plan and gave him one of the professorships, Professor of Insects and Worms. In those times, his title meant that he was responsible for all invertebrate animals.

It did not seem to matter to Lamarck that he knew nothing about invertebrates. Almost no one knew anything about them. So, Lamarck set about studying and organizing the growing invertebrate animal collection in the museum. It was the least prestigious position among the professorships, but it was better than being an assistant curator.

Lamarck labored on the invertebrate collections and published works on zoology and taxonomy of living forms as well as on invertebrate fossils. It was while conducting these studies that Lamarck began to formulate and refine a theory about life and its history. He drew on ideas from Buffon, his former patron, as well as contemporaries like Geoffroy Saint-Hilaire. Nevertheless, the details of the theory were his and came to him through the study of invertebrates, living and fossil.

---

[16] I expand on the theories of the Neptunists in *Geology Through Lyell's Eyes*.

FIGURE 5-24. One of the museum buildings within the Jardin des Plantes.

Lamarck began to formulate a theory about evolution or transmutation. In his view, organisms changed in a particular direction as a consequence of the use or atrophy of particular organs during their lives. Then, with such characteristics acquired during their lives, organisms could pass on those changed characteristics to their offspring. Thus, Lamarck's explanation of the diversity of life today and through time relied on progress. That is all things strive to perfection, so they change in a particular direction. Fossils seemed to bear out that view. Also, his theory of progressive change explained that there could be change (as substantiated by the fossil record) without extinction. All life was a continuum.

Like Lamarck, Georges Leopold Chretien Frederic Dagobert Cuvier (1769-1832) managed to survive the French Revolution. Saint-Hilaire noticed Cuvier and invited him to come to Paris and work in the Museum where he soon rose to Professor of Animal Anatomy. He created the discipline of comparative anatomy and applied that to fossil vertebrate animals. His amazing knowledge of anatomy, particularly of skeletal anatomy, allowed him to reconstruct whole animals from fragmentary evidence. He deduced more than the animal's appearance. He relied on the anatomy to infer aspects of the functional design of an animal and from that he could determine the ecology and behavior.

Through his study of fossil vertebrates, Cuvier verified the concept of extinction. He reasoned that because each species is a stable biological unit any change would be destabilizing. So, transmutation could not occur. Different animals in the fossil record, then represent other stable units that no longer exist. They did not change out of existence; they just went out of existence.

Cuvier came to believe that the earth was very old and generally stable. However, sometimes a change or revolution would occur and a new creation would populate the earth. Mastodons and mammoths resembled modern elephants because they function in similar environments. The general design is functional and the slight variations between species occur because of differences in requirements following a revolution.

Cuvier's work on great beasts living and dead put him in the public spotlight. The disagreement between Cuvier and Lamarck (and Saint-Hilaire) also caught the public's attention. While praising Lamarck's work on Invertebrate Zoology, the charismatic Cuvier attacked the notion of transmutation.

Largely through the influence of Cuvier, and his ridicule of transmutation, Lamarck's ideas were not well received in his day. In fact, Lamarck who did not fare well throughout his career came to a particularly ignoble end. He began to go blind during the last 10 years of his life. He ended his days on December 28, 1829, blind and penniless. He did not have money for a proper funeral and was buried in a rented grave from which he was removed five years later.

Cuvier fared much better. While he lived, Cuvier became one of the most famous scientists, indeed one of the most famous men, in Europe. He flourished under the rule of Napoleon and the succeeding monarchy. By the time of his death in 1832, Cuvier had been made a Baron of France.

The methods established by Cuvier allowed the study of extinct vertebrates and their interpretation. His influence in France lingered and stifled transmutationist theories. Thus, Britain became the seat of evolutionary thought where Darwin published *The Origin* 27 years after Cuvier's death. Curiously, Darwin through natural selection provided the theoretical explanation for transmutation that assumed extinction and denied that life progressed. The facts of transmution and of extinction had been established before Darwin. He provided the theo-

retical framework in which the two concepts made sense. Very quickly most of the biologists came over to the view of Darwinism.

THE BONE WARS
So that in the nature of man, we find three principal causes of quarrel. First, competition; secondly diffidence; thirdly, glory. -Thomas Hobbes

Exciting finds in paleontology lent support to Darwinian evolution and began to complete an understanding of the pageantry of life. Then as now no finds caught the public imagination like those of the dinosaurs. Although Richard Owen, the scientist who coined the term dinosaur, saw dinosaurs as supporting a Cuvier-like theory, and remained an anti-evolutionist throughout his life

In 1824 William Buckland published a description of a large carnivorous reptile that he called *Megalosaurus*. In the next year Giddeon Mantell published his discovery of another extinct reptile. He had sent a sample to Cuvier who pronounced it part of an extinct hippopotamus. Mantell was not convinced and pursued the problem until he noticed the resemblance between the fossil teeth and those of a South American iguana. Thus Mantell called his discovery *Iguanodon*, a name that means iguana tooth. The British scientists used reptiles as models to reconstruct their fossils and presented them as large, splay-legged lizards.

Following the American Civil War, two men, Othniel Charles Marsh (1831-1899) and Edward Drinker Cope (1840-1897) began to collect, describe, and name a vast array of extinct vertebrates from North America. Included in their accomplishments were discoveries of 130 species of dinosaurs. Their collections increased knowledge about the diversity and structure of these great beasts. Also, they discovered attractions that still astound visitors to museums throughout the world. However, what began as a tentative collaboration degenerated into all-out warfare on the American frontier and in the popular press.

O. C. Marsh began to study at Yale with the support of his uncle George Peabody. Marsh graduated with honors and completed his study in Europe. He convinced his uncle to fund the creation of a museum at Yale and to support him as its director. Thus in 1865 Marsh became a professor at Yale without teaching responsibilities and a chair endowed by his uncle.

In 1864 Edward Cope returned to the United States after a similar tour of Europe and its museums. Likely, his father sent Cope abroad to avoid the draft during the war. They were Quakers and adamantly opposed to involvement in warfare. Cope returned, married and took a teaching position at Haverford. However, he disliked the distractions of teaching and soon quit his post.

Cope took his inheritance, sold one of his farms, and moved to a site near Haddonfield in New Jersey. This was a calculated move on his part. Cope had studied under Joseph Leidy who had found the first dinosaur remains in the quarries near Haddonfield, New Jersey. Cope moved there to be close to the fossil beds and to begin the life of an independent natural historian and researcher in 1867.

It seems that Cope took Marsh through the Cretaceous localities where the dinosaurs (already published by Cope) had been found. Probably Marsh returned to some of the areas and paid the local collectors to send him their finds. Quickly, Cope discovered that he had been squeezed out of many areas that he had considered his domain.

About the same time, Cope showed Marsh a skeletal reconstruction of a plesiosaur called *Elasmosaurus* from Kansas. Marsh pointed out that the skeleton had been assembled backwards. That is, Cope had put the animal's head on the tip of its tail. Cope had already had a running commentary about the reconstruction with Joseph Leidy. To add insult to injury, Marsh not only sided with Leidy, but also published the critique[17]. Cope subsequently spent considerable time and money trying to buy up all copies of the article[18] (see Figure 5-25).

By the 1870's, both men mounted independent expeditions to the American west. Both groups began to collect fossils from the Eocene beds of the Bridger Basin of Wyoming. The competition brought on by the proximity was too much. Marsh accused Cope of stealing fossils. Although they tried to remain somewhat civil in public, an irreparable rift had formed between the two men.

---

[17] Marsh continued the insult on the public stage by publishing a series letters to newspapers like the New York Herald well into the 1890's.

[18] Cope sent out the following circular in an effort to retrieve the articles with the incorrect reconstruction of *Elasmosaurus platyurus*:

An error having been detected in the letter press of the "Synopsis of the Extinct Batrachia and Reptilia of North America," by Edward D. Cope, it will be necessary to cancel and replace one of the forms. The author therefore requests that the recipient of this notice would please return his copy of said work to the author's address, at his expense, postpaid, with Part II, of the same work, which will be sent to those who have received Part I.

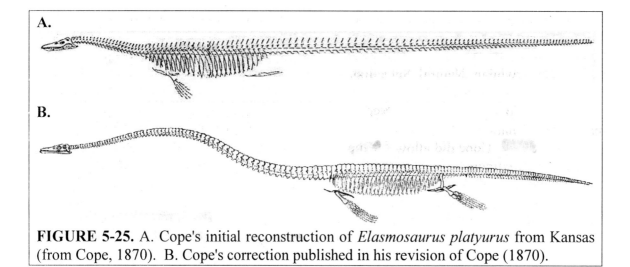

FIGURE 5-25. A. Cope's initial reconstruction of *Elasmosaurus platyurus* from Kansas (from Cope, 1870). B. Cope's correction published in his revision of Cope (1870).

In 1877 Arthur Lakes found a huge vertebra near Golden, Colorado and notified Marsh of the discovery. Marsh asked him to ship the bone to him, but was so slow in his correspondence that Lakes wrote to Cope about the find. This started a series of expeditions that culminated in some of the most impressive dinosaur discoveries to date. In particular, they had collected good specimens of the long-necked sauropods of the Jurassic.

The same year, Marsh's men found a spectacular site near Como Lake in Wyoming. By this time, Marsh's men did everything possible to mislead Cope's collectors. They hid and communicated by code. Still, such a find could not remain hidden. Cope visited the area personally in 1879.

Tons of fossils moved back to the respective laboratories in the east. Tons more were destroyed by careless digging and sabotage. Both teams were under orders to destroy any fossils that they could not ship so that they would not "fall into the wrong hands".

Marsh was so swamped by his paleo riches that he personally did not go into the field again after 1874. Cope continued to collect with his crews mainly be-cause his resources were much more modest than those of Marsh. The two men collected more than dinosaurs. Marsh collected a sequence or series of fossil horses and specialized in Cretaceous toothed birds. Cope collected everything.

The two men differed in important ways. Cope tended to think in grand terms. He was a theoretician but was not very careful with details. Sometimes he would publish based on single bones or ill-considered fragmentary material. He was so prolific that he published more than one paper a month, even during his leanest years. Indeed, in his career, he published more than 1200 scientific papers, a record unequaled in modern science. These were journal articles and books, some of them were hundreds of pages long. In addition, he wrote hundreds more popular articles.

Marsh, on the other hand, was a stickler for details. His caution, almost to the point of paranoia, caused him to be slower to publish. Furthermore, Marsh, who had quite a large staff for preparing his fossils, forbade anyone in his employ to publish on fossil vertebrates. Instead, he would periodically quiz the staff almost in outline form and frequently used their responses verbatim in his own publications.

Marsh had become a staunch supporter of Darwinian Natural Selection. Perhaps because of that or his Quaker upbringing, Cope developed a Neolamarkian explanation for the evolution of life. In this case, Cope did allow for the occurrence of extinction.

More imperious, but a much better politician, Marsh worked his way into the hierarchy and funding circles of science. He became president of the National Academy of Sciences and worked with John Wesley Powell who was director of the U.S. Geological Survey. Marsh managed to cause all sources of funding to dry up for Cope after the mid 1880's.

To control publications, Cope had purchased the *American Naturalist* in the 1870's. However, the feud between Cope and Marsh had so disgusted most members of the scientific community that they refused to publish in it or subscribe to it. It was not long before Edward Cope was in great financial difficulty. Finally, in desperation, he sold part of his collection to the American Museum of Natural History.

Earlier, Cope lashed out in the popular press, particularly the *New York Herald*. He accused Marsh of plagiarism, and everything else he could think of. He continued his attacks until he caught the attention of the Congress which cut funding to the U.S. Geological Survey thereby eliminating Powell's proposed reforms regarding settlement of the west in 1892. Also, almost all appropriations for paleontology disappeared, and Marsh had to withdraw from the U.S. Geological Survey. Cope had begun to reap his revenge.

Cope became president of the American Association for the Advancement of Science succeeding O. C. Marsh in 1895. In the same year, The University of Pennsylvania appointed Cope to Leidy's former chair of Zoology and Comparative Anatomy. The turn of fortune in the twilight of Cope's life reflected a downturn in Marsh's. The 1890's saw the Peabody money dry up. Marsh was reduced to asking Yale for a salary and had to mortgage his house.

THOUGHTS IN A MUSEUM

If the survival of what we value in nature, or of civilization, or even of our species depends on dreamers being awakened, it may take more than squabblers on a shrinking raft to do it. Science's tragedy may be humanity's.

-David Rains Wallace

I thought of the dilemma of cooperation as I walked through the Musee National d'Histoire Naturelle in Paris earlier this month. At one point, I stood in the hall of extinct animals. All about me were fossils of animals described by Marsh. I touched facing the giant ground sloth that Cuvier had prepared and characterized.

How might the science have benefited if Lamarck and Cuvier had cooperated. What if the more eloquent and erudite Cuvier had not ridiculed Lamarck? I know that this is idle speculation, but they held the pieces of Natural Selection between them. Might they and others in the Musee National d'Histoire Naturelle produced such a theory?

Suppose that Cope and Marsh had cooperated? Would the fossils have been removed and described more carefully? Would others have stayed in the field of paleontology and brought about even greater advancement in knowledge of the past? We will never know.

I do know through my experience that scientists do not work in isolation. It has become rare to see a scientific publication with a single author. Individual scientists may worry about priority, credit for discovery and publication. However, such things need not lead to ridicule, jealousy or greed. When that happens, we all lose.

FIGURE 5-26. Lamarck in the Jardin des Plantes. The inscription on the statue says, Founder of the Theory of Evolution.

I observed that of the players in the Lamarck-Cuvier rivalry, Lamarck, the apparent loser, was the only one with a statue on the Jardin des Plantes grounds (Figure 5-26). Similarly, Cope is honored by having the principle American journal of Herpetology called *Copea*.

I saw Marsh's name on some of the fossils in the great hall dominated by a large *Diplodocus* skeleton, and I thought back on a day in late fall nearly 30 years ago. I had not spoken to Mike for about a week. We saw each other on the cam-

pus, and I approached him tentatively. I looked at him, smiled and asked, "Well, am I going to be Cope or Marsh?" We laughed and then made plans for another field trip.

-2002, revised 2006

References:

Bowler, Peter. 1992. *The Fontana History of the Environmental Sciences.* Fontana Press. London.

Cope, Edward D. 1870. *Extinct Batrachia, Reptilia, and Aves of North America.* Transactions of the American Philosophical Society. New Series. 14:1-253.

Hellman, Hal. 1998. *Great Feuds in Science.* John Wiley and Sons, Inc. New York.

Jaffe, Bernard. 1944. *Men of Science in America.* Simon and Schuster. New York.

Jaffe, Mark. 2000. *The Gilded Dinosaur, The Fossil War Between E.D. Cope and O.C. Marsh and the Rise of American Science.* Crown Publishers. New York.

Lyell, Charles. 1990 [originally published 1830-33]. *Principles of Geology With a new Introduction by Martin J. S. Rudwick. Vols. 1-2.* The University of Chicago Press. Chicago.

Nordenskiold, Erik. 1927. *The History of Biology.* Tudor Publishing Co. New York.

Osborn, Henry Fairfield. 1931. Cope: Master Naturalist. Princeton University Press. Princeton.

Rudwick, Martin J. S. 1997. *Georges Cuvier, Fossil Bones, and Geological Catastrophes.* The University of Chicago Press. Chicago.

Shor, Elizabeth Noble. 1971. *Fossils and Flies, The Life of a Compleat Scientist, Samuel Wendell Williston.* University of Oklahoma Press. Norman, OK.

Wallace, David Rains. 1999. *The Bonehunter's Revenge.* Houghton Mifflin Co. New York.

Questions to Think About

1. What is a crinoid? Why might such an animal fossilize so well?

2. What are some of the critical steps in the formation of a fossil like a crinoid?

3. Why did Lamarck begin to accept a view of transmutation (species changing over time)?

4. What theory did Cuvier champion?

5. What was the foundation of the rivalry between Cope and Marsh?

6. In what ways were Cope and Marsh different? How were they similar?

7. Mark Jaffe argues that American science was propelled from being a backwater gentlemen's occupation to a highly developed profession that had significant government support as a consequence of the Cope-Marsh feud. What do you think?

8. How did the Cope-Marsh controversy negatively affect American science?

9. The rivalry between Cuvier and Lamarck was more passive than that of Cope and Marsh, but it did affect science in France. What was that effect? What is the implication of the statue of Lamarck in the Jardin des Plantes today?

10. How is most science done today?

THE DINOSAUR WITH A THUMB ON ITS NOSE

A GIFT

Frenzy yourself into sickness and dizziness –
Christmas is over and Business is Business
Franklin Pierce Adams

Just before Christmas in the early 1960's my parents took me to one of the best bookstores in Tulsa and asked me to pick out a book as one of my gifts. I looked around for a short while but my eyes kept coming back to a large formatted book filled with color, sepia, and black and white plates. The book was called *Prehistoric* Animals by Joseph Augusta, illustrated by Zdenek Burian. Of course, it was one of the most expensive books in the place, and my parents indicated that I should not get my hopes up. Anyway, I did and dreamed of that book until Christmas morning. I remember sneaking down in the wee hours of that morning to look at the tree. There, in anticipation of my action and to buy a little more sleep for themselves, my parents

had placed the book with a note on it, " You can open this now." I did. By morning, I had read the whole thing (there is not much text) and studied all of the plates. One of them illustrated a kangaroo-like *Iguanodon* plodding across the page (Figure 5-27).

This was the standard reconstruction of most bipedal dinosaurs then. They stood upright with their tails dragging on the ground and their heads on a gracefully curved neck. The reconstruction of animals like *Iguanodon* had a history that went back nearly 200 years. Then, like today, their posture, behavior, etc. were based on similar animals that are alive today. This came from the then fledgling discipline of comparative vertebrate anatomy. Georges Cuvier (1769-1832, France), the most celebrated scientist of his day, was the principal architect of the comparative method that supported the study of dinosaurs from their discovery to the present.

FIGURE 5-27. My Christmas gift open to the page with the illustration of *Iguanodon* by Zdenek Burian.

CUVIER'S METHOD

I got into Cuvier's sanctum sanctorum yesterday, and it is truly characteristic of the man. In every part it displays that extraordinary power of methodizing which is the grand secret of the prodigious feats which he performs annually without appearing to give himself the least trouble...   -Charles Lyell

Georges Cuvier[19] was born to a Huguenot family near Stuttgart in 1769. He showed early promise as a natural historian and was sent to university by the Duke of Wurtenberg. After working as a tutor in Normandy, his work on marine animals attracted the attention of the scientific elite in Paris. Cuvier accepted a research position in Paris and spent the rest of his professional life working on the anatomy of animals, particularly vertebrate animals there.

In 1795, just months after he arrived in Paris, the skeleton of an elephant was discovered in the Gypsum mines of Monmartre (this was the source of the original Plaster of Paris). Elephants in Paris! Some assumed that the presence of the animals could be explained easily. For example, the elephants were part of Hannibal's army and just got lost on their way to Rome.

Cuvier examined the bones and realized that they did not conform to the bones of the two known elephant species, the African or the Indian Elephant. They were so big that he called the new elephant *Mammothus*. He also supposed that the mammoths were no longer alive anywhere on the earth because they were just too big to remain unnoticed. The only other alternative was that the elephants from the gypsum quarry represented a species, which was no longer alive. This was a bold statement and set

the stage for the acceptance of the concept of extinction.

Soon, Cuvier began to be brought a wide assortment of fossil bones. It became clear to him that the bones represented many species, which are no longer alive. Also, they seemed to fall into particular periods of time. Extinct mammals were found in younger rocks than extinct reptiles, etc. He explained the succession of fossils as a series of creations each of which was destroyed to prepare for the next creation (much like the Biblical Flood).

Cuvier realized that each major group of animals had its own distinctive architecture. From that he defined the principle of "the correlation of parts" which stated that the anatomy of every bone, muscle and bodily organ was interrelated. Thus, a reconstruction of an extinct animal could be made by comparing its remains to the structure of similar living animals. Because of his encyclopedic knowledge of comparative anatomy, Cuvier was able to reconstruct almost any animal from fragmentary remains by applying his principle of the correlation of parts.

ELEPHANTS, & KANGAROOS

The Megalosaurs and Iguanodons rejoicing in those undeniably most perfect modifications of the Reptilian type, attained the greatest bulk, and must have played the most conspicuous parts, in their respective characters as devourers of animals and feeders upon vegetables, that this earth has ever witnessed in ... cold-blooded animals.   -Richard Owen

Thus, an English physician named Gideon Mantell took some fossil bones to Cuvier in 1823. Mantell had found the fossil bones, teeth, and a curious horn-like structure in the south downs of

---

[19] Find more about Cuvier in *Rivals*.

England over a 5 year period. He was convinced that the bones represented an extinct animal of enormous proportions. When he showed them in England, Geologists said that the fossils were not very important. Even Cuvier disputed their age and said that they were nothing more than a collection of extinct hippopotamus and rhinoceros bones.

Undaunted, Mantell believed that the fossils were the remains of an extinct reptile. He spent many hours in the Hunterian Museum in London where he compared his fossils with the bones and teeth of living reptiles. Finally, he met Samuel Stutchbury who was doing research on iguanas. Stutchbury recognized the teeth as similar to those of certain Central American iguanas. Mantell was thrilled and called his new animal *Iguanodon* (iguana tooth).

He applied Cuvier's principle to the reconstruction of the extinct animal. If it was an iguana, the bones and teeth suggested that *Iguanodon* must have been more than 60 feet long! The animal walked on all four legs, was a herbivore and had a large horn on its nose.

Mantell presented his work to the Royal Society in London and published the report in 1825. There he presented his new animal as a member of huge reptiles that lived on the earth long before mammals. This time his report was accepted because an eminent British Geologist, William Buckland, had published on the remains of another large, extinct reptile which he called *Megalosaurus* (big lizard). However, Buckland's monster was a carnivore. Upon reviewing the evidence, Cuvier magnanimously admitted his own errors and agreed with the interpretations of Mantell and Buckland.

It was not long before other giant prehistoric lizards were found. Richard Owen (1804-1892), a British anatomist and paleontologist, began to study the enormous reptiles and realized that they were very different from lizards. In 1841 he noted several unifying features that defined them as a separate group within the reptiles. Although he called them Dinosauria (terrible lizards), Owen explained that his intent was to label them as the "fearfully great lizards".

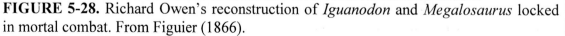

FIGURE 5-28. Richard Owen's reconstruction of *Iguanodon* and *Megalosaurus* locked in mortal combat. From Figuier (1866).

A lost world of giant lizards fired the imagination of Victorian society. Owen reconstructed the animals and had the monetary support to hire Benjamin Waterhouse Hawkins to make life-sized models of many Dinosaurs including *Megalosaurus* and *Iguanodon* for London's Crystal Palace in 1854. At the opening of the exhibition, a legendary dinner party was held. The guests were seated within one of the *Iguanodon* models. The point was that these animals were big!

Owen used elephants and large mammals as models for his reconstructions. Instead of the splayed legs of a lizard, he had given them large column-like legs. Owen's *Megalosaurus* resembled a scaly bear with a long lizard-like head. The *Iguanodon* also had a heavy rhinoceros-like body, complete with the horn on its nose (see Figure 5-28).

By 1881 Richard Owen became the first curator of the British Museum of Natural History. The star attraction was (and still is) its collection of dinosaur fossils. Ironically, in 1880, several dozen complete skeletons of *Iguanodon* were found in a coal mine in Bernissart, Belgium.

The task of mounting the Iguanodons of Bernissart for the Belgian Royal Museum fell to a young French mining engineer named Louis Dollo (1857-1931). His first task was to remove the fossil bones of 40 Iguanodons that had been taken from the mines. Then he had to prepare them for exhibit. He immersed himself in the task so completely that he did not take a vacation for 22 years (the first mounted skeletons took 25 years to complete).

Figure 5-29 illustrates Dollo's reconstruction of *Iguanodon*. This time, the animal looked more like a kangaroo with a dragging tail and an upright stance. His *Iguanodon* was a far cry from Owen's rhinoceros. The most important result was that *Iguanodon* stood upright on its strong hind legs. Also, it had a horny beak like a turtle or a bird. Its pelvis was birdlike as well. The spike which had been interpreted as a horn for the past 60 years turned out to be a highly modified thumb. Dollo interpreted a fissure in the skull as support for a very large tongue. So, he assumed that the animal ate much like a giraffe with a long, prehensile tongue. He assumed that the tail, flattened laterally, would have made it a powerful swimmer in avoiding predators.

The Natural History Museum of Paris attempted to acquire a skeleton of one of the Bernissart Iguanodons at the turn of the 20th century. However, the public outcry against exporting their national treasures forced Paris to accept a plaster cast, the plaster cast that I saw. The Dollo reconstruction remained the last word in *Iguanodon* structure, appearance, and behavior. Dinosaurs remained big, slow, cold-blooded animals that moved through swamps in slow motion. Indeed, in the face of the arrival of mammals, dinosaurs seemed destined to extinction. Indeed, Dollo himself suggested that the dinosaurs became extinct because their brains were not sufficient to allow them to compete with mammals. This view of progress in evolution (a view that Darwin did not have) has been challenged by new ideas about how dinosaurs lived and became extinct.

NEW VIEWS OF DINOSAURS

The work of paleontologists – the scientists who work on fossils – is truly a detective story, an unceasing search for new clues to unravel the mysteries of the ancient world.
  -David Norman

When I was a graduate student just completing my degree in Zoology before I went to the Botany-Microbiology Department at the University of Oklahoma, I decided to take a graduate-level vertebrate paleontology course just for fun. I was a little concerned to learn that I was the only non-geology student in the class. However, my concern melted away when a 30-something man walked into the room and told us in a heavy accent that he had been a student of Joseph Augusta, the author of my *Prehistoric Animals* book of many Christmases ago. It was one of the most enjoyable courses of my graduate career. He still taught the Dollo version of bipedal dinosaurs. However, he did hint that there were other interpretations that were being considered. Since then, for the past 25 years David Norman, Robert Bakker, Jack Horner, and others have found evidence to suggest that dinosaurs were much more active and complex than we were able to believe when they were just big reptiles. It seems that large herbivores like *Iguanodon* almost certainly were warm blooded and ran in herds. They had the complex behaviors which are common to active herd animals. They probably laid their eggs in rookeries and cared for their young. In his reexamination of the Bernissart skeletons, David Norman, curator of the Sedgewick Museum at Cambridge, has reinterpreted many aspects of Dollo's reconstructions. The most notable change was that the tail was held stiffly by tendons such that the animal could not have dragged it (Figure 5-29). Also, the structure of the neck, pelvis, etc. all suggest that *Iguanodon* walked with its body held almost horizontally such that it occasionally dropped to all four feet (this has been borne out by such impressions in *Iguanodon* trackways).

FIGURE 5-29. Models of *Iguanodon* produced by the British Museum of Natural History, 15 years apart. The model on the left has a kangaroo-like stance while the model on the right swivels at the hip with it tail extended stiffly as interpreted by David Norman.

Norman also showed that Dollo's long tongue hypothesis was based on a faulty interpretation of the skulls. The horny beak likely just clipped the leaves and branches that it fed on. Also, he suggested that the sides of the mouth were covered with a cheek like mammals and not open like the jaws of a lizard. Thus, Iguanodon could chew (an adaptation suggested by the battery of hundreds of well-worn and easily replaced molars).

Were Cuvier, Mantell, Owen, Marsh and others wrong? Not really; reconstructions based upon fragmentary evidence are always difficult. Their models of *Iguanodon* were based on certain ideas about its animal associations. When dinosaurs were considered lizards, they were reconstructed as lizards (just as Cuvier's principle of the correlation of parts required). Then, *Iguanodon* became a large reptile that stood on its hind legs. Still, its tail dragged along behind it as it plodded along.

Now, the new interpretation requires a different group of animals to use for comparison. In the new interpretation of dinosaurs Cuvier's principle is still valid, but the animal group with which they are compared has changed from reptiles to birds.

-1995, revised 2002

References::

Augusta, Joseph and Zdenek Burian. n.d. *Prehistoric Animals.* Spring Books. London.

Bakker, Robert T. 1986. *The Dinosaur Heresies.* Zebra Books, Kensington Publishing Corp. New York.

Bakker, Robert T. 1995. *Raptor Red.* Bantam Books. New York.

Colbert, Edwin. 1983. *Dinosaurs, an Illustrated History.* Hammond Inc. New York.

Cuvier, Georges. 1863. *The Animal Kingdom Arranged According to its Organization.* Henry G. Bohn. London.

Desmond, Adrian J. 1975. *The Hot-Blooded Dinosaurs, A Revolution in Paleontology.* The Dial Press. New York

Figuier, Louis. 1866. *The World Before the Deluge.* Cassel, Peter, Galpin & Co. New York.

Gould, Stephen Jay. 2002. *The Structure of Evolutionary Theory.* Belknap. Harvard. Boston.

Horner, John R. and James Gorman. 1988. *Digging Dinosaurs.* Harper and Row, Publishers. New York.

Lessem, Don. 1992. *The Kings of Creation.* Simon & Schuster. New York.

Norman, David. 1991. *Dinosaur!* MacMillan. New York.

Spalding, David A.E. 1993. *Dinosaur Hunters.* Prima Publishing. Rocklin, CA.

Trefil, James and Robert Hazen. 2000. *The Sciences, An Integrated Approach.* John Wiley & Sons, Inc. New York.

Wilford, John N. 1985. *The Riddle of the Dinosaurs.* Vintage Books. New York.

Questions to Think About

1. Distinguish between the different reconstructions of *Iguanodon.* Why were different model animals proposed? What happens to the reconstructions when different model animals are used?

2. What led Cuvier, a firm believer in creation, to accept that some animals must have become extinct?

3. What is Cuvier's comparative method?

4. Who discovered *Iguanodon?* Who named it?

5. What is the relationship between Richard Owen and dinosaurs?

6. Recall the different reconstructions of *Diplodocus* (See *A Rock, A Razor, and a Dinosaur*). How was the interpretation of *Diplodocus* similar to that of *Iguanodon?*

TRILOBITE TALES

TREASURE

At last I found a trilobite. The rock simply parted around the animal, like some sort of revelation. -Richard Fortey

I was a college student at a school in Arkansas during the first years of the 1970's. Then, I majored in Biology but I had become completely absorbed in collecting fossils which were plentiful in the Ozark Plateau. These were mainly marine deposits from the mid Paleozoic. Some of the locations were very rich with abundant and diverse forms of extinct animal remains. Some, like clams and snails, were familiar. Others like crinoids, nautiloids, and brachiopods, were even more common and became familiar. I came to know them well and could recognize them from tiny fragments or exposed parts. However, trilobites (see Figure 5-30), more than all of the other organisms, fired my imagination and kept me looking.

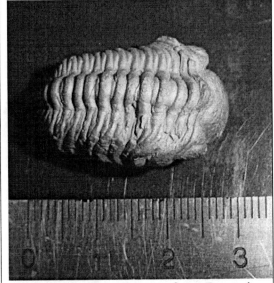

FIGURE 5-30. *Phacops* from Devonian beds of central Oklahoma. The scale is in centimeters.

They attracted me in part because they were relatively rare and because they were so exotic in appearance. They occurred almost always as dissociated parts, particularly the tail or pygidium. However, parts of the head also survived, but more rarely. These so occupied my attention that I ordered books on fossils and then the great volumes O and P on Trilobites and related animals from the Treatise of Invertebrate Paleontology (1959). I struggled through the two volumes and attempted to master the terminology as well as I could. My struggle was compounded by the frustration that there was no one at my college who could help me with the technical terms. The foundation of my frustration was that a particular fundamentalist perspective determined the college curricular philosophy. Still, I searched for fossils and attempted to explain their occurrences and meanings. By the end of my fourth year there, I had amassed quite a nice collection.

Then, I searched for fossils as one might search for treasure. I did not really study them. I possessed them. Then they began to possess me. My fossil hunting continued through my graduate school days in Oklahoma where I collected some beautiful specimens from Ordovician and Pennsylvanian fossil beds.

Apart from their exotic beauty (Yes, I find them beautiful), what is the value of a trilobite? Why would anyone spend time studying them? What secrets can they reveal?

TRILOBITES AS ANIMALS

Aquatic Arthropoda with preoral antennae and remaining appendages of typical or modified trilobite type, biramous appendages characterized by the presence of lateral gill branch attached to very base of walking leg. Introductory description of Trilobites by Leif Stormer in the Treatise of Invertebrate Paleontology (1959).

Although trilobites have been gone for hundreds of millions of years, we can know much about them. First, we know that they existed. They were animals, in particular Arthropods, which include insects, crustaceans, spiders, etc. As such they had a hard outer or exoskeleton, jointed appendages, and a segmented body. The body plan of the typical trilobite included three general regions (cephalon or head, thorax, and pygidium; see Figure 5-31). Also, the body of the animal had three longitudinal lobes (a central axial lobe flanked by two pleural lobes) that traversed the three body regions (thus the name trilobite, three-lobed animal).

The cephalon was a shield-like head to which a pair of antennae attached. Also, trilobites had complex compound eyes, prominent features on most whole specimens. The pygidium was made of a fusion of the terminal segments into a terminal shield-like structure. Both the head and tail were inflexible, but the thorax was made of multiple articulated segments that allowed the animal to bend. In fact many of them could roll up in what can only be interpreted as a defensive posture (see Figure 5-32).

The exoskeleton was made of chitin impregnated with calcium carbonate. This biomineralized skeleton made its survival as a fossil much more likely than if it had been made of chitin alone.

Also, like other arthropods, the animals had to molt or cast off the exoskeleton and grow a new one at successive stages in their growth because the exoskeleton did not stretch with them as they grew. Thus, any one animal left several cast molts throughout its life. The calcium carbonate hardened skeleton and the numerous molts (5 or more) of any one individual, increased the likelihood of preservation as a fossil, a remarkably unlikely event.

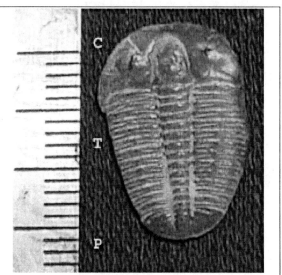

FIGURE 5-31. *Elrathia*, a small (about 2cm long) but very abundant animal that shows the dorsal anatomy of a typical trilobite. I have labeled the cephalon (C), thorax (T), and the pygidium (P). Note the eyes and the three longitudinal lobes.

Because the molts from the youngest and smallest to the adult form could be preserved, we now have been able to reconstruct their somewhat complex development. The smallest instar (larval stage) had a single segment. This form was very small (around a millimeter long) and likely lived as a member of the free-floating plankton, as many marine arthropods do today. In successive molts, the animal separated the head from the pygidium and then added thoracic segments, one per molt. Curiously, they seem to have added the segments from the top of the pygidium until they attained their full adult size.

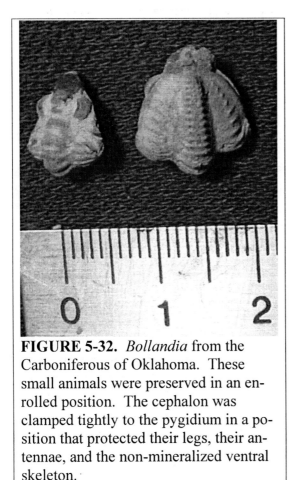

FIGURE 5-32. *Bollandia* from the Carboniferous of Oklahoma. These small animals were preserved in an enrolled position. The cephalon was clamped tightly to the pygidium in a position that protected their legs, their antennae, and the non-mineralized ventral skeleton.

Some exceptional fossil beds preserved the most delicate structures of trilobites. The most famous site is a mid Cambrian outcrop in British Columbia called the Burgess Shale, which was discovered by Charles Doolittle Walcott (1850-1927; USA), former head of the Smithsonian Institution in Washington, D.C. The trilobites contained in those shales had their legs, antennae, and internal organs preserved as thin carbonized films. They showed that the legs resembled those of crustaceans (shrimps and their relatives). That is, each walking leg had an additional leg-like lobe that must have functioned as a gill (the combined walking leg and gill is called a biramous leg; see Figure 5-33). They had a pair of biramous legs on each thoracic segment. We can infer that they used their legs to walk over the bottom mud or to burrow in the sediment. The numerous tracks and burrows that match the coexisting trilobites in width support such an inference. The legs also functioned to gather food, tear it into small pieces and transfer the pieces to the mouth, which was located on the underside of the cephalon. Again, this is similar to the feeding mode of the legs of many aquatic arthropods today.

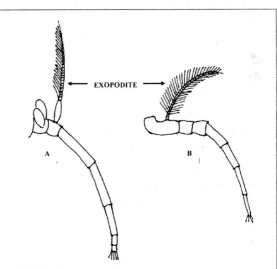

FIGURE 5-33. Biramous legs made of the jointed walking leg and a feathery gill. A. The biramous walking leg of a crayfish (crustacean). B. The biramous walking leg of a trilobite (after an illustration by Sam Gon).

Perhaps, the strongest evidence that they were bottom-dwellers is that they had flattened bodies with eyes on the upper surface of the cephalon. The eyes were compound, some of which had thousands of tiny calcium carbonate crystalline lenses. Many species lost their eyes presumably because they lived in environments where eyesight was not necessary (burrows or deep ocean sediments). Some abandoned the typical trilobite scavenger lifestyle and took to the open ocean. Their bodies were bullet-like and their eyes were huge. The phacopid trilobites (see Figures 5-30 and 5-34) had eyes with larger lenses, but fewer of them. The physics of the lensing system suggests that they had quite good visual acuity.

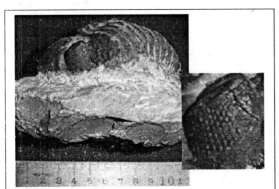

FIGURE 5-34. A large *Phacops* from Devonian deposits in Morocco. Note the relatively large lenses (see the enlarged eye in the inset). Also, the eyes were as large as the whole animals in Figure 5-32.

LESSONS IN EVOLUTION

The most erroneous stories are those we think we know best – and therefore never scrutinize or question.

-Stephen Jay Gould

It was while studying the Devonian[20] phacopids, especially their eyes that Niles Eldridge documented the stability of trilobite species over periods of millions of years and then a sudden (sudden in Geological time is on the order of hundreds of thousands of years) change followed by stability, etc. In particular, he documented changes in the number of rows of the crystalline lenses of various

---

[20] Consult *Reading the Earth* for descriptions of the periods of the Paleozoic Era.

Phacops species (see the insert in Figure 5-34). A species would show stability with regard to the number of rows followed by a change in number. These changes seemed to correlate with the changes in species. He realized that many other fossil groups also document stasis followed by rapid change followed by stasis. Together with Stephen Jay Gould (1941-2002), he called this mode of evolutionary changed punctuated equilibrium.

This met stiff resistance from the strict Darwinians. They subscribed to a view that said change occurs gradually, and, given enough time, new species appear. They argued that the appearance of stasis and rapid change was just an artifact of the fossil record. Really, gradual change had occurred. This debate has been quite acrimonious over the past 25 years, but the stasis appears to be real.

More recently, Ken McNamara studied the Cambrian genus *Olenellus.* Here, he documented true gradual change in the number of body segments in mature adults. Thus, evolutionary change might be gradual or sudden. The solution to this dilemma can be found in the realization that living things are not putty to be formed gradually or suddenly into something new. Instead, all living things exhibit variation in many characteristics. The variations meet with differential success from one generation to the next in response to one or more selective pressures. Suppose that a species of *Phacops* was very successful and ranged across areas that were isolated from each other. A satellite population with relatively few individuals could undergo profound change in just a few generations to become a new species. Certainly, most of these would not be more successful than their parent species. However, occasionally one could be and displace the parent species if they were to mix together again. On a geological time scale the displacement would appear sudden. Note, however, that this still invokes gradual change. This explanation of speciation was proposed by Ernst Mayr decades ago and has been taken up as the main explanation for punctuated equilibrium.

Gradual change might occur in a species that is subject to a particular long-term selective pressure which produces directional change. Thus, one species changes into another gradually. Both explanations for species change apply. Trilobites in all of their forms throughout the Paleozoic were molded by them.

Another problem about trilobites concerns their relationships with other arthropod groups. They have been tossed about over the years as members of the crustacea, as members of their own distinct group, and as members of the chelicerates (the group that includes spiders, horseshoe crabs, and their relatives). One problem had been that trilobites were about the earliest successful arthropods to appear in the fossil record. Thus, they were presumed to be among the most primitive of the whole phylum and gave rise to one or more of their lines. Recent analyses of arthropod structures by a method called cladistics suggests that trilobites are allied to spiders and their relatives in a line called the Arachnomorpha or spiderforms (see Figure 5-36)

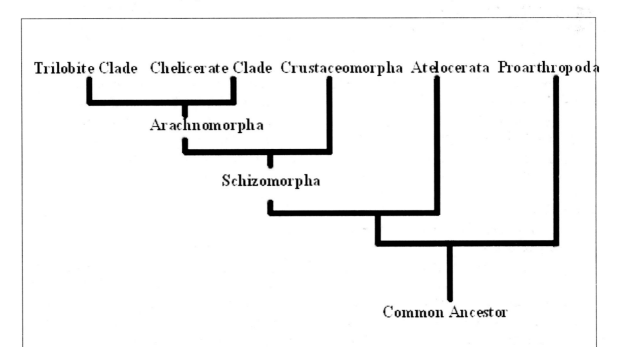

FIGURE 5-36. An evolutionary tree generated by cladistic analysis of all major groups of Arthropods. The schizomorpha, a term that refers to the presence of the biramous limb, includes the Crustaceomorpha and the Arachnomorpha. Most of the Arachnomorphs have lost the biramous limb. This suggests that rather than being primitive arthropods, trilobites were quite advanced. Modified after Sam Gon (2003).

Figure 5-36 and its ramifications are quite interesting. First, it suggests that within the schizoramid groups the biramous limb is primitive. Thus, the occurrence of biramous limbs in trilobites and crustaceans do not demonstrate close relationship. This is important because Darwin and others considered the biramous limb to be the key to the relationship. Now, the trilobites are seen as one of the arachnomorph lines, and highly evolved as Arthropods go.

THE CAMBRIAN EXPLOSION

It cannot be doubted that all the Cambrian and Silurian trilobites are descended from some one crustacean, which must have lived long before the Cambrian age, and which probably differed greatly from any known animal.

-Charles Darwin

The seeming paradox of the early appearance of trilobites and their apparent advanced body underscores the problem of the appearance of animals in the Cambrian Period. Just before the Cambrian, animals are found as trace fossils (tracks of soft-bodied worms, etc.) or relatively simple sea pen like organisms (animals attached like the soft corals). Within 50 million years, however, the Burgess shale documents a bewildering array of arthropods and almost all other phyla, including our own. This sudden appearance of animal groups and the appearance of almost all animal phyla in such a short period of time has been called the Cambrian Explosion.

How could this have happened? Stephen Jay Gould suggested in his popular book, *Wonderful Life*, that some mechanism independent of typical evolution occurs at the outset of a kingdom-level organization. This could have been true of animals in particular because they are multicellular with distinct tissues and structures coordinated through a pattern of development. Perhaps the developmental sequences were sloppier in the earlier days? Regardless, Gould pointed to the variations in form of arthropods and all other animals in the Burgess shale to sug-

gest that a maximum level of difference in possible body plans of the animals had developed quickly. Then, the history of the animal kingdom became the loss of major portions of the body plans with a few becoming dominant and highly diverse. Of course, Gould's may have been a very articulate presentation, but it certainly was not the last word. Almost immediately, the scientific community rejected his idea. But how could they object? Didn't the fossils confirm Gould's view?

In the last decade, advances in molecular biology have allowed the comparisons of DNA and other nucleic acids from one organism to the next. The relationships can be inferred based on cladistic analyses of the sequences of the bases in the nucleic acids. Related organisms can be studied relative to the base order of particular genes. However, much of the DNA housed in the nucleus and elsewhere is not functional, so changes in those sequences are neutral (they likely will not help or harm the organism). Such changes seem to occur at a steady rate and provide a molecular clock by which time of a group can be determined. When this method was applied to the Animal Kingdom, the molecular clock suggested that animals appeared 650-1,000 million years ago. That was more than 100 million years before the Burgess Shale animals! If true, why did the early animals not leave any fossils?

Richard Fortey, also a trilobite researcher, suggested that the earliest animals were small, microscopic. This is true of most of the aquatic crustaceans today. Likely, these have had quite a long history, but no fossils have been found of them except for one animal in the gut of a fossilized fish. He suggests that conditions in the Cambrian were such that an increase in size was both possible and selected for. What could have prompted such a change? Fortey and others claim that predation appeared in the early Cambrian. As carnivores became better at capturing their prey, some animals responded to the pressure by increasing their size. This would also allow for more substantial protective coverings like the mineralized and often spiny exoskeletons of trilobites. Arthropods were not alone in making such hard parts (the only parts that tend to leave fossils) bivalves like clams, brachiopods and other shelled animals appeared at this time, too.

Fortey's own work with trilobites showed that trilobites of the age of the Burgess shale across the globe were different from each other and already elaborate. Thus, they must have appeared as a group well before the Burgess Shale time to have achieved the observed diversity in form. They only became common as fossils when predation favored the heavier biomineralized exoskeleton of the trilobite.

Another and more compelling body of evidence is the diversity of the soft-bodied animals in the Burgess Shale which through a still unknown mechanism preserved the most delicate parts of soft-bodied worms as well as arthropods without biomineralized exoskeletons. A tally of the animals preserved suggests that 95% of all of them would not have left fossils under typical conditions.

EXTINCTION OF THE TRILOBITE
There are some cases when there was no obvious change in the earth's environment and yet a major group declined and became extinct. This was perhaps the case of the extinction of the trilobites. -Ernst Mayr

Trilobites participated in the Cambrian Explosion and were dominant organism throughout the Paleozoic Period. Indeed, their diversity increased from 26 families at the beginning of the Cambrian Period to 63 families by its end. They declined to 42 families by the end of the Ordovician Period (490-443mya). Then, a major extinction event occurred and they dropped to 19 families in the Silurian (443-417mya). Their diversity continued to erode through the Devonian Period (417-354mya) from 17 families to 5. What happened to them?

Extinction events like the one at the end of the Ordovician leads to a bottleneck in evolution. That is, all species that appeared after the Ordovician came from fewer body plans and restrictions in their possible variation imposed by that. Certainly, trilobites were not without success after that. There were about as many species of trilobites in the Silurian as in the Ordovician. *Phacops* and its relatives were common in the Devonian.

After the extinctions of the Devonian Period, trilobites were small and seemed to be restricted to shallow water habitats. This proved to be their undoing at the end of the Permian Period (290-248mya) when the mass extinction event eliminated about 95% of the groups that left fossil remains. Unfortunately for the trilobites, shallow marine environments were among the hardest hit. The Paleozoic Era ended and so did the reign of the trilobite.

TRILOBITE TALES
I find the creative part of the scientific process can be explained rather clearly at the trilobite scale. –Richard Fortey

I recall a fellow student trying to convince me of the falsity of evolution by claiming that trilobites had been discovered on the bottom of the Mediterranean Sea. He went on to say that evolutionists have been working hard to hush it up because it would cause the whole theory to collapse. I remember listening to him and dreaming of how wonderful it would be to find such an animal skittering over the ocean floor. Without thinking, I laughed and said that I know if scientists were to find living trilobites only death would shut them up.

A living animal would allow for confirmation of the relationship of trilobites to the other arthropods. It would permit the studies of behavior, physiology, development, etc. There may be some in the uncharted depths of the oceans. If so, their contribution would be a resounding confirmation of the interrelationships of all living things.

In Richard Fortey's words, trilobites are eyewitnesses to evolution. Their delicate crystalline eyes beheld some of the strangest animals that ever graced this planet. Now, paleontologists try to peer through the trilobite's eye but can do so only darkly. Illuminated by experience and informed imagination paleontologists pursue the past to provide us with more trilobite tales.

-2003

References:

Bowler, Peter. 1992. *The Fontana History of the Environmental Sciences.* Fontana Press. London.

Eldredge, Niles. 1995. *Reinventing Darwin, The Great Debate at the High Table of Evolutionary Theory.* John Wiley and Sons, Inc. New York.

Fortey, Richard. 2000. *Trilobite! Eyewitness to Evolution.* Alfred A Knopf. New York.

Gon, Samuel M. 2003. *A Pictoral Guide to the Orders of Trilobites.* Copyright by Samuel M. Gon.

Gould, Stephen Jay. 1989. *Wonderful Life. The Burgess Shale and the Nature of History.* W.W. Norton and Co. New York.

Gould, Stephen Jay. 2002. *The Structure of Evolutionary Theory.* The Belknap Press of Harvard University Press. Cambridge, Mass.

Harrington, H.J., et al. 1959. *Arthropoda 1.* In: Raymond C. Moore, ed. *Treatise on Invertebrate Paleontology. Part O.* Geological Society of America, University of Kansas. Lawrence.

Mayr, Ernst. 2001. *What Evolution Is.* Basic Books. New York.

Morris, Simon Conway. 1998. *The Crucible of Creation.* Oxford.

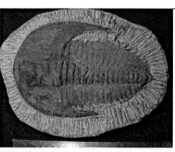

FIGURE 5-35. *Paradoxes* primitive middle Cambrian trilobite. Note that there is almost no pygidium. The fossil is about 30cm long.

Questions to Think About

1. Describe the general structure of a trilobite.

2. How do we know the developmental history of trilobites?

3. What is a biramous leg? How does it show a relationship with the crustaceans?

4. How can we know the physics of vision in the trilobites?

5. What is the difference between gradual change and punctuated equilibrium?

6. Figure 5-36 suggests that trilobites are related to what major arthropod group?

7. What is Gould's hypothesis about the origins of body plans?

8. Why did early animals suddenly appear according to Richard Fortey?

9. What happened to the trilobites after the Devonian extinctions?

10. Why are there no trilobites today?

ICE AGES

ON THE HILLS

Yesterday and the previous days I had most interesting work in examining the marks left by extinct glaciers.

        -Charles Darwin

I thought of Darwin's words as I sat on the hills overlooking Galich, a provincial town north of Moscow in Russia. The hills are steep and grassy. In areas flat enough to allow it, the townspeople have set up garden plots.

FIGURE 5-37. A view to the northwest from the Galich hills. Note the old part of the town with the lake beyond.

The old portion of the town rests in a narrow belt of land between the hills and a lake to the north. The land on the other side of the lake is farmed and has scattered villages with a landscape of low topography. The pastoral setting deceives the onlooker into assuming that the landscape has always been this way. However, if I had stood on the Galich hills only 13,000 years ago (a blink of the eye in geologic terms) and looked to the north, I would have faced the craggy ice wall of the terminal end of a glacier.

What is the evidence for the glacial origin of landscape features in Galich and other areas in North America and Europe? What causes Ice Ages to commence? What causes them to end? These are questions that relate to the nature of climate and its causes. However, to understand climate, one must understand some fundamentals of weather.

WEATHER[21]

If winds are the spirit of the sky's ocean, the clouds are its texture.-Guy Murchie

Most of us understand weather as clear or rainy. Particularly at his time of year when central Pennsylvania is caught in the grip of winter (and the groundhog saw his shadow!) that following the weather becomes more than a passing interest. Will we have another snow storm? Will it melt before I have to shovel it?

Here in the Northern Temperate Zone, we experience seasonal weather. That is, warm to hot summers and cool to cold winters. For example Harrisburg, PA (about 40°N), has a mean July high temperature of 29C (85F) and a mean January low temperature of -6C (22F). The range in temperature is a consequence of the tilt of the earth's axis relative to the plane of the earth's orbit around the sun. In particular, the Northern Hemisphere experiences summer when the North Pole tilts toward the sun and winter when the North Pole tilts away from the sun. The consequence is more than tilt. During summer sun light strikes the ground closer to a 90° angle.

---

[21] See *Clouds: The Keys to Understanding Climate, Weather, and the Hydrologic Cycle* for more information about weather. Also, I discuss the tilt of the globe in *Maps as Models*.

Also, the days are longer, so the ground is exposed to more light. All of this adds up to more heat (Figure 5-38).

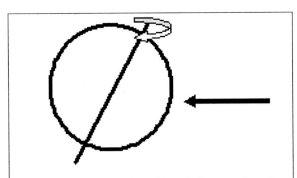

FIGURE 5-38. The tilt of the earth relative to the sun during the summer in the Northern Hemisphere.

The overall temperature then depends upon the amount of solar radiation that an area receives. This applies on a daily cycle as well. As warm air expands and spreads northward from the equator, it meets the cold air from the North Polar Region. At the convergence, warm air (which is lighter than cold air) rises and the cold polar air falls. However, air cools as it rises and turns to the east to form the jet stream. This fast-flowing river of air, once called the "storm track", may develop meanders that allow cold air to dip deep into the United States (see Figure 5-39).

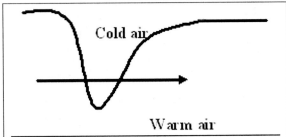

FIGURE 5-39. A dip in the Jet Stream, a convergence between the cold polar air mass and the warmer temperate air mass. The Jet Stream flows to the east and the dip propagates eastward as well.

Because warm air can hold more moisture than can cold air, the collision of such air masses leads to the rapid cooling of warm air and the condensation of its water to form clouds. If warm enough, the clouds can release excess moisture as rain or, at this time of year, as snow.

Alfred Wegener[22], the developer of the theory of Continental Drift, gave his life on an expedition to Greenland in 1930 to study the storm track. Now, weather satellites routinely monitor the movements of storm fronts and allow accurate prediction of weather changes (see Figure 5-40).

FIGURE 5-40. Satellite map of Temperate North America on February 8. Note the band of clouds along the northern tier of states.

The weather map (Figure 5-41) of the United States for February 8 shows a large portion of the country dominated by high-pressure systems. Air in high-pressure systems tends to sink. As air sinks, it becomes warmer, and its ability to hold water increases. Thus, those areas tend to be cloud-free and fair. Conversely, low pressure systems tend to have rising air masses. As air rises, it cools and may produce clouds and pre-

---

[22] Read more about Wegener in *Y2K, Deep Time, and Theory Choice in Geology*.

cipitation. Note that the jet stream (the jet stream lies along the northern front boundary) remains far to the north under the influence of high pressure to the south.

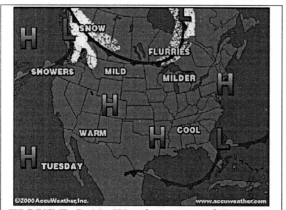

FIGURE 5-41. Weather map of Temperate North America that was based on Figure 5-40 and thousands of ground-based weather stations.

Despite the occasional unexpected snowstorm, the daily or seasonal ups and downs of weather are somewhat predictable and explainable. It would appear that major changes in weather patterns are fixed and unchanging. Indeed, based on past events since weather data have been recorded, there have been only minor and explainable shifts in weather. It would appear, then, that changes in climate, an integration of weather over about 30 years or an extended period, should occur very slowly, on the order of millions of years. How could an area such as Galich have been ice-bound so recently in geologic time? What is the evidence for the Ice Age?

EVIDENCE OF ICE AGES

I have worked upon the glaciers as an amateur, devoting my summer vacations, with friends desirous of sharing my leisure, to excursions in the Alps.

-Louis Agassiz

The Northern Hemisphere is covered with geological oddities that are relatively young. There are boulders that are out of place (called erratics). There are long mounds of jumbled rock called moraines. There are circular kettle lakes embedded in jumbled rocky substrates. There are long parallel scratches (or striations) on rocks like those in Central Park (they predate graffiti by thousands of years).

Further large-scale bits of evidence include shapes of valleys. For example, valleys that are carved by streams tend to be V-shaped. However, many young valleys like Yosemite Park are U-shaped. This is a signature of glacial activity.

Two hundred years ago, European geologists knew of such features, but they assumed that such curiosities were evidences of the flood. Louis Agassiz (1807-1873), a Swiss paleontologist and zoologist, became interested in geology through his passion for the study of fish. In his study, he realized that striations, moraines, and erratics could best be explained if glaciers covered much of Europe and North America in an earlier age.

Agassiz even spent summers in a hut on a glacier in the Alps. He and his companions recorded movements of the ice and noticed that the middle part of the glacier moved faster than the sides. He studied valleys below glaciers and saw striations and moraines. He surmised that the existing glaciers had expanded and retreated, and an Ice Age occurred when there was a general expansion of glaciers.

Agassiz moved to the United States in 1848 to recover from his debts. He took the chair of natural history at Harvard and created the museum of Comparative Zoology there. In the United States he saw many more examples to support his glacial theory.

Although the winter ice on my driveway appears particularly stubborn and static, it can move quite quickly as a glacier. When ice is piled to a thickness of hundreds of meters, the weight causes the whole mass to deform and flow almost as a plastic. In addition, melt water flows down to the bottom of the glacier and forms a lubricating layer.

Moving ice picks up stones (large and small) and incorporates them into the mass of the glacier. If they happen to lie at the edge as it slides past pavement rock, scratches or striations are formed. As ice moves, an equilibrium is established at the end where the rate of melting equals the replacement due to flow. At that point, the suspension of ice-rock begins to deposit its load of stones and finely ground rock in a mound called a moraine. The outwash and erosion caused by the continuous melt at the toe of the glacier created the depression that is now Galich Lake (see Figure 5-42).

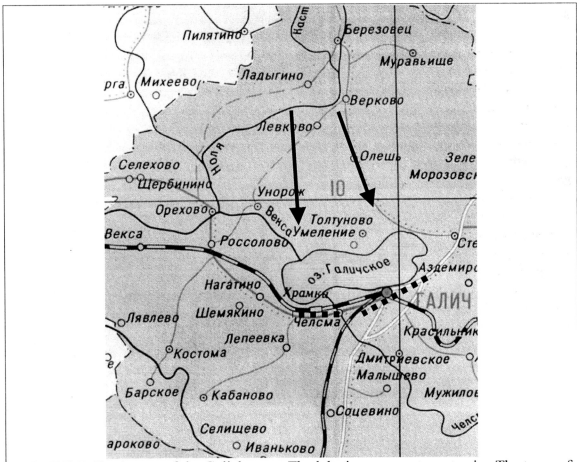

FIGURE 5-42. A map of the Galich area. The lake is on an east-west axis. The town of Galich sits on the southeast part of the lake. Arrows indicate the direction of the ice flow. Dashed lines indicate approximate positions of the moraines.

410

The explanation of geological features as a consequence of an Ice Age or glacial action is relatively straightforward. Still, it took nearly twenty years for the glacial theory to be accepted in Europe. Charles Darwin recognized Agassiz's explanation almost as it was formulated and began to reexamine his own interpretations of regional geological features in light of it. Paradoxically, Agassiz used the glacial theory to support his creationist views. He assumed that the earth was covered to the extent that all life was extinguished and the Creator started over again.

Thus for Agassiz, the cause of the Ice Age was clear. The Creator caused it to clean the slate and prepare the world for humans. Others sought a mechanism to explain how the earth could plunge into a deep freeze.

CAUSES OF ICE AGES

I have always suspected Agassiz of superficiality and wretched reasoning powers, but I think that such men do immense good in their own way. See how he stirred up all Europe about glaciers. -Charles Darwin

Around the beginning of the 20th Century, a Swedish chemist named Svante Arrhenius (1859-1927) considered the idea that atmospheric concentrations of carbon dioxide and water vapor could help to form an atmospheric blanket that kept the earth warm. Or put another way, average global temperatures should be related to the concentrations of those gasses.

He was the first to propose the Greenhouse effect[23]. That is, when sunlight strikes the earth's surface, some

is absorbed and released as infrared radiation (heat). Carbon dioxide absorbs infrared radiation and, therefore, holds that heat in the air.

Arrhenius pondered the problem and wondered how the atmosphere could change its concentration of carbon dioxide sufficiently to affect global climates. One day he looked out of his window and saw industrial smokestacks billowing smoke into the air. He realized that could lead to a change and began to calculate how much carbon dioxide would have to decline in order to cause enough global cooling to cause an ice age. He estimated that cutting current carbon dioxide concentrations in half would be sufficient to do it.

Atmospheric carbon dioxide could decline if the oceans became more efficient in their uptake, global photosynthetic activity would increase, and/or volcanic additions of carbon dioxide would decrease. These mechanisms are hard to explain, however, and likely work together in concert with other variations, particularly variations in orbit.

James Croll (1821-1890), a Scottish geologist and physicist, attempted to explain climate change in the 1860's by invoking changes in the earth's orbit, thereby changing the amount of solar energy striking the earth. The three orbital changes are: axial tilt, orbital eccentricity, and precession of the equinoxes.

Figure 5-43 illustrates axial tilt. The earth tilts 23.5° from normal relative to the sun. However, its tilt varies from 24.5° to 21.5°. As the earth becomes less tilted, its seasonal changes become less severe. This cycle has a period of about 41,000 years.

---

[23] See *Gaia: Science, Pseudoscience, or Fruitful Error* for some more background on climate change.

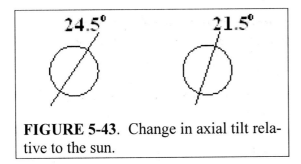

FIGURE 5-43. Change in axial tilt relative to the sun.

Like all other planets, the earth travels in a nearly, but not quite, circular path around the sun. The degree to which the orbit deviates from a circle is its eccentricity. That means the earth varies in its distance from the sun. At its closest (perihelion), the earth receives about 6% more solar radiation than at it most distant point (aphelion). However, now the earth nearly has its most circular (or least eccentric) orbit (see Figure 5-44). When at maximum eccentricity, the amount of solar radiation that strikes the earth could vary by as much as 20-30%. That could have a profound impact on global climates. This cycle has a period of about 100,000 years.

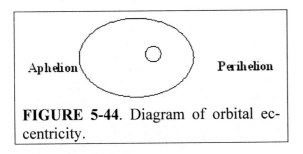

FIGURE 5-44. Diagram of orbital eccentricity.

Precession means that the earth wobbles slightly as it spins on its axis. Today, the Northern Hemisphere is in its summer (July 4) at aphelion. This should minimize the receipt of solar radiation by the Northern Hemisphere given the present eccentricity. Think of that during the summer; it could be 6% warmer than it is! This cycle has a period of about 23,000 years.

Milutin Milankovitch (1879-1958), a Serbian engineer, became interested in the Ice Ages and climate change, particularly the relationship between orbital changes and climate. He began to calculate the relationship as a soldier for the Serbian army during World War I. He was taken prisoner, and his Hungarian captors allowed him to continue with his project. Milankovitch found a good fit between the cycles of orbital variations and the four Ice Age cycle during the Pleistocene period. The Milankovitch cycles use Croll's orbital patterns, which explain variations in the total amount of solar radiation that strikes the earth, to explain variations in seasons and global locations of solar energy.

Considering something as complex as climate, other mechanisms certainly must come into play. For example, consider the Gulf Stream. It is a warm ocean current that brings warm tropical water northward along the western Atlantic and then bathes Western Europe. The impact is on regional climates is profound, particularly on winter temperatures. Consider Glasgow, Scotland and Moscow, Russia. Both cities fall around (56° N). Glasgow has a mean January low temperature of 1C(34F) while Moscow has a mean January low of -13C(9F). The difference is that Glasgow is near the ocean and influenced by the warm Gulf Stream. Moscow sits in the middle of the Eurasian landmass. If the Gulf Stream were to stop or be diverted, Glasgow could have winter temperatures comparable to Juneau, Alaska (average January low 18.7F or -7.4C), also on the ocean and at (58° N), but not bathed by a warm ocean current.

Indeed, the north Atlantic seems to be particularly important on a global scale. Wally Broecker has produced compelling evidence to suggest that the Gulf Stream is only a small part of a global conveyor system that controls global climate (see Figure 5-45). The westwardly subtropical air causes the mid Atlantic to move to the west and to lose water in the subtropics through evaporation and then deposit it across Central America into the Pacific Ocean. The westward flow of water also bumps into Central America, which deflects the current to the north. Thus, the Gulf Stream, slightly saltier and, therefore denser, flows toward the pole where it cools and becomes even denser. There, in the north Atlantic, the water of the Gulf Stream sinks and begins a global journey as an ocean bottom counter current. The sinking of the north Atlantic water also serves to pull the warm water of the Gulf Stream northward.

The sub oceanic current meanders southward toward the Antarctic where it turns to the east and flows past the southern tip of Africa into the Indian Ocean. There, it splits into two currents. One becomes a northward current that rises as it runs into India. The other flows south of Australia and northward into the Pacific Ocean where it may rise and retrace its journey back to the Atlantic as a warm, less salty surface current. The circulation is not rapid. In fact, it might take 1,000 years or so to make a complete circuit.

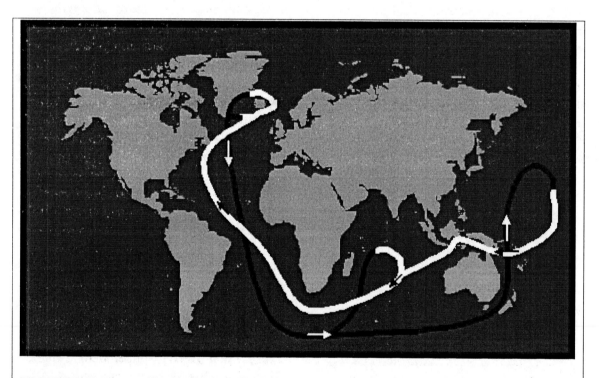

FIGURE 5-45. An illustration of Broecker's "conveyor". The flow of the cold deep water current is the black line, which flows generally eastward. The surface current (the white line flows westward and becomes what we know as the Gulf Stream. The uppermost part of the surface current becomes denser and sinks between Iceland and Greenland.

The descending water in the North Atlantic also may take with it large amounts of excess carbon dioxide and lock it away in the slow-moving depths. It could also deposit the excess carbon dioxide as carbonate on the ocean bottom. Thus, for multiple reasons, Wally Broecker sees the Global Climate Conveyor as key to explaining the stability of Earth's climate, especially during the warm interglacial periods. Thus, the distribution of landmasses over the planet can affect ocean currents by deflecting them. Tectonic activity, a mechanism with a much longer period than the Milankovitch cycles, determines continental distribution.

Around 600 million years ago, the continental landmasses were distributed through the tropics. Even so, there was a time when they were unaffected by ocean currents because the oceans had frozen solid to a depth of 1 kilometer.

SNOWBALLS & SLUSHBALLS

When water turns to ice does it remember one time it was water?

-Carl Sandburg

The Pleistocene Ice Ages and others through the past half billion years have left their characteristic marks, though much more faded. Glacial striations on continental rock and evidence of tropical icebergs suggest that the earth may have frozen solid just as animals appeared. What could have happened to bring about such an environmental calamity? The cause had to be stronger than the convergence of the Milankovitch cycles.

Earlier than 3.2 billion years ago, oxygen-generating photosynthesis evolved. We know that the chemistry of the ocean began to change at the end of the Archaean Eon (3.9-2.6 billion years ago) from an atmosphere with trace amounts of oxygen and higher amounts of carbon dioxide. Oxygen concentrations steadily increased during the Proterozoic Eon (2.6-0.52 billion years ago) to one very much like ours today[24]. Rocks laid down in the oceans during that time tell of a changing chemistry in the oceans until free oxygen began to occur in the atmosphere.

Evidence suggests that photosynthesis run-amok may have been responsible for the dilemma. Fossils show that photosynthetic organisms were quite common, even as long ago as 2.1 billion years. By 600 million years ago, they may have sucked enough carbon dioxide from the air to cause a significant drop in global temperatures. Some estimates of the paleoclimate suggest that global temperatures may have plunged to -45C. Even so, the oceans could not have frozen solid in this scenario because of submarine volcanic activity.

Support for a softer version of the snowball has grown over the past several years. This modification is called the Slushball. In this view, only the polar and temperate oceans froze. The tropical oceans, though ice free, likely had legions of icebergs plying their waters. This scenario allows for the persistence of life, particularly photosynthetic life, during the cold times.

Either way, the reduced photosynthesis and normal volcanic activity allowed for a rebound of carbon dioxide in the atmosphere, and the earth warmed up. It then suffered about 10 million years of very warm greenhouse conditions followed by another deep freeze. The environmental paroxysms continued through several more cycles and then dampened out.

---

[24] I expand on this topic in *Red Planets and Microbes*.

An interesting corollary of the Snowball-Slushball theory holds that photosynthesis occurred almost unchecked until herbivorous or grazing animals evolved. Then, the rapid changes in atmospheric carbon dioxide ceased. Animals had arrived just in time to save the planet.

CLIMATE CHANGE
Change, that is the only thing in the universe which is unchanging.
                                    -Helmuth Wilhelm

The past 600 million years has seen climatic shifts and swings but none so dramatic as the snowball earth. Has the planet finally settled down? Well, taking the evidence of paleoclimatology, the only thing that is normal about climate is change. By that statement, I do not mean to give aid and comfort to those who claim that we should not worry about climate change. Indeed, it should serve as a warning.

Ice cores taken from Lake Vostok in the Antarctic and the central Greenland ice sheet (see the locations in Figure 5-46) provide a nearly unbroken climatological record for the past 100,000 years. In the record of the ice scientists like Richard Alley have been able to read temperature, atmospheric chemistry, the strength of prevailing winds, relative snowfall, etc. as they changed throughout the Holocene Period. The details all add up to a very important conclusion. Climate can change rapidly. That is, the climate of the temperate zone can change significantly in a matter of a century or a decade. In fact, the resolution of the ice cores (they are in layers and read like tree rings) suggests that some of the changes occurred in a matter of a few years.

"Recent" climatological fluctuations produced a relatively warm, benign weather patterns during the Medieval period. That was followed by a sudden cold period known as the Little Ice Age (ca. 1350-1900; The Medieval Warm Period was a mild period that lasted a few centuries prior to the LIA). During that time, the Thames froze routinely. Also, a Norse settlement that had established itself on the coast of Greenland disappeared. In a similar way, civilizations all over the globe responded to changes in climate from the disappearance of the Maya to the expansion of the Romans and the Mongols. Climate change turned Palestine, "a land flowing with milk and honey" into the arid to semi-arid desert that it is today. Such climatic changes can be seen clearly in the ice core records. However, these fluctuations that have doomed civilizations are mere twitches in the climatic record of the past 100,000 years (see Figure 5-46). Alley and others have shown that rapid climatic fluctuations are the norm, and some have been very large and very sudden. Prevailing view is that such rapid climatic changes could be brought about by an abrupt halt of the Climatic Conveyor. This could happen by an influx of freshwater into the North Atlantic (through increased rainfall, for example) that would keep the water in the north Atlantic from being dense enough to sink. That would stop the "pull" that creates the Gulf Stream and the climate of Britain would rather suddenly be like that of southern Alaska.

The past 100 years has been warm, and it seems as though the Little Ice Age has ended. This anthropogenic (human-generated) increase in temperature goes hand-in-hand with a concomitant increase in carbon dioxide. However, the "end" of the Little Ice Age fluctuation might have been brought about by the anthropogenic increase in carbon dioxide. If so, we could still be in the Little Ice Age, and at its end, the rebound in temperature could be catastrophic for the biosphere and the global economy. Given our present concerns about global warming, this is a frightful possibility.

I thought about these things as I sat on the hills in Galich and looked out over the town and lake. A wall of ice and desolation seemed impossible on that summer's day. Yet those same hills bear witness and speak of a time so close to us that it is almost within human memory. How will we use the insight that the past has given us?

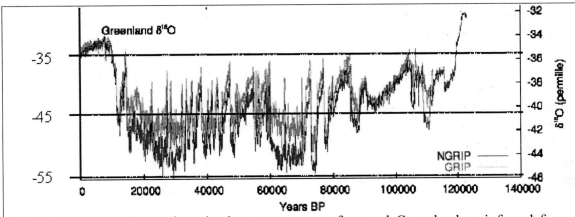

FIGURE 5-46. Fluctuations in the temperature of central Greenland as inferred from oxygen isotopes in ice core data. Note the large, rapid temperature fluctuations. The axis on the left is approximate temperature at the time of the formation of ice in degrees centigrade. The Little Ice Age is one of the small blips on the left hand side of the graph. This graph is modified from Wickipedia at: http://en.wickipedia.org/Wicki/image:Ice-core-isotope.png from a figure created by Leland McInnes.

-2000, revised 2005

References:

Agassiz, Louis. 1866. *Geological Sketches.* Houghton and Mifflin Co. New York.

Alley, Richard B. 2000. *The Two-Mile Time Machine.* Princeton University Press. Princeton, NJ.

Benarde, Melvin A. 1992. *Global Warning... Global Warming.* John Wiley and Sons. New York.

Bianche, G.G. and I.N. McCave. 1999. *Holocene Periodicity in North Atlantic Climate and Deep Ocean Flow South of Iceland.* Nature 397: 515-517.

Bowler, Peter. 1992. *The Fontana History of the Environmental Sciences.* Fontana Press. London.

Broecker, Wally. 1997. *Thermohaline Circulation, The Achilles Heel of our Climate System: Will Man-Made CO_2 Upset the Current Balance?* Science 278: 1592-1588.

Broecker, Wally. 1999. *Climate Change Prediction.* Science 283:179.

Broecker, Wally. 2001. *Glaciers that Speak in Tongues and other Tales of Global Warming.* Natural History 110(8): 60-69.

Croll, James. 1845. *Climate and Time in their Geological Relations: A Theory of Secular Changes of the Earth's Climate.* D. Appelton & Co. New York.

Firor, John. 1995. *Rhythm of the Earth.* In: *Scientific American Triumph of Discovery.* Henry Holt and Co., Inc. New York.

Hecht, Alan. 1985. *Paleoclimate Analysis and Modeling.* John Wiley and Sons, Inc. New York.

Hoffman, Paul F., A.J. Kaufman, G.P. Halverson and D.P. Schrag. 1998. *A Neoproterozoic Snowball Earth.* Science 281: 1342-1346.

Hoffman, Paul F. and Daniel P. Schrag. 2000. *Snowball Earth.* Scientific American 282(1): 68-75.

Huggett, Richard John. 1997. *Environmental Change, The Evolving Ecosphere.* Routledge. London.

Hughen, K.A. et al. 1996. *Rapid Climate Changes in the Tropical Atlantic Region During the Last Glaciation.* Nature 380: 51-57.

Lyell, Charles. 1990 (originally published 1830-33). *Principles of Geology With a new Introduction by Martin J. S. Rudwick. Vols. 1-2.* The University of Chicago Press. Chicago.

Manabe, S. and R.J. Stouffer. 1995. *Simulation of Abrupt Climate Change Induced by Freshwater Input to the North Atlantic Ocean.* Nature 378: 165-167.

Mayewski, Paul A. and Frank White. 2002. *The Ice Chronicles, The Quest to Understand Global Climate Change.* University Press of New England. Hanover, NH.

Raymo, M.E., K. Ganley, S. Carter, D.W. Oppo, and J. McManus. 1998. *Millenia-Scale Climate Instability During the Early Pleistocene Epoch.* Nature 392: 699-702.

Taylor, et al. 1997. *The Holocene-Younger Dryas Transition Recorded at Summit, Greenland.* Science 278: 825-827.

Trefil, James and Robert Hazen. 2000. *The Sciences, An Integrated Approach.* 3rd Edition. John Wiley and Sons, Inc. New York.

Williams, Jack. 1995. *The USA Today Weather Almanac.* Random House, Inc. New York.

Questions to Think About

1. What is the difference between weather and climate?

2. What factors determine the climate at any place on earth?

3. Which way does the storm track go in the northern temperate zone?

4. How do we know that there were ice ages?

5. What factors seem to control the occurrences of ice ages? Who first proposed them?

6. How does Wally Broecker's climate conveyor work?

7. What is the "Snowball Earth" hypothesis?

8. What does the ice on Greenland tell us?

9. What was the "Little Ice Age"?

10. What does the science of ice ages teach us about climate change?

CLOUDS: KEYS TO UNDERSTANDING WEATHER, CLIMATE, AND THE HYDROLOGIC CYCLE

A MEMORIAL DAY TRIP

If you don't like the weather in Oklahoma, just wait a minute.   -Will Rogers

I recall a particular windless, sultry Memorial Day in Tulsa. A group within my extended family had decided to go to a reservoir outside of the city for a day of picnicking and swimming. We secured a van for the purpose, and spent the day trying to be comfortable under a nearly cloudless sky. After a day in the Oklahoma sun, we returned in late afternoon. I was elected to drive. From a distance I could see a large anvil-topped thunderhead building over the city, and the first thing that came to mind was "maybe it will cool things off." As we approached, we saw that the cloud had grown to monstrous proportions and periodic lightening flashes punctuated its blackness. The whole scene looked as though an angry god was about to take vengeance on the city, a notion that was not far from being wrong.

Rain began to fall in unrelenting sheets so that the windshield wipers became completely ineffective. When I could see, the water had filled the street to above the curb and formed shallow streams that were growing. We made it to my mother's home, which stood on relatively high ground and took shelter in the basement. There, we sat, sometimes by candlelight, and told stories, ate popcorn, and waited. The storm raged throughout the evening and began to die down in intensity only near midnight.

However, the authorities urged listeners by radio to stay in their homes, because most roads were flooded and very dangerous.

By morning, the rain had stopped, but Tulsa had become a shallow lake, and the small hill on which our house sat was one of many islands. I went for a walk in the neighborhood and saw downed trees, cars in odd places, and even one car sitting atop another. As though mocking the destruction on the ground, pillows of fair weather cumulus clouds dotted the sky as the mercury climbed and gave way to another hot afternoon. The news and weather programs that day (and for days after that) announced that we had received 11.5 inches of rain in a single storm.

Weather and clouds are related to each other. Furthermore, the discovery of clouds as physical entities that could be described, labeled, and categorized, was a crucial link in understanding weather and the great Hydrologic Cycle of water from the oceans to the atmosphere, and back, ultimately, to the oceans again. The description of the general features of the great cycle had been known since before Greek Natural Philosophy, but an understanding of clouds, cloud formation, and the physics of clouds was absolutely necessary to connect the atmosphere to the ocean in order to help explain why parts of the earth were deserts and others were replete with rain.

A CLASSIFICATION OF CLOUDS

It is not in the least amiss for those who are involved in meteorological research to give some attention to the form of clouds. -Lamarck

Jean Baptiste Pierre Antoine de Monet chevalier de Lamarck[25] (1744-1829; France) was one of the very first to attempt to use a classification system as a way to support a theory of evolution. He had been made the curator of worms (invertebrates) at the Musee Nationale in Paris. In that position, he attempted to make sense of the diversity of all animals without backbones and build on the classification system of Linnaeus, many years earlier. He also tried to apply a method of classification to clouds, other natural chaotic structures. Lamarck saw that clouds seemed to occur in five different types:

- Hazy clouds (en forme de voile)
- Massed clouds (attroupes)
- Dappled clouds (pommeles)
- Broom-like clouds (en balayeurs)
- Grouped clouds (groupes)

He published his classification system of clouds in 1802 and expanded it to twelve types in 1805.

Lamarck wrote that the purpose for such a classification system was to group them according to their causes. That is, he expected that their shapes were related to how they were formed. Thus, his categories were linked to potential explanations of their formation.

In 1802, an Englishman named Luke Howard (1772-1864) also saw a need to classify clouds. He had been raised a Quaker, sent to a Quaker school, and later in life became one of the leading members of the Society of Friends. Beyond that he did not have special education in the sciences. Indeed, he was a successful pharmacist. Although he was only an amateur scientist, he had become a very prolific one. It was at a meeting of amateur scientists that Howard presented his classification system for clouds. He categorized them into four basic types and gave them descriptive Latin names:

- Cumulus (Latin, heap)
- Stratus (Latin, layer)
- Cirrus, (Latin, curl)
- Nimbus (Latin, rain)

The first three were named for their forms while the last one was named for its action, precipitation. He recognized that clouds by their nature change and can change from one form to another. While others had seen this as a problem with a descriptive taxonomy, Howard expanded his system to accommodate the transitional stages. For example, cumulus clouds could begin to bunch together. As they did so, they formed a kind of broken layer of bunched clouds, which he called cumulo stratus.

Other transitional clouds included:

- Cirro-Stratus (small, rounded clouds in a layer)
- Cirro-cumulus

His classification system was almost immediately successful and almost universally adopted. The reasons that the world adopted Howard's system, as opposed to that of Lamarck likely are complex. However the consensus seems to be that Lamarck used French phrases while Howard used the more universal (and neutral) Latin terms. Also, Howard's system resembled the very successful Latin classification system that

---

[25] Lamarck has been introduced in several essays. However, *Rivals* describes him most thoroughly.

Carolus Linnaeus[26] had created for living things. When meteorologists all over the world had a means to categorize clouds by formal definitions, then they could communicate aspects of clouds.

FIGURE 5-47. . High waves of cirrus and developing mid-level clouds as the leading edge of a warm front moves from south to north at the end of February 2005.

FIGURE 5-48. . This is a cumulus cloud that a cumulo-nimbus (note the snow shower falling from the left end of it).

CLOUDS AND WEATHER

The sky, too, belongs to the landscape. The ocean of air in which we live and move, in which the bolt of heaven is forged, and the fructifying rain con-

densed, can never be to the zealous Naturalist a subject of tame and unfeeling contemplation. -Luke Howard

Clouds form when air becomes supersaturated with water, which then condenses. There are several ways in which air can become supersaturated: it can gain water, it can become cooler, or it can change its ability to hold water due to change in air pressure. Cloud formation usually involves all three components. Fog is a special type of cloud whose formation is indipendent of air pressure because it develops on the ground from air that is saturated and then cools off (usually through radiative cooling).

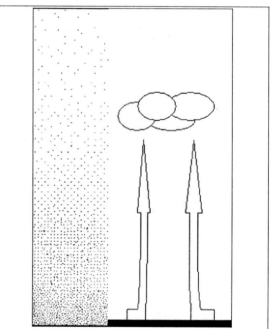

FIGURE 5-49. A Diagram of cloud formation from thermal convection. The column on the left illustrates the relative density of air molecules with height due to pressure changes. The arrows indicate the movement of warmer, moisture-laden air into higher, less dense, cold levels where the moisture condenses to form clouds.

---

[26] See *Kingdoms* for an explanation of the Linnaean System.

Most clouds develop as air rises. A simple case would be that of a thermal (see Figure 5-49). Air near the ground is heated through the day, and begins to rise displacing the cooler air above it. It carries moisture that had dissolved at the temperature and pressure near the ground. As it rises, air carries moisture from near the ground at near sea-level atmospheric pressure. However, air higher in the atmosphere has less air over it pressing down; so, the air molecules are farther apart and the air column is cooler, a mechanism called adiabatic cooling. The water dissolved in the air at the temperature and pressure on the ground condenses at the more rarified, cooler temperatures at higher levels, and clouds are made. This is not always benign. The thunderstorm that Tulsa experienced on the Memorial Day was due to the thermal convection from the heat island of the city. In a way, the city brought down destruction on itself.

A similar situation can be seen when moisture-laden air encounters a barrier, like a mountain (see Figure 5-50). As air is forced up and over the mountain, water condenses so that the windward side of the mountain has a wet climate with frequent rainfalls. As the air passes up and over the mountain, it descends on the other side. The warmer, denser air can hold much more water, but most of that has been wrung out of it. So, the other side is very dry, often desert, sitting as it does in the rain shadow of the mountain.

Of course, the global situation that influences weather and cloud formation usually is much more complex (go to Ice Ages for a more complete explanation). The atmosphere is made of air masses that have different temperatures and interact with each other. The line along which air masses collide is called a front.

If a mass of warm air collides with a mass of cold air, the warm air tends to override the denser cool air (see Figure 5-51). The outcome is a gradual change from high cirrus clouds followed by midlevel stratus that gives way to low level stratus that frequently becomes a nimbus.

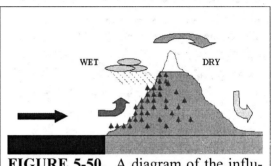

FIGURE 5-50. A diagram of the influence that a barrier like a mountain can have in a on regional climates. The windward side of the mountain has frequent rainfalls while the leeward side is a desert in the rain shadow of the mountain.

Cold fronts have a different structure from warm fronts. Because the approaching cold air is denser than the warm air that it is moving into, it tends to form a bulge. Along the leading edge, warm air is forced upwards. There, immense towering thunderheads that give rise to many of the spring and summer severe storms can form (see Figure 5-52).

During the winter many of the cold fronts come down from the Arctic air mass. Such cold air is very dense and tends to be associated with high pressure cells. As such, it tends to descend from the high, dry layers and produce those clear, bright, cold winter days (see Figure 5-53). This is similar to the descent of air on the rain shadow side of a mountain.

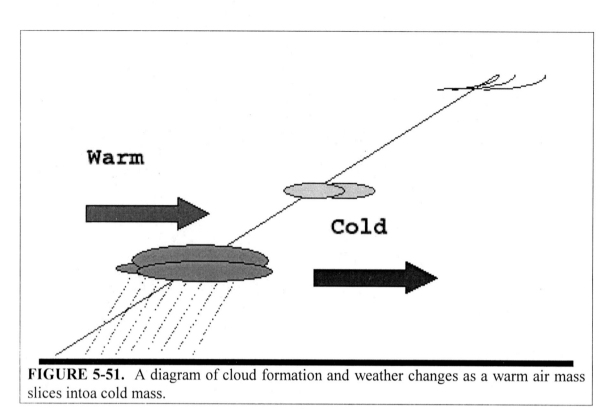

FIGURE 5-51. A diagram of cloud formation and weather changes as a warm air mass slices intoa cold mass.

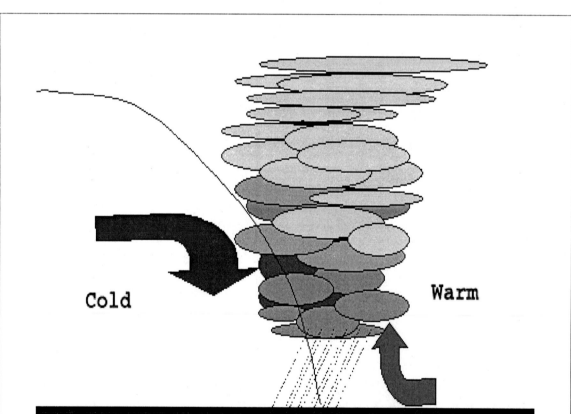

FIGURE 5-52. A cold front moves into a mass of warm air. The cold air, being denser, does not override the warm mass, but moves into it along a bulging interface. It tends to force the warm air to rise along the bulge , and can form severe weather.

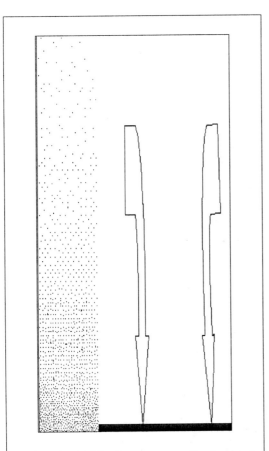

FIGURE 5-53. A diagram of why high pressure tends to form a cloudless sky. The high pressure column tends to make the air descend from high, dry air. Thus, there is no source of dissolved water that would tend to give rise to clouds.

THE HYDROLOGIC CYCLE

The hydrologic cycle is the perpetual movement of water throughout the various components of Earth's climate system.

Thomas Pagano & Soroosh Sorooshian

Clouds are among the most visible of the components of Earth's climate system, but the amount of water actually contained in them is diminishingly small compared to the amounts in the oceans or on land (see Figure 5-54). Indeed, most of the water held by the atmosphere is not in the forms of clouds. Nevertheless, they are necessary as conduits of water from the oceans to land. Furthermore, evaporation removes heat from the oceans and serves to transfer it from warmer, tropical regions toward the poles.

A major pool of water, particularly freshwater, can be found in glaciers and other ice fields. Some are at high altitudes, but most occur at high latitudes. Glaciers can contain as much as 70% of all freshwater (though freshwater is only 2.5% of the total amount of water on Earth). Although permanent ice has so much water locked up, it does not figure significantly in the hydrologic cycle, because the exchange rates are so low. For example, glacial ice renews itself at the rate of about 10,000 years while atmospheric water renews itself about every 18 days. So, although there is less water in the atmosphere than in polar ice, the contribution to the hydrologic cycle by polar ice is negligible. Water comes to land solely by means of precipitation. Much of it flows on the surface, or infiltrates into the ground to become groundwater, but eventually makes its way back to the ocean ($37 \times 10^{12} m^3/yr$). As water returns to the ocean, it carries nutrients and sediments with it. Surprisingly, though, almost twice as much water ($62 \times 10^{12} m^3/yr$) goes back into the atmosphere from land through evaporation and the movement through plants called transpiration

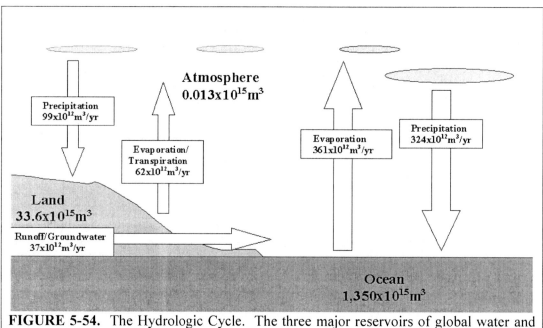

FIGURE 5-54. The Hydrologic Cycle. The three major reservoirs of global water and the rates and types of movement between the reservoirs.

The most impressive exchange occurs between the ocean and the atmosphere where nearly 80% of the water evaporated returns as precipitation. Clouds thus generated increase the albedo or reflectivity of the Earth[27] and affect the global heat energy budget (Glacier and ice reflect light/heat about as well as clouds do). Heat energy imparted to the atmosphere through evaporation, serves to moderate temperatures toward the poles. Indeed, in climate change (global warming) scenarios, the temperatures at the poles will see a much greater increase than those at the equator for that reason.

A deeper understanding of the hydrologic cycle will allow us to better explain questions like:

- What happens to cause and maintain an ice age?[28]
- How do the cold periods of the ice ages end?
- What happened to bring about the end of the snowball (or shush ball) Earth?
- How did the hydrologic cycle operate during such periods?
- How did the hydrologic cycle operate during times when the earth was much warmer?

For example, during the time of the mid-Cretaceous (the last period in the great Age of the Dinosaurs), the Earth was much warmer than it is today. Estimates based on oxygen isotopes in rock laid down at the time suggest that the average global temperature was about 8C higher than it is today, due in part to 3-4 times the current levels of atmospheric CO_2. The increased atmospheric

---

[27] See *Gaia: Science, Pseudoscience, or Fruitful Error* for an explanation of albedo and its consequences for climate.

[28] See *Ice Ages* for an explanation of how ice ages develop and for the concept of the snowball or slushball Earth.

temperatures also produced increased evaporation rates and a much more active hydrologic cycle. Consequences for the planet were profound. Global precipitation rates were up more than 25% over the present day. This led to the formations of nutrient-depleted lateritic soils well into the temperate zone[29]. Also, the differences between the temperatures of the tropical and polar regions were much smaller.

The Cretaceous scenario would seem almost like paradise, particularly as I think about scraping the windows of my car at the end of another Pennsylvania winter. Shouldn't we welcome climate change that would bring about increased global temperatures? Unfortunately, the devil is in the details, most of which have yet to be discovered. First of all, I am sure that the anticipation would turn more to dread if you were to read this in mid-July. The most important questions, though, center around what would a more active, energetic hydrologic cycle be like? Clearly, a warmer atmosphere is a more energetic atmosphere, which produces storms of greater energy levels. Imagine an Earth in which hurricanes come at category 6 over an ocean that has expanded by the temperature increase. This is just one type of disaster that I can anticipate. However, the nature of a complex system, like the hydrologic cycle, is that most outcomes cannot be anticipated by examining the components of that system[30]. That is why the amount of water in the atmosphere is not as important as the exchange rates between the atmosphere and the land, the mediators of which are clouds. Thus, the study and understanding of clouds and cloud formation are vital to our understanding of weather, climate, the hydrologic cycle, and what the Earth might be like by the end of the 21st Century.

Luke Howard provided the foundation by which clouds could be categorized and classified. This he provided the foundation that led to the development of modern meteorology by assigning a common set of terms and concepts to a dynamic system by which others could communicate and then begin to explain. The aspect of common language is important because science is a community of people who just won't shut up. They constantly evaluate and reinterpret evidence as skeptics and "devil's advocates". They communicate explanations for phenomena, and all that must be done with the terminologies of their respective disciplines to seek with greater precision nature's subtle truths.

Unfortunately, charlatans among politicians, the business community, and policy makers prey upon the minds of an uninformed public. They present the discussion within the scientific community as lack of qualified knowledge. Nothing could be farther from the truth; scientists seek a precision of knowledge that they do not now have. Nevertheless, a less precise understanding is infinitely better for a society to use than that of outright ignorance fueled by greed. In 1995, the phrase "Global Warming" in legitimate scientific literature was rare. Now the phrase along with the more general variant, Climate Change, is quite common. Certainly, the community of scientists sees the tempest ahead. Will we as a society ignore the signs and drive headlong into the storm?

- 2005

---

[29] See *A Few Inches* for an explanation of different soil types.
[30] See *Butterflies* for an expansion on this concept.

References:

Gedzelman, Stanley. 1989. *Cloud Classification Before Luke Howard.* Bulletin American Meteorological Society. 70(4): 381-395.

Hamblyn, Richard, 2001. *The Invention of Clouds.* Picador. New York.

Holton, James. 1992. *An Introduction to Dynamic Meteorology. Third Edition.* Academic Press. New York.

Pagano, Thomas and Soroosh Sorooshian. 2002. *The Hydrologic Cycle.* IN: Michael MacCracken and John Perry, eds. *Vol 1. The Earth System: Physical and Chemical Dimensions of Global Environmental Change. Encyclopedia of Global Environmental Change* (Ted Munn, editor-in-chief). John Wiley and Sons, ltd. Chichester.

Peterson, Larry, Gerald Haug, Konrad Hughen, Ursula Rohl. 2000. *Rapid Changes in the Hydrologic Cycle of the Tropical Atlantic During the Last Glacial.* Science 290:1947-1951.

Pierrehumbert, Raymond. 2002. *The Hydrologic Cycle in Deep-Time Climate Problems.* Nature 419: 191-198.

White, Tim, Luis Gonzalez, Greg Ludvigson, and Chris Poulsen. 2001. *Middle Cretaceous Greenhouse Hydrologic Cycle of North America.* Geology. 29(4): 363-366.

http://observe.arc.nasa.gov/

Questions to Think About

1. What are the four major categories of clouds?

2. Why, although he presented a cloud classification system earlier, was Lamarck's system ignored?

3. Who created the cloud classification system that we use today?

4. What is the major difference in the way that a cloud forms and fog forms?

5. How can a thermal form a cloud? In what way is that similar to the way in which a barrier like a mountain forms clouds?

6. How can a mountain be responsible for the formation of a desert? What is that called?

7. Clouds frequently form at the margins of air masses. How do the structures of warm and cold fronts differ?

8. Why does high pressure produce clear skies?

9. What is the hydrologic cycle? What are the major "reservoirs" of water within the cycle?

10. Why are glaciers and permanent ice fields not considered important in the hydrologic cycle?

11. How can the Cretaceous Period inform us about global warming?

A FEW INCHES

CREATING A GARDEN

No occupation is so delightful to me as the culture of the earth, and no culture comparable to that of the garden.

-Thomas Jefferson

I moved into my house in Central Pennsylvania during the winter of 1982. The yard occupied nearly an acre with some trees (mainly Black Walnuts) and a small garden plot. Most of it was one large, uninterrupted lawn with an area to the side that had been a barn, which the former owners used as a place to dump trash and coal ash. I was determined to turn the lower part of the yard into a large garden. But first I had to fix the eyesore of the dump area.

I started by hauling away the big stuff like tires, an old washing machine, and defunct car parts. Then, I staked an area that I would enclose with a low rock wall and fill with soil (the former owners had left a great pile of topsoil in the mess below). While digging in the area of the trash heap, I uncovered some interesting yellowish stones. They were somewhat chunky but cleaved nicely. I used them to lay up much of the stone wall through the month of March as I had time to do it.

I became busy with projects in the house and at the university as April approached so I could not spend much time on the wall. Then, a large snowstorm hit, followed by a warm spell. I was happy to be able to get back outside and work on the rock wall again, but all I saw was a mound of yellowish stuff where the wall had been. I discovered that I had been building with frozen clumps of coal ash. So the wall had melted! You see, having come from Oklahoma, I had no experience with frozen ground.

FIGURE 5-55. The raised bed area 18 years later. Note the low stone wall (lower arrow) and coal ash heap (upper arrow).

The wall fiasco did not discourage me as a gardener even though a neighbor said that I was "dumber than dirt." I spent the next several years converting the lower part of the yard from unbroken lawn to garden plots. Quickly, I discovered that the whole area had been a 19th century tannery under one roof. Some of the beds were underlain by stone rubble, others by coal ash, and others by old buggy parts, empty ink wells, and even an old headstone.

I dug in leaves, grass clippings and compost. I encouraged earthworms and kept exposed soil covered with mulch. Slowly, year-by-year, the garden soil in the plots became blacker, more friable, and more productive. My main struggle in creating my garden had been to build topsoil in a place where it had been depleted, and to establish a stable soil structure rich in organic matter.

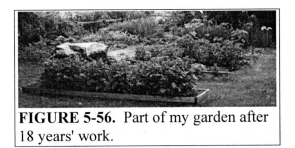

FIGURE 5-56. Part of my garden after 18 years' work.

STRUCTURE OF THE SOIL

This mantle of soil which nearly everywhere envelops the lands has a very great significance for us human beings.
    -Charles Schuchert & Clara LeVene

If you were to take a spade and dig down through soil, you would see that it contains a fairly definite and repeatable structure (see Figure 5-57). The uppermost layer usually is dark and made mainly of partially decayed plant material. This is the humus layer, also called the O horizon. Humus is poorly consolidated and easily moved aside, almost like a mulch layer.

The uppermost mineral soil layer has humus in it, but it also contains mineral components. This is the topsoil or A horizon. Because water typically moves down through the soil, substances that dissolve in water move down through the topsoil layer. Since nutrients such as nitrates, phosphates, and potassium tend to be water soluble, they tend to move out of the topsoil and into the B horizon.

The B horizon tends to accumulate dissolved substances. Thus, it is called the zone of accumulation or the subsoil. The line of demarcation between the A and B horizons often is quite distinct in undisturbed soil. The lowest level or C horizon contains rubble of the parent rock material and grades down to bedrock. The ideal structure of soil as depicted in Figure 5-57 rarely shows itself so nicely (Figure 5-58). Highly disturbed soils from plowing or fill might show no layers at all.

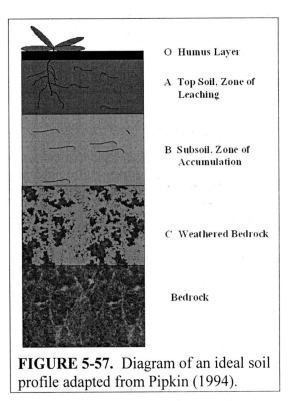

O Humus Layer

A Top Soil, Zone of Leaching

B Subsoil, Zone of Accumulation

C Weathered Bedrock

Bedrock

FIGURE 5-57. Diagram of an ideal soil profile adapted from Pipkin (1994).

Still, soils mean different things to different people. For example, to the engineer, soil means a platform on which things might be built, whereas to the farmer, soil is the medium within which crops can be grown. These different things and different reasons to classify soils have led to a chaos of designations and classification systems.

A SCIENCE OF SOIL.

All soils (with the trifling exception of the thin stratum of vegetable mold which covers the ground in certain localities) are formed from the disintegration of rocks .-Joseph Le Conte

Certainly, soil has been important to humankind as long as there have been builders and farmers. Designations of soils, then, depended upon the intended purpose. For example, the designation of rich, fertile soil had little meaning for the builders of the Tower of Pisa, but that designation would be the main purpose for the farmer.

FIGURE 5-58. Real soil profiles rarely are as clear as those of Figure 5-57. However, here the O, A, B, and C horizons are quite distinct.

Some early experimental work on soils included ways to make them more fertile. Justus von Leibig (1803-1873), a somewhat pugnacious German chemist, argued that fertilizers containing phosphates and potassium would increase crop yields. He attributed little importance to the structure of soil as long as it contained the appropriate elements.

Geologists of the 19th century saw soil as disintegrated rock. Thus soil served as a matrix from which growing plants derived support, water, and necessary elements. Water and nutrients then came and went as a kind of balance sheet. For example, phosphate removed by plant crops could be added in the form of fertilizer or some other form. This balance sheet view is still applied by many growers, particularly lawn fanciers.

Although much work had been done to map soils and work on ways to increase the fertility of soils, the study of soils did not become a science until the 19th century. Several independent scientists realized that soils were more than just "weathered rocks" and formed as a consequence of a variety of factors.

Independently, scientists in the United States and in Russia developed a deeper understanding of soils and their formation. However, the main credit for summarizing a new understanding of soils goes to the Russian scientist, Vasili Dokuchaev (1846-1903). He and his colleagues studied the deep, black Chernozyom soils of Siberia. As a consequence of their studies, they realized that soils are unique natural entities with properties that stem from their formation.

Dokuchaev and his colleagues recognized that soils formed as a consequence of a variety of processes and attributes. Thus they realized that a combination of properties as well as geology determined the nature of soil. With this realization in the U.S. and Russia, the study of soils became a new science called Pedology.

FACTORS OF SOIL FORMATION

[Soil is]...*a unique body having a definite genesis and distinct nature of its own and occupying an independent position in the formations constituting the surface of the earth.* -G.N. Coffey

In particular, Dokuchaev and the Russian school of soil science said that there are five properties that determine the development and nature of soils. These attributes are:
1. Climate.
2. Organisms.
3. Relief (or topography).
4. Parent Rock or Geology.
5. Time.

Climate can have an enormous impact on the ecology of terrestrial systems. Average temperatures, precipitation, etc. determine the kinds of weathering that rocks are subjected to (e.g. ice, water, wind, heat). For example, the amount of rainfall can determine how rapidly the A horizon is leached of soluble compounds. Temperatures determine the rate at which soil processes can function.

The average temperature regime and precipitation characteristic of a climate determine soil moisture and evaporation rate. Certainly, an important source of soil moisture is precipitation. However, relative humidity (a factor that is temperature-dependant) determines the rate at which water evaporates. For example, with the same amount of precipitation, soil in the subarctic remains wetter than soil in the subtropics.

Organisms, particularly plants, grow in the soil and return organic material to the soil. Their leaves cover the ground as a humic mulch. Indeed, dead plant material makes up the O horizon. Also, plant roots penetrate soil horizons, injecting organic material deep into the ground (see Figure 5-59).

Although less substantial in bulk, animals of the soil can have an important impact on soil and its development. Darwin studied the action of earthworms on soil (he called soil "vegetable mould"), and how they cause layers to mix, aerate, and accumulate organic material[31]. He noted that the action of earthworms could have profound impact on soil and the landscape by their constant stirring or bioturbation. For example, he set out a grid of white chalkstones on the surface of a field next to his house at Down. After 29 years, he and his son dug a trench in the field and discovered that the white stones had sunk 7 inches into the soil, a movement

that he attributed to the action of earthworms. Since then, his conclusions have been borne out for most areas of the Temperate Zone. In the Animal Kingdom only ants and termites come close to the impact of earthworms on soil structure.

FIGURE 5-59. Top of the leaf litter (above) and the leaf litter removed (bottom).

Relief, topography or slope determines depth of the soil as well as its moisture. Soils at the top of a slope tend to be thin because the fine components constantly wash downslope (see Figure 5-60). Thus, soil tends to be deep at the bottom of a slope as it accumulates fine material from above.

Similarly, water easily runs off of a steep slope, but moves relatively slowly over more horizontal soils. As water moves slowly, it can soak into soil and allow for greater soil moisture. Depressions in the landscape allow for accumulation of water and the formation of wa-

---

[31] This is the topic of my essay, *A Tale of Two Stones.*

terlogged or wetland soils. More than simple slope, topography determines exposure of the soil to sunlight and prevailing winds. Also, elevation has a direct impact on ambient temperatures. Thus, topography can produce or modify some of the same factors that characterize climate.

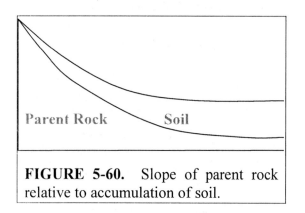

FIGURE 5-60. Slope of parent rock relative to accumulation of soil.

Parent rock material weathers or erodes by chemical and mechanical means to produce pieces. This rubble that overlies bedrock is called regolith and may be produced in place or transported from some distant source. Regardless, the composition of the parent material determines much of the chemistry of the resulting soil. In the Ridge and Valley Province of Central Pennsylvania, some valleys have soils produced by the weathering of limestone. They tend to be less acidic, well buffered and higher in nutrients than soils derived from shales and sandstones.

The mineral components of soils consist of a mixture of cobble and gravel, clay, silt, and sand. These designations do not refer to particular minerals, although they do have particular properties. Cobbles and gravels are stones that are greater than 2mm in diameter. The larger cobbles resist water movement and other modes of erosion. Sands (0.07-2mm in diameter) behave like gravel except that they erode much

more easily. Sand feels gritty between the fingers or on the tongue (yes, Pedologists taste soil).

Silt is very fine (0.004-0.074mm in diameter). Typically, it is slightly elastic when wet but has no cohesive strength when dry. A simple test for the presence of silt would be to rub soil on paper and allow it to dry. Silt will fall apart or rub away easily.

Clay is finer than silt (less than 0.004mm in diameter). It has strong elastic properties and remains strong when dry. Clay compacts easily and binds chemically to water. The fine spaces tend to exclude air pockets and openings in which free water (water available to plants) might accumulate. Because clay can bind to water, it can shrink and expand depending on its hydration.

Soil with too much clay feels heavy and hard to dig. Most of the soil in my garden was heavy clay 18 years ago. I built raised beds and added sand and a considerable mass of organic material to them. The clay is still there but it is diluted by the other stuff that makes it friable. The transition has been slow (but I had soil to start with).

Weathering of parent rock material to make the mineral components of soil takes a great deal of time. James Hutton[32] (1726-1787) recognized that such weathering in soil production would take enormous amounts of time. His ponderings about such processes led to his premise that the earth is uncounted years old.

Indeed, soil does take a long time to develop. Soils with a weakly developed profile (an A horizon directly over a C horizon) might be on the order of hun-

_____

[32] See *Geology Through Lyell's Eyes* and *Y2K, Deep Time, and Theory Choice in Geology* for more about James Hutton.

dreds to a few thousands of years old, whereas well-developed soils could be 40,000 to hundreds of thousands of years old.

Hans Jenny (1902-1993) in the U.S. developed the concepts of Dokuchaev and others. He recognized the importance of looking at the five factors collectively and spent his professional career trying to quantify them. He especially stressed the importance of time in the formation of soils.

Classification systems based on the engineering properties of soils, the agricultural properties of soils, etc., had been produced for more than 100 years. The yearbook of Agriculture in 1938 published a taxonomy of soils based upon development and color. Guy Smith (1902-1981) spent his professional career, trying to produce an informative and manageable classification system. He based much of his work on quantifiable properties of soils rather than their colors or inferences about their genesis. He published the "seventh approximation" of soil taxonomy in 1975.

Although the U.S. system of soil taxonomy is widely used, Brazil, Canada and Russia have their own systems of soil taxonomy. The need to communicate precisely about soil type is great. There may be as many as 50,000 different types of soil in the U.S. alone. Imagine how many types there are on a global scale.

EROSION & DESERTIFICATION
A few inches between humanity and starvation. -Anonymous

All sciences require a common set of terms in order to allow for effective communication. Pedology approaches that situation but has not achieved it yet. Effective communication is a necessary tool in approaching solutions to issues related to soil. In human terms, there are fewer issues that are greater than those of soil erosion and desertification.

Here in Pennsylvania, the most important problem with soil has to do with water-borne erosion. The gradual loss of topsoil is a consequence of farming practices and other human activities that tend to remove the organic layer from the soil surface. It is not uncommon to see even the most pristine streams become turbid after rainstorms. Figure 5-61 shows an almost pristine section of Penns Creek after a storm event. Runoff (in this case strictly agricultural) has changed a normally clear stream into a murky turbid stream. The load of suspended silt and clay will flow into the Susquehanna River and ultimately into the Chesapeake Bay.

FIGURE 5-61. A "pristine" section of Penns Creek following a storm event and agricultural runoff.

Some solutions rely on different types of plowing, or maintaining a plant cover (called a green mulch) over the soil. One of the easiest solutions is the use of undisturbed vegetation next to steams. The "green belt" traps soil particles before they can get into waterways.

Other areas with marginal climates can change to desert as a consequence of human activity. For example, on lands that border the Sahara Desert, the plant cover has been removed from the surface by overgrazing and poor farming practices. The loss of cover allows rapid drying of the top soil and its loss through wind erosion. If that is followed by a period of drought, marginal land becomes desert and this process is called desertification.

Such a thing happens here in the U.S. as well through intensive agriculture of marginal lands. The Dust Bowl of the 1930's is not the only example. Large parts of the Southwestern U.S. can no longer support agriculture. The San Joachin Valley of California is one of the most productive agricultural areas in the world. However, its productivity depends upon intensive irrigation in a near desert environment. Water used in irrigation has dissolved substances in it. As the water evaporates in the low humidity of the San Joachin Valley, dissolved salts accumulate until the soil cannot support the growth of plants.

Even the tropics suffer a kind of desertification. For example, rainforest soils tend to be deficient in nutrients, mainly because soluble nitrates, etc. are washed out of the soil by the prodigious rainfall. Therefore, nutrients there tend to be tied up in the biota. Tropical laterite soils tend to be heavy clay enriched in iron oxides. When the plants cover is removed, the exposed nutrient-poor clay turns to a hard, brick-like consistency and requires many years to return to its former productivity.

With the help of an amelioration of the climate, quick and decisive action has reversed the desertification of the Dust Bowl region in the central U.S. Similar action is required to save marginal lands and tropical areas. Considering these global problems, I take some comfort in the small gains made in my garden.

As the global human population exceeds six billion, the loss of topsoil becomes an all important consideration. It not only fouls streams but also can profoundly affect agricultural production and the world's ability to feed humanity. Also, given the generation time necessary for the production of well-developed soil, it should not be considered a renewable resource. Rather, we need to think of soil, *the few inches between humanity and starvation*, as a gift to be cherished and cared for. As the teacher of Ecclesiastes said, "*The profit of the earth is for all, the king himself is served by the field.*"

-2000

References:

Bowler, Peter. 1992. *The Fontana History of the Environmental Sciences.* Fontana Press. London.

Darwin, Charles R. 1985 (original published in 1881). *The Formation of Vegetable Mould, Through the Action of Worms.* The University of Chicago Press. Chicago.

Ehrlich, Paul R. and Anne H. Ehrlich. 1996. *Betrayal of Science and Reason, How Anti-Environmental Rhetoric Threatens our Future.* Island Press. Washington, D.C.

Gardner, Gary. 1996. *Shrinking Fields: Cropland Loss in a World of Eight Billion.* Worldwatch Paper 131. Washington D.C.

Huggett, Richard John. 1997. *Environmental Change, The Evolving Ecosphere.* Routledge. London.

Jenny, Hans. 1941. *Factors of Soil Formation.* McGraw-Hill. New York.

Johnston, J.F.W. 1857. *Lectures on the Applications of Chemistry and Geology to Agriculture.* C.M. Saxton & Co. New York.

Keller, Edward A. 1996. *Environmental Geology.* 7th ed. Prentice Hall. Upper Saddle River, NJ.

LeConte, Joseph. 1898. *Elements of Geology.* D. Appleton & Co. New York.

Lyell, Charles. 1990 (originally published 1830-33). *Principles of Geology With a new Introduction by Martin J. S. Rudwick. Vols. 1-2.* The University of Chicago Press. Chicago.

Pipkin, Bernard W. 1994. *Geology and the Environment.* West Publishing Co. St. Paul, MN.

Trefil, James and Robert Hazen. 1998. *The Sciences, An Integrated Approach.* John Wiley and Sons, Inc. New York.

Questions to Think About

1. What is the general structure of soil?

2. How did soil science develop in Russia and the U.S.?

3. What are the factors that determine soil type?

4. What are the contributions of Hans Jenny and Guy Smith?

5. What are the main environmental problems suffered by soil?

6. What is the difference between soil and dirt?

7. What is meant by a soil taxonomy? How might it be useful?

8. What is erosion?

9. What is desertification?

10. How is soil "a few inches between humanity and starvation"?

A NEW STORY TO BE TOLD EVERY DAY

A FLOOD

The face of the water, in time, became a wonderful book....And it was not a book to be read once and thrown aside, for it had a new story to be told every day.

                    -Mark Twain

I grew up in Tulsa in an older part of the city close to the Arkansas River. The river defined much of the city in those days. Through Tulsa, the Arkansas River flowed nearly from the north to the south and divided the city into east and west Tulsa. I grew up in the north side on the eastern side of the river.

The river also provided a water source for three oil refineries (all situated on the west side of the river). Still, the periodic stench from those great plants drifted over to my side of the river almost daily. Similarly, the outline of the distillation towers and the arcane network of pipes along such a long stretch of the river provided an industrial backdrop to the relative wildness of the river.

My friends and I often went down there to play in the sand and long sinuous, braided networks of warm water. Old oil drums, driftwood and a variety of metallic objects occupied us for many hours. However, nothing quite caught our interest as much as looking for and playing in quicksand did. We made certain that one of us had a long, sturdy stick while the others of us ran and jumped into spots that we had identified as quicksand. In a few instances, we slipped into the sand up to our chests and "swam out" with the aid of the stick and a good pull.

The lazy summer days spent on sand and water made the river almost a personal playground or a large affable friend. But this friendly giant often became a raging monster during the times of the spring rains.

My father, as did all firefighters, went to help to build up the riverbanks with sandbags in their struggle to contain the river and prevent it from causing loss of life and property damage along the river-front. Sometimes they won the conflict, but often they did not. Then, in 1964 the Corps of Engineers completed Keystone Dam above Tulsa at the confluence of the Arkansas and Cimarron Rivers. The dam and those upriver were supposed to absorb water during a flood event and release it slowly downriver so that Tulsa would not experience the repeated flood events of the past. Soon, the sandbagging obligations became part of the history of Tulsa. The dam was in place.

The power and majesty of floods have left their marks in human history and in the myths and stories of most cultures. The story of the flood of Noah is not the only one. Mesopotamia had the flood story of Gilgamesh. Indeed, indigenous cultures all over the Americas, Europe, Asia and Australia have such stories with their particular variations in response to the destructive and cleansing power of moving water.

Creeks and rivers not only provide water but also transportation systems, power and (in some cases) protection. Agriculture depends upon the actions of moving water to provide for rich soils and irrigation. Long has it been in the interest of our species to understand moving water and appreciate its proclivities to predict its fury and to try to tame it. Thus, the stories passed down accumulated wisdom about rivers, their structures and their behaviors. Much later came the descriptive science.

STRUCTURE OF STREAMS

It is the longest river in the world – four thousand three hundred miles...It is also the crookedest river in the world, since in one part of its journey it uses up to one thousand three hundred miles to cover the same ground that a crow would fly over in six hundred and seventy-five.-Mark Twain

By their very nature, rivers and creeks are highly dynamic systems. Not only do they change moment to moment as water replaces water on its way to the sea, but the whole system can undergo dramatic change as in the Arkansas River floods. The dynamism is a direct result of the nature of flowing water in a somewhat pliable basin (geology and soils) with variable rainfall and temperature (climate).

The anatomy of a stream includes water moving downhill in a natural groove or channel. Streams include all waters that flow through a channel, regardless of size. Rivers are large streams while creeks are smaller streams. Most of its water flows along the deepest portion of the stream. Not only does the main channel carry most of the water, but it moves with the greatest velocity because its water is least affected by friction with the sides and bottom.

Water flowing down steep slopes tends to move swiftly in relatively straight channels. However, as hillside or mountain streams begin to level out and water velocity drops, channels naturally begin to deviate from a straight line. Consider the Yukon River illustrated in Figure 5-62. The flowing water has carved a winding river basin through the landscape. This is not unusual among rivers with relatively low slope or relief. The broad S-shaped curves in the river are called meander bends.

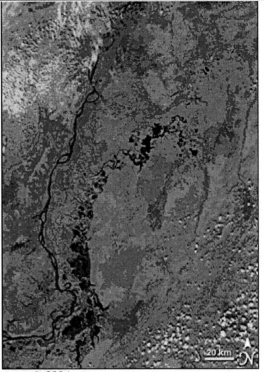

June 5, 2006

FIGURE 5-62. A satellite view of the Yukon River. This river has low relief with well-developed meander bends and braided stream regions. The image was acquired by NASA's Terra Satellite and posted on NASA's Earth Observatory: http://earthobservatory.nasa.gov/

As water rounds a meander bend, it moves faster at the far end of the curve where it cuts away the bank. Slower water on the inside of the bend tends to deposit a point bar. As the meander grows into a larger and larger loop, the bend becomes unstable and a new channel slices across the point bar to make a cut off. This new basin is called an oxbow lake and will persist as a lake until it eventually fills with sediment and organic debris.

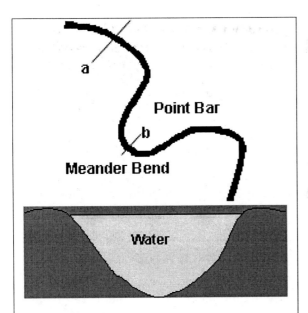

FIGURE 5-63. The top diagram illustrates the channel of the Yukon River in the lower-left quadrant of Figure 5-62. Meander bend and point bar are indicated. The middle diagram illustrates a cross-section of the river at a (see top diagram). The bottom diagram represents a cross-section of the river at b (at the meander bend on the top diagram).

Some parts of the Yukon River have multiple parallel or reticulate channels. Often, they appear as wider parts of the stream with multiple islands. This type of channel is called a braided stream.

THE WATER'S BURDEN

Oh Shendandoah, I long to hear you.
Away, you rolling river
Oh Shendandoah, I long to hear you
Away, I'm bound to go
'Cross the wide Missouri.

-Anonymous

The rolling turbulence of the waters in a moving stream or river provides the energy to allow for sediment transport. As water flows down a stream, turbulence creates internal eddies, which, added together produce a net downslope move-

ment. However, the internal water movements keep silts and clays in suspension, called suspended load. If the turbulence is great enough, even sands and small stones can be kept in the water column. The velocity of the water has the greatest impact on turbulence and on the water's ability to carry suspended material. Some of the sediment load occurs as bed load, i.e. the movement of material along the bottom, as it is dragged along by the movement of water.

When water moves into a reach of lower slope or some other slower-moving section, turbulence falls, and it cannot hold as much material in suspension. Bed load transport drops off, too. Thus, the silt-laden Mississippi River enters the Gulf of Mexico, and the velocity drops. Turbulence drops and the sediment settles out into an expanding delta at its mouth (see Figure 5-64).

Conversely, riffles are shallow with water at high velocity. At these places, the more turbulent and energetic water exports small components of the substrate like sands and silts. Thus, typical riffles contain only stones, gravels and cobbles.

Rivers and streams often rise out over their banks and extend into the surrounding area. In floods such as these, the larger mass of water moves swiftly. However, as it recedes, much of its excess suspended load drops out and fills the surrounding flood plain with finer silts and clays. Because water moves in the channel all of the time, smaller particles tend to be washed out compared to the flood plain. The sediments and their soils created by deposition are called alluvium.

To a degree, the velocity of the water determines the total amount of water that moves down a stream, and that moving volume would be easy to estimate if streams did not vary in depth from month to month or day to day. However, such

440

dynamic systems respond quickly to storm events, so as a stream rises, the total volume moving down the stream increases. This discharge can be estimated by calculating the cross-sectional area of a stream and its velocity. Because streams are not rectangular in cross-section, all streams have to be calibrated so those discharge estimates can be made.

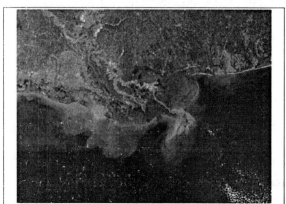

FIGURE 5-64 A satellite view of the Mississippi River delta. The image was acquired by NASA's Terra Satellite and posted on NASA's Earth Observatory: http://earthobservatory.nasa.gov/

Figure 5-65 illustrates a theoretical stream in cross-section. A gage measures depth, but the volume represented by each increase in a foot, usually increases the cross-sectional area dramatically. However, once calibrated, gauging stations provide valuable information on water flow, flooding events, etc.

On March 21, 2000 in central Pennsylvania, we experienced a period of rain. During nearly two days, more than three inches of rain fell in the surrounding area. Figure 5-66 shows that the gauging station on Penns Creek showed a rapid increase in stream discharge (given in cubic feet per second) with a relatively rapid decline following the storm event. The gauging station on the Susquehanna River at Sunbury, however, showed a more sluggish or de-

layed response as creeks from the area discharged their excess water into the river.

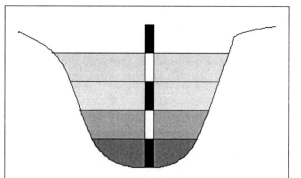

FIGURE 5-65. A diagram that shows the relationship between height of the water in a stream and its cross-sectional area. Each gauging station site on a stream must be measured and calibrated independently.

CARVING THE LANDSCAPE

I climb so high that the men and boats are lost in the black depths below and the dashing river is a rippling brook, and still there is more canyon above than below. All about me are interesting geologic records. The book is open and I can read as I run. -John Wesley Powell

The power of rivers to carve the landscape has been appreciated by geologists since the 19th century. Even before that, Leonardo da Vinci, who had a consuming interest in the science and engineering of water, considered streams and their actions. Da Vinci began an ambitious project to write an extended treatise on the motion and measurement of water that eventually grew to 35 books. In his treatise, he speculated on the force of moving water and its action in shaping the valleys in which they occur.

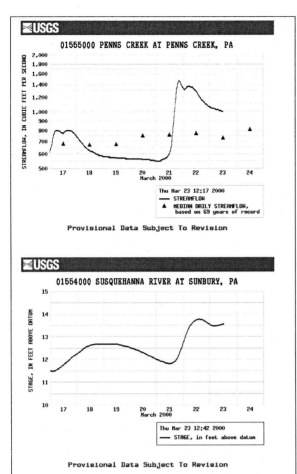

FIGURE 5-66. The top graph shows discharge measurements for Penns Creek from March 17-23, 2000. The bottom graph shows the same information for the Susquehanna River at Sunbury, PA. The data come from gauging stations maintained and operated by the USGS. Reported at http://www.usgs.gov/

By and large, geologists assumed that the earth had undergone a large upheaval or several upheavals. The cracks and surface irregularities thus formed became valleys down which rivers flowed. The catastrophic interpretation of landform formation found a challenger in James Hutton's publication of the *Theory of the Earth*. John Playfair, a mathematician and supporter of Hutton, suggested that given enough time, a stream could cut and shape its valley. In fact, he claimed in 1802 that to suppose that rivers flowed through ready-made conduits was "infinitely improbable."

Charles Lyell in his *Principles of Geology* described rivers and streams in a very modern way. He characterized the formation of meanders and transportation of sediment. Mainly, however, he stressed that streams were agents of erosion. This litany repeated itself throughout the 19th century.

One of most interesting explorers during the 19th century was Major John Wesley Powell, a Civil War veteran who had lost his right arm at the battle of Shiloh. After that he saw action at Vicksburg and in Georgia. He returned to Illinois where he taught geology at Illinois Wesleyan University. While there, he came up with a plan to explore the Colorado River and the Grand Canyon (a name given to it by Powell). In 1869 he and nine others began a 1000 mile trip from the Green River to below the Grand Canyon. The trip had many hardships, including dangerous rapids and starvation. Of the ten explorers that started, six finished the trip. His colorful account was quite readable and included numerous observations on the geology and anthropology of the region.

Powell considered the problem of the Grand Canyon. In particular, how could the Colorado River cut down through such an immense plateau? If it did, it would have had to begin as a trickle and only much later join the Colorado River when it cut down deep enough. Powell assumed that an easier explanation was that the river preceded the uplift of the plateau and remained at about the same level as the canyon rose about it. Thus, he interpreted rivers, although dynamic and changeable, as stable drainage features that literally were older than the hills.

Powell became famous and commanded respect as a consequence of his exploration. He convinced congress to fund another expedition to the canyon and ultimately became head of the U.S. Geological Survey. His confirmation of the erosive power of water and the uplift theory for the explanation of the Grand canyon became incorporated into geological dogma soon thereafter.

FIGURE 5-67. An illustration of the Grand Canyon from Powell's first expedition. From *The Exploration of the Colorado River and Its Canyons* (1895).

A STREAM IN ITS VALLEY
Let the fields and the gliding streams in the valleys delight me. -Virgil's Georgics

At the end of the 19th century the consideration of landforms and how they came about, a discipline called Geomorphology, began to consider the constructive as well as the destructive power of water in sculpting a landscape. Although geomorphologists considered other agents such as ice and wind, they considered moving water as the principal instrument of change. During the first half of the 20th century, they developed a growing understanding of the link between a stream and its valley.

One of the main spokespersons for the importance of moving water in geomorphology was (and remains) Luna Leopold, son of Aldo Leopold. He and others defined the drainage basin as a geomorphic unit. That is, a stream, its floodplain, and its valley became interrelated and inseparable components.

So, rivers periodically rise and go out of the banks of their channel and flow into the flood plain. The resulting alluvium tends to be finer silts and clays in the floodplain of the stream with coarser substrates in the channel of the stream. The point is that the floodplain belongs to the river and is part of the river. The cycles of deposition and erosion work together throughout the valley.

THE RIVER'S EDGE
The Susquehanna seizes your soul as quickly as it grabs the prow of a canoe on a bright June morning.
                                    -Susan Stranahan

Rivers tell many stories about themselves and where they have been. The Arkansas River is a large, wide prairie river. It has a broad alluvial plain through which a shifting channel courses. During some parts of the year, the water in the small channel can be reduced nearly to a trickle while most of it flows through the sand. On either side, the land rises as matched terraces. The terraces have been augmented with extra fill to make levees for flood control.

The system of dams down the river causes the river to slow down as it encounters the reservoirs behind the dams. Less turbulent water causes the river's silt load to come out of suspension and to be dumped in the reservoir basins. The consequence is that Keystone Lake and others are silting up. As more volume becomes taken with silt, the reservoir can hold less water, and it becomes less effective in mitigating floods. A time will come when the reservoir will no longer be effective and the "tamed" river might once again come charging down on the city.

I live in the Susquehanna River valley now, just below the confluence of the two branches in the upper part of Figure 5-68. Rather than the broad, flat prairie river, the Susquehanna flows over a hard bedrock. It is constrained in places by the ridges that it cuts through in its course to the Chesapeake Bay.

The Susquehanna is a beautiful river that deserves our appreciation and respect. Most of the time it is a lovely part of the background in the Central Pennsylvania area. However, there are times when it awakens and comes roaring down the valley with destruction in its path. Here, the floodplain is, indeed, part of the river, a reality that the river has made clear numerous times since I moved here 19 years ago.

The region has established an uneasy truce with the river by the construction of levees for flood control. But on the other hand, more construction (parking lots, roads, etc) which favors rapid runoff as well as significant loss of wetlands that once held water to release it slowly to the river, also has occurred during the past 19 years. As the development of the Susquehanna River floodplain increases so does the potential for greater economic impact of flooding.

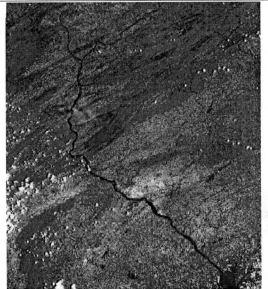

FIGURE 5-68. The lower Susquehanna River from north of Sunbury, PA to the Chesapeake Bay. Note how it cuts through the ridges of the Appalachians before it emerges to the relatively flat piedmont. This is from a Landsat image acquired in June 1977. The image is from http://www.nasa.gov/

As I write this essay, the radio announces that there is a flash flood warning. This is just another story that the river might tell. All rivers carry their stories with them. They change moment to moment but within that chaos they can be stable for millions of years. They sculpt the landscape with the power to create and to destroy.

-2000; revised 2003

References:

Bowler, Peter. 1992. *The Fontana History of the Environmental Sciences.* Fontana Press. London.

Dana, James D. 1863. *A Text-Book of Geology.* Ivison, Blakeman, Taylor, & Co. New York.

Figuier, Louis. 1867. *The World Before the Deluge.* Cassell, Petter, Galpin & Co. New York.

Huggett, Richard John. 1997. *Environmental Change, The Evolving Ecosphere.* Routledge. London.

Keller, Edward A. 1996. *Environmental Geology.* 7th ed. Prentice Hall. Upper Saddle River, NJ.

LeConte, Joseph. 1898. *Elements of Geology.* D. Appleton & Co. New York.

Leopold, Luna B. 1997. *Water, Rivers and Creeks.* University Science Books. Sausalito, CA.

Leopold, Luna B., M. Gordon Wolman, and John P. Miller. 1992. 1995 [first published 1964]. *Fluvial Processes in Geomorphology.* Dover Publications, Inc. New York.

Lyell, Charles. 1990 [originally published 1830-33]. *Principles of Geology With a new Introduction by Martin J. S. Rudwick. Vols. 1-2.* The University of Chicago Press. Chicago.

Pipkin, Bernard W. 1994. *Geology and the Environment.* West Publishing Co. St. Paul, MN.

Powell, John W. 1961 [first published in 1895]. *The Exploration of the Colorado River and Its Canyons.* Dover Publications, Inc. New York.

Stranahan, Susan Q. 1993. *Susquehanna, River of Dreams.* The Johns Hopkins University Press. Baltimore.

Tenney, Sanborn. 1860. *Geology.* E.H. Butler & Co. Philadelphia.

Trefil, James and Robert Hazen. 1998. *The Sciences, An Integrated Approach.* John Wiley and Sons, Inc. New York.

Vallentin, Antonina. 1938. *Leonardo da Vinci, The Tragic Pursuit of Perfection.* The Vicking Press. New York.

All over the globe the myriad raindrops rushing in rivers to the sea are with tireless energy working to obliterate existing continents.

-John Fiske

Questions to Think About

1. Why do you think that flood stories seem to be pan global and pan cultural?

2. Distinguish between the terms creek, river, and stream.

3. How does a meander bend form? What is its fate?

4. Distinguish between clay, silt, sand, and cobble.

5. What characteristics of the stream affect its ability to transport clay, silt, sand, and cobble?

6. How does a stream gauge work?

7. Why do creeks and the rivers that they feed respond to storm events differently?

8. Who was John Wesley Powell, and what contributions did he make to our understanding of streams?

9. What is the concept of geomorphology? How did the work of Luna Leopold give rise to it?

10. Why might flood insurance be difficult to acquire in certain places of the U.S.?

FOUND A PENNY, PICKED IT UP...

A PENNY

Found a Penny. Picked it up, and all the day I had good luck.   -Anonymous

I had spent much of my teenage years playifng in large rivers and the occasional creek (although in Oklahoma, creek-sized streams were called rivers). Anyway, I saw streams only as bodies of water in which to swim or fish, or maybe to find the odd soft-shell turtle in. Still, if asked what lived in streams, I'm sure that I would have answered fish.

That changed when I went to college. I remember a particular field trip in a general zoology class. We went to a part of Arkansas that had clean, shallow fast-moving streams. The instructor set us loose in the riffles to just see what we might find[33].

I still remember how astounded I was to see that the rocks were almost alive; mostly with small insects skittering back to the undersides of rocks when I turned them over. I collected insects and put them into alcohol. I was about to leave when I saw a strange animal on the upper surface of a stone. It was flattened and prehistoric, almost trilobite-like, in its appearance[34]. I carefully scraped it off the rock and was not very surprised when I learned that it was called a water penny (see Figure 5-69). I was much more surprised when I learned that it was the larva of a beetle in a larger group called Riffle Beetles.

One of the texts in that class was *Fresh-Water Invertebrates of the United States by Robert W. Pennak.* It was an old book even then (published in 1953),

but the information was particularly useful to help make sense of the collection that I had made that day. The text said that riffle beetles typically occur in streams "where the water is shallow and swift." That an insect could say something about the nature of the stream made quite an impression on me. Certainly, I felt very lucky to have found that "penny".

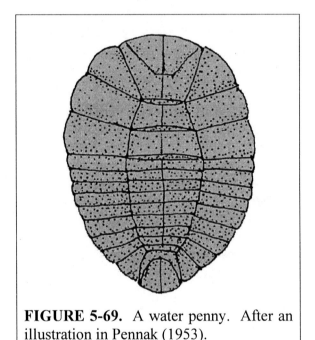

FIGURE 5-69. A water penny. After an illustration in Pennak (1953).

STRUCTURE OF STREAMS

You cannot step into the same river twice.
  -Russian proverb

The proverb alludes to the defining feature of streams, a gradient down which water flows in a valley. Thus, particular water masses constantly come in and replace those that have gone downstream. Of course, this is obvious to anyone who has contemplated a stream, but it has important consequences for the nature of the physical, chemical and biotic components of the system.

---

[33] Read *A New Story to be Told Every Day* for a description of the physical nature of streams.
[34] See *Trilobite Tales* for a description of trilobites.

Streams grow in size and amount of water transported as they flow from their headwaters to their mouths. Generally, this is because the farther a stream travels, the larger the area drained by it. This is manifest by the coalescence of small streams or tributaries to make a larger stream. Stream Ecologists and Geomorphologists define this as stream order. That is, a first order stream has no tributaries. After two first order streams join, the resulting stream is a second order stream and so on. The proviso is that a stream increases in order only after it merges with a stream that is at least the same order as itself.

Upland streams exhibit low stream order, steep gradients with turbulent water, coarse substrate, and relatively low temperature (Figure 5-70). Lowland streams exhibit high stream order, and lower gradients with less turbulent water (Figure 5-71). The substrate tends to have smaller silt particles and higher temperatures.

As streams increase in size and stream order, they drain a larger area. This may seem obvious and unnecessary to mention. Nevertheless, the larger drainage area means that a much greater area influences high order streams. Usually that translates to high order streams carrying a greater dissolved nutrient and suspended sediment load.

The nature of the flow-through system makes it stable. Such a thing would seem to be a paradox. After all, streams flow and, therefore, constantly change. But that they flow creates stability in the drainage basin that can last for many millions of years. By contrast, very few lakes seem to persist for more than tens of thousands of years[35].

FIGURE 5-70. A low order reach of Middle Creek in Central Pennsylvania.

FIGURE 5-71. A higher order reach of Middle Creek.

ECOSYSTEMS[36]
All flesh is grass.   - Isaiah 40:6.

Living things are similar to streams in that they, too, are flow-through systems. In this case, however, it is energy rather than water that flows through an organism. Generally, food (mainly proteins, fats, nucleic acids, and carbohydrates) is the form that energy takes in an organism. As liv-

---

[35] See *A New Story to be Told Every Day* for an explanation of the stability of streams.

[36] I cover the development of the Ecosystem concept in *Ecosystems: Form, Function, and Wonder.*

ing things use food, much of the energy is dissipated as heat and other forms (movement, etc). Some food is changed and converted to the formation of the organism in growth.

Ultimately, all food originates from the process of photosynthesis in which solar energy is stored in the organic (carbon-containing) compounds of food. Food produced by photosynthesis is called primary production. Thus, photosynthetic organisms are the primary producers.

All living things take food and use it for the living process. This is called respiration. Even the primary producers use food that they have made for their respiration. Fortunately, for the rest of living things, primary producers usually make more food than they use in respiration.

Those things that feed directly on the primary producers are called herbivores. Carnivores, in turn, may feed upon herbivores. However, at every step, the food molecules in the bodies of living things can be traced back to photosynthesis; so, in a very real sense, *all flesh is grass*.

The sequence of primary producer to herbivore to carnivore is called a food chain (Figure 5-72). The steps in the chain are called trophic levels. Primary producers occupy a lower trophic level than herbivores, etc. Still, this sequence is quite simple compared to the reality of a living community of organisms. Most often, the relationships of the eaters and eaten form a web or net-like structure (Figure 5-73).

A community is the collection of organisms in a given area that live together and interact in the extended food web. Organisms within the community also exist on a variety of scales. The smallest include bacteria and algae. Some algae are large and exist at the size scale of invertebrates like insects, snails, and clams. Some of the invertebrates are quite large and overlap the scale of fish. Indeed, some aquatic insects prey upon small fish. Aquatic plants tend to exceed the scale of fish. Certainly, the range from bacterium to large plant and fish represents a continuum in scale. Nevertheless, often work in streams focuses on the fish community, the attached algae community, or the aquatic insect community.

Ecologists began to consider the flow of energy through the living community. In this view, a living individual is an analog for the flow of energy through a whole community of organisms. This was called the ecosystem.

In an ecosystem, food enters the whole system via primary production. Some of that energy is expended in the respiration of the primary producers, and some is converted to new living mass of the primary producers. Of the living mass that is formed, much dies and is respired by bacteria and fungi (the decomposers), and herbivores consume much of what is left. The conversion of energy from one trophic level to the next is not very efficient so that 100g of primary producers might make less than 10g of herbivores that would make less than 1g of carnivores. The one-way energy flow through a food web makes a fairly stable system.

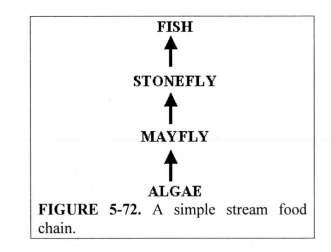

FISH

↑

STONEFLY

↑

MAYFLY

↑

ALGAE

FIGURE 5-72. A simple stream food chain.

449

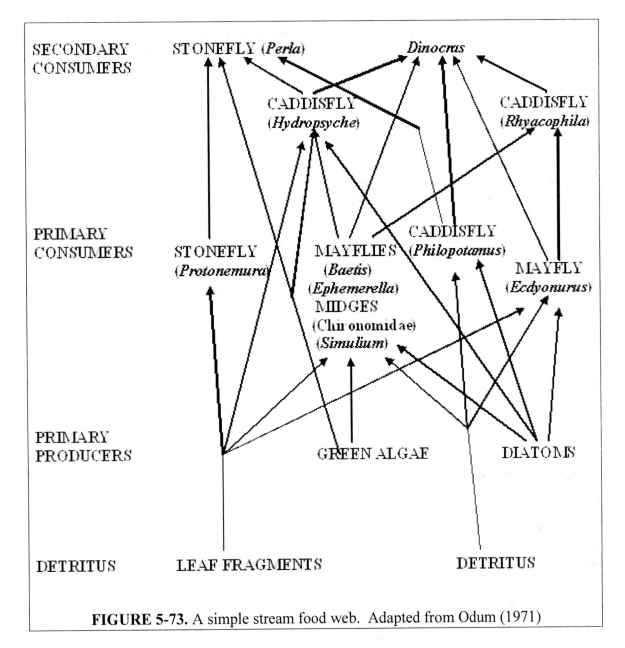

FIGURE 5-73. A simple stream food web. Adapted from Odum (1971)

Streams are unusual as ecosystems go. The upstream reaches typically are shaded with most of the food coming into the water from the outside. This usually occurs in the form of leaves and other plant debris. The paradox is that overall community respiration usually exceeds community photosynthesis in the water of an upland stream. The reverse tends to be true for lowland streams. There, primary production within the water of the stream tends to exceed community respiration.

AQUATIC INSECTS
Big things come in small packages.
-English/U.S. Proverb

Streams are governed by moving water. That is particularly true for the things that live in that moving water. Many fish accommodate that by being powerful swimmers. However, at the scale of aquatic insects, most accommodate the problem of moving water by being streamlined and attached to a solid substrate like a stone or stick. Often, they cling to the undersides of stones and avoid the problems of current and turbulence altogether. Such organisms are called benthic (bottom-dwelling) invertebrates. Choose almost any stream and examine the benthic invertebrates. The number and mass of the invertebrates will far exceed the number and mass of the fish because the benthic organisms occupy a lower trophic level than do the fish.

Taxonomically, most aquatic insects fall within a few insect orders that include mayflies (Ephemeroptera; see Figure 5-74), stoneflies (Plecoptera; see Figure 5-75), caddisflies (Trichoptera; see Figure 5-76), dragonflies (Odonata; see Figure 5-77), true bugs (Hemiptera), flies (Diptera), and beetles[37] (Coleoptera). Although other groups are represented, these are the most common ones in typical streams of the Northeastern US.

They can be classified also into four broad groups according to ecological function: shredders, collectors, scrapers and predators. Shredders feed on large items of organic debris like leaves. Collectors filter much smaller organic particles, either suspended in the water or mixed with the sediments. Scrapers feed on attached algae (periphyton). Predators feed on shredders, collectors and scrapers as well as other predators.

Most aquatic insects live in the water as larvae and in the air as adults. That reduces competition between the life stages and allows the adults to disperse far and wide in search suitable habitats in which to lay their eggs. Almost all adult insects have wings.

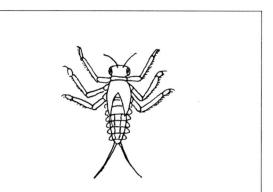

FIGURE 5-74. Mayfly larva. These have two or three bristle-like tails and visible gills on their abdomens. Almost all are herbivores as collectors or scrapers.

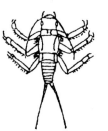

FIGURE 5-75. Stonefly larva. These have two stout bristles at the tip of the abdomen and no visible abdominal gills. Almost all are predators some are shredders.

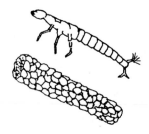

FIGURE 5-76. Caddisfly larva. They can be recognized by their habit of constructing cases of debris, sand, and silk. Mostly herbivorous as shredders, but some make silk nets with which they can collect suspended food particles.

---

[37] Beetles make up the most diverse group of animals. Likewise, those with aquatic larvae also come in many larval forms. Recall that the water penny is a beetle (Figure 5-68).

FIGURE 5-77. Dragonfly larva. All members of this group are predaceous. Dragonflies have no visible gills, but their relatives, the damselflies, have three leaf-like gills on the posterior end of the abdomen.

Upland streams are dominated by shredders and collectors. Mid-range streams have collectors and grazers. Lowland streams in which the water is slow and allows the growth of plankton encourage the growth of collectors.

Others like the flies (mosquitoes, midges, blackflies, horseflies, etc.) have aquatic larvae that are more or less maggot-like with no jointed legs. Certainly, the aquatic insect larvae are big things ecologically, but they come in small packages. They dominate upland stream reaches and mediate the flow of energy through high order streams in the lower reaches.

DIATOMS

What is worth most is often valued least.
-Aesop's Fable, The Stag at the Pool

Attached algae grow throughout a stream. However, they cover stones and any hard substrate that is given enough light and continuously wet conditions. Algae are one-celled, colonial or filamentous photosynthetic organisms. As such, they are primary producers. Of the attached algae, diatoms are among the most informative groups. In the first place, there are many species, but they

can be differentiated on the basis of the ornamentation of the cell wall. Diatom cell walls are made of silica or glass. In fact, each cell has two overlapping silica walls that might be covered with rows of holes, slits, bumps, nodules, and ribs.

Rocks that are covered with diatoms typically appear brown-green and are very slick. Usually, they impart a strong fishy odor. Nevertheless, they frequently have a variety of grazers feeding on them.

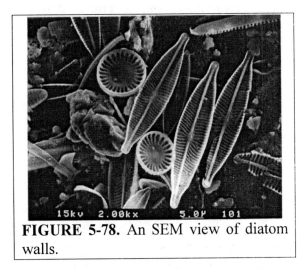

FIGURE 5-78. An SEM view of diatom walls.

Figure 5-78 shows the two main types of diatoms. Those that are elongated and bilaterally symmetrical are called the Pennate Diatoms and dominate in fresh, particularly running water environments. The circular or radially symmetrical cells are called the Centric Diatoms and they dominate in marine environments.

Well, so what? Who cares about such smelly, slimy things? They are so small that they must be seen with a microscope. How important are they? Well, in the middle and lower reaches of streams, they are very important from an ecosystem perspective. They are among the dominant primary producers. They are the "grass" that eventually could become the flesh of a trout.

IN PRAISE OF THE SUBTLE

Loving Nature is not the same as understanding it.
-Gary Larson, *There's a Hair in my Dirt.*

I have been studying streams for some years now. Often I am asked why I don't just measure the temperature or check the levels of nutrient pollutants instead of wasting my time on algae and insects. The truth of the matter is that the algae and insects say more about the water and health of the creeks that I study than chemical tests of the water can. The answer can be found in the proverb, You can never step into the same river twice. Because water flows, it changes constantly. The things that live in that water have particular tolerances for ranges in oxygen, temperature, salinity, pH, nitrate, phosphate, etc. Their occurrences integrate all environmental factors and their fluctuations over the life span of the community in question.

Most insect communities occur over a year or more. Thus, their occurrences help to understand long-term fluctuations in the stream and its health. Diatom communities grow over a matter of weeks and help to make sense of short-term fluctuations. Together, the "small things" and the "least valued" in the stream usually say more about the health of the drainage than most other measures.

I'm not sure why the water penny from so long ago left such a lasting impression on me. Then, I knew that I loved nature and was intrigued by such a strange thing clinging to a rock. However, I knew that I wanted more than the intrigue; I wanted to understand. It is the understanding that we as scientists seek. Only through understanding can we mitigate the blunders and reduce the likelihood that we will make mistakes as we seek maintain an environment for ourselves and our children.

-2000, revised 2004

References:

Bowler, Peter. 1992. *The Fontana History of the Environmental Sciences.* Fontana Press. London.

Huggett, Richard John. 1997. *Environmental Change, The Evolving Ecosphere.* Routledge. London.

Hynes, H.B.N. 1970. *The Ecology of Running Waters.* University of Toronto Press. Toronto.

Jeffries, Michael and Derek Mills. 1990. *Freshwater Ecology, Principles and Applications.* Belhaven Press. New York.

Lampert, Winfried and Ulrich Sommer. 1997. *Limnoecology, the Ecology of Lakes and Streams.* Translated by James F. Haney. Oxford University Press. Oxford.

Larson, Gary. 1998. *There's a Hair in My Dirt.* HarperCollns Publishers. New York.

Leopold, Luna B. 1997. *Water, Rivers and Creeks.* University Science Books. Sausalito, CA.

Leopold, Luna B., M. Gordon Wolman, and John P. Miller. 1992. 1995 [first published 1964]. *Fluvial Processes in Geomorphology.* Dover Publications, Inc. New York.

Odum, Eugene P. 1971. *Fundamentals of Ecology.* W.B. Saunders Co. Philadelphia.

Pennak, Robert W. 1953. *Fresh-Water Invertebrates of the United States.* The Ronald Press Co. New York.

Wargo, Matt and Jack Holt. 1998. *Determination of Stream Reaches in a Ridge and Valley Creek Using Diatom Periphyton Communities.* Journal of freshwater Ecology. 13(4): 447-456.

Questions to Think About

1. What is a water penny?

2. How does a stream typically change from its headwaters to its mouth?

3. What is an ecosystem?

4. What is the nature of the food chain and how can it be described within the eco-system concept?

5. What is the meaning of food web? How does it complicate the ecosystem con-cept?

6. Insect larvae that live in moving water have typical characteristics, even though the insect groups are only distantly related. What are those common characteris-tics?

7. What are some of the most common aquatic insects?

8. Why did I not show an illustration of a typical coleopteran (beetle)?

9. Why are diatoms important in understanding the health of a stream?

10. What did Gary Larson mean when he wrote: Loving nature is not the same as un-derstanding it. What are some implications of that statement?

THE CHILDREN OF SIR GILBERT WALKER

WRONG...AGAIN?

If the sun shines on Groundhog Day;
Half the fuel and half the hay.

-American saying.

None can deny that this past winter season has been unusually cool and snowy here in the northeast. We just went through a spell in which I recorded 19 consecutive days with high temperatures below freezing. In fact, the mean temperature in my backyard for the month of January was –4.9C. Also, during the month I recorded 26 days with some snowfall. Anyway, I am tired of shoveling snow and nursing along water pipes that might freeze again. If only we could have an early spring. With that as incentive, I await the forecast of Punxsutawney Phil, Pennsylvania's famous Groundhog. The "custom" of Groundhog Day is an import from Germany where on Candlemas Day, the midway point between the Winter Solstice and the Spring Equinox, a hedgehog predicts the likelihood of an early spring. As a predictor of weather the rotund rodent can boast a 39% accuracy rate. Although his predictions come true at about the same rate as those of the hedgehog, his accuracy is still 11% less than the penny in my pocket. Thus, I am more inclined to look for other explanations than the prognostications of a hibernating rodent.

I recall another Groundhog Day five years ago (1998) when Punxsutawney Phil saw his shadow at Gobbler's Knob and thereby "pronounced" that winter would linger 6 more weeks. That winter had been unusually warm. In fact, it seemed as if the whole winter had been an early spring. It seems that both the cold winter of 2002-03 and the warm winter of 1997-98 had the same cause, a little boy in the Pacific Ocean.

A BAD BOY

When disasters arrive, they hurt the rich but cripple the poor.

-Tim Radford, Kenya 1997.

The weather has not been uniformly mischievous across the globe during the winter of 2002-03. Indeed, the onset of mid fall rains and heavy winter snows here in the Northeast have brought welcome relief from an extended drought that we have suffered. Such global climatic changes from the norm seem to occur with some regularity. Recall the winter of 1997-98. For us that time was relatively warm and nearly storm-free. However, conditions were not similarly benign across the globe. In fact, it produced a mosaic of global effects, most of them bordering on disastrous. The West Coast and southeastern US experienced much wetter than normal winters and more severe storms. Similarly, the coasts of Ecuador and Peru were wetter than normal while Australia and Southeast Asia suffered extreme drought. All in all, though, despite the money that I saved in home heating bills that winter, the global damage wrought topped 8 trillion dollars.

The standard whipping boy for such global climatic anomalies has been called El Niño (or the boy). This weather pattern received its name in the 19th century because of the unusually wet winters that manifest themselves in South and Central America during the celebration of another December event, Christmas. So, El Niño refers to the Christ child, and records in western South America going back to the early 18th century suggest that El Niño occurs about every 8-10 years.

El Niño is a product of changes in the central Pacific Ocean where the water becomes unusually warm. This sets in motion a cascade of global-scale changes that impact weather in all parts of the world, not just the Pacific basin. An explanation of these changes and their impacts on global weather requires an understanding of the unusual density and thermal properties of water.

A HEAT SINK

A great advance in the theory of heat was made when Joseph Black (1760) introduced the distinction between temperature and the quantity of heat.

-G. Allard 1964

Water has an unusually high Specific Heat. That is, it can absorb large amounts of heat without changing temperature. For water, 1 gram (also 1ml) water absorbs 1 calorie of heat to rise 1 degree centigrade. In general, Specific Heat is calories per gram to raise the temperature one degree. So, water has a specific heat of 1 (1calorie/1gram). Most substances like metals have specific heat values in the range of 0.2 or lower.

The concept of specific heat was first stated by Joseph Black (1728-99), a Scottish physician who also studied chemistry and physics. [Among other things Black discovered that carbon dioxide was a product of respiration, fermentation; and burning charcoal. Also, he discovered that carbon dioxide when dissolved in water behaved as an acid; and that it is probably found in the atmosphere.] Also, Black recognized that water absorbed heat as it changed form from ice to water or from water to steam. Black called this phenomenon Latent Heat and it is quite high for water. Ice at 0C must absorb 79.72 calories per gram to change to water at 0C. Water at 100C must absorb 540 calories per gram as it evaporates. So, the total of heat (as calories) held by water is much higher than by metals or most other substances at the same temperature.

These properties of high specific heat and latent heat mean that water resists changes in temperature, and moderates the climates of lands near water, a property that G. E. Hutchinson called "thermal inertia". So, islands and coastal areas tend to have climates with fewer sudden shifts in temperature and dampened extremes in summer and winter. This effect is apparent even in inland areas, particularly near large lakes. The climate of Michigan, a state surrounded by the Great Lakes, is much more moderate than that of Wyoming. Similarly, areas with humid climates are more moderate than desert areas.

TABLE 5-2. Relationship between average July high and low temperatures and relative humidity of selected U.S. cities between 41 and 42 degrees North.

City	temperature range	relative humidity
Chicago, IL	17-29	54%
Cheyenne, WY	12-29	39%
Providence, RI	17-28	62%

The concept of thermal inertia can be seen in the relationship between humidity and temperature range for July as indicated in Table 1. Both Providence and Chicago are near bodies of water and have nearly identical average temperature ranges (11 and 12C, respectively). Cheyenne is inland plains with a lower relative humidity and a higher range in temperature (17C).

Water experiences remarkable density (weight per unit volume) properties. Water is 1 gram per cubic centimeter at around 4 degrees centigrade, and it becomes less dense as it gets warmer. Waters of different densities resist mixing to the degree that whole rivers like the Gulf Stream (warm water) flow within the cooler North Atlantic.

Water's most anomalous property of density occurs below 4 degrees centigrade. That is, water becomes less dense. Indeed, ice at 0 degrees centigrade is 8.5% lighter than water at 0 degrees centigrade. Almost all other substances are denser as solids than liquids. If water did not have this strange property, most of the planet's water would be locked away as a frozen "bedrock" below 200 meters in the ocean.

HOLD THE ANCHOVIES

Scientifically, the study of El Niño has led us to a genuinely new understanding of the nature and strength of the interplay between the earth's oceans and atmosphere, and the implications this has for all aspects of climate.

-Stephen Zebiak 1994

Because the earth turns toward the east, water tends to be slightly displaced to the west. Cold subsurface water then moves up to replace the displaced water on the western edges of continents. This phenomenon can be clearly seen off the west coast of Peru and Chile where cold, nutrient-rich deep ocean water rises to the surface. Photosynthetic plankton make use of the nutrients and provide rich grazing for zooplankton and fish, particularly anchovies.

In 1904 after several devastatingly dry years in India, Sir Gilbert T. Walker (1868-1958), a director-general of British observatories in India, was given the task of determining a way to predict years of weak monsoons. He poured over weather data from across the Indian and Pacific Oceans. Finally, in the 1920's he found an almost mirror-image relationship between the air pressure on Tahiti (the eastern Pacific) and Darwin, Australia (western Pacific). These fluctuations or oscillations in air pressure also correlated with the monsoons of India. When the pressure over Tahiti was high and low over Darwin, India could expect a typical monsoon season. He explained this phe-

nomenon by the normal prevailing flow of air, and Walker called it the Southern Oscillation.

Jacob Bjerknes (1897-1975), a meteorologist whose father began the research that defined the polar-temperate air mass boundaries and led to the discovery of the northern jet stream, defined mechanisms by which temperate cyclones determined the weather[38] over the northern temperate zone.

A cyclone is a large region of rotating air. For example, in the Northern Hemisphere air in a low pressure cell have rising air and turn in a counter clockwise direction. As the air rises and cools, water in it condenses, and clouds are formed. Low pressure cells or cyclones are storm cells, the extreme of which develop into hurricanes (in the Atlantic Ocean; see Figure 5-79).

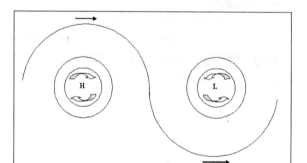

FIGURE 5-79. The movement of air in a surface anticyclone (high pressure cell) and cyclone (low pressure cell). The high pressure cell (H) is formed by converging air that falls and rotates in a clockwise direction. The low pressure cell (L) is formed by diverging air that rises from the surface and rotates in a counter-clockwise direction.

Air in a high-pressure cell sinks, and in so doing, the circulation about the point of highest pressure is in a clockwise direction. Thus, they are called anticyclones. Since in a high pressure cell

---

[38] Other essays on weather and climate in this collection include: *Butterflies, Ice Ages,* and *Clouds: the Keys to Understanding Climate, Weather, and the Hydrologic Cycle.*

the cool air sinks and warms and cool air can hold less water than warm air, the air in an anti-cyclone tends to be relatively dry. That manifests itself as clear skies. The weather-making cells progress across the globe by winds formed at the zones where major air masses collide. That is what happens at the boundary between the Northern Temperate Westerlies and the cold (and denser) northern polar air mass where the difference in pressure creates a narrow westerly river of air called a jet stream. Temperate cyclones are moved along by the motion of the jet stream. Also, cyclones can distort the boundaries of the jet stream so that it has ripples that circle the globe, and cause incursions of cold air deep into the south (or north from the perspective of the southern hemisphere).

Bjerknes put the air pressure and sea temperature components together and explained El Niño as a coupled event. He called it ENSO (El Niño Southern Oscillation) in recognition of that. During normal years the atmospheric circulation moves westward over the equatorial Pacific Ocean. Air above the cold water in the east is chilled and, therefore, holds less water. However, the air picks up moisture on its westward trip across the Pacific and is carried very high with an associated low pressure on the western side of the Pacific. This is the wet region. High pressure and dry air are associated with the regions of sinking air. During such normal years, the low level trade wind with a very high level counter circulation is called the Walker Circulation (Figure 5-80).

During times of ENSO the eastern equatorial Pacific Ocean becomes so warm that it prevents the cold nutrient-rich water from rising to the surface. The resulting diminished growth of photosynthetic plankton produces a cascade of effects that cause the anchovy fisheries to collapse. Anomalous Walker Circulation associated with ENSO is a pattern of rising air that forms over the central Pacific

(Figure 5-81). This produces unusually wet winters over the central pacific and the west coast of South America. Also, the western Pacific, which receives moist air from the Walker circulation generated trade winds, is left dry.

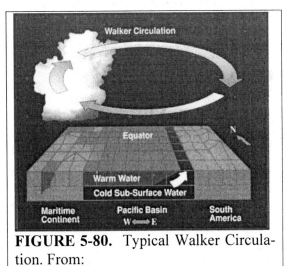

FIGURE 5-80. Typical Walker Circulation. From: http://nsipp.gsfc.nasa.gov/enso/

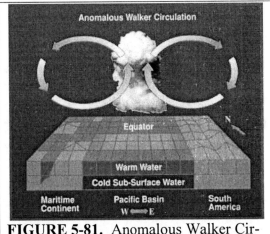

FIGURE 5-81. Anomalous Walker Circulation associated with El Niño Southern Oscillation. From: http://nsipp.gsfc.nasa.gov/enso/

Warmer ocean temperatures associated with El Niño have been associated with periods of prolonged and intensified Pacific hurricanes. At the same time Atlantic hurricanes were weaker due to weaker high-level winds and stronger low level equatorial winds that served to "shear off" the growing storms before they fully developed.

The 1997-98 ENSO event was much stronger than any previously recorded. It caused more damage than the devastating 1982-83 event. The area of unusually warm water in the mid Pacific exceeded 1.5-2 times the size of the continental U.S. There, water was as high as 3.5 to 5C above normal.

It seems that the reverse phenomenon is also possible. That is, the eastern Pacific Ocean can become cooler than normal. At first (and still some of the literature) called this Anti-El Niño. However since this literally means the Anti-Christ, meteorologists chose to call it La Niña, the girl.

La Niña is not entirely benign. This weather pattern can send stronger than normal trade winds to the west. As a consequence, Australia can receive record rainfalls as it did during the La Niña events of 1973-74 and 1988-89. Brisbane's worst flooding in this century occurred in January 1974 and in inland Australia in March 1989.

The ultimate cause of these climatic fluctuations remains a mystery. It does appear that ocean levels on the eastern side of the Pacific Ocean may be associated with the oscillation. A possible scenario is that the cold deep Pacific water sloshes back and forth in a slow oscillation. When the cold water is close to the surface in the east, the cold current is strong and climate is normal or experiences La Niña conditions. On the other hand when the deep water moves away from the surface, warmer than normal conditions prevail and El Niño prevails. Such deep ocean waves would explain the periodicity of ENSO. However, the cause of such a wave is another big question. It might be as simple as the action of earth's rotation on the water in its basins. Other causes have been suggested. Even Darwin suggested that the periodic warming of the Peruvian current could be due to volcanic action in the Pacific basin.

ATLANTIC WEATHER MAKERS

We've been aware of the NAO for years, but we haven't been able to come up with a way to forecast it. 'We just don't really have a grasp of the physical mechanisms.
-Vernon Kousky of the National Weather Service's Climate Prediction Center 1997.

A similar kind of pattern of High-Low oscillation seems to exist in the North Atlantic. It is called the North Atlantic Oscillation (NAO), and it is one of the most important weather makers for the USA, Canada and Europe. Like Walker's Southern Oscillation, the North Atlantic Oscillation is a pattern of areas of high and low air pressures and winds over the North Atlantic that is most prominent in winter. Unlike El Niño, which lasts around a year and occurs every three to seven years, the North Atlantic Oscillation is stable for around a decade before it changes. From 1980 to 1994 the NAO sent mild Atlantic winds across Europe in the winter, a pattern that made the seasons mild and wet in northern Europe. It also made southern Europe and parts of North Africa dry.

Data from the years 1899 to 1993 show a strong correlation between the NAO and the presence of European warmth and northwest Atlantic cold. The strongest correlations in this century have occurred since 1980. So, it seems clear that the NAO is largely responsible for the unusually warm and wet winters observed across much of Europe over the past 15 years. Normally, this pattern produces mild winters in the northeastern U. S. However, when the pressure over Iceland rises and the pressure over the Azores falls, Arctic air can invade the northeastern U.S. as it did in 1995 and triggered the snowy winter of 1995-96 in the northeast and brought unusually cold weather to Europe and rain to southern Europe.

The big question about the NAO its relationship with ocean temperatures. That is, is it merely an atmospheric phenomenon or is it connected with ocean temperatures as is ENSO. This is very important as it relates to prediction because ocean temperatures change slowly and would allow meteorologists to anticipate a climatic shift as they did early in 1997 for that ENSO event.

As it happens, the NAO is on the end of perhaps the most well-know ocean current, the Gulf Stream. Benjamin Franklin first charted this river of warm water. As it flows northward into the cooler water of the North Atlantic, it gives up its heat slowly and mixes as its density approaches that of the rest of the surrounding ocean. Still, the core of the current is visible in infrared satellite imagery off southeastern Canada.

The warm water courses across the Atlantic and spills over the British Isles giving them a much milder climate than their position on earth warrants. For example, Britain is as far north as Labrador and Hudson Bay.

There is some evidence that heavier than usual amounts of rain in the Caribbean and equatorial Atlantic might produce pockets of cool water in the Gulf Stream. Upon their arrival in the northern British Isles, the pockets of cooler water could cause cooler weather and heavier than normal snow falls in northern Europe. If they cause a change in the North Atlantic Oscillation, the impact could also be felt in the northeastern U.S.

CLIMATE AND OUR CHILDREN

When the history books are written 50 years from now, the most important thing NASA will have done is provided the information to the political establishment about what are the causes, sources and forces of global change so we can mitigate them and have further hope for our children on this planet

.-Daniel S. Golden 2000.

The understanding of local weather and its connection to global patterns came slowly. Local data collection was spotty until the 20th century. Indeed, if local weather data had not been collected and published, Walker would not have been able to find his Southern Oscillation. Since that time the understanding of global patterns has grown at a geometric pace. No technology has been as useful in understanding region-wide and global weather patterns as much as space-based data collection and observation. Mainly this is accomplished by a fleet of weather satellites positioned over the globe. Although expensive, the return on our investment in space hardware and exploration has been a phenomenal increase in our understanding of weather-related phenomena, and with understanding comes better means of prediction (certainly better than can be offered by Punxsutawney Phil). That translates to saving lives, resources, and property. Now we recognize that such phenomena are global and have had significant impacts on human history. Although much is known about ENSO, many more long-term questions and its climatic relatives have yet to be answered. Perhaps the most important question is the relationship between ENSO and global climate change, a question that cannot be answered without adequate continued investment. The story of ENSO is one of ongoing discovery. It is a part of the story that Daniel Golden referred to and its understanding has implications for all people who live on this on this planet, for their children, and for those who are yet to be born.

El Niño and La Niña, the climatic children, have been known for several hundred years. Sir Gilbert Walker provided a connection and Jacob Bjerknes supplied the theoretical perspective that allowed meteorologists to make the association between mid Pacific water temperatures and weather patterns in Southeast Asia. So, in a sense, El Niño, La Niña, and their north Atlantic cousins are Sir Gilbert Walker's children. Unless we develop an adequate understanding of the phenomena, they will become like the children described by Shakespeare in Henry V, v, ii, who...*grow like savages,...*

-1998, revised 2003

References:

Aguado, Edward and James E. Burt. 2001. *Understanding Weather and Climate.* 2nd edition. Prentice Hall. Upper Saddle River, NJ.

Caviedes, Cesar N. 2001. *El Niño in History, Storming Through the Ages.* University Press of Florida. Gainesville.

Fox, Karen Celia. 1998. *El Niño's Atlantic Cousin.* Earth 7(2):20-21.

Goody, Richard. 1995. *Principles of Atmospheric Physics and Chemistry.* Oxford University Press. New York.

Hutchinson, G. Evelyn. 1957. *A Treatise on Limnology. Volume 1. Geography, Physics and Chemistry.* John Wiley & Sons, Inc. New York.

Monastersky, Richard. 1995. *Tropical trouble, two decades of Pacific warmth have fired up the globe.* Science News 147(10): 154-155.

Monastersky, Richard. 1997. *El Niño cooks up unusual hurricane season.* Science News 152(16): 245.

Monastersky, Richard. 1997. *Spying on. El Niño, the struggle to predict the pacific prankster.* Science News 152(17): 268-270.

Monastersky, Richard. 1998. *As globe warms, hurricanes may speed up.* Science News 153(7): 103.

Neuberger, Hans and John Cahir. 1969. *Principles of Climatology, A Manual in Earth Science.* Holt, Rinehart, & Winston, Inc. NY.

Trefil, James and Robert Hazen. 2000. *The Sciences, An Integrated Approach.* 2nd editionn. John Wiley & Sons, Inc. New York.

Wetzel, Robert G. 2001. *Limnology.* 3rd ed. Academic Press. NY.

Questions to Think About

1. How is El Nino measured?

2. Why does ice float?

3. What is Walker Circulation?

4. How does El Nino differ from La Nina?

5. What did G. E. Hutchinson mean by "thermal inertia"?

6. Who was Sir Gilbert Walker?

7. How does El Nino affect the anchovy catch off Chile and Peru?

8. What is oscillating in Walker's *Southern Oscillation*?

9. What could be the consequence of a Northern Oscillation in the Atlantic Ocean??

10. Light provides heat for water as well as energy for what living process?

NATURE'S STOREHOUSE

HOOVER DAM

This morning I came, I saw, and I was conquered, as everyone would be who sees for the first time this great feat of mankind.

-Franklin Delano Roosevelt, 1935 at the dedication of Hoover Dam

I stood on the top of Hoover Dam and leaned over to see it gracefully plunge 727 feet to the Colorado River below, almost like a frozen waterfall. I had to fight my sense of vertigo to look at it so long, but I just couldn't take my eyes off of it. Hoover Dam was more than a structure, it was a monument to technology in the desert (see Figure 5-82). Hoover Dam's primary purpose was flood control and to maintain a controlled and reliable source of water that supplied more than 25 million people throughout the southwest via a system of canals. However, other products of the dam were non-resource-depleting electric power and Lake Mead National Recreation Area.

FIGURE 5-82. Aerial view of Hoover Dam. Note how narrow and deep the canyon is. The lower part of Lake Mead can just be seen above the dam. The Colorado River is in the lower part of the photograph. Courtesy of the U.S. Department of the Interior, Bureau of Land Reclamation.

The task of building the dam was one of the largest construction projects attempted by the U.S. President Coolidge signed the Boulder Canyon Project Act on December 21, 1928 and President Hoover signed a bill making the first appropriation available for commencing work. Finally, on March 11, 1931 contracts were awarded to Six Companies Inc., of San Francisco, to build the dam for $49,000,000, the largest government contract up to that time. As expensive as that sounds, it was less than 6% of the cost of the MGM Hotel and Casino in nearby Las Vegas.

In addition to the problems of supplying the materials for the dam, the contractors had to recruit, house and feed thousands of workers in the desert. They built Boulder City for this purpose. At the peak of construction, more than 5,000 people were employed on the gigantic project in Black Canyon. Ninety-six workers died building the dam. Work continued nonstop and was completed in four years. President Roosevelt dedicated Hoover Dam on September 30, 1935. Upon its completion Hoover Dam backed up the Colorado, Virgin and Muddy rivers to form Lake Mead.

According to the U.S. Department of Interior, the completed dam is 727 feet high, 1,244 feet long, 660 feet thick at the base, and 45 feet thick at the top. It weighs 5,500,000 tons and contains 3,250,000 cubic yards of concrete. The total volume of the dam exceeds that of the largest Egyptian pyramid. It has two spillways that protect the dam and powerhouse from overflow, and they are each large enough to float a battleship.

Lake Mead, named for a former U.S. Commissioner of Reclamation Elwood C. Mead, is one of the largest reservoirs in the world (see Figure 5-83). At the dam, the water is over 500 feet deep. When full, the lake is 110 miles long and reaches into the lower part of the Grand Canyon. It has a shoreline of more than 550 miles and a surface area of 255 square miles. Lake Mead has a capacity of 28.6 million acre feet of water. An acre-foot is equivalent to one acre of land covered by one foot of water, or the amount of water used by a family of four in a year. In fact, Lake Mead contains enough water to cover Connecticut 10 feet deep.

FIGURE 5-83. A Landsat7 image of Lake Meade. Hoover Dam is at the far left. The Colorado River enters at the far right. Image from: http://www.nasa.gov.centers/goddard/

In 1963 the Colorado River was impounded once again. Glen Canyon Dam was closed, and Lake Powell a reservoir upriver from the Grand Canyon and below the confluence of the San Juan and Colorado Rivers, began to fill. The lake that was formed became the second largest reservoir in the United States. It is about 187 miles long with 96 side canyons, and it has 1960 miles of shoreline, more than all of New England.

Lake Powell, like Lake Mead, provides for water storage, flood control, recreation, and hydroelectric power to the southwestern U.S. Despite this, some now question its advantages

against loss. The Navajo nation lost two of its most sacred sites and others have been made inaccessible. Other historically important sites have also been lost.

Sediment that is suspended in the turbulent Colorado River used to travel from the muddy head waters to the Gulf of California in Mexico. Because reservoirs are much less turbulent than free-flowing rivers, they hold much less suspended sediment. Thus, the reservoirs on the Colorado (or any river for that matter) function as sediment traps. The effect has been dramatic. Average sediment concentrations in the lower Colorado dropped from 1,500 parts per million (ppm) to around 7ppm. This has led to the net loss of beaches and sandbars (necessary for many native fish species) along the Colorado.

The lower, more regular flow below Glen Canyon Dam has led to a more extensive growth of marsh plants along the banks of the Colorado. Whereas these increased riparian zones have become added habitat for native and exotic (non-native) species, their full impact has yet to be appreciated.

Water from Glen Canyon Dam is drawn from deep in the lake. Deep water tends to be cold and vary little in temperature. Although this is ideal for many exotic trout species, native warm water species suffer from the cold, clearer water. At least three native fish species have disappeared from the river below Lake Powell. Other native fish like the Humpback Chub, the Flannelmouth Sucker, and Razorback Sucker struggle to survive and compete with

The Bureau of Land Reclamation, the agency responsible for management of Lake Powell, has initiated a $60 million project that will pull water from the lake at different depths to simulate seasonal temperature variations. Given the problems with Lake Powell, the Sierra Club has called for Lake Powell to be drained to restore Glen Canyon and address the environmental problems posed by the dam. Although this political solution has gained momentum in the southwest, too many people rely on the water and power provided by Lake Powell. Future management scenarios will have to address these environmental realities one way or another.

Maybe, the greatest environmental problem posed by the impoundments on the Colorado River is the loss of water to the river itself. Not only is water removed for consumption by Arizona, Nevada, and Southern California, but also large bodies of water in the desert lose much of their water to evaporation. Thus, the mighty 1,400-mile Colorado River is reduced to an intermittent trickle where it crosses the border into Mexico.

ECOLOGY AND TECHNOLOGY

Modern technology
Owes ecology
An apology.   -Alan M. Eddison

The Colorado River story points out the complexity of environmental issues and the different purposes that people of good faith have in studying and managing the environment. Today, the media presents ecologists, environmental engineers, and environmentalists almost interchangeably. However, their underlying philosophies make them very different.

Ecology[39] is a science and generally considered a branch of Biology. By science, I mean that the purpose of ecological work is to explain how nature works. For example, an appropriate ecological question would be to define the current

range of the Razorback Sucker in the Colorado River. How is that range related to ambient temperature? What do they eat? What factors are most important in successful spawn?

In some ways, Ecology is both the youngest and oldest of the Biological disciplines. Greek philosophers like Aristotle described living things in nature. By and large, this descriptive method was called Natural History. By the 18th and 19th centuries, what could be called ecology was a kind of descriptive natural history called Natural Theology. In this view, nature is in perfect balance as provided by the Creator. (In general, the view of nature in perfect balance is not very different from the messages in most nature programs on television).

Increasingly through the 19th century explanations of nature were reduced to aspects of physics and chemistry, a trend that Ernst Mayr called physicalism. Alexander von Humboldt (1805) was one of the first biologists to employ a physical measurement as an explanation for the distribution of plants when he noted that plant distributions were determined by temperature.

Darwinian evolution[40] was another major influence on ecology. It was a major challenge to Natural Theology in that the "balance of nature" was the consequence of cruel struggle, competition and random fate. In the latter part of the 19th century Ernst Haeckel, a German evolutionary biologist coined the term ecology. He meant it as the science that studies the economy of nature. Today, the dominant view of ecology is that of an economic model with energy and nutrients as the currency of exchange. In general, the science of ecology can be divided into two subdisciplines: autecology and synecol-

---

[39] The concept of ecology is described in *Found a Penny...* and *Ecosystems: Form, Function, and Wonder.*

[40] See the essays *Parasites and Darwin's Intellectual Triumph* and *The Mentor and the Heretic.*

ogy. Autecology is the ecology of a species and is the approach most often taken by zoologists (biologists who study animals). Synecology is the ecology of communities or associations of living things and is most often the approach taken by botanists (biologists who study everything else).

Technology, though often confused with science, really is just the manipulation of nature to solve a practical problem. The problem could be as simple as how to attach a stack of papers or as complex as how to land on the moon. Throughout the bulk of the history of humankind, technology has been separated from science. However, in the past 200 years the association of science and technology has become very strong, so strong in fact that it is difficult to separate them. Engineers are technologists who have a strong foundation in mathematics and the physical-chemical scientific principles that underlie their particular disciplines.

An environmental engineer could design drainage for a town, construct wetlands, or manage a lake like those who are responsible for the management of Lakes Powell and Mead. For efficient solutions to problems, it is necessary to simplify the problem as much as possible. Simplifying complex systems can lead to unforeseen problems like the decrease in suspended sediment below Glen Canyon Dam led to a decrease in sandbars and a decrease in native fish species. However, it is the environmental engineers who are seeking solutions based on designing new outflow structures from dams and varying the amount of water that is being discharged.

Environmentalism grew out of the conservation movement that had its roots in the 19th century. This is a political movement and it is based (somewhat) on scientific principles. Ecologists find much environmental talk somewhat disturbing because the basic belief is that nature is a whole, almost living entity. There is almost a mystical or religious aspect to some of their writings. By and large, the environmentalists view the reductionist approach of ecologists with great suspicion. Conversely, holistic theories that come from within ecology like the Gaia Hypothesis of James Lovelock and the Biophilia Hypothesis of E. O. Wilson are seen as too mystical.

Environmentalists range from those who promote proper management to a complete "return to nature." Sometimes the "return to nature" is based on a distorted view of what nature is. Good intentions that are based on emotion rather than science can lead to bad consequences. Consider the Arbor Day call to plant a tree. Rather than promote the planting of native vegetation, the Arbor Day association treats trees as trees. Out of a whole bundle of five plants that I received from the Arbor Day association several years ago, the only plant that was native to Central Pennsylvania was the Flowering Dogwood. Indeed, the Arbor Day movement began as an attempt to plant trees across the treeless plains, a sentiment that I do not share.

Still, it is the environmentalists that argue the value of endangered species and environmental problems in the public forum. They make the public aware of endangered fishes like the Razorback Sucker, and they champion causes like the draining of Lake Powell.

FISH STORIES

World-wide lakes and rivers contain at least 8,400 fish species, or roughly 40% of the Earth's species of fish that have been identified to date. In turn, this means that these freshwater ecosystems support almost one-quarter of the planet's known biodiversity in less than 0.01% of the planet's water.

-Norman Myers, 1997

The stories of fishes in freshwater ecosystems are mixtures of successes and failures. That such a small percentage of the Earth's total water (0.01%) contains so many species of fish (~8,400) makes such systems particularly vulnerable to changes. As with the Colorado River stories, technology, science, and culture continue to clash over inland waters with their species caught in the struggle. Such struggles now occur in the Susquehanna River and Africa's Lake Victoria.

The Susquehanna River, one of the largest rivers in the eastern U.S. is the major contributor to the Chesapeake Bay. At the turn of the 20th century and earlier, the Susquehanna supported an extensive Shad fishery, now they are all but gone.

The American Shad is in the herring family and important to eastern rivers because it is anadromous. That is, shad can change from marine to freshwater and migrate up rivers to spawn, very much like salmon. Young shad grow and mature for 4-5 years in the ocean and then return to the rivers in which they were spawned. The migrations used to occur in the spring and the catch at the end of the last century amounted to nearly 27million tons along the eastern seaboard. Now, however, the Conowingo Dam near the mouth of the Susquehanna River effectively eliminates the movement of shad upstream.

There was a bitter debate about the responsibilities of those managing the Conowingo Dam to provide help to the migrating fishes. In 1987 a federal mandate declared that the managers of the dam must assist the shad in their migrations. This was a triumph of the partnership between ecologists (who worked out the biology of the shad and their ecological requirements), environmentalists (who popularized the plight of the shad and made it a political question), and the engineers (who constructed lifts, and fish ladders to assist the shad in their passage over Conowingo Dam). The shad have responded and are beginning to be seen once again in the Susquehanna River.

A less optimistic prognosis exists for the fishes of Lake Victoria, the world's largest tropical lake and source of the Nile River. Lake Victoria and its associated lakes (Lake Malawi, etc.) have had water in them for the past four million years. In that relatively short period (geologically speaking) a bewildering array of fish in the cichlid family has evolved. Some estimate range as high as 1,500 species of cichlids in the same period of time that saw our own line separate from the other apes.

Called furu by those who live around Lake Victoria, the native cichlids are rather small (rarely more than 6 inches long; see Figure 5-84). They have evolved myriad feeding strategies. Some feed on attached algae. Some feed on insects or other furu. Some have specialized to eat the scales from the sides of fishes. There is a hint that at least one species is adapted to eat the eyes of living cichlids.

Many cichlids are mouth brooders. That is, the male entices a female to lay eggs in a nest and then drives her away. After he fertilizes the eggs (often of several females), he takes them into his mouth and holds them until they hatch. The fry continue to use the adult's mouth as a refuge until they are big enough to fend for themselves. One furu has exploited this as a food source and sucks the young out of the mouths of brooding males.

FIGURE 5-84. A cichlid from Lake Victoria .

Lake Victoria is shared by the central African countries of Uganda, Kenya, and Tanzania. In a move to boost the economy, these countries began to stock the lake with Nile Perch, a large (up to 6 feet long) predatory fish about 10-15 years ago. Very quickly the exotic Nile Perch began to take over the lake. When the perch were caught, their stomachs were filled with furu. Within several years the relative number of furu began to decline precipitously. Now, up to 300 species of furu may be extinct in Lake Victoria.

Nile Perch have not declined as the furu disappeared. They shifted to other food sources, shortening and simplifying the local food chains. An international effort is now underway to catalog the furu and to save them by sending threatened species to aquaria for captive breeding programs. How do the Africans feel about this change? By and large, they prefer to catch the large Nile Perch. Some Tanzanians have begun to call them "savior".

Unfortunately, the Nile Perch fishery may not be sustainable. With the loss of furu and simplification of the lake system have come other environmental problems. The lake now regularly experiences blooms of bluegreen algae, photosynthetic bacteria. When the blooms die back, they settle into the deeper portions of the lake where their decomposition uses up the oxygen. Certainly, Lake Victoria is a very different lake from what it was before the introduction of the Nile Perch.

NATURE'S STOREHOUSE
You may note that the waters are Nature's storehouse, in which she locks up her wonders.
　　　　-Isaak Walton, *The Compleat Angler*

Clearly, rivers and lakes are nature's storehouse, with their treasures of biological diversity, clean energy, and useful water. That is why we try to lock them up behind dams and cultivate their wealth. However, without adequate knowledge, we cannot begin to anticipate potential consequences of our actions. Barry Commoner expressed the problem in his first law of ecology: *Everything is connected to everything else*[41]. In simplifying complex systems, we can forget or ignore a multitude of connections that exist within the water, between the water and the land, and between human culture and the ecosystem. I write as an aquatic ecologist and fully acknowledge my bias in expressing its importance. However, it is the ecology that informs environmental management and advises environmental action.
　　　　　　　　-1998, revised 2005

References:

---

[41] Barry Commoner's 4 Laws of Ecology are:
1. Everything is connected to everything else.
2. Everything must go somewhere.
3. Nature knows best.
4. There is no such thing as a free lunch.

Commoner, Barry. 1971. *The Closing Circle, Nature, Man, and Technology.*

Goldschmidt, Tijs. 1996. *Darwin 's Dreampond, Drama in Lake Victoria* . MIT Press. Cambridge , Mass.

Huntley, Brian J. 1988. *Conserving and Monitoring Biotic Diversity, Some African Examples.* In: E.O. Wilson, ed. *Biodiversity.* National Academy Press, Washington, D.C. pp. 248-260.

Hutchinson, G. Evelyn. 1957. *A Treatise on Limnology. Volume 1. Geography, Physics and Chemistry.* John Wiley & Sons, Inc. New York .

Leopold, Luna B. 1997. *Water, Rivers and Creeks.* University Science Books. Sausalito , CA .

Mayr, Ernst. 1997. *This is Biology, the Science of the Living World.* The Belknap Press of Harvard University Press. Cambridge , Mass.

Myers, Norman. 1997. *The Rich Diversity of Biodiversity Issues.* In: M.L.

Reaka-Kudla, D.E. Wilson, & E.O. Wilson, ed. *Biodiversity II.* Joseph Henry Press. Washington, D.C. pp. 125-138.

Stranahan, Susan Q. 1993. *Susquehanna, River of Dreams* . Johns Hopkins . Baltimore and London .

Sweeney, Mary E. 1996. *Malawi Cichlids: Mbuna.* YearBOOKS, Inc. Neptune , NJ .

Thornton , Kent W., Bruce L. Kimmel, and Forrest E. Payne. 1990. *Reservoir Limnology: Ecological Perspectives.* John Wiley and Sons, Inc. New York .

Trefil, James and Robert Hazen. 1995. *The Sciences, An Integrated Approach.* John Wiley & Sons, Inc. New York .

Wetzel, Robert G. 2001. *Limnology, Lake and River Ecosystems.* 3nd ed. Saunders College Publishing. New York .

Zimmerman, Michael. 1995. *Science, Nonscience, and Nonsense, Approaching Environmental Literacy.* Johns Hopkins University Press. Baltimore .

Questions to Think About

1. Why was Hoover Dam built?

2. Why was Glen Canyon Dam built?

3. In what ways did the two dams change the nature of the Colorado River?

4. How did the changes impact some of the biota, particularly fish?

5. What are the differences between an ecologist, an engineer, and an environmentalist?

6. What are the two different types of ecology?

7. Why is the biodiversity of inland water so delicate and so important?

8. How did the Conowingo Dam impact the American Shad in the Susquehanna River? What changes are being made to mitigate the problems?

9. How did the introduction of the Nile Perch affect the biota of Lake Victoria? Is there a possibility of mitigating their impact?

10. What are Barry Commoner's Laws of Ecology? Do they seem to have been formulated for ecologists, engineers, or environmentalists?

CHAPTER 6: CHANGING IDEAS IN BIOLOGY

I have walked over these roads;
I have thought of them living.
-Ezra Pound *Provencia Deserta*

These living arches grace the path to the large church in the square of Zarcero in central Costa Rica. Like the ribs of an ancient beast, the trimmed plants have a segmented appearance. Also, they exist on a nested series of biological scales that range from a population of trees to populations of cells and subcellular components.

The essays concentrate on evolutionary theory (*Parasites and Darwin's Intellectual Triumph, The Mentor and the Heretic, Nature's Bounty, Origins, Language a Nurture of Nature* and *Our Great Leap Forward*), the foundations of cell and molecular biology (*A Vital Science*, and *A Horse and Molecular Biology*), systematic biology (*The Systematics Wars, Kingdoms*, and *E Pluribus Unum*), and Ecology (*Ecosystems, Wetlands, Succession in a Sceptic's Garden*, and *Islands and their Lessons in Biogeography*). These essays focus on the fundamental underlying characteristics of life as well as the diversity of living things. Ultimately, the quest to learn about other living things teaches us much about ourselves.

PARASITES AND DARWIN'S INTELLECTUAL TRIUMPH

A BOIL?

The study of parasitic adaptation is one of the most important buttresses of evolutionary theory.
       -Hans Zinsser (1934)

Several months ago a colleague from the Mathematics Department asked me to speculate about the most highly evolved species on the planet. I tried to convince him that the concept of "most highly evolved" had little meaning in modern biology. He then changed the question to be the most complex species. Without hesitation, I responded that any number of organisms that we call parasites would qualify for that position.

Parasites include all manner of living things from every kingdom of life. They are marked by tuning their life histories and physiological processes to those of their host organisms. Some of them have more than three different hosts. The concomitant complexity in life cycle is usually balanced by a simplification in body form, as the host becomes the habitat for the parasite.

I have been the host of a myriad of parasites. I have suffered infectious diseases, the annual flu, colds, fungal diseases, etc. However, my most memorable parasitic visitation was that of a type of fly called a Botfly (*Dermatobia hominis*). I began to notice the organism two years ago within a week of my return from Costa Rica. A boil began to rise on my wrist where I had noticed a particularly itchy mosquito bite. I tried to lance the boil myself but found only swollen tissue (see Figure 6-1). I went to my local physician who tried twice to lance the swollen area. Out of desperation, she sent me to a regional hospital where they took biopsies to determine the nature of the infection.

In the mean time, the boil would occasionally cause acute pain and a large flow of blood. The odd nexus of symptoms caused almost everyone to scratch their heads especially when the report came back from the dermatological biopsy that neither a bacterium nor a fungus caused the "boil". On an off chance, I asked the university physician what it might be. He looked at the wrist and said that it appeared to be a parasite of some sort. I went straight back to my lab and put my wrist under a dissecting microscope. There, I saw the movement of a black and tan striped animal under my skin. Periodically, it stuck its breathing tube out through a hole in the raised area. I realized in a moment that I was the host of a parasitic insect. Within minutes I had found the culprit in my parasitology books and called the physician who had already come to the same conclusion. Within the hour, he removed a 1 cm long maggot from my wrist (See Figure 6-2). The month of uncertainty finally had an explanation. All of the symptoms began to make sense in retrospect.

The lifecycle of the human botfly is tuned to two different kinds of organisms. First, the female botfly locates an appropriate blood-feeding insect, a mosquito or a biting fly. Somehow, the female lays an egg on or near the head of the other insect while it is resting. The blood-feeding insect then seeks out an appropriate mammalian host (humans are just one of several possible hosts). While the insect is taking a blood meal, the botfly egg drops off and secures itself to the skin of the host. It quickly hatches and burrows into the skin. There, it causes a cellulitis-like response where it grows embedded in a plentiful food supply. The maggot maintains an opening to the outside through which it extends its air tube. When the maggot is ready to pupate, it backs out of the skin of the host and drops to the ground. After a brief pupal stage underground, the mature fly emerges to continue the life cycle, which is elaborate but effective. Although it is uncomfortable, the botfly is rarely fatal to its host.

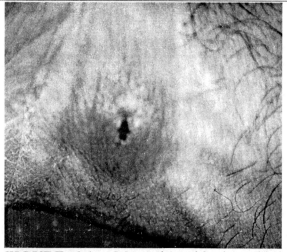

FIGURE 6-1. My wrist with the raised "boil" and the open hole at the apex of the swelling.

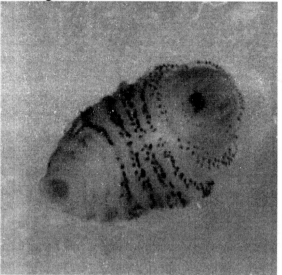

FIGURE 6-2. The botfly maggot that came from my wrist in December 1999. The total length of the animal is about 1 cm. Its head is on the right and the abdominal end with the air tube is on the left.

Much of the world is controlled by the occurrences of a broad range of parasites such as malaria, sleeping sickness, ascariasis as well as infectious diseases and spore-disseminated bacteria (like anthrax). That is particularly true of those diseases that can exist in a debilitating chronic form. Such an extended sublethal disease erodes the human potential of a population at the same time that it consumes the financial support of the society in which the disease occurs.

In some cases, parasitic diseases are so pervasive that their incidences might be nearly 100%. That was the case of Chagas' disease in certain areas of Central and South America through the 19th Century. While on his voyage of discovery, Charles Robert Darwin (1809-1882) visited the areas of South America in which malaria and Chagas' disease were endemic. Indeed, Darwin describes the Benchuca bug (*Triatoma infestans*), a large South American bed bug that is the intermediate host for the causative agent of Chagas' disease, and its ability to suck a large volume of blood in a very short time. Almost certainly Darwin became infected with the trypanosome (*Trypanosoma cruzi*) that produces the disease somewhere in Chili (See Figure 6-3). He became acutely ill from September 20 to the end of October, 1834.

DARWIN EXPLAINED?
But it is...a principle feature of his life, that for nearly forty years he never knew one day of the health of ordinary men, and thus his life was one long struggle against the weariness and strain of sickness.

-Francis Darwin

When an infected bug feeds on a victim, it quickly engorges itself with blood and more than doubles its size. As it bloats, the bug typically defecates. Trypanosomes in the feces can be moved into the wound created by the bug when the sleeping person scratches the wound. At first, the infective cells seek out tissues of the lymphatic system and multiply. Then, they break out into the circulatory system as swimming trypanosome cells as in Figure 6-3. This is the acute phase and lasts a relatively short period. Following that, the trypanosome takes up residence in tissues like the heart and intestines. There, they cause chronic malaise and digestive problems, both of which were Darwin's complaints in later years.

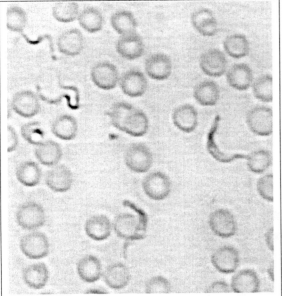

FIGURE 6-3. A human blood smear from a person infected with *Trypanosoma cruzi*, the causative agent of Chagas' disease. Note the C-shaped flagellated cells among the circular red blood cells.

Darwin was not always sickly as his son described him. Indeed, as a young man Darwin routinely went on hunting trips. Throughout the time that he was the Ship's Naturalist aboard the H.M.S. Beagle (1831-1836), Darwin showed enormous strength and endurance as he explored rainforests, mountains, rivers, plains, etc. His energy also poured through his writings and were manifest in his many interests and attention to detail in his journals as presented in his publication of the *Voyage of the Beagle*.

Upon his return to England, Darwin found that he was something of a celebrity among the scientists of Britain. His collections and preliminary notes on the voyage had excited the scientific community as much as those of Von Humboldt (1769-1859), a generation earlier. Darwin dove into organizing his field notes and collections for publication.

His initial problem was how to organize the collections. Only Richard Owen (1804-1892) and Charles Lyell (1797-1875) came forward to offer help with them. Darwin had to cajole and attempt to enlist experts in botany, zoology, and geology to help him in the organization. Darwin soon lamented that "the collectors so much outnumber the real naturalists that the latter have no time to spare." Nevertheless, he gradually recruited naturalists to begin working on his collections. He was particularly successful in finding zoologists to take "whole tribes of animals."

Darwin married his cousin, Emma Wedgwood in 1839 and moved into a small house in London. Soon thereafter Darwin began to experience the chronic ill health that would plague him for the rest of his life. By 1842, Darwin and his wife moved to an estate in the village of Down, south of London. They chose it because it was quiet and in the country. Darwin lived there for the rest of his life and conducted most of his observations and experiments there. They lived on money that they had inherited from their parents. Furthermore, Darwin made shrewd investments and later had some income from his many books. He became completely absorbed in the science that he had begun during the voyage and spent the rest of his life as a gentleman scientist with a fairly rigid work schedule. He vowed to return to London about twice each month so that he could remain active in the scientific establishment there and kept up that routine as long as his health permitted.

A Darwin afflicted with Chagas' disease was still very active as a scientist. He wrote extensively on all areas of natural history: geology, zoology, and botany. He experimented with anatomy and physiology. In 1846 he tried to organize his collection of barnacles and noticed that the taxonomy of the group was in such disarray that the task was impossible. Furthermore, a quick survey of the group indicated that he had collected entirely new groups of barnacles. His barnacle project grew in scale and occupied him until 1854 when he produced a massive three-volume treatise (2 volumes on living and 1 volume on fossil barnacles published between 1851 and 1854). Thus, Darwin became one of the most skilled natural historians in Britain and almost all self-taught.

THE ORIGIN OF *THE ORIGIN*

To Charles Lyell, Esq., F.R.S. this...is dedicated with grateful pleasure - as an acknowledgement that the chief part of whatever scientific merit this journal and the other work of the author may possess, has been derived from studying the well-known and admirable Principles of Geology.
- Charles Darwin (1845)

Darwin took a copy of Lyell's *Principles of Geology* (Vol 1) when he left on the voyage of the Beagle. He read the book and assimilated its message of uniformitarianism[1]. Later, he had copies of volumes 2 and 3 shipped to him during the voyage. His observations showed him first hand that the earth was tremendously old and that much of what he saw could be explained more easily given large expanses of time.

Darwin was delighted to make Lyell's acquaintance after his return. The friendship that developed between the two men was genuine and lasted throughout their lives. Lyell was one of the few allowed into the estate at Down and had a great influence on the science of Darwin.

Volume 2 of *Principles of Geology* treated the possibility of "the transmutation of species" (a phrase that means evolution in today's usage). Lyell began the second volume by considering the views of Jean-Baptiste Pierre Antoine de Monet, Chevalier de Lamarck[2] (1744-1829, France) who worked as a naturalist at the National Museum of Natural History (Musee National d'Histoire Naturelle) in Paris. First, he worked at the poverty level as an assistant with the plants in the Jardin des Plantes. Then, in the wake of the French Revolution, Lamarck was appointed professor of Invertebrates (Insects and Worms in the language of the day). At the time few, including Lamarck, knew anything about the "lower" animals. However, the numbers and diversity of invertebrate species also demonstrated to him that species could change. He published his view of evolution in 1801 in which he proposed that organisms were constantly climbing the ladder of life. They changed by passing on acquired characteristics to the next generation driven by an urge for perfection in form.

Lamarck suffered a deafening silence from the scientific community and the scorn of his colleague, Georges Cuvier (1769-1832) who believed that species were immutable. He believed that species could not change because all parts of an individual were beautifully integrated into a whole that was ideally suited to its environment. Nevertheless, he did recognize that animals occurred in related groups, some of the species were extinct. For example, the woolly mammoth was extinct but its parts were homologous (equal to) those of living elephants. Thus, he could take a single bone from an animal like a woolly rhinoceros and reconstruct the whole animal. Cuvier's encyclopedic knowledge of the vertebrates allowed him to compare anatomical structures

---

[1] See *Geology Through Lyell's Eyes*

[2] Consult *Rivals* for more background about Lamarck and his feud with Cuvier.

of animals living and extinct. Thus, he created the discipline of **Comparative Anatomy.**

Cuvier reconciled the immutability of species with comparative anatomy and extinction by supposing that the earth had suffered a succession of catastrophes, each followed by a separate creation. Similar animals in each creation must have occupied similar habitats and, therefore the necessity for similarity in form. Lyell, himself, adopted the view of Cuvier in the first editions of *Principles.* Thus, Darwin was well-acquainted with the philosophies of Lamarck, Cuvier and Lyell with regard to species and their mutability. Still, fresh from his voyage in 1836, when Darwin began to organize his journals, he noticed how many of his observations could be explained if species were mutable. He began to keep a series of notebooks in which he recorded any facts relevant to the species question. Later, Darwin claimed that even while in South America he noticed that certain observations were explainable only with the "supposition that species gradually became modified." Still, Darwin claimed that he did not become convinced of the mutability of species "until two or three years had elapsed."

Curiously, Darwin's own grandfather, Erasmus Darwin (1731-1802) explored the mutability of species in a major work called *Zoonomia, or the Laws of Organic Life* (1794-1796). Charles never met his grandfather who died seven years before he was born. Later, Darwin said that he did read his grandfather's work, but it made little impression on him when he was young. He claimed to have reread the book after his return from his voyage and commented, "I was much disappointed; the proportion of speculation being so large to the facts given." On Darwin's death, Thomas Henry Huxley claimed that "Erasmus was an anticipator of Lamarck, and not of Charles Darwin." Thus, Charles' belief in the mutability of species grew from his struggle to make sense of nature, not from a particular preconception about species.

DARWIN AS PARASITE?

The sick man is a parasite of society.
                          -Friedrich Nietzsche (1888)

Curiously, no one questioned the notion of a species. Lyell's, Lamarck's, and Darwin's treatments of species were quite modern in their outlooks. Indeed, a good working definition of species was independent of a belief in the fixity of a species. For example, Carolus Linnaeus[3] (1707-1778) who defined the modern system of classification was a staunch believer in the inerrant unchanging character of species. Nevertheless, the general definition of a species was (and is) a group of organisms that can breed and produce viable offspring. That is, they must breed true. The real question was whether some individuals within a species might breed almost true and, therefore, allowed for a change.

Darwin's study of his samples and notebooks demonstrated how much individuals might vary and still remain within the same species. Could variability alone lead to new species? Darwin said that he struggled with this issue until 1838 when he happened to read an essay by Thomas Malthus (1766-1834), a political economist, called *Essay on the Principle of Population* (1798). Malthus asserted that the standard of living in England must decline because the lower classes produce too many offspring and use up finite resources. Unless, the lower classes were regulated, then famine and poverty were in the future. (He speculated that such were natural outcomes visited upon human populations by God to keep them from becoming indolent.)

---

[3] Read more about Linnaeus and his contributions in *Kingdoms.*

Darwin wrote that he was "well-prepared to appreciate the struggle for existence" after reading Malthus. He realized that species would tend to produce offspring in excess of the resources available. Thus, those individuals with more favorable variations would tend to survive. An accumulation of such differential survival would lead to a new species. Darwin wrote, "Here, then I had at last got a theory by which to work." He called the new theory natural selection and began to seek evidence of its operation in nature. His notebooks began to fill with observations and later in 1842, Darwin wrote a sketch of the theory that he expanded into a 230-page essay in 1844. He set aside the essay with a letter to his wife and funds for its publication in the event of his sudden death. In that event, he named Charles Lyell as his preferred editor for the work.

Why did Darwin not publish his book in its 1844 form? The essay generally laid out the arguments that he would expand on in *The Origin of Species*. He knew that the theory was important, but that it would generate much controversy. So, Darwin waited and gathered information.

Loren Eiseley suggested that Darwin actually received his inspiration from a Calcutta apothecary named Edward Blyth (1810-1873) who had published on "the struggle for existence" in 1835 and 1837 in *The Magazine of Natural History,* a journal that Darwin often read and referenced. Later, Blyth entered into an extended dialogue with Darwin about the mammals and birds of the Indian subcontinent and Southeast Asia. Indeed, Blyth may have introduced Darwin to the branching tree metaphor of life (although Lamarck had used it 30 years earlier). Eiseley claims that the formulation of the theory of natural selection actually came from Blyth and that Darwin invented the Malthus explanation years later.

Curiously, Darwin wrote his expanded essay in the same year that Robert Chambers (1802-1871) anonymously published *Vestiges of the Natural History of Creation.* Chambers was a publisher and popular writer from Scotland with a particular interest in geology. His small but ambitious book attempted to explain the origins of the solar system and of life, the known geological periods, the development of life (evolution), and the origin of our species. He claimed that inanimate nature obeyed the Law of Gravitation while animate nature (life) obeyed the Law of Development. The book generated such controversy in the English-speaking world that Chambers retained his anonymity until years after his death. Although controversial, *Vestiges* was successful and was published through more that 12 editions (1844-1884). Later Darwin claimed that the book helped to introduce and therefore prepare people to accept the idea of evolution. However, *Vestiges*, like his grandfather's *Zoonomia*, was long on speculation and short on facts.

Darwin bided his time particularly with his work on barnacles. Through that eight-year exercise, he learned first hand the challenges of taxonomy (classification) and the remarkable variation that can occur within a group and within a species. Still, later he mused, "I doubt whether the work was worth the consumption of so much time."

Meanwhile, Darwin was in communication with naturalists all over the world. He plied them with questions about species of all types. He visited the barnyards and became a member of a local pigeon fancier's club. There, he saw first-hand the power of selective breeding from the common rock dove to the myriad forms available in his day. His notebooks continued to fill with information. Lyell advised Darwin to write a more complete manuscript of his ideas in 1856. Darwin began the project of his species book, a book that was to have been much more massive than the *Origin.* He communicated his views openly with Lyell and other members of his inner circle like the botanist Joseph Dalton Hooker (1817-1911). He even communicated the essence of his theory of natural selection to another botanist in the U.S. named Asa Gray (1810-1888). These "bold" moves saved Darwin and allowed the priority of the discovery to go to him.

In the summer of 1858 Darwin opened his mail and read a communication from Alfred Russel Wallace[4] (1823-1913), a collector and naturalist working in the Malay Archipelago (what is now Indonesia). The enclosed essay, *On the Tendency of Varieties to Depart Indefinitely from the Original Type,* was, in Darwin's words, "exactly the same theory as mine." His first inclination was to relinquish priority to Wallace and just see to the publication of his essay. However, Lyell and Hooker convinced Darwin to write a short paper and publish jointly with Wallace. Darwin did that. They published in *The Journal of the Proceedings of the Linnean Society in 1858* with a copy of a letter that Darwin had sent to Asa Gray in 1857. Professor Haughton of Dublin retorted, "that all that was new in them was false, and what was true was old."

Was Darwin a parasite on other's ideas? Eiseley claimed that Haughton's comment referred to the real contributions of men such as Blyth, Chambers, and Lamarck. Did Darwin really get his inspiration for natural selection from Malthus or Blyth or Chambers or Wallace? Ernst Mayr said that Darwin's theory was inspired by the writings of Charles Lyell. Curiously, Wallace also claimed to have been inspired to conceive natural selection by reading Mathus' essay.

Where did the theory come from? Does it really matter? Of these men only Wallace

---

[4] Find more information about Wallace in *The Mentor and the Heretic* and *Islands and Their Lessons in Biogeography.*

articulated the theory as clearly as Darwin did, but Darwin had much, much more evidence. The manuscript from Wallace forced Darwin's hand, and he quickly prepared a manuscript, a 300+-page book that Darwin referred to as an abstract.

THE SPECIES BOOK

To anyone who studies the signs of the times, the emergence of the philosophy of Evolution...is the most portentous event of the nineteenth century. -Thomas H. Huxley

Darwin said that the book "cost me thirteen months and ten days' hard labour" and was published in November 1859 under the title, *Origin of Species.* He called his book "one long argument" in which he attempted to convince the reader that species changed over time and the mechanism of that change was natural selection. He began the argument as had other authors (e.g. Lamarck, Blyth, Chambers, and Wallace, etc.) with an examination of the power of selective breeding in shaping organisms. He considered the breeds of dogs, plants, and pigeons and summed up his conclusions with, "Over all these causes of change I am convinced that the accumulative action of selection, whether applied methodically and more quickly, or unconsciously and more slowly, but more efficiently, is by far the predominant power."

Darwin noted that house cats vary little because of their nocturnal (and therefore uncontrollable) breeding habits. Still, many cat breeds have been generated since Darwin's day. Consider the differences between my two cats (see Figure 6-4) and the relatively few generations required to produce them. This is a striking example of Darwin's argument about variation under domestication.

He then considered variation under nature. In this chapter, he gave example after example (primarily of plants) of how large, widespread, dominant groups show the greatest variability.

He argued that the subgroups thus generated could give rise to new species through the struggle for existence by a parade of examples primarily from the animal kingdom. He argued that in the struggle of life any form with a slight advantage over another will "survive and multiply."

FIGURE 6-4. My two cats, Lyuba (left) and Benny (right).

Darwin then deftly turned the argument by uniting the remarkable variability of organisms within a species with the struggle for existence. Just as organisms under domestication change in response to selective breeding, so do they change in nature as a consequence of the struggle of life. Thus nature tends to select for traits that are beneficial and cause a change from one species to the next. Similarly, the rise of new successful species must lead to the extinction of those that are displaced. In this way, natural selection drove the changes of life throughout its history. Here, Darwin employed the metaphor of the branching tree to describe the theory of descent with modification to explain life and its history.

Darwin explored problems with the theory of natural selection. Namely, how were variable traits inherited (this was long before a good working theory of genetics)? How could complex organs like the eye evolve without large leaps in structure? He finally settled on the solution that however traits are inherited they include all of the former adaptations in the history of the organism. Thus, by small steps through the agency of natural selection even a structure as marvelous as the eye could evolve. Similarly, he did consider the imperfection of the fossil record and concluded that the gaps in the record just represent gaps in time during which large changes could occur in living things.

The final chapters of the *Origin* carried the strongest weight of evidence. In these, he used natural selection and descent with modification to explain the distributions of livings over the globe. For example, the finches of the Galapagos Islands are all rather similar in form and resemble a kind of finch on the mainland of South America. However, the island finches vary considerably with regard to their beaks (See Figure 6-5). Some of them are adapted to eating seeds, some have changed to a beak suited to catching insects. One evolved a woodpecker-like beak with an elaborate behavior to pull insects out of wood.

Clearly, the Galapagos finches happened to find themselves on the islands as a consequence of storms or other means. Natural selection allowed them to diversify and occupy a variety of habitats excluded from them on the mainland. Nevertheless, the woodpecker finch would easily be displaced by a real woodpecker if it were to make it to the islands.

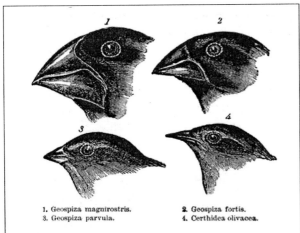

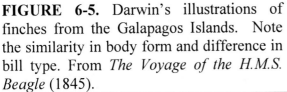

1. Geospiza magnirostris.   **2.** Geospiza fortis.
3. Geospiza parvula.   4. Certhidea olivacea.

FIGURE 6-5. Darwin's illustrations of finches from the Galapagos Islands. Note the similarity in body form and difference in bill type. From *The Voyage of the H.M.S. Beagle* (1845).

Just as organisms tend to be more similar to each other the closer that they are in time, they also tend to be more similar the closer that they are to each other on the earth. Darwin put it this way:

...the more nearly any two forms are related in blood, the nearer they will generally stand to each other in time and space; in both cases the laws of variation have been the same, and modifications have been accumulated by the same power of natural selection.

Finally, Darwin argued that the system of classification itself was a manifestation of the relationships between living things. For example, consider the orchids pictured in Figure 6-6. *Phalanopsis* is more closely related to other species of *Phalanopsis* that it is to the *Dendrobium*. In a Darwinian sense, the orchids are related through a common ancestor. They are related more distantly to oats (*Avena sativa*) through a common ancestor and they are related to common cats (*Felis domesticus*) through an even more distant ancestor. The relationships would branch like a tree with some lines becoming

extinct while others might branch many times. Thus, the similarities that are used in a classification system (similarities in anatomy, development, etc.) simply show the characters or sets of characters that are inherited from a common ancestor.

At the end of the book Darwin tries to present how exalted he views this explanation of life. He challenged directly the view of special creation by the following:

When I view all beings not as special creations, but as the lineal descendants of some few beings which lived long before the first bed of the Silurian system was deposited, they seem to me to become enobled.

Thus Darwin presented his grand view, and in the last paragraph invoked the Law of Gravity to connect natural selection to physical law.

FIGURE 6-6. Two orchids, *Phalanopsis* (left) and *Dendrobium* (right). Although different, they posses the characteristic structures of orchids.

The first edition of *Origin* was published by subscription; so, it sold out within hours of its release in November of 1859. The second edition that followed around the beginning of 1860 likewise sold out. Then, Darwin waited for the storm while he occupied himself with other projects.

THE DARWIN CREW

I finished your book yesterday...Since I read von Baer's Essays nine years ago no work on Natural History Science I have met with has made so great an impression on me.

-Thomas Henry Huxley (1859) to Darwin

Thomas Henry Huxley[5] (1825-1895) was one of the rising stars of British natural history, particularly comparative anatomy, when he became one of the first converts to Darwin's vision. He published a very favorable review of the *Origin*, and set out to defend the view at every turn. His tenacity earned him the name of Darwin's Bulldog.

Perhaps, Huxley's most famous defense of Darwinism came in 1860 when a great debate on evolution had been staged at Oxford. Huxley was one of the speakers for the Darwinian view while Archbishop Samuel Wilberforce spoke for the opposition. Huxley almost left the debate but was persuaded to stay by Robert Chambers. Richard Owen, who had developed a great dislike for Huxley, instructed Wilberforce on the appropriate arguments, particularly the scientific weaknesses of Darwinism.

Huxley and others spoke for and against Darwin. Wilberforce took the podium and delivered an oration that ended with a question to Huxley, "Was I descended from an ape on my grandmother's or my grandfather's side?" Huxley is supposed to have said to those near him, "The Lord hath delivered him into my hands." Later Huxley claimed to have made this reply:

If then the question is put to me would I rather have a miserable ape for a grandfather or a man highly endowed by nature and possessed of great means of influence and yet who employs these faculties and that influence for the mere purpose of introducing ridicule into a grave scien-

tific discussion, I unhesitatingly affirm my preference for the ape.

Thus, the debate ended.

Other debates continued throughout science and western society. Huxley, Gray, and Hooker almost immediately became advocates for Darwinian science. Much later Lyell finally sided publicly with the Darwinists. Wallace, who did not quite like the term, natural selection, coined the term, Darwinism. Darwin himself stayed away from the fray and remained content to let others come to his defense.

The concept of evolution swept through the scientific world with the same kind of fury that Newton's view of the universe had nearly 200 years earlier. Quickly, evolution, and less so the theory of natural selection, became knit throughout the life sciences. The integration of biology and evolution was nearly complete by 1870. Indeed, that all living things share a history of common descent became the unifying principle of biology and, therefore, made it a coherent discipline.

Western society accepted evolution because it appeared to provide some support for progress of the human species. For that reason, society never quite accepted the full implication of natural selection. Unfortunately, evolution also manifest itself in all types of perversions, all of which sought to find a scientific support for the notion that might makes right.

---

[5] Find more about T.H. Huxley in *A Tale of Two Stones*.

ORIGIN'S THEORIES

Darwin's views on evolution are often referred to as The Darwinian Theory. Actually, they consist of a number of different theories that are best understood when clearly distinguished from each other.

-Ernst Mayr

Plasticity of understanding and acceptance of evolution occurred within science, particularly during the first fifty years following the publication of *The Origin*. In fact, many who said that they accepted evolution rejected natural selection. That was because *The Origin* presented five different concepts according to Ernst Mayr, one of the leading evolutionary theorists of the 20th Century (see Table 1). Mayr presented them as five theories. I interpret them slightly differently.

I consider the nonconstancy of species to be a fact. That species changed over time was clearly demonstrated, even before 1859. However, no one said it more clearly or authoritatively before *The Origin*. This nonconstancy of species is the fact of evolution.

That all organisms are the products of descent from common ancestors is the principle that unifies the science of Biology. It is this concept that makes clear the underlying similarities of living things. Thus, we can explain why all living things are cellular in their fundamental structures, why they use proteins made of L-amino acids, why they use carbohydrates made of D-sugars, and why they use the same set of nucleic acids to store and transmit information. The list of underlying similarities is quite long, but the point is clear. The study of life, at least life on planet Earth, is fundamentally the same.

The gradualness of evolution grew from the study of paleontology and the application of the Principle of Uniformatarianism. Darwin's application of Lyell's book with this as its fundamental principle to observa-

tions that he made on the voyage of the Beagle was his earliest clue that life changed over time, because there was so much time for it to happen. The strict adherence to this theory caused Darwin to reject the notion that life could evolve in leaps and jumps. Thus, life could have no discontinuities (also a strict application of the principle of common descent).

TABLE 6-1. The concepts of evolution presented in *The Origin* according to Ernst Mayr (2001).	
The nonconstancy of species	Fact
The descent of all organisms from common ancestors.	Principle
The gradualness of evolution	Theory
The multiplication of species	Theory
Natural selection	Theory

Evolution is the source of biological diversity or the multiplication of species. This theory, also a consequence of the principle of common descent, assumes that the extravagance of life that we see on earth today came from the repeated separation of species over time. This was one of the few theories that Darwin illustrated in *The Origin* (see Figure 6-7). A corollary to this theory suggests that life has continually grown in diversity throughout its history with brief interruptions caused by mass extinctions.

The last, and Darwin's most valued theory was natural selection. Curiously, very few of those in his close circle thought that life evolved by natural selection. Then, the theory fell to the scientific rubbish bin following the discovery of Mendel in 1900 when mutations seemed to be the way that species changed. Theodosius Dobzhonsky, Julian Huxley, and Ernst Mayr, in the first half of the 20th century reconciled the problem in what was called, The New Synthesis. In this view, mutation was the source of variation on which natural selection operated. Darwin's precious theory was restored.

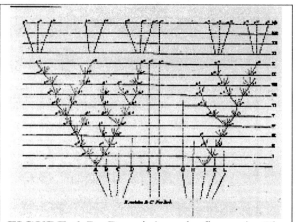

FIGURE 6-7. Darwin's only figure in *The Origin*. It was an illustration of the branching tree-like nature of evolution.

OUR INHERITANCE

"Natural Selection" is the key-stone of my Book & I have very great confidence it is sound.
-Charles Darwin (1858) in a letter to Hooker

Darwin succeeded in convincing science of the fact of evolution and struggled through the rest of his life to convince biologists of natural selection, the most creative contribution of Charles Darwin. He continued to explore aspects of natural selection in his books[6] that followed *Origin* until his death in 1882. He was buried in Westminster Abbey right next to Isaac Newton.

Natural selection as an explanation of evolution began to fall out of favor through the end of the 19th and the beginning of the 20th Centuries. Then, science began to see it at work in a most terrible way. Insects that had once been controlled by pesticides could

---

[6] I have listed his books and dates of publication in *The Mentor and the Heretic*.

no longer be held in check. More recently, the indiscriminate overuse of antibiotics led to the selection of highly resistant strains of staph, and tuberculosis. Other parasitic diseases such as malaria again became epidemic.

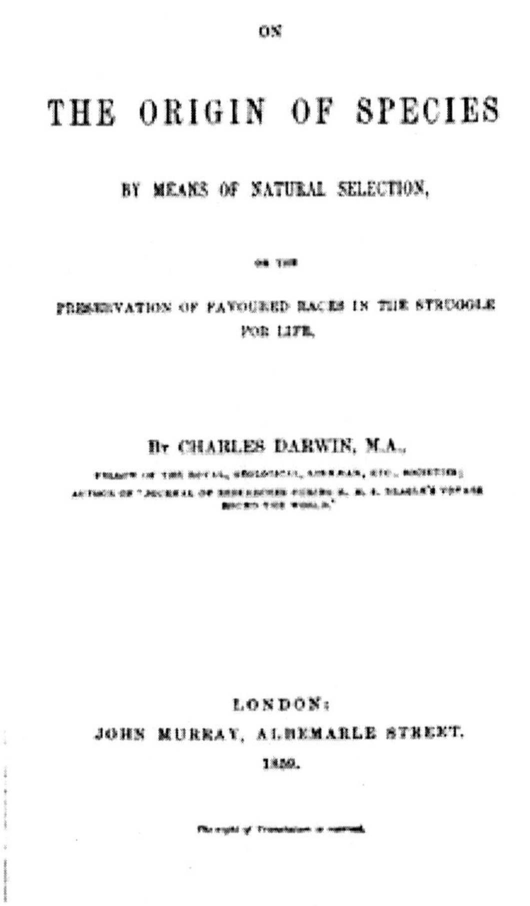

ON

THE ORIGIN OF SPECIES

BY MEANS OF NATURAL SELECTION,

OR THE

PRESERVATION OF FAVOURED RACES IN THE STRUGGLE FOR LIFE,

By CHARLES DARWIN, M.A.,

FELLOW OF THE ROYAL, GEOLOGICAL, LINNÆAN, ETC., SOCIETIES;
AUTHOR OF "JOURNAL OF RESEARCHES DURING H. M. S. BEAGLE'S VOYAGE
ROUND THE WORLD."

LONDON:
JOHN MURRAY, ALBEMARLE STREET.
1859.

The right of Translation is reserved.

FIGURE 6-8. The title page of the first edition of *Origin of Species*.

Some evidence suggests that the trypanosomes that cause Chagas' disease jumped from Guinea pigs to humans after the first wave of human settlement entered South America. The triatomid bug intermediate host found humans to be a convenient and nutritious meal. The trypanosomes found the physiology of humans to be compatible to that of the original Guinea pigs. Natural selection did not have to work very hard to do the rest. By the time it had infected Darwin, *Trypanosoma cruzi* had become well adapted to its human hosts. Without doubt, parasites are the clearest and most tragic examples of Darwinian evolution at work.

-2001, revised 2005

References:

Beeson, Paul B. and Walsh McDermott, eds. 1975. *Textbook of Medicine.* 14th edition. W.B. Saunders Co. Philadelphia.

Bowler, Peter J. 1992. *The Fontana History of the Environmental Sciences.* IN: Porter, Roy, ed. *Fontana History of Science.* Fontana Press. London.

Browne, Janet. *Charles Darwin, Voyaging.* Princeton University Press. Princeton, NJ.

Browne, Janet. *Charles Darwin, The Power of Place.* Princeton University Press. Princeton, NJ.

Burkhardt, Krederick, ed. 1996. *Charles Darwin's Letters, A Selection 1825-1859.* Cambridge University Press. New York.

Chambers, Robert. 1870 (originally published 1844). *Vestiges of the Natural Histroy of Creation. With a Sequel.* Harper & Brothers, Publishers. New York.

Darwin, Charles. 1979 (originally published 1859). *The Origin of Species.* Gramercy Books. New York.

Darwin, Charles. (originally published 1845). *The Voyage of the H.M.S. Beagle.* 2nd edition. The Heritage Press. New York.

Darwin, Francis, ed. 1958 (originally published in 1992). *The Autobiography of Charles Darwin and Selected Letters.* Dover Publications Inc. New York.

Darwin, Francis, ed. 1896. *The Life and Letters of Charles Darwin.* Vol 1-2. D. Appelton & Co. New York.

Desmond, Adrian and James Moore. 1991. *The Life of a Tormented Darwin.* Warner Books, Inc. New York.

Diamond, Jared. 1998. *Guns, Germs, and Steel, The Fates of Human Societies.* W.W. Norton and Co. New York.

Eiseley, Loren 1961. *Darwin's Century: Evolution and the Men Who Discovered It.* Doubleday, Anchor Books. New York.

Eiseley, Loren. 1979. *Darwin and the Mysterious Mr. X, New Light on the Evolutionists.* Harcourt Brace Jovanovich. New York.

Gould, Stephen Jay. 2002. *The Structure of Evolutionary Theory.* The Belknap Press of Harvard University. Cambridge, Mass.

Holt, Jack R. and Patricia Nelson. 2001. *Paths of Science.* Kendall/Hunt. Dubuque.

Huxley, Thomas Henry. 1896. *Darwiniana.* D. Appleton & Co. New York.

Huxley, Thomas Henry. 1896. *Man's Place in Nature.* D. Appleton & Co. New York.

Irvine, William. 1955. *Apes, Angels, and Victorians, The Story of Darwin, Huxley, and Evolution.* McGraw-Hill Book Co, Inc. New York.

Keynes, R. D., ed. 2001. *Charles Darwin's Beagle Diary.* Cambridge University Press. Cambridge.

Lloyd, Elisabeth. 1994. *The Structure and Confirmation of Evolutionary Theory.* Princeton University Press. Princeton, NJ.

Loewenberg, Bert James, ed. 1959. *Charles Darwin: Evolution and Natural Selection, An Anthology of Writings of Charles Darwin.* Beacon Press. Boston.

Lyell, Charles. 1990 (originally published 1830-33). *Principles of Geology.* Vol 1-3. University of Chicago Press. Chicago.

Mason, Stephen F. 1962. *A History of the Sciences.* Collier Books. New York.

Mayr, Ernst. 1991. *One Long Argument, Charles Darwin and the Genesis of*

Modern Evolutionary Thought. Harvard University Press. Cambridge.

Mayr, Ernst. 2001. *What Evolution Is.* Basic Books. New York.

Milner, Richard. 1994. *Charles Darwin, Evolution of a Naturalist.* Facts on File, Inc. New York.

Ruse, Michael. 1999. *The Darwinian Revolution, Science Red in Tooth and Claw.* The University of Chicago Press. Chicago.

Simmons, John. 2000. *The Scientific 100, A Ranking of the Most Influential Scientists, Past and Present.* Citadel Press. New York.

Wallace, Alfred R. 1890. *Darwinism.* Mac-Millan & Co. London.

Zinsser, Hans. 1963. *Rats, Lice and History, The Biography of a Bacillus.* Little, Brown, and Co. Boston.

Questions to Think About

1. Why was the botfly infestation difficult to diagnose?

2. When was Darwin infected with *Trypanosoma cruzi*? Why does this seem likely?

3. How did Darwin spend his time in the 20 years after his return from the voyage of the Beagle?

4. How did the *Principles of Geology* help Darwin to develop his evolutionary theories?

5. Distinguish between the evolutionary views of Lamarck, Cuvier, and Darwin.

6. How did the essay on population by Thomas Malthus help Darwin to develop Natural Selection?

7. How may Blyth and Chambers have helped Darwin in the development of evolutionary theory?

8. Hooker, Gray, Lyell, and Wallace all played prominent roles in the creation of *The Origin*. What were they?

9. What types of evidence did Darwin draw upon and use in the presentation of his "long argument"?

10. Darwin presented 5 concepts (Mayr called them 5 theories) of evolution in *The Origin*. What were they?

THE MENTOR AND THE HERETIC: ARCHITECTS OF NATURAL SELECTION

RECOLLECTIONS

You are young, replied Athos, and your bitter recollections have time to be changed into sweet remembrances.
-Alexandre Dumas, *The Three Musketeers*

Every history is beset with contingency and coincidence such that one may look back through the sequence of events and look for the important ones that steered a course to a particular historical outcome. One of the most important events in navigating my own life started with my mother giving me enough money for a haircut, and then sending me on my way. I jumped on my bicycle and began the mile-long ride to the shopping center. However, overcome with fatigue, I returned and said that I was too tired to go. That unexpected response caused my mother to give me a closer look. She saw that the whites of my eyes had a yellowish tinge and immediately called the pediatrician. After his examination, I went to the hospital for tests, and soon the confirmation arrived. I had infectious hepatitis. At that time, the treatment was not very sophisticated. I was put on a strict low-fat diet and isolated from everyone except my parents and grandparents. That was how I lived 6 months of my eighth year.

I was never in pain, but tired easily. Because I spent most of my time in bed, my father bought a small television set to keep me company. I watched Mr. Ed and Truth or Consequences until I was sick of TV. One day, my father brought me a model airplane. I struggled to build it, and made quite a mess in the process. He brought other model kits, which I built, too. Each one was better than the last. Then, my mother brought me a boxed edition of The Three Musketeers. I struggled through the language of the first few pages, but by then Dumas' story hooked me and would not let go.

Neither of the things that I began doing during my illness had anything to do with science directly. Yet, I mark the beginning of my path as a scientist from that experience in that both model building and reading fostered a habit of mind that was necessary in science; however, those habits were not restricted to science and could have put me on any path. That my illness occurred in 1959, two years after Sputnik-I went aloft, and the United States put science education into high gear, likely nudged me in the direction of science, too. Indeed, many other events influenced me as course corrections, but my mother claimed that I came out of the illness a changed boy. Though I suffered from poor penmanship because cursive writing was taught in the third grade, from that point forward I began to assert myself as a student both in and out of the classroom.

We all have our own stories about life-changing events and coincidences. For me, no story is more fascinating than that of Charles Robert Darwin (1809-1882) and the twists and turns in his life that made a connection with a younger naturalist named Alfred Russel Wallace (1823-1913). Their lives had some similarities and some important differences[7]. Their interactions usually were very warm, but there were periods of dis-

---

[7] I have elaborated on the lives of the two men, particularly as their interaction led to *The Origin of Species* in *Parasites and Darwin's Intellectual Triumph* and *Islands and Their Lessons in Biogeography*.

487

agreement and disappointment. Together, they brought about the biological revolution that gave birth to modern biology.

DARWIN'S VOYAGE
No pursuit at Cambridge was followed with nearly so much eagerness or gave me so much pleasure as collecting beetles. - Charles Robert Darwin, *Autobiography* (1892)

Charles Darwin began a life in which he seemed to be foreordained to follow his father and grandfather and to be trained as a physician. As a boy, he enjoyed a comfortable life in the large house of a wealthy family. Gardens, servants, and many books surrounded him. However, as a student, Charles seemed to be very lazy, and in his words, *I did not distinguish myself at Dr. Butler's Day School.* Furthermore, Charles hated the study of medicine and failed to complete his studies at Edinburgh University. His father was disappointed in Charles, but wanted to secure a profession for him. After a long talk, Charles and his father decided that the position of country parson would be the best position for someone who showed so little ability.

Charles was not really lazy, but his interests lay elsewhere. He enjoyed nature: collecting beetles, rocks, and marine animals. For a time he was completely obsessed with hunting, particularly with shooting game birds. While at Edinburgh, he made friends with a black taxidermist who taught Charles the skill. Charles became adept at the art and practiced on the many birds, etc. that he managed to shoot. Since the position of a country parson would provide Charles with a comfortable life and allow him to continue his passion for the outdoors, he enrolled in Christ's College at Cambridge University in 1827 to study for the ministry.

There his interests continued to lean toward field biology (natural history). Charles developed a passion for collecting things, both biological and geological. He wrote in his autobiography that he became so successful and single-minded about his collection that he had to hire a "laborer" to help him. Together, they scraped moss off trees and "rubbish at the bottom of barges". He collected from tidal pools, dead trees and rock outcrops. He collected birds on the wing and pressed plants. He gained such a reputation as a collector that he was asked to join botanical and geological forays. Darwin's skill and tenacity attracted the attention of John S. Henslow (1796-1861), a clergyman and professor of Botany, who took the young man under his wing as Charles' mentor. Together, they went on many long field trips to collect plants. Also, Adam Sedgewick (1785-1873), a geologist who was trying to work out the Paleozoic time sequence, chose Charles to accompany him on a geological collecting expedition to northern Wales.

Despite those experiences, nothing prompted his collecting urge more than insects, especially beetles. He wrote, it was the mere passion for collecting" that drove him. Nevertheless, he did make modest contributions to science as a student and even saw some of his beetles illustrated in Stephen's *Illustrations of British Insects*.

When Charles managed to pass Greek and graduation was in sight, Henslow intervened. He recognized that Charles had become a much better naturalist than a clergyman, and steered the young man toward an opportunity that would change his life. Henslow got wind of an opening for a gentleman naturalist aboard the H.M.S. Beagle, a former warship that was being refitted to map the coast of South America. The Beagle already had a commissioned naturalist, the customary responsibility of the ship's surgeon. However, Captain Robert Fitzroy wanted this to be a grand expedition of discovery and prepared to pay the salary of a second naturalist from his own pocket. Another and more pressing reason for Fitzroy, only 26 at the time, was that he feared he would succumb to madness like the previous captain of the Beagle and sought out a gentleman companion for the voyage. Henslow thought that Charles would be perfect for the position and prevailed on him to apply. Although Charles' father objected, he finally relented through the intercession of his father-in-law (and Charles' grandfather), Josiah Wedgewood. Then, Fitzroy nearly turned him down because Charles' nose betrayed a streak of laziness (according to the pseudoscience of physiognomy). Nevertheless, and despite all of the obstacles, Charles sailed on December 27, 1831 as part of an expedition that was supposed to last for two years. He returned to England nearly five years later.

Among the books that he took with him was *Principles of Geology,* volume 1 by Charles Lyell (1797-1875), which was published one year earlier. He received volumes 2 and 3 at various ports of call in South America. The three volumes argued that the earth was very old and that surface features of the earth should be interpreted accordingly. Thus, an application of unbroken natural law and process, given immense amounts of time, could account for the landforms, geology and the biology of earth. This was the principle of uniformitarianism, and Darwin began to apply it to his observations.

Darwin took his job as naturalist very seriously and outstripped the resources of Fitzroy. Darwin's father ended up paying for and supporting much of Charles' scientific needs: his books and his equipment. Soon, he supplanted the surgeon, a drunkard who was booted from the ship as soon it reached Brazil, as the ship's naturalist. However, Darwin never was officially appointed the naturalist. That meant that his collections did not belong to the British government. He could dispose of them as he saw fit, and he took full advantage of that opportunity. He crated and shipped boxes and boxes of pressed plants, rocks, fossils, skeletons, animal skins, and insects back to England. He sent back so much stuff that Charles was becoming very famous among scientists in Britain (something that he did not know at the time). After spending much time on the east coast of South America, Captain Fitzroy took the Beagle around Tierra del Fuego and up the west coast. The ship then left the continent of South America and stopped at an archipelago on the equator called the Galapagos Islands. There, Darwin saw giant land tortoises on many of the 14 islands. He was struck by a comment made by a missionary who claimed that he could tell which island any tortoise came from by the shape of its shell, an observation that Darwin confirmed. Other things like mockingbirds showed the same diversity in geographic variation.

Darwin was enthusiastic but not careful in making his collections on the Galapagos. He was content only to collect tortoises, mockingbirds, and finches and record that they came from the island chain. Later, back in England, Darwin lamented that he had been so careless. Fortunately, Darwin's butler kept more careful records of the collections and particular locations. Thus, Charles saw that not only were there different kinds of finches on the Galapagos Archipelago, but that there were slight variations between populations of the same kinds of finches from island to island. Darwin recognized in the cases of finches, tortoises, and mockingbirds, that they had each come from a single ancestral type.

In retrospect, his stop at the Galapagos Islands was very important to Darwin. The chapter on the Galapagos is one of the only chapters that is illustrated in *The Voyage of the Beagle.* Although the Galapagos Islands are rarely mentioned in *The Origin of Species*, they do play a prominent role in the arguments that he makes about the immigration of species from a landmass to islands and the subsequent speciation of the immigrants.

Darwin returned to England on October 2, 1836. He began to organize his notes and collections and publish on them right away. He used this time to recover from the ravages of the disease, and to find a wife. He never recovered from the disease that beset him for the rest of his life. However, he was successful in finding a wife when he married his cousin named Emma Wedgewood on January 29, 1839. They set up housekeeping in London, but the constant distractions of the city and Charles' recurring illness forced them to look for a place outside of London but close enough for day trips. They found a place of refuge in the village of Downe, south of London in 1842. There, they purchased a house that would become Darwin's citadel against the chaos of the world and where, supported by his investments and income from his writings, he would live the life of a gentleman scientist.

In June 1845, Darwin published *The Voyage of the Beagle.* This and his other books about his voyage of discovery made him famous in England (long before he published *The Origin*) and helped to inspire a new generation of naturalists, collectors, and explorers. In secret Darwin opened a series of notebooks in which he explored the "abominable mystery" of the species question. His observations in South America as well as the Galapagos led him to understand that related species occupied the same or neighboring regions. Also, related species could be separated from existing ones through time. This supported the concept that species change, a notion that was accepted by many naturalists at the time. The abominable mystery was how they might change. While he also occupied himself with other projects, Darwin spent the next twenty years wrestling with the mechanism that he would come to call Natural Selection.

He got the final and vital clue from reading a tract by the Reverend Thomas Malthus who argued that laws intended to help the poor would, in the end, only do them and the country great harm. His line of reasoning was that support in the form of free housing, food, etc., would only keep an unproductive segment of the population alive while they would be free to increase their numbers. That is because a population tends to increase geometrically while the necessities (food, shelter, etc) would increase only arithmetically. Thus, a time would come when the poor would outstrip the resources of even a wealthy empire like that of Great Britain. His essay from 1798 had been a politically hot topic for 40 years and helped to postpone the initiation of the Poor Laws in Britain. Darwin read the tract a few months before his marriage hoping to gain some insight about the potential problems that inbreeding might produce within his family. The essay shed little light on that concern, but it did illuminate an important aspect of the species question that Darwin had wrestled with since he first saw the biotic extravagance of the rainforest. He finished reading Malthus on October 3, 1838 and directly began the development of a theory about how species might change in nature. The theory he called natural selection as a reference to the creative act of artificial selection that produced so many breeds of plants and animals for agriculture, horticulture, etc. In this case, however, the creative agent was nature itself.

For example, if populations of flies or beetles were allowed to reproduce, they would yield so many offspring that the environment could not support them. So, within a species, there is a struggle for survival. As Darwin said, *Individuals having any advantage, however slight, over others, would have the best chance of surviving and procreating their kind.* This was his core concept of natural selection.

Darwin delayed publication of his theory because he had seen how science had vilified those who had presented similar scenarios of species changing over time. He was cautious and wanted to make an airtight argument. Still, he did not want the priority for the discovery to be taken from him; so, he wrote a sketch in 1842, which he expanded in 1844 as an essay and gave it to his wife in a sealed envelope to be published in the event of his death.

WALLACE IN THE TROPICS

An earnest desire to visit a tropical country, to behold the luxuriance of animal and vegetable life said to exist there, and to see with my own eyes all those wonders which I had delighted so much to read of in the narratives of travelers, were the motives that induced me to break through the trammels of business and break the ties of home.

-Alfred Russel Wallace (1853)

Among those who were inspired to explore and collect by Darwin's *Voyage of the Beagle* were two young men from the lower classes in Britain, Henry Walter Bates (1825-1892) and Alfred Russel Wallace (1823-1913). Wallace was born January 8, 1823 in Usk, Monmouthshire, England. His family was not wealthy, so his education was marginal (He later described his schooling experience as dreadful. He had to bring his own candles and ink. Curiously, he also said that he found geography to be very boring.) Then, after his father died, his time in the classroom came to an end. He worked for a while as a surveyor and then as a "drawing master" at the College of Leicester (pronounced lestah).

While at Leicester, he met Henry Walter Bates who taught him methods of collecting and identifying plants and insects. Wallace and Bates traveled to the Amazon basin in 1848 where they began to work as professional collectors. They intended to earn their fortunes by collecting pressed plants, bird and mammal skins, and insects (particularly butterflies) for museums and wealthy Victorian private collectors. Also, they hoped to generate legitimate scientific knowledge and publish their results upon their return. They secured the support of Samuel Stevens, a successful natural history auctioneer, in a business relationship that would serve them well.

They traveled up and down the Amazon River and parted company in 1850. Bates spent more time exploring the lower part of the Amazon and then went up to the headwaters of the Amazon. Why they separated on the Rio Negro (Black River) in March 1850 is lost to history. Neither of the men mentioned why they separated except to note that it was better that they did. Wallace explored the Rio Negro and crossed over to the headwaters of the Orinoco River (See Figure 6-9). In 1854, after four years of careful and successful collecting, Wallace crated up his treasure of skins, skeletons, insects and pressed plants and carefully nursed them down to the city of Belem. Not only had he made collections of dead things, but also he collected live monkeys, birds, even a Toucan. He knew that he could get top dollar for these upon his return. His collection was enormous and impressive. Combined with the material that Bates gathered, the two documented nearly 15,000 species, about 8,000 of which were new to European science.

Bates remained in Amazonia for 11 more years. He spent most of his time around Ega, from which he explored the upper Amazon to the foothills of the Andes. Finally, stricken with malaria and overcome with homesickness, Bates returned to England with his collection in tact.

FIGURE 6-9. A map of northern South America that delineates the Amazon (A), Rio Negro (N), and Orinoco River (O) basins. Wallace went up the Rio Negro (N) and Orinoco River (O) and while Bates went westward to the headwaters of the Amazon (A) in the Andes Mountains. I generated this map using:
http://shareware.miningco.com/compute/shareware/library/education/bledmaps.htm

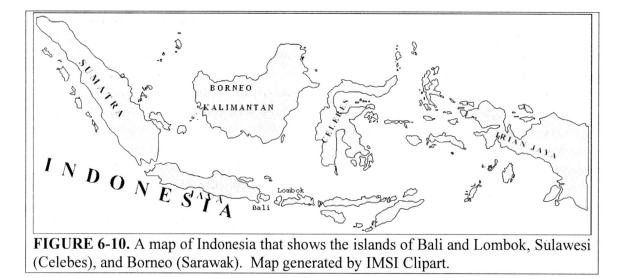

FIGURE 6-10. A map of Indonesia that shows the islands of Bali and Lombok, Sulawesi (Celebes), and Borneo (Sarawak). Map generated by IMSI Clipart.

On the other hand, Wallace seemed cursed on his return to England. Only a few days out of port, his ship with a hold full of resin caught fire. He had barely enough time to save a metal box that contained a small portion of his journal, a few pressed plants, some other specimens, and two shirts. He described the nightmare of pulling away from the burning ship and watching his monkeys leaping through the masts to escape the flames. Wallace returned to England in financial and scientific ruin. He had no specimens to sell and no notes on which to base any scientific works. Fortunately, Sevens had insured Wallace's collections; so, he had a small amount of money from that and earlier shipments of specimens to Britain. With the few notes that he saved and his memories, Wallace wrote two books on his return and supported their publication with his meager earnings. The first book was *Palm Trees of the Amazon*, which was criticized by Sir William Hooker, curator of the Royal Botanic Gardens at Kew, who said, *this work is certainly more suited to the drawing room table than to the library of a botanist.* He followed that with *Travels on the Amazon and Rio Negro* in 1853.

After about a year, Wallace felt as though his fortunes had closed in on him.

As a collector, he was a failure; as a scientist, he was irrelevant. Naturalists of Britain did not take his book seriously for the same reason that he failed as a collector. Wallace had no supporting data, neither notebooks nor samples. At that time, Britain was awash with popular travelogues, and Wallace's book became just another one of them. Staring into the face of the kind of failure and poverty that had plagued his father, Wallace turned to the only thing that he knew how to do well. He planned another trip of collection and exploration in the tropical jungles. However, this time he planned to go to a place that was even more exotic and unexplored than the Amazon Basin. He prepared to sail to the Malay Archipelago[8], the land of the orangutan and the bird of paradise (see Figure 6-10). Again, his venture was supported in part by the business relationship that he had with Stevens. Together, they reasoned that natural history collections would be even more valuable if they were taken from a largely unexplored tropical region. So, Wallace secured free passage aboard a ship to Southeast Asia.

---

[8] Also known as the as the Spice Islands or the Mollucas in what is now Indonesia.

THE MALAY ARCHIPELAGO

Situated upon the Equator, and bathed by the tepid water of the great tropical oceans, this region enjoys a climate more uniformly hot and moist than almost any other part of the globe, and teems with natural productions which are elsewhere unknown.

-Alfred Russel Wallace (1874).

He arrived in Singapore in 1854 and began to collect in the area and on the northwestern part of Borneo, then known as Sarawak. There, Wallace collected 320 different species of beetles in only 14 days during his first year. The rainy season that followed gave him time to ponder the implications of such diversity and he wrote a theoretical paper that summed up his observations of biological diversity, geography, and geology. In summary, he concluded that related species arise in neighboring areas (geography) but are separated by time (geology). This, he called the Sarawak Law, and mailed his paper to England for publication. It was published in *The Annals and Magazine of Natural History*, and Wallace waited for the reaction of the scientific community but received only silence. He was most curious to hear of Charles Lyell's reaction because he felt that Sarawak Law was a direct consequence of the application of the principle of uniformitarianism[9]. Also, Lyell was the most influential natural historian in Britain at the time. Finally, a year after he mailed his manuscript, Wallace wrote to a fellow explorer whom he thought would be more accessible. He wrote to Charles Darwin and established a correspondence that lasted through the rest of his stay in the Malay Archipelago.

Wallace's paper had indeed made an impact on Lyell, who, although committed to the fixity of species at the time, began to keep a notebook in which he explored evidence for the transmutation of species. In the mean time, he and others drew Darwin's attention to the paper and its implications. Darwin needed no one to tell him that Wallace was hot on the trail of the mystery he had been pursuing for 20 years. At that point, he took Lyell and Joseph Hooker (1817-1911), son of Sir William Hooker and the next director of Kew Gardens, into his confidence about Natural Selection. Lyell advised that he should get something into print. Thus, Darwin began work on his great species book, a great work that he never completed. The next year, Wallace became more adventurous and explored the island of Celebes (now known as Sulawesi). While there he sought to promote the Sarawak Law by writing a second theoretical paper that was published in *The Zoologist*.

From Celebes, Wallace branched out to the smaller and lesser-known members of the island chain. In his travels Wallace took careful notes of the plants and animals on the different islands. He was particularly surprised when he compared the animals on two neighboring islands called Bali and Lombok. Bali was very close to Java and, not surprisingly, had many kinds of animals in common with those on Java and the continent of Asia. Lombok, on the other hand, was only 25 miles from Bali but its animals were more like those of Australia and New Guinea. Wallace assumed that the difference was due to shifting ocean water levels. The islands of Java, Sumatra and Bali were on the continental shelf in relatively shallow water. They would have been connected if the water level had been 200 feet shal-

---

[9] Read more about Lyell and the principle of uniformitarianism in *Geology Through Lyell's Eyes.*

lower. Lombok, however was separated from Bali by a very deep trench. Those two islands would never have been connected. So, like Darwin, Wallace saw that immigration of species from a continent was important in the initial colonization of the island. However, after the species were established on the island, they often diverged from the continental species and became unique.

In 1858, Wallace found himself on the island of Ternate, sick with tertian malaria[10]. Wallace later claimed that while he languished in his malarial stupor, the mechanism for natural selection came to him in a flash. Like Darwin, his experiences with the diversity of life, and the inspiration of Lyell's *Principles* guided his thoughts. More importantly, Wallace claimed that he, too, had been mulling over the essay by Mathus at that time. While in his malarial fever, he hit upon the mechanism of natural selection and wrote up his brilliant paper on a day or on those days when he felt somewhat normal in February of that year. He wrapped up the twenty pages and took them to a passing ship for transport to England. He sent the manuscript to the naturalist with whom he had been in correspondence, Charles Darwin. He asked Darwin's indulgence to read over the manuscript and forward it to Charles Lyell if it had merit. Darwin later recorded that he received the packet on June 18, 1858 and was stunned. He said to Lyell that Wallace's paper was almost an outline of the book that he had been working on for the past 20 years.

A DELICATE ARRANGEMENT?
You cannot tell how I admire your spirit, in the manner in which you have taken all that was done about establishing our papers.
     -Charles Darwin, in a letter to Wallace

Darwin was nearly in a panic after he received Wallace's ternate paper. He forwarded the manuscript to Charles Lyell with a note in which he said that he wished that he had heeded Lyell's warning. Lyell and Hooker suggested that Darwin and Wallace both should jointly publish the theory of natural selection. Darwin, cautious but unwilling to give up priority, accepted the solution with gratitude.

Darwin had anticipated such a problem with Wallace's publication of the Sarawak Law; so, he had stepped up the work on the manuscript of his big book, which was nowhere near publication and by that time had grown to a manuscript of more than a half million words with no end in sight. He had secured his priority in other more subtle ways. He had divulged his theory to Lyell and Hooker. He had written his essay of 1844. Also, in 1857, he sent a more polished explanation of natural selection to Asa Gray, an American Botanist with whom he had been in correspondence. So, Lyell and Hooker presented a set of manuscripts to the secretary of the *Linnaean Society* on July 1, 1858. The manuscripts read into the proceedings on that day began with a letter from Lyell and Hooker that explained how the two men had independently formulated the theory of natural selection. They followed their letter with a chapter that described the mecha-

---

[10] In this disease, the blood parasites are synchronous in their growth such that they tend to lyse the infected red blood cells at about the same time. As the cellular debris and parasite waste products flood into the bloodstream, fever takes hold and makes the body feel cold as the body's thermostat resets. Then, as the fever comes down and the thermostat resets at a normal level, the body feels hot. The familiar chills and fevers are followed by a day of recovery. On the third day, the victim will feel somewhat normal before the cycle begins again.

nism of natural selection from Darwin's 1844 essay and a synopsis of the letter to Asa Gray. Finally, they read Wallace's Ternate paper.

Some, like Arnold Brackman[11] suggest that Darwin, Lyell, and Hooker formed a conspiracy against Wallace to relegate the true discoverer of natural selection to a brief footnote in history. Why would they do that? Well, Darwin was their friend and confidant. More importantly, Darwin was of the proper class. This and other works about the Darwin-Wallace affair have given plenty of ammunition to conspiracy theorists, some of whom (chiefly John Langdon Brooks) say that Darwin was not even scooped, but he stole the whole concept of natural selection from Wallace in the greatest conspiracy-cover-up in the history of science.

The conspiracy argument centers on the date that Darwin received the package from Ternate. It seems that immediately upon receipt of the paper, Darwin wrote a response to Wallace, but he dated it the 18th. The question is was it the 18th of June as Darwin said or was it the 18th of May? If it were May, then Darwin would have had a month to work with Wallace's paper and insert concepts, etc. into his big book. Another letter sent to Bates' brother at the same time as the Ternate paper did arrive around the 18th of May. To use such circumstantial evidence as the main support for such a conspiracy is irresponsible. Other evidence indicates that it is as Darwin said. Michael Shermer points out that Darwin's daily routine did not vary all through May and into June. Then, he became focused on this one issue after the 18th of June. Furthermore, Darwin had already written out, though somewhat awkwardly, an outline of his theory in

1842, 1844, and finally in 1857, all *before* the receipt of the Ternate paper.

One insensitive and just plain stupid assertion was that Darwin was so ashamed of the subterfuge that he sent his "henchmen" to do his dirty work at the meeting of the *Linnaean Society*. Nothing could have been farther from the truth. He had one child who was very ill and another (Charles Waring Darwin) who had died of scarlet fever and was being buried on the same day as the presentation.

When Wallace was informed of the arrangement, he was delighted. He felt that he was fortunate to have a theory that allowed him to share the spotlight with one such as Charles Darwin and to have it be important enough to be presented by scientific luminaries like Charles Lyell and Joseph Hooker. Fundamentally, Wallace was not bothered by the situation at all. Indeed, throughout his life, he referred to evolution by natural selection as *Darwinism*.

Darwin abandoned his big book and began work on a much smaller abstract that would be full of supporting examples but light on references. Darwin's detractors said in that format Darwin could avoid the acknowledgement of Wallace's contribution to his central theory. Darwin published *The Origin of Species by Means of Natural Selection* in November 1859. The theory of natural selection, which received little notice after its debut at the Linnaean Society, rippled through science and began to transform biology.

Finally, Wallace decided to return to Britain and began his preparations in 1861. He became obsessed with the possibility of bringing back a living orangutan and birds of paradise. In part, this would erase the ignominy of tragic loss of his living Amazon collection.

---

[11] A journalist who wrote *A Delicate Arrangement, The Strange Case of Charles Darwin and Alfred Russel Wallace* in 1980.

The orangutan died en route and one of the Birds of Paradise died before the trip. However, he did manage to keep two of them alive through the arduous trip and arrived in London on April 1, 1862.

EMERGENCE OF A HERETIC

An Overruling Intelligence has watched over the action of those laws, so directing variations and so determining their accumulation, as finally to produce an organization sufficiently perfect to admit of, and even to aid in, the indefinite advancement of our mental and moral nature. -Alfred Russel Wallace (1869)

Initially, Wallace moved into his mother's house and attempted to recuperate from the lingering effects of malaria, a malady from which he never fully recovered. Wallace did what he could to prepare and organize his collections according to geography, an important tenant of his Sarawak Law. Wallace found that he had broken into the ranks of the scientist super-elite in Britain. Soon, he made the acquaintance of Charles Lyell and Herbert Spencer (1820-1903). He was honored by membership in the Royal Society, chaired at that time by Thomas Henry Huxley (1825-1895), who was one of the most eloquent proponents of evolution. Later in June Wallace and Darwin met at Down House, Darwin's home[12].

Like Darwin, Wallace's third goal on his return was to find a wife. He met Annie Mitten the daughter of a well-known botanist, and they were married in 1866. Unlike Darwin, though, he could not rely on the financial support and backing of a wealthy family. Also, he was still uncertain about his ability to survive on income from his writing after the two disastrous attempts following his return from the Amazon. In addition, he was not a good or stirring speaker; thus, almost all avenues that allowed him to continue his beloved study of natural history were closed to him. His inability to find steady work did not dampen his enthusiasm for study, though. He published numerous articles (more than 700 through his lifetime), one of which was written based on observations that he made of the landscape in Wales during his honeymoon.

He published numerous papers with natural selection as a central theme during the years after his return. Finally, buoyed up by his success in publishing articles, Wallace tried once again to write a book. This was called *The Malay Archipelago* (1869), and it was a financial success, at last[13]. He followed that in 1870 with a book about natural selection.

Wallace tended to use natural selection as the only law for the structure of living things. It worked for most things. However, Wallace was at a loss to explain human intellect and morality as having been produced by natural selection. He had lived among primitive peoples in the Amazon and the Malay Archipelago, and was struck by their capacity for higher thought and a moral sense that he considered to be superior to many cultured Europeans. How could this be possible, particularly, in his opinion, because higher levels of thought and elevated and strict mores were either counter productive or completely unnecessary for the survival of the individual. He considered natural selection to be completely blind to the future usefulness of a trait; so, something else, some other

[12] Wallace claimed that he had met Darwin in the insect gallery of the British Museum before his voyages. Darwin did not remember the encounter.

[13] I elaborate the importance of this book to science in *Islands and Their Lessons in Biogeography*.

He considered natural selection to be completely blind to the future usefulness of a trait; so, something else, some other law, must have guided the evolution of the human mind.

Wallace became converted to the spiritualist fad that was sweeping Europe during the mid 19th Century. His sister, Fanny, an ardent follower, introduced him to séances and mediums soon after his return. At first he was skeptical, but once he became a convert, he embraced the spirit world completely. Then, he used the spirit world as the dimension in which thought and morality resided. He exposed this concept in 1869 during a review of Lyell's 10th edition of *The Principles of Geology.* Darwin was completely taken aback and asked Wallace if he was going to murder their child (natural selection) by making such assertions.

Almost as an answer to Wallace's objections, Darwin produced the *Descent of Man* in 1871. In this 2-volume work, Darwin argued that human evolution operated by a particular modification of natural selection, a modification that he called sexual selection. This mechanism assumed that the selection of mates, particularly the selection of the male by the female in many different vertebrate groups (e.g. birds, mammals), is the most important driving force of evolution.

Consider the Bird of Paradise, the extravagant plumage of the male would seem to run counter to its ability to evade predators and to catch food. Indeed, the extraneous feathers should even impede its ability to fly. However, its appearance announces its presence and allows it to attract a female in spite of the difficulties. The final word is that new varieties and species do not arise by the survival of individuals but by the differential reproduction of individuals. That is, those who leave more offspring are the ones whose

traits determine the nature of the group. Darwin expanded that argument in his next book, *The Expression of Emotion in Man and Animals* (1872) in which behavior itself is treated as a trait that can evolve[14].

Wallace, who by that time was completely captured by the spirit world argument, rejected Darwin's argument. In part, he explained that such modifications ran counter to natural selection. Wallace then followed with a book on miracles and spiritualism (1875). This set him clearly on a path at the fringe of science. Wallace did not abandon science, however. His publications after that helped to establish the science of ecology called biogeography.

No more telling difference between Darwin and Wallace can be seen than by an examination of their published books, which I take as a representative subset of their overall record of publication. Compare Tables 1 and 2. After the publication of *The Origin*, Darwin continued with the theme of evolution by natural selection. All of his books, except the one about his grandfather Erasmus read almost as chapters of his proposed big book. Thus, in effect, Darwin did write it and published it in installments from 1859 to 1881, one year before his death. Wallace's record of publication is much more eclectic, though (see Table 2). Some of his books were about natural selection, ecology, and natural history. He also wrote books in support of spiritualism and many aspects of social policy. Like Darwin, he continued to publish throughout his life. In fact, he published two books in his last year.

Because of the quality of Wallace's scientific publications, particularly those on biogeography, Darwin pushed for a

---

[14] This book is the focus of *Language, a Nurture of Nature.*

royal pension to support him. Influential scientists of the day (e.g. Joseph Hooker) were reluctant to sign a petition to that effect because of Wallace's blatant gullibility with regard to spiritualism. Darwin managed to push it through, though, and Wallace received support until his death, 31 years after Darwin died

TABLE 6-2. Darwin's published books and the dates of the publication of their first editions.

	TITLE
1840	*Journal of Researches During the Voyage of the Beagle.*
1842	*Structure and Distribution of Coral Reefs*
1846	*Geological Observations on Volcanic Islands and Parts of South America*
1851-1854	*Monographs on the Cirripidae*
1859	*The Origin of Species*
1862	*The Various Contrivances by which British and Foreign Orchids are Fertilized by Insects*
1868	*Variation of Plants and Animals under Domestication*
1871	*Descent of Man*
1872	*Expression of Emotion in Man and Animals*
1875	*Insectivorous Plants*
1875	*Movements and Habits of Climbing Plants*
1876	*Effects of Cross and Self Fertilization in the Vegetable Kingdom*
1877	*Different Forms of Flowers and Plants of the Same Species*
1879	*Life of Erasmus Darwin*
1880	*Power of Movement in Plants*
1881	*Formation of Vegetable Mould Through the Action of Worms*

TABLE 6-3. Wallace's published books and their dates of publication.

	TITLE
1853	*Palm Trees of the Amazon and their Uses*
1853	*A Narrative of Travels on the Amazon and Rio Negro*
1869	*The Malay Archipelago; The Land of the Orang-utan and the Bird of Paradise*
1870	*Contributions to the Theory of Natural Selection, A Series of Essays*
1875	*Miracles and Modern Spritiualism. Three Essays*
1876	*The Geographical Distribution of Animals*
1878	*Tropical Nature and Other Essays*
1879	*Australasia*
1880	*Island Life*
1882	*Land Nationalisation*
1885	*Bad Times; An Essay on the Present Depression of Trade*
1889	*Darwinism*
1891	*Natural Selection and Tropical Nature*
1898	*The Wonderful Century; Its Successes and its Failures*
1900	*Studies Scientific and Social*
1903	*Man's Place in the Universe*
1905	*My Life*
1907	*Is Mars Habitable?*
1908	*Notes of a Botanist on the Amazon and Andes*
1910	*The World of Life; A Manifestation of Creative Power, Directive Mind, and Ultimate Purpose*
1913	*Social Environment and Moral Progress*
1913	*The Revolt of Democracy*

CONTINGENCY & COINCIDENCE

Contingency...becomes a residual domain for details left unexplained by general laws. Stephen J. Gould (2002)

One can hardly think of Wallace without some comparison with Darwin. The two men shared many characteristics. Indeed, their paths to the discovery of natural selection seem to have been eerily similar: they both studied the abundance of life offered by the tropics, they both studied islands, and they both interpreted their results in light of Lyell's necessary, but they were not sufficient to give rise to the theory. Other explorers had the same set of experiences. Why did they not discover it? Much has to be explained by accident or coincidence. By coincidence, Darwin read Malthus when he did. By coincidence, Wallace struck up a correspondence with Darwin, and by coincidence, Wallace sent Darwin the manuscript of his Ternate paper. Did these accidents indicate the hand of fate or some design? Of course not. Wallace had to be in communication with someone, and fortunately, it was with Darwin. If someone with Darwin's scientific stature and enormous collection of supporting facts had not presented natural selection and evolution to the world, their acceptance would have been much slower. Perhaps, Biology, a discipline that is united by the principle of evolution, would have fragmented in the 19th Century. However, things did happen as they did just because they did.

Coincidences occur all of the time. For example, Abraham Lincoln and Charles Darwin were born on the same day. Nothing more can be made of that coincidence except that the two men were the same age (at least up to Lincoln's assassination).

Was my decision to become a scientist a coincidence or was it contingent upon my having contracted hepatitis? I will never know. I cannot imagine a life other than the one I have lived.

Certainly, the coincidence of Wallace contacting Darwin from Ternate with a manuscript about natural selection did cause Darwin to act. Up to that point he did not seem in a great hurry to finish his big book. Without that contingency[15], he might never have finished it. Any number of naturalists who also were concerned with the species question might have

scooped him. Coincidence and contingency shape human history just as they shape natural history, so that some events in the history of life appear to have a purpose and a direction. Of all of the ape lineages, ours was the only one to adopt an upright or bipedal gait. We might have developed the human mind, complex language and social system without going bipedal, but we did. So, although "what if" scenarios are fun to play with, they do not provide much help in understanding how the history of life did come about.

The problem is when belief in a false concept colors the interpretation of an observation. Fortunately, science is a community so that one person's opinion or interpretation does not go unchallenged. As Darwin put it, a false interpretation is not as bad as a false observation (a fabricated observation). The interpretation can be reexamined; falsified data cannot. Wallace did not falsify information; he was just gullible when it came to the scientific explanation of the spirit world. For more than 100 years spiritualist claims have been examined and rejected by science. Similarly, beliefs in UFO's, lake monsters, intelligent design, etc. all fall outside of the realm of science. Such pseudosciences have appeal and attract many followers. The dangerous followers are those who in their zeal to promote their idea or themselves, falsify or intentionally produce illusions intended to fool "the believers". The lies of such frauds only cause small setbacks in science, but they present themselves as legitimate, sometimes alternative, means of understanding nature to the public at large. Such views might be legitimate in a spiritual or cultural sense, but they are not in a material sense. That is the danger to our civilization. If science is not taught as scientists

_____

[15] I explain Gould's concept of contingency in the history of life in *Lost Worlds.*

do it, then the presentation to the public is nothing more than a perversion shaped by illusion and falsification. Wallace, remembering his own miserable educational experience, wrote and spoke for science education reform through his life after his return from the Molluccas. If such a reformed science education had been in place for Wallace, he might have had the appropriate theoretical instruments to avoid the traps of the spiritualist frauds.

I think that I would have liked both Darwin and Wallace, though Darwin would have been very hard to get to know. Not only was he shielded in the citadel of Down House, but rarely opened up even to his closest friends. Of the two, Darwin was the mentor. He was slow, methodical, careful, and also pessimistic. Wallace, the heretic, was quick, less careful, but more adventurous, and very optimistic. Certainly, science benefited from the attributes of both men, the architects of natural selection and the founders of modern biology.

-2005

References:

Beddall, Barbara, G., ed. 1969. *Wallace and Bates in the Tropics, An Introduction to the Theory of Natural Selection.* The MacMillan Co. London.

Bowler, Peter J. 1992. *The Fontana History of the Environmental Sciences.* IN: Porter, Roy, ed. *Fontana History of Science.* Fontana Press. London.

Brackman, Arnold. C. 1980. *A Delicate Arrangement, The Strange Case of Charles Darwin and Alfred Russel Wallace.* Times Books. New York.

Browne, Janet. *Charles Darwin, Voyaging.* Princeton University Press. Princeton, NJ.

Browne, Janet. *Charles Darwin, The Power of Place.* Princeton University Press. Princeton, NJ.

Burkhardt, Krederick, ed. 1996. *Charles Darwin's Letters, A Selection 1825-1859.* Cambridge University Press. New York.

Chambers, Robert. 1870 (originally published 1844). *Vestiges of the Natural Histroy of Creation. With a Sequel.* Harper & Brothers, Publishers. New York.

Darwin, Charles. 1979 (originally published 1859). *The Origin of Species.* Gramercy Books. New York.

Darwin, Charles. (originally published 1845). *The Voyage of the H.M.S. Beagle.* 2nd edition. The Heritage Press. New York.

Darwin, Francis, ed. 1958 (originally published in 1992). *The Autobiography of Charles Darwin and Selected Letters.* Dover Publications Inc. New York.

Darwin, Francis, ed. 1896. *The Life and Letters of Charles Darwin.* Vol 1-2. D. Appelton & Co. New York.

Desmond, Adrian and James Moore. 1991. *The Life of a Tormented Darwin.* Warner Books, Inc. New York.

Eiseley, Loren 1961. *Darwin's Century: Evolution and the Men Who Discovered It.* Doubleday, Anchor Books. New York.

Gould, Stephen Jay. 2002. *The Structure of Evolutionary Theory.* The Belknap Press of Harvard University. Cambridge, Mass.

Holt, Jack R. and Patricia Nelson. 2001. *Paths of Science.* Kendall/Hunt. Dubuque.

Huxley, Thomas Henry. 1896. *Darwiniana.* D. Appleton & Co. New York.

Irvine, William. 1955. *Apes, Angels, and Victorians, The Story of Darwin, Huxley, and Evolution.* McGraw-Hill Book Co, Inc. New York.

Keynes, R. D., ed. 2001. *Charles Darwin's Beagle Diary.* Cambridge University Press. Cambridge.

Lloyd, Elisabeth. 1994. *The Structure and Confirmation of Evolutionary Theory.* Princeton University Press. Princeton, NJ.

Loewenberg, Bert James, ed. 1959. *Charles Darwin: Evolution and Natural Selection, An Anthology of Writings of Charles Darwin.* Beacon Press. Boston.

Lyell, Charles. 1990 (originally published 1830-33). *Principles of Geology.* Vol 1-3. University of Chicago Press. Chicago.

Mason, Stephen F. 1962. *A History of the Sciences.* Collier Books. New York.

Mayr, Ernst. 1991. *One Long Argument, Charles Darwin and the Genesis of Modern Evolutionary Thought.* Harvard University Press. Cambridge.

Mayr, Ernst. 2001. *What Evolution Is.* Basic Books. New York.

Milner, Richard. 1994. *Charles Darwin, Evolution of a Naturalist.* Facts on File, Inc. New York.

Raby, Peter. 1996. *Bright Paradise, Victorian Scientific Travelers.* Princeton University Press. Princeton, NJ.

Raby, Peter. 2001. *Alfred Russel Wallace, A Life.* Princeton University Press. Princeton, NJ.

Ruse, Michael. 1999. *The Darwinian Revolution, Science Red in Tooth and Claw.* The University of Chicago Press. Chicago.

Schermer, Michael. 2002. *In Darwin's Shadow, The Life and Science of Alfred Russel Wallace.* Oxford University Press. New York.

Van Oosterzee, Penny. 1997. *Where World Collide, The Wallace Line.* Cornell University Press. Ithaca, NY.

Wallace, Alfred R. 1874. *The Malay Archipelago, The Land of the Orang-Utan and the Bird of Paradise.* MacMillan & Co. London.

Wallace, Alfred R. 1890. *Darwinism.* MacMillan & Co. London.

Wallace, Alfred, R. 1895. *A Narrative of Travels on the Amazon and Rio Negro.* 5th edition. Ward, Lock, and Bowden, Ltd. London.

Wheeler, Quentin D. and Rudolph Meier, eds. 2000. *Species Concepts and Phylogenetic Theory, A Debate.* Columbia University Press. New York.

Questions to Think About

1. What is the difference between contingency and coincidence? How do they figure into history or into science?

2. How does Darwin's early life contrast with his life from the voyage onward?

3. What were some of the main clues that Darwin used to devise the theory of natural Selection?

4. Why did Darwin delay publication of Natural Selection? What prompted him to publish?

5. How did Wallace come to the theory of Natural Selection?

6. What is meant by *the delicate arrangement*?

7. In what way was Wallace a heretic?

8. How do the lists of published books differ between Darwin and Wallace?

9. What evidence is there to suggest that Darwin and Wallace were on good terms from 1858 until Darwin's death in 1882?

10. What is the difference between a false observation and a false interpretation? **Are** they equally injurious to science?

A TALE OF TWO STONES

A VISIT TO DOWN HOUSE

Erasmus [Darwin's brother], *who hated the country, declared they ought to call the place "Down-in-the-Mouth."*

-Janet Browne

I have two stones, chalk and flint, on my desk among the clutter of papers, books, catalogs, old mail and post-its. The chalk is white and easily scratched with a fingernail. The piece of flint is hard and gray with sharp edges (see Figure 6-11). I picked them up this one summer's day in 1995 when I visited Charles Darwin's house and garden, an estate called Down House.

FIGURE 6-11. Two stones, chalk (left) and flint (right) that I picked up on Darwin's estate during a visit in the summer of 1995.

Darwin and his growing family moved from the hustle and bustle of London to the bucolic village of Downe in September of 1842. Both Darwin and his wife, Emma, had grown up in similar rural settings. The move was not greeted with universal delight, however. Many of his fellow scientists could not believe that Darwin would prefer to be in the country over the apartment in which they had lived in the political, social, and scientific capitol of Britain. In truth, Down House was only about 16 miles south of London, but the rail lines were not very conveniently situated. So, a trip to London could take up to half a day. That degree of isolation also meant that Darwin and his family were cut off from visitors, unless they spent the night there. He lived at his home in the village of Downe (an estate which he called Down House; see Figure 6-12) from 1842 until his death in 1882. It was at Down that Darwin carried out his research on barnacles, pigeons, orchids, earthworms, etc. It was in this atmosphere of a quiet country life that Darwin produced most of his scientific work, including publication of *The Origin of Species, The Descent of Man*[16] along with eleven other major works.

FIGURE 6-12. The front of Darwin's estate, Down House in the village of Downe, south of London. The two closest windows on the ground floor belong to his his study of more than 30 years.

---

[16] The timetable for the publication of these and other works is given in *The Mentor and the Heretic.*

Nearly an invalid since the voyage of the Beagle, Darwin lived comfortably with his family in the estate on an inheritance from his father. There, he was able to devote himself completely to his science without the distractions of society or of working at a profession. In this way, Darwin was a "gentleman" scientist, unattached to any academic institution or museum and the distractions of a profession. When needed, he enlisted the aid of his children and household servants, but generally did almost all of his work alone.

Darwin stuck to a very regular schedule throughout his life. He worked through the morning in his study. Then, when he felt well enough, and weather permitted, he walked a sand-covered path around his estate. It was called the sandwalk, though Darwin frequently referred to it as his thinking path (see Figure 6-13). From this vantage point he watched the annual cycle of nature.

Thus, Darwin walked from the back of his house past the kitchen gardens, greenhouse and meadow. Then, he passed through a low gate and walked a narrow path with hedges on one side and the meadow on the other. This was the same meadow that Darwin watched and studied through most of his 40 years at Down House.

DARWIN'S WORM BOOK

It is a marvelous reflection that the whole of the superficial mould over any such expanse has passed, and will again pass every few years through the bodies of worms. Charles Darwin (1881)

Darwin's health caused him to become a recluse. Nevertheless, he was very famous, but his notoriety bothered him very much. Others carried on the public fight about evolution in Darwin's name. Darwin, however, continued to write and conduct research. His many books after *The Origin* were concerned with other aspects of evolution, particularly as they illustrated natural selection. The topics that he explored ranged from orchids and domestic animals to the evolution of human beings. That is why his last book, which was about earthworms and their habits, seemed so out of place. He published *The Formation of Vegetable Mould through the Action of Worms, with Observations on Their Habits* in 1881, within a year of his death.

Many were disappointed or assumed that the worm book was the product of Darwin's senility. I am sure that they did not read his last book, or if they did read it, they misunderstood its intent. His book on worms is about their behavior in the soil, their impact on the structure of the soil, and their influence in shaping the landscape. The book showed the same careful work and attention to detail, which had distinguished his other writings. More importantly, the worm book is about how small changes can have a major impact when given enough time, a metaphor for the gradualistic nature of evolution. This was the lesson that must be understood in order to appreciate how evolution works. Darwin chose apparently insignificant creatures to illustrate his great lesson.

Darwin wrote a very brief autobiography at about the same time as the worm book. At the end of it, he examines his life and sums up his personal assessment this way, "With such modest abilities as I possess, it is truly surprising that I should have influenced to a considerable extent the belief of scientific men on some important points."

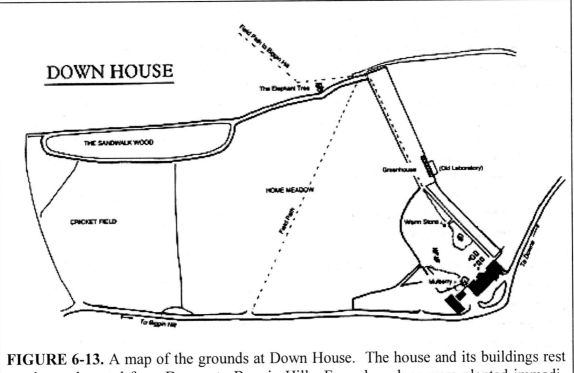

FIGURE 6-13. A map of the grounds at Down House. The house and its buildings rest nearly on the road from Downe to Boggin Hill. Formal gardens were planted immediately back of the house. However, most of it was fields, meadows and woods separated by hedgerows. Through these ran his sandwalk or thinking path. The map is taken from Titheradge (1981).

Darwin noticed that the pieces of flint and chalk, which had covered the fallow field in 1842, when he and Emma moved into Down House, had disappeared beneath the surface by 1871. He even set up an experiment by spreading broken chalk on part of the field (see Figure 6-14). Later, he dug up the chalk pieces and determined that the stones were "sinking into" the soil about 0.22 inches per year. He speculated that the continuous and unrelenting activity of earthworms had changed the face of his meadow. He examined other fields, buildings and other stones. He even examined the stones, which had fallen over at Stonehenge and noticed that the way that they were sinking into the ground was consistent with the action of earthworms.

The sandwalk led to a loop through a wooded area of beech, cherry, maple, yew and oak. When confronted by a particularly difficult problem, Darwin would stack flints at the beginning of the loop through the sandwalk wood. At each turn, he would whack a flint with his walking stick to keep track of the number of times around the loop. He often referred to problems as "one flint" or "two flint" problems. A very complex problem might require three flints.

FIGURE 6-14. An illustration from Darwin's Worm Book that showed the structure of the soil after earthworms had caused his chalk to "sink" into the ground.

As I walked the sandwalk I could view a landscape that was very similar to what Darwin might have seen. There was a valley with a patchwork of fields surrounded by hedgerows. These were punctuated by great white exposures of chalk, a rock that dominates the landscape of southern England. Not only are there great exposures of chalk (the White Cliffs of Dover are made of chalk) but also the ecology of the Downs region is determined by the alkaline and porous nature of the chalk deposits. The great chalk deposits of England are more than 1,000 feet thick in places and occur over much of Europe. The deposits were laid down during the Cretaceous period, the last great period of the dinosaurs. In fact, Cretaceous comes from the Latin *Creta* which means chalk[17].

ON A PIECE OF CHALK

But the mind is so constituted that it does not willingly rest in facts and immediate causes, but seeks always after a knowledge of the remoter links in the chain of causation.

-Thomas Henry Huxley (1868)

In 1868, Thomas Henry Huxley (1825-1895), delivered a talk called *On a Piece of Chalk* to The Working Men of Norwich. The popular lecture was later published as an essay in Macmillin's Magazine as an essay. His lecture illustrated the same theme as Darwin's Worm Book would in 1881. Huxley attempted to show that chalk, its occurrence and abundance, were the consequences of the actions of single-celled organisms acting by unchanging natural law over immense amounts of time.

Much earlier, before the publication of *The Origin*, Huxley had delivered a withering attack on the concept of transmutation as presented by the anonymous (now known to be and then assumed to be publicist Robert Cham-

bers) author of *The Vestiges of Creation*. This book was published in 1844 and presented arguments from scattered evidence that life had changed over time. However, his facts were jumbled and his mechanism was easily attacked. Darwin knew that he would have to win Huxley over by facts and logic. He did not know if Huxley would become a convert, but he did not want Huxley's eloquent wit to be pitted against him and his theory.

In 1856, Darwin had invited Huxley, Joseph Hooker (1814-1879), and Thomas Wollaston (1822-1878) and their families to Down House for a weekend. Darwin had great respect for the three men, but especially wanted to cultivate Huxley's belief in the transmutation (evolution) of species. Huxley was sharp-witted and a terror as an enemy. The conversation among the four men turned to the species question, particularly, the inability to define the boundaries between certain ones. Apparently, Huxley left Down House agreeing in concept that species might change.

In a letter to Huxley accompanying an advanced copy of *The Origin* Darwin said, "I know there will be much in it which you will object to." Huxley read the book with interest and gave the highest praise when he responded, *"How extremely stupid of me not to have thought of that!"* At that point, Huxley was a convert and a crusader[18]. Darwin was reluctant to fight for his ideas in a public way. However, Huxley relished a good fight and engaged in public debates, and wrote many general interest essays with the theme of evolution. Huxley's tenacity, as well as his appearance, earned him the nickname of "Darwin's Bulldog."

Within four years of the publication of *The Origin*, Huxley answered a challenge by Richard Owen (1804-1892, England) who said that the human brain is unique and, therefore, humans could not be the

---

[17] I explain this in *Reading the Earth.*

[18] Find more about Huxley's contributions in *Parasites and Darwin's Intellectual Triumph.*

product of evolution. Huxley showed that the human brain was structurally identical to that of the chimpanzee. In addition, he showed that muscle for muscle and bone for bone, humans were more similar to apes than apes were to monkeys.

Later, Huxley argued "The doctrine of evolution in biology is the necessary result of the logical application of the principles of uniformitarianism to the phenomena of life." In his essay, *On a Piece of Chalk*, Huxley describes the biological nature of chalk. That is, if you examine chalk with a microscope, you can see that it is made of countless one-celled organisms called Foraminifera (this literally means window-bearer; see Figure 6-15)). The forams make a calcium carbonate shell, which is covered with holes. The dominant forams are called *Globigerina* and are about 0.5 to 1 mm across. How many of these would have to die and layer out on the bottom of an ocean to make a deposit 1,000 feet thick? Then, how long would it take for the sea bottom to rise and begin to weather away? The theory of gradualism, the principle of uniformatarianism, and enormous amounts of time provide the framework within which evolution can work.

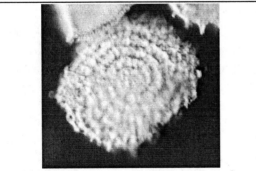

FIGURE 6-15. A low power microscopic view of a foraminiferan from a piece of the chalk from Darwin's garden.

MY THINKING PATH WALK
It is interesting to contemplate a tangled bank... -Charles Darwin (1859)

I returned to my group after I walked the oval of the sandwalk wood for the second time. There, I picked up pieces of flint and chalk and proceeded down the path, past the meadow and wild hedges. I stopped and looked at a bank, overgrown with brambles and vines. There, the last paragraph of *The Origin* came alive.

It is interesting to contemplate a tangled bank, clothed with many plants of many kinds, with birds singing on the bushes, with various insects flitting about, and with worms crawling through the damp earth, and to reflect that these elaborately constructed forms so different from each other, and dependent upon each other in so complex a manner, have all been produced by laws acting around us. There is a grandeur in this view of life with its several powers having been originally breathed by the Creator into a few forms or into one; and that, while this planet has gone circling on according to the fixed law of gravity, from so simple a beginning endless forms most beautiful and most wonderful have been and are being evolved.

Indeed, there is a grandeur in seeing ourselves connected thus with the life that surrounds us, supports us, and is part of us. Darwin gave us the way to explain and begin to understand that connection. More importantly, they gave us a reason to care about the organisms with which we have a connection. Darwin's earthworms and Huxley's forams teach us the same lesson: the earth is very old, and given enough time, even the most humble of creatures can literally change its face.

FIGURE 6-16. I am walking Darwin's Sandwalk path in the summer of 1995.

-1995, revised 2005.

References:

Brent, Peter. 1981. *Charles Darwin, A Man of Enlarged Curiosity.* Harper and Row, Publishers. New York.

Bowlby, John. 1990. *Charles Darwin, A New Life.* W.W. Norton & Co. New York.

Browne, Janet. 1995. *Charles Darwin, Voyaging.* Princeton University Press. Princeton.

Browne, Janet. 2002. *Charles Darwin, The Power of Place.* Alfred A. Knopf. New York.

Darwin, Charles R. 1859. *The Origin of Species by Means of Natural Selection.* D. Appleton & Co. New York.

Darwin, Charles R. 1881. *The Formation of Vegetable Mould, Through the Action of Earthworms, with Observations on their Habits.* John Murray, Albemarle Street. London.

Desmond, Adrian and James Moore. 1991. *Darwin, The Life of a Tormented Evolutionist.* Warner Books, Inc. New York.

Eisley, Loren. 1961. *Darwin's Century, Evolution and the Men Who Discovered It.* Doubleday & Co. Garden City, NY.

Huxley, Thomas Henry. 1868. *On a Piece of Chalk.* IN: 1874. *Lay Sermons, Addresses, and Reviews.* Macmillan & Co. London.

Huxley, Thomas Henry. 1889. *The Coming Age of the 'Origin of Species.'* IN: Loewenberg, Bert James, ed. 1959. *Charles Darwin: Evolution and Natural Selection.* Beacon Press. Boston.

Irvine, William. 1955. *Apes, Angels, and Victorians, The Story of Darwin, Huxley, and Evolution.* McGraw-Hill Book Co, Inc. New York.

Kudo, Richard R. 1966. *Protozoology.* 5th edition. Charles C. Thomas, Publisher. Springfield, Illinois.

Lloyd, Elisabeth. 1994. *The Structure and Confirmation of Evolutionary Theory.* Princeton University Press. Princeton, NJ.

Milner, Richard. 1994. *Charles Darwin: Evolution of a Naturalist.* Facts on File, Inc. New York.

Titheradge, Philip. 1981. *The Darwin Museum at Down House, Downe, Kent.* Beric Tempest. London.

Trefil, James and Robert Hazen. 1995. *The Sciences, An Integrated Approach.* John Wiley & Sons, Inc. New York.

Questions to Think About

1. What are the types of stones that I found on the grounds of Down House?

2. What was Darwin's daily routine at Down House?

3. Why did he want to cultivate the friendship and support of Thomas Henry Huxley?

4. Why did Darwin write a book about earthworms? How did it fit into the themes of his writings after the publication of *The Origin*?

5. What experiments did Darwin perform with earthworms?

6. How did Huxley earn the name, "Darwin's Bulldog"?

7. What point did Huxley intend in *On a Piece of Chalk*?

8. What is the importance of foraminifera in Huxley's essay?

THE SYSTEMATICS WARS: SCHOOLS OF MODERN TAXONOMY

A COURSE EVOLVES

The first step in a survey of natural history...should be the acquisition of some familiarity with the system of names and the system of classification, with the word equipment used by naturalists.   -Marston Bates (1950)

I have taught a course on the diversity of life almost every year that I have had university teaching appointments. Even as a graduate student I taught or assisted in such courses. Through that period, the appreciation for the diversity of life within the biology curriculum has waxed and waned. Moreover, the subject itself has undergone considerable change from 1970 to the present. At first, all of life was divided into plants (Botany) and animals (Zoology). This dichotomy seemed natural and went all the way back to the time of Aristotle (384-322 BCE). Such was my training in college and graduate school. The first courses that I taught on biological diversity as a new professor was called Plant Diversity and covered all living things that were not considered animals. Someone else taught zoology. Then, the five-kingdom system finally took hold and the course evolved into something called Plants, Protists, and Fungi, which was similar to Plant Diversity but incorporated the animal-like protists into a standard survey of botany. Finally, after the animal kingdom had been eliminated from the other introductory courses, the course became Systematic Biology and embraced all living things with emphases on biodiversity and phylogenetic relationships. Throughout all iterations of the surveys, evolution had been the focus.

The evolution of the survey courses pretty much reflects the three common theoretical schools of classification[19] that had developed since the Modern Synthesis[20]. They were:

1.   Evolutionary Taxonomy
2.   Numerical Taxonomy
3.   Phylogenetic Taxonomy

The three schools produce taxonomic hierarchies that resemble each other, and are fundamentally the same in some of their assumptions, particularly that all things have evolved from a common ancestor and that the classification reflects their degree of kinship. Nevertheless, the followers of the three schools have had some bitter fights from during the past 35 years.

Ernst Mayr (1904-; Germany & USA), an architect of the evolutionary taxonomy school said that classification has always had two functions: a practical and a scientific one. The practical function of taxonomy always has been a way to organize life, a kind of giant roadmap of all living things. The scientific purpose, at least since Darwin, has been to reflect the degree to which they are related to each other. Similarly,

---

[19] Classification is the arrangement of taxa in a heirarchary. Taxonomy and systematics both refer to the theory of classification.

[20] The Modern Synthesis was a way to accommodate the conflict between the Darwinists and the Mutationists of the early 20th Century. Ernst Mayr (and some other biology luminaries like Theodosius Dobzhonsky, George Gaylord Simpson, and Julian Huxley) worked out how Mendelian genetics explained the hereditary part of evolutionary theory while natural selection explained the way organisms change.

the tension between the classification systems is the tension between the practical and the scientific.

MODERN TAXONOMIC SYSTEMS

If a classification system is based strictly and exclusively on the monophyly of the included taxa, it is a genealogical ordering system. -Ernst Mayr (1997)

Classical classification systems before Darwin also had a similar tension between the practical and the general, but a general function that was not based on evolutionary relationships. In a world in which life did not evolve, the classification system assumed that species were invariant or could undergo some minor changes. Either way, the general object of classification was to find the character or characters that defined the essence of the group. That was how Carolus Linnaeus[21] (1707-1778; Sweden) defined the format of the taxonomic system that we still use today. However, his fundamental philosophy could not have been more different from the taxonomists of today. He defined the taxonomic hierarchy with the understanding that life did not change. Thus, the differences and similarities between taxa were the consequences of the similarities and differences between their essences.

Darwin recognized that the Linnaean taxonomic hierarchy and the particular relationships between species would have been the consequence of descent with modification, the principle of evolution (see Figure 6-17). Thus, he used classification as evidence for evolution, and it figured prominently in *The Origin*. Following Darwin's lead, taxonomists began to use the essentialistic classifications to infer evolutionary relationships. Also, classification systems could be altered according to new evolutionary inferences. That became the goal of evolutionary taxonomy.

In the early days of evolutionary taxonomy, though, the purpose of systematics (= taxonomy[22]) had been to define classification systems based on evolutionary lines (phylogeny) defined by fossils and by other disciplines like comparative anatomy. This led to a near fruitless search for "missing links". The discipline matured in the late 19th and early 20th Centuries to recognize the population, not the species, as the unit of evolution. Thus, the use of statistics became appropriate in the study of evolutionary relationships leading to classifications.

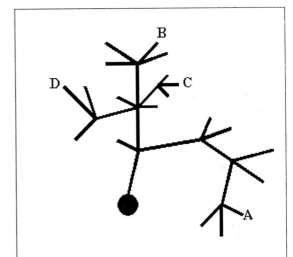

FIGURE 6-17. Redrawn from an early illustration by Darwin showing the tree-like pattern produced by lineages derived by descent with modification from a common ancestor (black circle).

---

[21] You can find much more about Linnaeus and the initiation of his system in the essay called *Kingdoms.*

[22] The equivalence of the terms is only approximate. Systematics includes the diversity of all living things and the evolutionary relationships that bind them. Historically, taxonomy has been a component of systematics, and includes: identification, classification (how things are ordered into a hierarchy), and nomenclature (how things ---- ---- ed) according to Winston (1999).

This was the nature of systematics through much of the 20th Century. In this way, Evolutionary Taxonomy seemed to be the legitimate heir of Classical Taxonomy. Unfortunately, such systems required specialists who seemed to apply arbitrary criteria for determining definitions of particular families, genera, etc. For example, within the insects, the orders and level of difference between orders seemed consistent, but an insect order could not be compared to a mammalian order. Could taxonomic hierarchies be created such that ordinal-level differences were consistent? This was not a problem for those who used biological classification for practical purposes, but it was very unsatisfactory for a few who insisted that biological classification reflect the branching tree of evolutionary descent with modification.

The introduction of the computer allowed for the development of statistical comparisons between many characters with multiple character states. If so, then comparisons between taxa could be made using a large matrix of taxa and characters such that the matrix was filled with observable character states. The characters were not ordered nor were they weighted. This would allow for a pristine, classification, untainted by preconceptions. The dream was to make taxonomy free and independent of theory, and, thereby, objective.

Peter H. A. Sneath (UK), who had employed such methods in the classification of bacteria in the 1950's joined Robert R. Sokal (USA), a biological statistician. Together, they founded this school with the publication of *Principles of Numerical Taxonomy* in 1963. That term was used interchangeably with Phenetics, a reference to the comparisons of phenotypes. The numerical methods mainly employed similarity indices between taxa based on their respective character states. The resulting hierarchy of similarities would produce a tree-like diagram, a diagram reflecting their biological classification and their evolutionary relationships.

Numerical taxonomy produced a renaissance in systematics. The obvious power of having an objective means of classifying organisms was very appealing. Also, because it was theory-free, it could be used to explore evolution without the logical fallacy of circular reasoning.

Unfortunately, the promise of phenetics has not been fulfilled. Such pure objectivity is illusory because within science, all operations are theory-laden. Other difficulties include the treatment of characters. Within numerical taxonomy, all characters are equal, and, therefore, biased toward unimportant easily observed ones.

Willi Hennig (1913-1976, Germany) was an entomologist who was not satisfied with classification systems. He recognized that the classification produced by evolutionary taxonomy was subjective, and its methods could neither be codified nor repeated. On the other hand, classification produced by numerical taxonomy was arbitrary and based on the characters chosen. Hennig proposed that numerical-like methods be adopted. However, some rules needed to be assumed. First, character states should be identified as primitive (plesiomorphic) and derived (apomorphic). That taxa share primitive characters (symplesiomorphic) is uninformative. Only shared derived characters (synapomorphic) are informative about their evolutionary histories, and, therefore, their systematic relationships. Also, because many trees can be derived from a single character X taxon matrix, the tree with the fewest number of changes (most parsimonious) would be the best according to Occam's

Razor. The proper statistical test, then would be a test of parsimony.

The attraction of phylogenetic taxonomy was that its methods were repeatable algorithms and that it used phylogenetic inference as its guiding principle. It was not, and made no pretense to be, theory-independent. Hennig presented this philosophy in 1966 in a book called *Phylogenetic Systematics*. His followers were few at first but grew within the Numerical Taxonomy community. The coexistence between the two philosophies, however, broke out into an acrimonious philosophical civil war.

THE SYSTEMATICS WARS

We old survivors of the systematics wars sit around nursing our post-traumatic stress disorder and telling our war stories to the few who will listen.

-Joseph Felsenstein (2001)

The systematics wars between the three schools began in the 1970's. The evolutionary taxonomists were concerned with variable rates of evolution and taxonomic evidence that considered such problems. Thus, they argued that a strict algorithmic approach to taxonomy would ignore one of the most important aspects of evolution and speciation. Nevertheless, evolutionary taxonomists were being nudged out of favor. Mayr, one of the principle critics of the new taxonomic schools called the phylogenetic taxonomists cladists in reference to the branch (clade) and the systematic importance given to clades. It was intended as a derogatory remark, but the phylogenetic taxonomists began to wear that as a badge of honor.

Sokal attempted to demonstrate that parsimony, one of the fundamental tenets of phylogenetic taxonomy, was inappropriate and that clusters of similar taxa should define a classification system. Through the 1970's the differences between the pheneticists and the cladists grew increasingly rancorous until a full break came at the 1979 meeting of the Numerical Taxonomy meetings at Harvard. Following that meeting, an all out bitter fight ensued where cladists attempted to take over systematics by controlling its journals and societies.

What were they fighting about? Well, consider seven theoretical taxa (A, B, C, D, E, F, G). In this case, we will consider only two characters (I, II). The two dimensional distances between the taxa based on their characters and differences between their character states are given in Figure 6-18, which is a solution to a character-taxon matrix. A dendrogram based on their proximity or similarity is given in Figure 6-19. Taxa A, B and C form a cluster in which they differ by a taxonomic distance of 2. Taxa F and G form a similar cluster. Taxa D and E are more alike and are separated only by a taxonomic distance of 1.

A cladistic analysis of the same set of taxa and characters likewise is based on a matrix of taxa and characters (see Figure 6-20). The solution to this matrix, however, is based on parsimony and a diagram that requires the fewest number of changes in character states from the base of the tree or cladogram (see Figure 6-21) to the ends with the taxa. In this case, the character I has 3 states and character II has 5 states. The cladogram is identical to the dendrogram of Figure 6; however, the difference in philosophy becomes clear when considering how the states of the characters change from the base of the tree to the taxa in question.

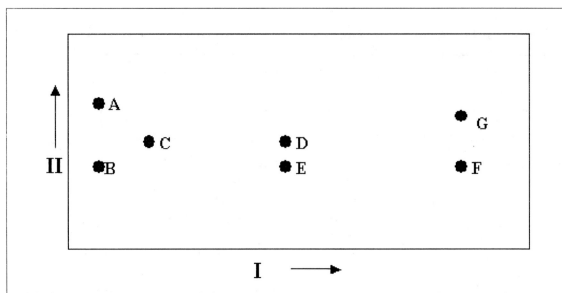

FIGURE 6-18. A diagram of distance between taxa A-F based on the states of two characters.

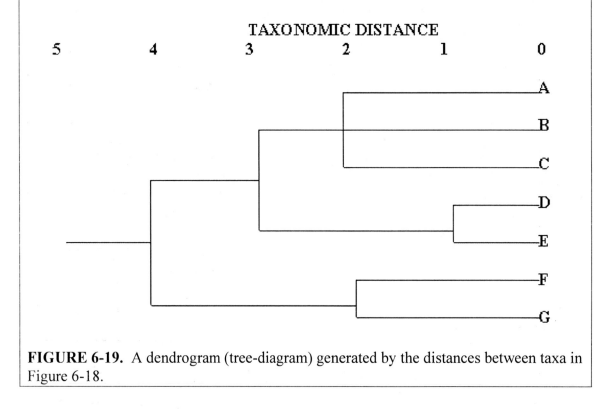

FIGURE 6-19. A dendrogram (tree-diagram) generated by the distances between taxa in Figure 6-18.

TAXA	CHARACTER I	CHARACTER II
A	2	0
B	2	3
C	2	4
D	1	2
E	1	2
F	0	0
G	0	1

FIGURE 6-20. A Character X Taxon matrix for taxa A-G and characters I and II. Character I has three states (0, 1, 2) and character II has five states (0, 1, 2, 3, 4).

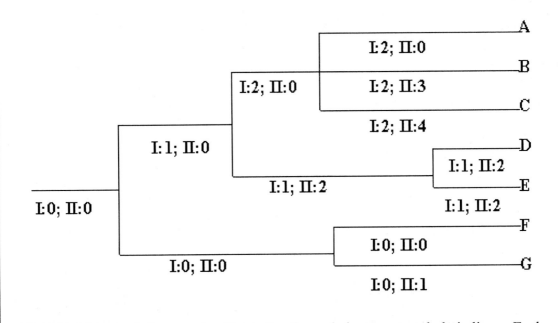

FIGURE 6-21. A cladogram that illustrates three clades or monophyletic lines. Each internode is labeled according to the characters and their states.

The primitive states of both characters in this example are 0 and 0. Note that as you work your way up the cladogram, taxon F retains both primitive states. Its sister taxon, G, exhibits the primitive state for character I, but character II has changed from 0 to 1. This monophyletic branch is called a clade. The clade that terminates in taxa D and F shows changes in both characters from the base of the tree. However, the two taxa cannot be differentiated based only on the two characters. Clade A-C is defined by character I, state 2, but character 2 varies among all thee of them. Thus, the cladogram also charts the evolution of characters within each clade. Note that in this example, there are no reversals in characters, that is, the states never reverse to an earlier form from the base to the terminal taxa.

These are very simple examples, but they illustrate the fundamental differences between the phenetics and cladistics. Now, imagine a matrix with 100 or more characters, each with more than one expressed character state. The number of solutions to such a large matrix could be greater than the number of atoms in the universe. This is true for both algorithmic methods, but more so for cladistic methods. Have they just traded the complexity of biodiversity for the mathematical complexity of linear algebra? Fortunately, the principle of parsimony and other statistical methods allow for the determination of the best solutions.

Phenetics, because it made no pretense at constructing phylogenies, did not consider fossils to be important in the interpretation of characters, particularly in direction of change. The use of fossils in determining evolution and fundamental relationships has a long history in the Darwinian era[23]. They play a major role in the classification systems of the evolutionary taxonomists. Cladists, because they were interested in constructing classification systems that reflected phylogenies, also began to consider fossils and their importance in determining primitive character states, etc. Even cladists armed with fossil evidence did not assume that the cladogram was a phylogeny, but they assumed that a phylogeny could be constructed from a cladogram.

Consider the question of the relationship between birds and dinosaurs. This had been considered for some time. Thomas Henry Huxley[24] was the first Darwinian scientist to propose the connection between the two types of animals. The discovery of

Archaeopteryx, a clear intermediate between birds and dinosaurs, in 1861 seemed to underscore the connection. However, evolutionary taxonomists considered the relationship to be superficial. They assumed that birds had emerged from a dinosaurian line (or pre-dinosaurian line), but radiated into a group with class-status in the vertebrates. Cladists interpreted the evidence differently.

Suppose a very simple cladogram of four taxa and two characters: number of walking legs and presence of teeth (see Figure 6-22). The *Iguana,* a lizard, represents the primitive state for both characters: it walks on four legs and has teeth. From that form emerged a line, the dinosaurs, that had two walking legs. *Brachiosaurus,* a huge sauropod, returned to the 4-legged position. This represented a reversal in the clade. However, this reversal was borne out by fossil evidence. The other dinosaur, *Velociraptor,* was in a clade that included birds.

The cladistic interpretation of Figure 6-21 is that all taxonomic units (e.g. species, genera, families, etc.) must be monophyletic. So, if the dinosaurs were reptiles (like lizards) then the whole cladogram would represent reptiles and subgroups of reptiles. Although dinosaurs as reptiles might be palatable, birds as reptiles is not. The alternative is that modern reptiles like lizards are separate from the dinosaurs and birds, which together should make up a class Dinosauria, of which Aves would be a subclass. The alternative of allowing birds and dinosaurs to be separate groups would destroy the monophyletic (making them paraphyletic) aspect of the groups and is not allowed in the rules of cladistics.

---

[23] By this phrase, I mean after the publication of *The Origin.*

[24] Read more about T.H. Huxley in *A Tale of Two Stones.*

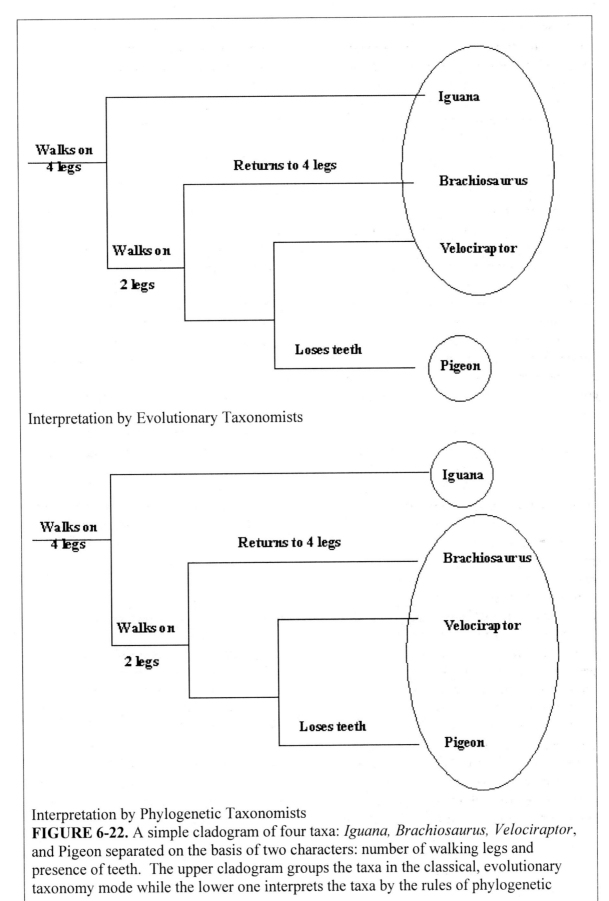

Interpretation by Evolutionary Taxonomists

Interpretation by Phylogenetic Taxonomists

FIGURE 6-22. A simple cladogram of four taxa: *Iguana, Brachiosaurus, Velociraptor,* and Pigeon separated on the basis of two characters: number of walking legs and presence of teeth. The upper cladogram groups the taxa in the classical, evolutionary taxonomy mode while the lower one interprets the taxa by the rules of phylogenetic taxonomy.

In cladistic terms, the *Iguana* is an outgroup genus. That is, it is related to, but not part of the organisms in question. Placing an outgroup in the cladogram causes the states of the characters to become polarized, and more likely produce a tree that reflects phylogeny. The resulting inferred phylogeny, then, is used to produce a classification.

The particular rules for converting cladograms to classifications brought about the ire of the evolutionary taxonomists. Although they agreed that the goal of classification should be to reflect evolutionary relationships, they (particularly Ernst Mayr and George Gaylord Simpson, 1902-1984, USA) said that the *a priori* assumptions made for the connection between evolution and classification in a cladistic analysis did not recognize the reality of evolution. In the view of the evolutionary taxonomists, some groups emerged from a line and then went through a rapid radiation that made them a separate group. The evolutionary taxonomist would have interpreted Figure 6-22 as the emergence of the birds (as a separate class) from a reptilian ancestor. The phenetecists would have rejected the analysis all together because they did not allow the incorporation of fossil or extinct groups. Besides, phenetic classifications were assumed to be artificial anyway.

All was not calm within the ranks of the cladists, though. Prior to the open warfare between cladistics and phenetics, a quiet revolution began to brew within the camp of the Phylogenetic Taxonomists. A group of cladists began to apply even more draconian methods than Hennig had. In essence, they believed that if all *a priori* evolutionary assumptions were purged, then the cladistic analyses generated could be used to test evolutionary hypotheses without the problem of circular reasoning. Members of the movement called themselves transformed cladists.

The cladists, transformed or not, rapidly won the systematics civil war. By the end of the 1980's cladistic analyses were quite common in the systematics literature. By the 1990's almost all publications dealing with systematics were based on cladistic analyses.

MOLECULAR TREES

Evolution at different amino acid and nucleotide sites is easily comparable: one change at one site is equivalent to one change at another. This is a huge advantage when we are weighing up conflicting evidence..

-Mark Ridley (2004)

Classification systems had all been based on morphological characters. However, the drawback of morphology (this includes anatomy, physiology, and development) is the relative paucity of homologous characters that span large groups. Also, the importance of morphological characters varies. The use of macromolecules, particularly biopolymers, like proteins and nucleic acids, however, provides a very large number of characters that are about equal in importance. For example, consider the insulin molecule, the first biopolymer to be sequenced. It has 51 amino acids linked in a particular order. Thus, insulin could be used as 51 different characters, each with 20 potential amino acids (thus, 20 characters states). Insulin is not universal, however, and it could not be used to distinguish humans from chimps.

Consider something even more universal, like nucleic acids (DNA and RNA). These are found in the nucleus, the mitochondria, the chloroplasts, and the cytoplasm. Comparable strands of nucleic acids could yield 100's to 1000's of characters, each with four character states (the four bases). With current molecular sequencing methods and instrumentation, such comparisons can be made with suitable speed. Such analyses have revolutionized our understanding of life.

At first glance it would seem that chromosomal DNA would provide the key to the fundamental relationships of all life. The problem, though, is that all organisms compared have to the same gene. They could be used to compare closely related organisms, but they could not be used to make a universal tree. Also, although such sequences might provide many characters (nucleotides), each one has only four possible character states. Short sequences might give results that appear to indicate homology. Useful sequences, therefore, must have hundreds or thousands of nucleotides. So, even though Transfer RNA is universal, the sequences are too small to be reliable and reflect changes of a long history. Ribosomal genes and RNA, however, are universal, highly conserved, and large enough to bear the changes from its history. In theory, ribosomal sequences should be adequate to elucidate the universal tree of life.

In the 1960's the Neutral Theory of molecular evolution appeared, expounded mainly by Motoo Kimura (1924-1994, Japan). This view held that genomes mutate at a particular rate. Thus, the number of differences in a genome provided a kind of molecular clock that timed the separation of species. This became the fundamental principle that guided molecular phylogenetics. Thus, when molecular methods began to be used in cladistic analyses, phylogenetic analyses began to proliferate, and, in some cases, provide many unexpected answers. One of the first based on rRNA was that life consists of three domains, two of which are bacterial.

The molecular sequences have come back to tell us more about ourselves. Consider Figure 6-23. This is a cladogram of 12 primate taxa and 900 characters (nucleotide positions from mitochondrial DNA). The outgroup is a Lemur (far left). According to the rules of cladistics, the Tarsier (far right) is one clade (clade 1). Saimiri is clade 2. Four different tailless monkeys in the genus *Macaca* make up clade 3. Clade 4 includes the great apes and *Homo sapiens.* However, by the rules of cladistics, we have to be part of the group that includes the great apes, or should I say, the other great apes?

This particular cladogram has branches that vary in length according to the number of changes in the branch. The macaques (monkeys within the same genus) show about the same variability as the apes above *Hylaobates* (gibbon). Another curious outcome is that any node can swivel without changing the tree length. If the *Pan-Homo* clade were to swivel, *Homo* (our genus) would be clearly within the great apes. This is not great surprise. Even Linnaeus placed chimpanzees within our own genus. Since then, the evolutionary taxonomists removed us to our own family, the Hominidae, and left the other apes in the family Pongidae. The cladists would have us united again.

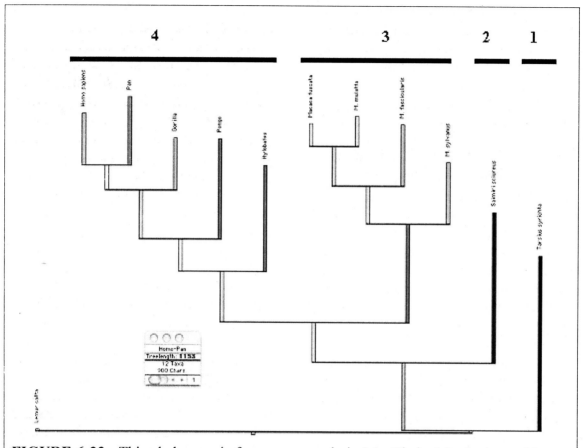

FIGURE 6-23. This cladogram is from an example in MacClade 4.0. It shows 12 taxa of primates with Lemur as the outgroup. It shows 4 clades that have been derived by comparing 900 nucleotides from mitochondrial DNA.

CLASSIFICATION REVISITED

The first step of science is to know one thing from another. This knowledge consists of their specific distinctions; but in order that it may be fixed and permanent distinct names must be given to different things, and those names must be recorded and remembered.

-Carolus Linnaeus from Smith (1821)

The classification of birds, reptiles, and our genus points to a major rift between the positions of cladists-pheneticists and classical taxonomists (more in the vein of evolutionary taxonomy). The Numerical Taxonomists were more extreme than all other groups in recognizing that the taxonomic system is artificial, and, therefore, the terminal taxa would not even be called species,

but referred to as Operational Taxonomic Units (OTU).

Both Phenetics and Cladistics, because they are inherently hierarchical, would seem to lend themselves well to the Linnaean classification hierarchy. The nodes of the cladogram (or dendrogram) could be given Linnaean taxonomic status. However, even with the current system, there are only 8 major categories if the domain is included as the highest taxon[25]. Then given multiplications of the main taxa with prefixes like sub-, super-, or infra, up to 20-24 taxonomic levels could be designated in any full hierarchy. However most dendrograms or cladograms with many taxa could have many nodes from

---

[25] The hierarchy would be: Domain, Kingdom, Phylum (sometimes Division in Botany), Class, Order, Family, Genus, Species.

521

the root to the terminal taxon. For that reason, some of the more rabid cladists, insist that the Linnaean system be swept away entirely. In its place would be a series of numbers that indicate the position of a terminal taxon and the nodes that lead to it. Such a system might sound fine in theory, but it abandons the practical need for classification as a retrieval system. Furthermore, the "true and final" cladogram on which the cladistic classification would be built is far, far away, both in time and complexity. Right now, fewer than 2 million species have been described. There may be as many as 10-100 million species. How many nodes would be required to separate them?

Another more subtle, but important point is that the need for a practical system is to support those who do not know the groups well. Colin Tudge suggested that most of those who work with particular types of organisms tend to think in terms of the species or genera. For them, the higher taxa have little meaning. I can say that this applies to me. I work with diatoms and dinoflagellates, both of which have higher taxa that I know only generally. However, I know the common freshwater species well.

So far, classical classification prevails. The cladistic modification likely will not be used in a major way any time soon. So, in a way, even the cladists lost this war.

A TRUCE?

So, we are waiting for the dust to settle down over these several decades, and we suspect that waiting for things to quiet down totally is as fruitless as spending hours each evening watching the sky for the next major meteor impact.

The Editors of *Taxon* (2000)

The classification systems created by molecular phylogenetics remain classical Linnaean in form. However, because molecular instrumentation and the power of the computer have provided for an almost cottage industry in systematics, the proliferation of classifications produced by molecular phylogenetics often are dissimilar, and, therefore, not practical, either. This aspect of practicality will not go away. Classification must be useful and usable. The information must be easily transferable. All of these practical attributes of classification systems are particularly valuable at a time when the inventory and discovery of biodiversity is so important. Molecular phylogenetic systems alone lead to questionable relationships anyway. As Max Taylor (1999) declares, the solution must be to tie molecular attributes to morphological characters. Only in that way can phyletically sound classification systems be made useful.

A crisis in systematics developed in the latter 1990's and culminated in the first years of the 21st Century. Single sequences had been very informative and had given much insight to the evolution of some organisms, but the method produced unacceptable relationships for groups in large hierarchical units. The eukaryotes, organisms with nuclei, seemed at first to conform to the five-kingdom system, four of which were eukaryotic. Then, some unexpected results appeared. The Fungi and Animals seemed to be sister groups (clades that branch from a common ancestor) and were lumped into a higher taxon called the Opisthokonts. However, more and more groups under phylogenetic scrutiny did not fit. Finally, in 1999 David Patterson declared that there are 60 to 120 groups that have no clear sister groups. Did that mean there could there be 60 eukaryotic kingdoms? Ribosomal RNA, mitochondrial and nuclear DNA sequences did not help. A possible solution had been proposed in 1992. If multiple datasets and trees were combined, the problems with any one or few datasets would be swamped. The analysis began to be used with hundreds of datasets after 2000. In 2001 Vincent Daubin, Manolo Gouy, and Guy Perriere of France performed such an analysis, called a supergroup analysis, for all prokaryotes and defined 11 coherent groups, which I interpret as 9 kingdoms of Eubacteria and 2 kingdoms of Archaea. Similar supertree analyses on eukaryotic groups revealed 5 supergroups, which, like the prokaryotes, contain about 11 kingdoms (see Figure 6-24). Not only did the supergroup analysis resolve the chaos of 60 sisterless groups into 5 supergroups, but also it found relationships between orphaned, seemingly disparate taxa in what is now called the Cercozoa. It confirms relationships between the red algae and the green plants, between the amoebozoa and the opisthokonts, and between the excavates and the dicristates. The resolution to the systematic chaos of the past 10 years seems to be at hand. Similarly, the general solution to the complete tree of life is within our grasp by the use of such powerful methods.

The systematics wars have died down to periodic skirmishes, but cladistics is the clear winner. Still, Phylogenetic Taxonomy is not a clean break from its rivals. Evolutionary Taxonomy is based on inferred phylogeny, but its methods are very subjective. Numerical Taxonomy is based on the similarities among groups, but not on a presumption of phylogenetic relationships. The methods of Numerical Taxonomy are algorithmic, and, therefore repeatable. Cladistics, in my opinion, takes the best of both schools: the phylogenetic basis of Evolutionary Taxonomy and the repeatable algorithmic methods of Numerical Taxonomy. Thus, the systematics wars brought about a revolution by replanting the tree of life and producing powerful methods to study it.

-2005

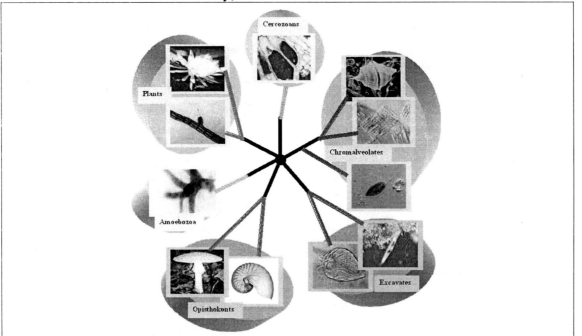

FIGURE 6-24. Eukaryotic supergroups after Sandra Baldauf (2003). Note that there are five independent clades from the unrooted tree.

References:
Bakker, Robert T. 1986. *The Dinosaur Heresies.* Zebra Books, Kensington Publishing Corp. New York.

Baldauf, Sandra. 2003. *The Deep Roots of Eukaryotes.* Science. 300 (5626): 1701-1703.

Cracraft, Joel and Niles Eldredge. 1979. *Phylogenetic Analysis and Paleontology.* Columbia University Press. New York.

Darwin, Charles R. 1873. *The Descent of Man and Selection in Relation to Sex.* D. Appleton & Co. New York.

Daubin, Vincent, Manolo Gouy, and Guy Perriere. 2001. *Bacterial Molecular Phylogeny Using Supertree Approach.* Genome Informatics. 12:155-164.

Editors. 2000. *Innovations in Plant Classification and Nomenclature.* Taxon 49:633-634.

Felsenstein, Joseph. 2001. *The Troubled Growth of Statistical Phylogenetics.* Systematic Biology. 50(4):465-467.

Gould, Stephen Jay. 1992. *We Are All Monkeys' Uncles.* Natural History 92(6): 14-21.

Hennig, Willi. 1966. *Phylogenetic Systematics.* Translated by D. Dwight Davis and Rainer Zangerl. University of Illinois Press. Urbana and Chicago.

Maddison, Wayne P. and David R. Maddison. 1992. *MacClade, Analysis of Phylogeny and Character Evolution.* Sinauer Associates, Inc. Sunderland, Mass.

Mayr, Ernst. 1982. *The Growth of Biological Thought, Diversity, Evolution, Inheritance.* The Belknap Press of Harvard University Press. Cambridge, Mass.

Mayr, Ernst. 1997. *This is Biology, The Science of the Living World.* The Belknap Press of Harvard University Press. Cambridge, Mass.

Patterson, David. 1999. *The Diversity of Eukaryotes.* The American Naturalist. 154(supplement): S96-S124.

Radford, Albert E. 1986. *Fundamentals of Plant Systematics.* Harper & Row, Publishers. New York.

Ridley, Mark. 1986. *Evolution and Classification, The Reformation of Cladism.* Longman Scientific and Technical. Essex, England.

Ridley, Mark. 2004. *Evolution, 3rd edition.* Blackwell Publishing. Oxford, UK.

Rosenberg, Alexander. 1986. *The Structure of Biological Thought.* Cambridge University Press. New York.

Simpson, George Gaylord. 1949. *The Meaning of Evolution.* Yale University Press. New Haven, CT.

Sneath, P.H.A. and R.R. Sokal. 1973. *Numerical Taxonomy.* Freeman. London.

Taylor, F.J.R. 1999. *Ultrastructure as a Control for Protistan Molecular Phylogeny.* The American Naturalist. 154(supplement): S125-S136.

Tudge, Colin. 2000. *The Variety of Life.* Oxford University Press. Oxford.

Winston, Judith E. 1999. *Describing Species.* Columbia University Press. New York.

Questions to Think About

1. What are the three schools of modern taxonomy? Who were their founders?

2. How do the three schools differ regarding to their fundamental bases or philosophies?

3. What are the two functions of classification?

4. What are the distinctions between pre-Darwinian and post-Darwinian (post *Origin*) taxonomy?

5. Why did I call the period between 1979 to the early 1990's the Systematics Wars? In what way was it a civil war?

6. What would be an advantage of algorithmic methods for classification?

7. Distinguish between character, character state, apomorphy, plesiomorphy.

8. What is the neutral theory of molecular evolution?

9. Are we members of the Hominidae or the Pongidae?

10. Aside from the Systematics Wars, what was the crisis in phylogenetic taxonomy in the 1990's? How was it resolved (at least so far)?

11. What is wrong with the five-kingdom system?

NATURE'S BOUNTY

NATURE'S BOUNTY

The parasitic plants on the trunks and branches, the wonderful variety of foliage, the strange fruits and seeds that lie rotting on the ground - taken together surpass description...

        - Alfred Russel Wallace

In October of 1999, I took a boat down a canal in the Tortuguero National Park on the north-east side of Costa Rica. The sky was clear, the water was very turbid. Herons, egrets and other water birds patiently waited for us to pass so that they could continue fishing and flew if we lingered too long or showed too much interest in them. Occasionally, we would see troops of Howler Monkeys in large Mahogany, Fig and Kapok trees lining the canals. More rarely, we saw a lone three-toed sloth.

Most of the trees were covered with epiphytes of bromeliads, orchids, and the occasional cactus. The bases of many trees expanded in triangular buttresses that made the trunks look like great rockets covered in leafy branches. Basilisk lizards guarded their territories at intervals along the banks.

The diversity of life in that rainforest was quite astounding and in great contrast with the relatively depauperate forests here in Central Pennsylvania. Why are there so many species of trees and insects? Why does Costa Rica have more than 400 species of butterflies? Why was the canal lined with Snowy and Little Blue Egrets, both of which are about the same size and probably eat the same fish? Why, and more importantly, how had this diversity of life come about?

FIGURE 6-25. Trees next to the water with buttress roots in the Tortoguero National Park..

ENTER NATURAL SELECTION

Being well prepared to appreciate the struggle for existence which everywhere goes on, it at once struck me that under these circumstances favorable variations would tend to be preserved and unfavorable ones to be destroyed. The result of this would be the formation of new species.

        -Charles Darwin

This exuberance of life also bothered 19th century naturalists. Why were there so many different species? Where did all of those species come from? Charles Darwin and a younger contemporary named Alfred Russell Wallace independently arrived at the same solution, a theory that we know as natural selection or Darwinism[26].

Simply put, the concept of evolution is that species change over time. That view is quite well established and among the accepted principles of science. Even before the time of Darwin the concept of

---

[26] This is a term that Wallace later used to describe Natural Selection. See my essay, *The Mentor and the Heretic*, for a more detailed description of the relationship between the two men, and controversy about the discovery of Natural Selection.

change over time was a valid interpretation of the fossil record and the amazing diversity of life that exploration had revealed.

The insight of Darwin and Wallace was not that living things changed, although Darwin provided many examples, observations, and experimental results to support that idea. The insight was an explanation for how species change. Darwin noticed the remarkable variations that dog and pigeon breeders had produced through selective breeding or artificial selection in relatively few generations. They argued that, given enough time, nature molds living things through a similar process called Natural Selection.

Darwin and Wallace both said that organisms produce many more offspring than can survive to reproduce. In the struggle for existence, those that are better suited to ambient environmental conditions have a better chance of surviving to produce offspring. Thus, nature "selects" certain individuals for speed, color, metabolic efficiency, or any particular collection of traits.

For example, the three-toed sloth that I saw had greenish fur. Surely, green would be beneficial to an animal that spends its time in the canopy of trees. In this case, however, the green is not caused by a pigment. The animal has hairs that are grooved in which algae grow. Thus, the animal is green because of photosynthetic pigments within the algae.

The important caveat to this scenario is that the variation must exist such that a particular trait can change. For example, if a given butterfly routinely lands on and occupies a particular purple flower, then it might have a better chance of survival if it became purple. However, that assumes that the purple variant can occur in that particular species. If purple does not occur in that species, there is a good chance that it will never occur no matter how much it might benefit the species.

Similarly, if black or orange fungi had begun to occupy those ridged hairs on the three-toed sloth, there would be a strong selective pressure for the animals to lose the ridges on their hairs.

That life changed did not originate with Darwin and Wallace. Indeed, it was an old concept whose roots went well into the 18th century. Even Charles' grandfather, Erasmus Darwin wrote about evolution or the transmutation of life in a poem called *Zoonomea*. Nevertheless, the concept suffered for lack of a mechanism that might explain how life changed. Jean Baptiste Pierre Antoine de Monet, Chevalier de Lamarck (1744-1829) was one of the first to propose a mechanism that did not invoke a supernatural designer. Although Darwin's theory of natural selection was substantially different, he acknowledged Lamarck as a pioneer in an attempt to explain how species change[27].

Lamarck had distinguished himself as a Botanist in France by 1778 with the *Flore Francaise* (Flora of France). Later, he accepted the chair of Insects and Worms (that is, of all Invertebrates, a term that Lamarck created) at the Musee National d'Histoire Naturelle (The National Museum of Natural History). Although he knew nothing about Invertebrates, Lamarck began an intensive study of them and soon became an expert.

---

[27] Darwin said, "Lamarck…first did the eminent service of arousing attention to the probability of all changes in the organic, as well as the inorganic world, being the result of law, and not miraculous interposition." The preface to editions 3-7 of the *Origin of Species*.

During this time, he noted similarities between living things and came up with an explanation for the similarities and overall diversity by saying that life continually changes or transmutates into new beings that are higher on the ladder of life.

His mechanism for transmutation was fairly complex. He believed that the environment caused an animal to change its behavior. That in turn caused a change in the use or disuse of particular structures and organs. Increased use caused structures to increase in size and disuse caused them to decrease in size. Thus, over time, a mouse could become an elephant.

Today, we refer to Lamarck's mechanism as the inheritence of acquired characteristics. Even then, Lamarck's views were not generally accepted. Georges Cuvier, a contemporary and colleague disregarded Lamarck's explanation in favor of a model of separate creations in the mode of the Natural Theology of the day[28].

Natural Theology was a religious view of the time that sought to illustrate the beneficence of the Creator by showing how much care had been taken in designing all other aspects of creation. The argument went that if the Creator could lavish such attention and care on the structure of the wing of an insect, imagine how much care he will take with one of his chosen. In the absence of a plausible mechanism to explain the diversity of life, the designer seemed to be the best explanation.

In the early days of exploration, the potential for the diversity of life was not known or guessed. The variety of living things found in the typical English countryside seemed to be the norm. The explorers changed that view.

Another more serious challenge came from anatomists and other field biologists. Why were there so many design flaws or inefficiencies in nature? For example, Stephen J. Gould pointed out that Pandas because they strip the leaves from bamboo while feeding require the use of a thumb. However, in their case, one of the wrist bones has expanded to provide them with an opposable digit (bears have no thumbs). Although the panda's "thumb" works it is inefficient and of poor design compared to the thumbs of monkeys and raccoons. Nature is full of such "Rube Goldberg" solutions.

DEMOCRACY AND THE SELF-CORRECTION OF SCIENCE

Freedom is a prerequisite for continuing the delicate experiment of science.
                              -Carl Sagan and Ann Druyan

Darwinian natural selection when proposed in 1859 provided a more plausible mechanism for the shaping of organisms that the concepts of acquired characteristics or of intellegent design. Very quickly, the scientific community came over to accept the views that life has changed over time and that it changed by means of natural selection.

Richard Dawkins pointed out in a recent lecture here in central Pennsylvania that natural selection is the only solution because it is so elegant as an explanation. By elegance, scientists mean that the solution has great explanatory power with relatively few postulates. In this case, natural selection explains the diversity of life and its underlying unity while postulating only that individuals within a species vary and those variations that offer greater chance

---

[28] For more about Lamarck and his relationship with Cuvier, please read my essay, *Rivals*.

of survival will tend to increase. That is all living things are descended from successful ancestors if success is measured in terms of offspring. In this way, as more and more changes occur, species diverge from an original type. Thus, by this mechanism, more than 5 million species of living things can be produced from a common set of ancestors. The concept of elegance is very important when scientists choose one or the other rival theory.

As a community, science is quite democratic. Ideas are openly discussed and presented in journal articles, meetings and books. It is the free flow of ideas and their open evaluation that is the real creative lifeblood of science. Indeed, I would argue that science is the oldest extant democratic institution on earth. This culture in the society of science creates a kind of natural selection of ideas, so that those today are indeed better and more elegant that those of 200 years ago. Thus, science, as a community, is continually introspective and self-corrective. No better example can be seen in the struggle to accommodate Mendelian genetics and evolution, especially with the mechanism of Natural Selection.

In the flow of ideas at the turn of the 20th century, biologists had become disenchanted with natural selection. The main problem was that there was no good explanation for heredity or how the changes could be passed on to offspring. With the discovery of Mendel's principles and the concept of mutation, some biologists began to wonder if natural selection could work at all. Perhaps, mutation or changes in big steps held the answer to how species change. This led to the concept of the hopeful monster. That is, mutation occasionally would produce a fundamentally different mutant (hope-

ful monster) in one large step. This kind of saltation seemed necessary in the early days of our understanding of genetics. August Weismann objected saying, "An abrupt transformation of a species is inconceivable, because it would render the species incapable of existence[29]." His concern was typical of the selectionist's stance in the dispute between adherents of natural selection and mutationism.

Finally, an accommodation or synthesis of the two evolutionary theories was brought about by biologists like Ernst Mayr, Julian Huxley, and Theodosius Dobzhansky. They saw that genetics held the key to how species vary (mutation) and transmit their particular traits (heredity). Natural selection held the key to how those variations might increase or decrease within a species. Modern evolutionary theory is a direct outcome of the synthesis that occurred in the 1930's and 1940's. Although mutationism was rejected as the sole mechanism for change (except of course in monster movies), its consideration and accommodation led to a deeper understanding of how living things evolve.

LYSENKO AND LIES
If the outstanding practitioners are going to support theories and opinions that are obviously absurd to everyone who knows even a little about genetics..., then the choice before us will resemble the choice between witchcraft and medicine, between astrology and astronomy, between alchemy and chemistry.
                                        -H. J. Muller

Mutationism did not make much headway among scientists in the Soviet Union. By and large, they tended to be selectionists in their views. The problem

---

[29] Quoted by Mayr (1985).

529

with natural selection was that it did not conform well with Marxist-Leninist doctrine because it supported a view that people could not change to adapt to particular situations in their environment. Rather, those who could change would have to be selected for and the others would have to be eliminated. Although Stalin seemed very willing to go the route of elimination, he was swayed by the Neo-Lamarckian views of Trofim D. Lysenko.

Lysenko suggested that a Lamarckian approach to species change might be more politically correct because change could be induced and passed on to the offspring. He had done plant-breeding experiments that seemed to corroborate his views. In particular, he exposed wheat to colder and colder temperatures in an attempt to cause them to respond to the change by becoming more cold-hardy and passing that trait on to the next generation.

Soviet geneticists and other biologists scoffed at the idea and rejected this Neo-Lamarckian theory. Stalin responded with vengeance and attempted to purge the scientific community of all vestiges of bourgeois theory. Those who did not swear allegiance to this theory were sent to gulag or disappeared entirely. Still, in the struggle of ideas, Soviet scientists showed remarkable courage and attempted to maintain an intellectually honest dialog within their portion of the scientific community.

Later, evidence showed that Lysenko's vernalization experiment were flawed with inadequate controls and defective experimental designs. In addition, his results were fudged or grossly misinterpreted. Soviet genetics, particularly plant breeding initiatives never recovered from this kind of external meddling and the Soviet Union was forced to purchase grain from the United States in the 1970's.

Note that although mutationism and Neo-Lamarckism challenged natural selection, all theories assumed that evolution or descent with modification had occurred. The question was how to explain the mechanism of that change. Mutationism arose within the scientific community and posed a serious intellectual threat to natural selection until the advent of the new synthesis. Neo-Lamarckism came from within the scientific community but never really posed an intellectual challenge to natural selection. Instead, it posed a political threat and exacerbated food shortages of the 1970's.

Creationism is something quite different. Duane Gish, a chief spokesperson of the creationist camp, stated quite clearly why Creation Science is not a science:

> By creation we mean the bringing into being by a supernatural Creator of the basic kinds of plants and animals by the process of sudden, or fiat, creation." We do not know how the Creator created, what processes He used, *for He used processes which are not now operating anywhere in the natural universe.*[30]

That is, Creation Science requires laws and principles that are not in existence. They cannot be tested, and they cannot be falsified. More importantly, as a theory goes, it is far less elegant because it requires a plethora of postulates, each of which is quite complex. Thus, the explanatory power of Creation Science occurs at the expense of the fundamental nature of science whose foundation re-

---

[30] Quoted by Stephen J. Gould (1983). Italics are Gish's.

530

quires a continuous flow of unbroken natural law.

More importantly, biologists do not practice Creation Science (also called Intelligent Design). I say this confidently as a member of that scientific community. Out of 68,833 papers indexed by BIOSIS from 1991-1997 on evolution and intelligent design, only one paper was indexed under intelligent design. Clearly, Creation Science does not represent an alternative point of view within the science of biology.

Indeed, the Creation Science is quite difficult to practice within the context of a science. One cannot set up falsifiable hypotheses without committing blasphemy. So, the practice seems to be aimed at showing why evolution is not true. That approach may work for the general uninformed public, but it is not how scientists choose theories. If Creation Scientists want to have their theory considered by the community of biologists, they need to show *how intelligent design is a better, more elegant explanation for the diversity of life.*

The conclusion of the courts, philosophers, and community of biologists is that Creation Science is not a science. It is not a viable alternative theory to Neo-Darwinian Natural Selection (or to Neo-Lamarckism, for that matter). The situation is not unlike that of Lysenkoism in the Soviet Union. Like Lysenkoism, Creationism is a political movement that is trying to impose a theory on the community of scientists from the outside, particularly as how biology is taught. Fortunately, the history of science does not have a single instance in which a theory became incorporated into the science as a result of external pressure.

That does not stop political attempts to undermine science in public school.

One of the most startling political moves by the Creationist camp occurred during the past six months in Kansas. There, the State Board of Education had assembled a committee to examine the science curriculum for the public schools in the state. The science education standards written by the panel of scientists pretty well followed the general guidelines of the National Science Teachers Association with evolution as a central unifying theme for biology. The Science Education Standards were submitted for approval on August 10 and 11, 1999.

At this point some of the board members, particularly Steve Abrams, offered amendments to the standards that were based on the premise that science is only that body of knowledge that can be repeated in the laboratory[31]. This definition of science would eliminate much of geology, ecology, and astronomy. Abrams and his followers argued that by this definition evolution was not scientific and therefore should be removed from the standards.

This turn to intellectual dishonesty may seem like a question of fairness to some. That is, if there are competing views present them or be silent about both of them. However, this is a scientific concept. Evolution is the central unifying principle of biology. Only the community of biologists can define for others, particularly educational groups,

---

[31] This scenario can be seen in the minutes of the State Board of Education at the time. The are recorded in the following on-line documents:

http://www.ksbe.state.ks.us/commiss/bdmin/039 9brdmin.html

http://www.ksbe.state.ks.us/commiss/bdmin/049 9brdmin.html

http://www.ksbe.state.ks.us/commiss/bdmin/089 9brdmin.html

what characterizes biology. Evolution does; Creationism does not.

THERE IS GRANDEUR IN THIS VIEW OF LIFE

Nothing in Biology makes sense except in light of evolution.

-Theodosius Dobzhansky

In describing evolution in *The Origin*, Darwin ended his book by saying, *"There is grandeur to this view of life."* Indeed, it is both a grand and liberating concept. On the one hand it pulls us into the circle of life, and on the other it helps to explain why we are all different.

On my trip to Costa Rica one encounter stands out in my mind. Our guide spotted a young three-toed sloth in a small tree at the water's edge. The animal was quite wet, and the guide explained that it had just swum the canal and pulled itself onto the tree. I pulled myself up to a notch to bring my head about level with the animal. Slung under a horizontal branch, the sloth slowly turned its head to study me briefly, dismissed me as a threat and returned its attention to the boat below. I do not know what may have passed through the sloth's mind in that the brief exchange of mutual contemplation. I found it to be thrilling.

I was a mammal and shared a lineage with the sloth. I was more distantly related to the Night Heron a short distance away in the same tree, which was more distantly related still. Surrounded by life so different, yet fundamentally similar, I felt like I was part of nature's grandeur, its bounty. Changed, I climbed down from the tree and as a member of just another species, walked back to my companions in the boat.

-1999, revised 2005

FIGURE 6-26. A three-toed sloth contemplating me in her territory.

References:

Dawkins, Richard. 1998. *Unweaving the Rainbow, Science, Delusion and the Appetite for Wonder.* Houghton Mifflin Co. New York.

Degler, Carl. 1991. *In Search of Human Nature, The Decline and Revival of Darwinism in American Social Thought.* Oxford University Press. Oxford.

Gilkey, Langdon. 1985. *Creationism on Trial, Evolution and God at Little Rock.* Winston Press. Minneapolis, Minn.

Gross, Paul, Norman Levitt, and Martin Lewis, eds. 1996. *The Flight From Science and Reason.* The New York Academy of Sciences. New York.

Gould, Stephen J. 1980. *The Panda's Thumb.* W.W. Norton & Co. New York.

Gould, Stephen J. 1983. *Evolution, Fact and Theory.* In: Gould, Stephen J. *Hen's Teeth and Horses Toes.* W.W. Norton & Co. New York. pp. 253-262.

Holton, Gerald. 1993. *Science and Anti-Science.* 1993. Harvard University Press. Cambridge, Mass.

Joravsky, David. 1970. *The Lysenko Affair.* The University of Chicago Press. Chicago.

Mayr, Ernst. 1985. *Weismann and Evolution*. Journal of the History of Biology. 18(3): 295-329.

Mayr, Ernst. 1991. *One Long Argument: Charles Darwin and the Genesis of Modern Evolutionary Thought.* The Belknap Press of the Harvard University Press. Cambridge, Mass.

Mayr, Ernst. 1997. *This is Biology, The Science of the Living World.* The Belknap Press of the Harvard University Press. Cambridge, Mass.

Montagu, Ashley, ed. 1984. *Science and Creationism.* Oxford University Press. Oxford.

Radnor, Dasie and Michael Radnor. 1982. *Science and Unreason.* Wadsworth Publishing Co. Belmont, Cal.

Sagan, Carl. 1995. *The Demon-Haunted World, Science as a Candle in the Dark.* Random House. New York.

FIGURE 6-27. A panoramic view of the Tortuguero Forest

Questions to Think About

1. What did I mean when I described the Pennsylvania forests as being relatively depauperate?

2. What is the relationship between Natural Selection and Variation?

3. What was Lamarck's view of evolution? How did it differ from that of Darwin?

4. What was the concept of Natural Theology (the discipline of natural history in which Darwin was trained)?

5. What does the phrase self-correcting mean? How is it importance to our advancement of understanding the natural world?

6. What is the difference between the Darwin-Wallace and the Mutationist versions of evolution?

7. What was Lysenkoism? What was its consequence?

8. Why is Creation Science not a science?

9. What is the importance of my statement: "Fortunately, the history of science does not have a single instance in which a theory became incorporated into the science as a result of external pressure."?

10. In what ways are theories judged by members of the scientific community?

ECOSYSTEMS: FORM, FUNCTION AND WONDER

DEAD FISH

A very ancient and fish-like smell.
-Shakespeare (The Tempest act II, sc 2)

I once accompanied a fellow graduate student to a reservoir near Jet, Oklahoma. The Great Salt Plains Lake was a brackish body of water, and we went to see if we could find marine algae growing there. That particular winter (1978) had been quite cold and the reservoir had frozen. I recall that we were not quite prepared for that because in Oklahoma lakes rarely freeze. We used some tire tools and an old ax in the trunk of my car to carve out holes large enough to allow the samplers to slip down into the water. The frigid water and stiff Oklahoma wind made the job of cutting ten different holes in the ice thoroughly uncomfortable.

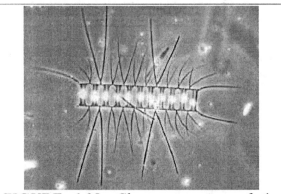

FIGURE 6-28. *Chaetoceros,* one of the common algae beneath the ice of the Great Salt Plains Reservoir.

As we broke through the ice at the sampling sites, the odor of hydrogen sulfide, the essence of rotten eggs, issued from each opening. Our sampling equipment indicated that the oxygen level just beneath the ice was quite high but it tapered off rapidly just centimeters below the surface. The high oxygen level was associated with the telltale brown-green peculiar to certain groups of algae, particularly the ones that we wanted

to find. That discovery made all of the cold and unpleasantness dissolve into the euphoria that only field scientists and curious children can know in similar circumstances.

We walked back to the car after our last sample and the background fetid odor became stronger. This time the rotten eggs mingled with a hint of fish. We crested the path and looked down toward the dam on our way to the parking lot. There, we saw fish, hundreds of dead fish, boiling up in the ice-free zone along the dam and spilling into the creek below. The likely cause of the massacre was oxygen depletion, a common malady in very productive or eutrophic waters.

RESPIRATION & PHOTOSYNTHESIS

Oxygen is the most fundamental parameter of lakes and streams aside from water itself. -Robert G. Wetzel (2001)

Oxygen in water can come from two sources. The most obvious one is the atmosphere. Air is about 21% oxygen and, therefore, an enormous reservoir of the molecular form, O_2. Gaseous oxygen dissolves into water relative to the temperature of water. For example, water at $0^{\circ}C$ can hold up to 14.62 mg O_2 per liter of water. However, water at $40^{\circ}C$ can hold only 6.41 mg O_2 per liter of water. Thus, temperature-wise, the lake should have had more than enough oxygen to support the fish. Recall though that the lake had a covering of ice that formed an effective barrier and cap to prevent the infusion of atmospheric oxygen into the lake.

The only other source of dissolved oxygen would have been through the process of photosynthesis. Simply put, algae and plants absorb light energy by means of chlorophyll. Then, they combine the hydrogen from water (H_2O) with the carbon from carbon dioxide to make carbohydrate molecules. They can then take the carbon molecule and use it as the backbone to make all manner of other necessary food compounds.

In the process of stripping water of its hydrogens, photosynthesis releases molecular oxygen as a waste product. So, increased rates of photosynthesis should allow for increased concentrations of oxygen in water. However, all living things (including plants) respire, that is, extract usable energy from food molecules. Most (but not all) living things use oxygen in the process of respiration or metabolism. Put another way, the net input of dissolved oxygen in a lake is the difference between photosynthetic input and metabolic uptake by the community of organisms.

To further confuse matters, metabolic rate is generally temperature-dependent. That is community oxygen uptake will be about twice as high at 20° C than at 10° C. However, photosynthetic rate is not so temperature-dependent. So, an aquatic community in cold water, given sufficient light, should have a much greater net oxygen production than a community in warmer water. Also, the colder water can hold more oxygen due to its increased solubility.

Well, the lake water was cold. Algae were in the lake. Why did the fish die? The answer is somewhat complex and requires a much more comprehensive view of the lake.

Consider a lake during the spring. This time it is moderately productive and lies in the northeastern U.S. The water is the same temperature throughout and easily mixed by the spring winds and storms (see Figure 6-29-A). The algal plankton (also called phytoplankton) get plenty of sunlight and grow well. The small planktonic animals, zooplankton, feed on the algae. In turn, small fish, etc. feed upon the zooplankton. As spring turns into summer, the upper water of the lake warms up and mixing ceases.

The resistance to mixing increases as the temperature differential increases. This condition is called stratification (see Figure 6-29-B).

Usually, a stratified lake has three well-defined layers:
- A warm upper epilimnion.
- A transition zone of rapidly changing temperature called a thermocline.
- A cold bottom layer called a hypolimnion.

Water tends to layer this way because colder water is denser than warmer water. Lakes that exhibit such strong stratification behave as if they were three distinct bodies of water and do not mix easily with each other. The epilimnion has direct contact with the atmosphere and unfiltered exposure to light. On the other hand, the hypolimnion usually has no particular source of oxygen because there is no photosynthesis and no exposure to the atmosphere.

During summer stratification in very productive lakes, the epilimnion can be saturated with oxygen while the hypolimnion can be completely depleted. This is counter to what the solubility curve dictates. The colder water of the hypolimnion should hold more oxygen, but in the absence of any sources, community metabolism can exhaust whatever became trapped there as it stratified.

As the lake begins to cool at the onset of fall, the difference in temperature between the epilimnion and hypolimnion decreases until the whole body of water mixes or turns over (see Figure 6-29-A). Such turnover events can be quite dramatic (and aromatic). I have seen lakes that one day were clear turn turbid and cloudy as anoxic water and suspended sediment from the bottom mix with the top layer.

The lake continues to cool through the fall and into winter. Then, fortunately, water exhibits anomalous behavior. Below about 4°C, water becomes less dense. The solid form of water becomes less dense still. Thus, ice floats and traps slightly warmer liquid water beneath it (see Figure 6-29-C). This is another kind of stratification called inverse stratification because the warmer water lies on the bottom.

In the case of an ice-covered lake, the sources of oxygen are gone and the whole body can behave as one large hypolimnion. Milky ice or a little snow cover over the ice can be enough to plunge a lake into anoxia. Sometimes, however, ice can be clear enough to allow photosynthesis to occur beneath it. In those cases oxygen can approach saturation beneath the ice.

With small variations this kind of annual cycle continues in concert with the seasons. The northern U.S. has cold winters so the kind of double mixing lake described in Figure 6-29 is common. The southern U.S. has mild winters and frozen lakes tend to occur only rarely (as in 1978 in northern Oklahoma). The seasonal responses of lakes are so dramatic and, in general, so predictable that they had been used as sources of food, ice, and recreation for thousands of years. The predictable environments had predictable groups of living things in them.

THE MICROCOSM

Life does not perish in the lake, nor even oscillate to any considerable degree, but on the contrary the little community secluded here is as prosperous as if its state were one of profound and perpetual peace.
-Stephen A. Forbes (1887)

By and large, this was the concept of the lake as viewed by early ecologists of the late 19th and early 20th centuries. They saw the lake or any environment as made of living (or biotic) components and non-living (or abiotic) components that influence the life in the lake. Stephan Forbes, an American ecologist, set the stage for this kind of understanding in his 1887 paper called *The Lake as a Microcosm*, a community of life.

The period that followed saw much research in Europe and the U.S. on describing the components of the lake communities. Those who studied lakes were called "Limnologists." The first significant studies of phytoplankton (floating algae) and zooplankton (small floating animals that usually feed on the phytoplankton) complemented the age-old understanding of fish communities. Explorations of more than just the impacts of temperature and seasons began to be important in ecological research. Earlier in the 19th Century Justus von Liebig[32] sought to understand what in the environment contributed to the growth of plants. He noticed that a potted plant might increase many times its original weight but take almost nothing from the soil. He reasoned that the carbon for its growth must come from the atmosphere. Nevertheless, the soil did change in weight slightly. Thus, he added ash of plants back to the soil and the "fertilized" plant grew much better. The impact of this research further strengthened the view that life existed at the mercy and under the control of the non-living environment.

---

[32] See *Chance and the Prepared Mind* for more about von Leibig.

The early Limnologists described the structure of lake communities quite well. They saw the importance of plankton and the rooted plants in the overall play of photosynthesis and metabolism and the importance of the different components within the trophic (level in the food chain) structure of the community.

Plants and algae make food by photosynthesis, thus they are called producers. They are consumed by herbivores that are consumed by carnivores. All living things ultimately die and decomposers (fungi and bacteria) process them thereby returning their components to the environment (see Figure 6-30).

By the middle of the 20th Century lake communities had structure. Their components were known and relationships studied. Still, the structure seemed empty because it had no function except to suggest that communities behaved as superorganisms.

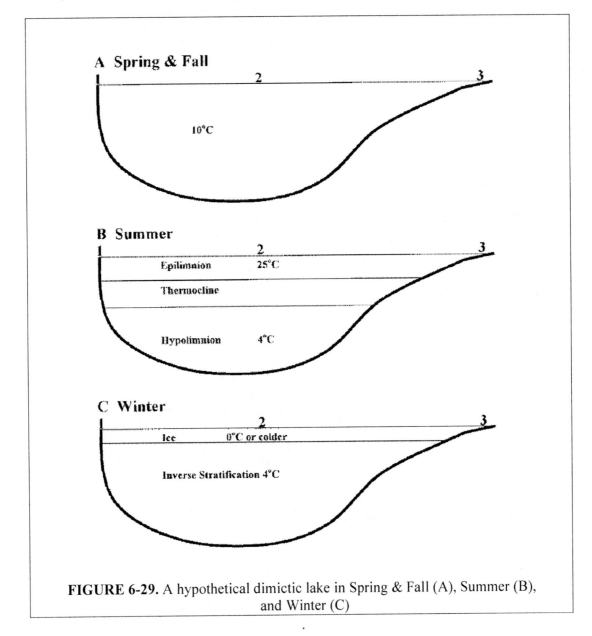

FIGURE 6-29. A hypothetical dimictic lake in Spring & Fall (A), Summer (B), and Winter (C)

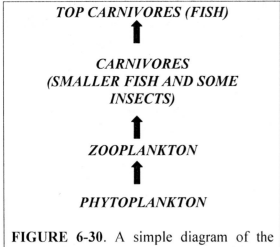

FIGURE 6-30. A simple diagram of the trophic levels in a generalized plankton community. Note that the decomposers have been omitted here but draw on each level of the food chain[33].

THE BIOSPHERE

The phenomena in the biosphere cannot lead to an understanding of the biosphere unless one takes into account the bond which unites it with the entire cosmic mechanism.

        -Vladimir I. Vernadsky (1926)

Vladimir Vernadsky[34] paved the way for an understanding of function in ecology as he contemplated the role of life from the perspective of a geochemist. Brought to chemistry by the lectures of Mendeleev[35] in St. Petersburg. He began to realize that the environment was a consequence of the synergism between the biotic and abiotic components of the environment.

Consider the Great Salt Plains Reservoir again. Under the the ice some photosynthesis did occur but not enough to counter the overall respiration or oxygen uptake of the living community, particularly the bacteria. Organic material in the water (dead plants, etc.) served as food for the microbial community which rapidly depleted the oxygen

level in the lake. Fish, even with a reduced metabolic rate and oxygen demand still required some oxygen. Also, the anoxic conditions, augmented by an ample food supply, allowed the development of anaerobic bacterial populations. These then released compounds like hydrogen sulfide, carbon dioxide, and methane, all of which added further stress to the fish. The dying fish, in turn, became food for bacterial growth as well.

In such conditions other things begin to happen. Phosphate, which is not very soluble in oxygenated water, leaves the sediment and dissolves. In surface waters, phosphate usually provides the limit to growth, so the total amount of living mass will increase until something else limits growth (This concept of the limiting nutrient came from von Liebig). In such a strongly reducing environment,[36] nitrate converts to ammonium and elements like iron, arsenic and, lead become more soluble.

In this scenario life did not fall prey to the impact of the abiotic environment. It altered the abiotic environment in a feedback loop that tended to stabilize itself into an anaerobic bacterial community. The total living mass, despite the loss of fish, probably increased, at least for a time.

Vernadsky saw the interconnections of biotic and abiotic as integral to the operation or function of the environment. He described this structure and function in a book called the Biosphere in 1929. Most importantly, this kind of environmental function precluded the need for a mystical biotic superorganism. The feedback loop (or cybernetic) system could create the observed stability of environments and the movements of materials through food chains. Unfortunately, at that time there was little contact between the scientific communities beyond the sphere of the So-

---

[33] Such a food chain is explained in *Found a Penny...*
[34] Find more about Vernadsky in *Succession in a Skeptic's Garden.*
[35] Mendeleev, the creator of the periodic table of the elements, is described in *Seeking Patterns.*

[36] I explain the concept of reduction and oxidation in *Old Books and Atoms.*

viet Union. In the West enough data had been gathered to begin to apply the biogeochemical approach, but it took a mind as expansive as Vernadsky's to accomplish it.

HUTCHINSON

I am an avid consumer of Hutchinson's words and syntheses with an appreciation similar to that held for Darwin; both are members of a group that appears only rarely in a particular discipline, perhaps once in a generation.

-Robert G. Wetzel (1993)

G. Evelyn Hutchinson (1903-1991) began his career as a biologist with an interest in insect physiology. That interest soon changed to questions related to the environment. He did work in Africa and then went to Yale where he taught from 1928 to 1971. There, he turned his attention to limnology and began a series of descriptive and experimental studies on Lindsay Pond.

He saw that ecology suffered from a lack of mathematical rigor. Aquatic ecology, in particular, had much descriptive data. He began to apply mathematics to aquatic ecology in the context of biogeochemistry. Whether this was through the direct influence of Vernadsky is difficult to say. He did read and cite Vernadsky's writings that had been translated into French.

Curiously, Hutchinson never acquired a Ph.D. He did not need one. His influence as a teacher and mentor of young ecologists resonated and continues to resonate throughout the discipline. In 1942 Raymond Lindeman, a student of Hutchinson, published *The Trophic-Dynamic Aspect of Ecology* from work that he had done on Cedar Bog Lake in Michigan. His work showed that the energy of the sun trapped by the producers became available to all other trophic levels in the lake. However, the transfer of food from one level to the next involved a loss in energy and biomass (see Figure 6-31).

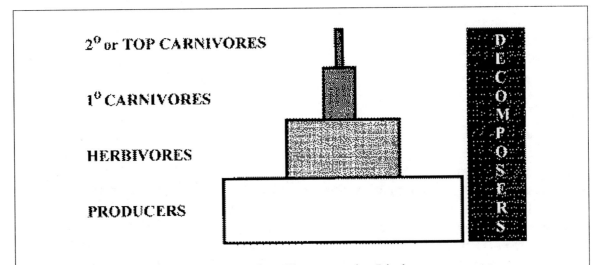

FIGURE 6-31. A simple diagram that illustrates the Lindeman concept as an energy pyramid of different trophic levels.

Lindeman calculated that the efficiency of respiration varied up the food chain. He found that producers lost 33% of their energy to respiration relative to growth while consumers lost about 62%. His work showed that simple food chains could not be very long and would tend to anastomose into more complex food webs. Although Lindeman died the year of the Cedar Bog Lake paper at the age of 27, his contribution to the science of ecology was enormous and formed the basis of the ecosystem concept.

THE ODUMS

Any unit that includes all of the organisms in a given area interacting with the physical environment so that a flow of energy leads to a clearly-defined trophic structure, biotic diversity, and material cycles within the system is an ecological system or ecosystem.

-Eugene P. Odum (1971)

Like Hutchinson, Eugene P. Odum began his career in physiology but shifted to ecology after he accepted a job with the Atomic Energy Commission. While there, his brother Howard T. Odum began to work under Hutchinson at Yale. Howard used to send Eugene copies of Hutchinson's lecture notes and sparked a long-standing correspondence between E. P. Odum and G. E. Hutchinson. Following the influences of Hutchinson and Lindeman, the Odums explored ecology as a system, and as such had to conform to the following attributes as defined by Georges Dussart:

- It has structure (internal order).
- Its components can be measured or described.
- Its attributes can be defined.
- It has emergent properties that cannot be predicted from the study of its components alone.

An ecological system or ecosystem has all of these attributes.

In the 1950's Howard and Eugene Odum conducted an ecosystem-level study on the Einiwetok Coral Atoll in the South Pacific. They measured and described the components of the atoll. They defined the attributes (trophic levels, etc.) and described the allocation of energy in the system. They found that in a mature and stable ecosystem, almost all of the energy was used for maintenance. That is, there was no net growth. In the ecosystem concept, living things become the conduit for energy and material from one trophic level to the next. So, the diversity of the living system and the interrelationships of all species become as important as the biomass and the materials. The complexity of the web together with the flow of energy work together to make a stable system. Thus, anything that would tend to simplify the biotic part of the system would destabilize the whole ecosystem

SOME CASE STUDIES

Lake management and restoration have focused upon problems particularly associated with excessive nutrient loading and poor land management.

-Robert G. Wetzel (2001)

The ecosystem approach was used to attack the problem of pollution in Lake Erie, a lake that had been pronounced "dead" in 1968. Curiously, this dead lake was actually suffering from an over-abundance of life. The influx of phosphates which then were used as components of detergents, had brought about massive algal blooms in Lake Erie. Organisms in the upper trophic levels could not process the food produced by the particular favored algae. Thus, the food webs began to be shortened and simplified. The ecosystem became unstable. With the requirement of proper sewage treatment and the elimination of phosphate in detergents, Lake Erie made an astounding recovery.

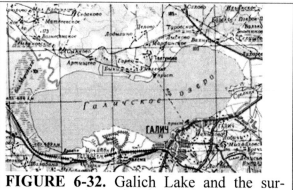

FIGURE 6-32. Galich Lake and the surrounding area. The grid lines over the lake are 4km apart.

I have studied Galich Lake, a lake in the upper Volga basin in Russia, since 1993[37]. It is a glacial lake that is approximately 16km long (E-W) and 4-6km wide (N-S) (see Figure 6-32). It has one major town, Galich, on its southern edge and two major inflows and one outflow. The average depth ranges from 1-1.5 meters, but the basin is filled with up to 9 meters of a slimy organic sediment called sapropel, which is formed under anaerobic conditions. The water has a slight brown tea-like color to it. The residents of the Galich area believe that the lake could be cleaned up by the removal of the sapropel. In addition, the sale of sapropel for fertilizer and pharmaceutical use could provide an economic boost to the town.

Similar sapropel harvesting programs have been started in other lakes of the region. The method of harvest requires that the sapropel is pumped up onto a floating barge. Water drains out of the spongy sediment as the harvester moves across the lake. Rostov Lake, a lake on which this method of harvest has been employed, has already experienced significant blooms of bluegreen algae[38] (a group of photosynthetic bacteria that respond to phosphate enrichment, see Figure 6-33). Although I did not measure phosphate, I suspect that the water draining from the collecting barges returns phosphate that has been trapped in the sediment for thousands of years. This method of harvest could increase the productivity level so that the hypolimnion routinely becomes anoxic. If that were to happen after the winter ice cover, the lake's fish community could be remarkably depleted and simplified. In this case I have no doubt that the cure would be far worse than the disease.

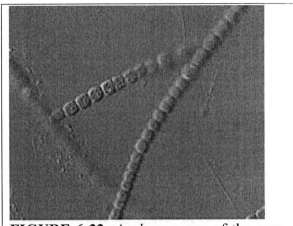

FIGURE 6-33. *Anabaena*, one of the common bluegreen algae in Rostov Lake.

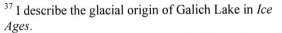

[37] I describe the glacial origin of Galich Lake in *Ice Ages*.
[38] I discuss bluegreen algae (also called cyanobacteria) in *Red Planets and Microbes*.

RETURN TO THE GREAT SALT PLAINS

Wheresoever the carcass is, there will be eagles gathered together.

-Matthew 24:28

Any cure for the Great Salt Plains Reservoir "fishkill" might prove to be a similar disaster. Many water birds now rely on that reservoir during their annual migrations. Besides, the lake freezes so rarely that tough environmental action would be unwarranted.

Anyway, the dead fish just formed the backdrop for what really impressed me on that day. Down the stream, driven by an unusually cold winter and supported by effective environmental laws and regulations, I saw almost 60 bald eagles lined up shoulder-to-shoulder feasting on the fish smorgasbord. Despite the assurance of Matthew, I could see it and explain it, but I could never have predicted that unforgettable sight. The memory of that event reminded me that although the science of Ecology has form and is developing an understanding of function, it would never lose its wonder.

- 2001

References:

Bowler, Peter J. 1992. *The Fontana History of the Environmental Sciences.* Fontana Press. London.

Brock, William H. 1992. *The Norton History of Chemistry.* W. W. Norton & Co. New York.

Forbes, Stephan A. 1887. *The Lake as a Microcosm.* (reprinted 1925 Bull. Ill. Nat. Hist. Survey. 15, 537-550).

Holt, Jack R. & Patricia A. Nelson. 2001. *Paths of Science, Explorations for Science Students and Educators.* Kendall/Hunt Publishing Company. Dubuque, Iowa.

Hudson, John. 1992. *The History of Chemistry.* Chapman & Hall. New York.

Hutchinson, G. Evelyn. 1957. *A Treatise of Limnology.* Vol I. *Geography, Physics, and Chemistry.* John Wiley & Sons, Inc. New York.

Hutchinson, G. Evelyn. 1967. *A Treatise of Limnology.* Vol II. *Introduction to Lake Biology and the Limnoplankton.* John Wiley & Sons, Inc. New York.

Hutchinson, G. Evelyn. 1975. *A Treatise of Limnology.* Vol III. *Limnological Botany.* John Wiley & Sons, Inc. New York.

Jeffries, Michael and Derek Mills. 1990. *Freshwater Ecology, Principles and Applications.* Belhaven Press. London.

Lindeman, Raymond L. 1942. *The Trophic-Dynamic Aspect of Ecology.* Ecology. 23:399-418.

Needham, James G. and J. T. Lloyd. 1916. *The Life of Inland Waters.* The Comstock Publishing Co. Ithaca, NY.

Odum, Eugene P. 1971. *Fundamentals of Ecology.* 3rd Ed. W. B. Saunders Co. Philadelphia.

Trefil, James and Robert Hazen. 2000. *The Sciences, An Integrated Approach.* 2nd ed. John Wiley & Sons, Inc. New York.

Wetzel, Robert G. 2001. *Limnology, Lake and River Ecosystems.* 3rd Ed. Academic Press. New York.

Questions to Think About

1. Why is oxygen such an important parameter in lakes and streams?

2. What are the sources of oxygen? Why can it disappear even when physical conditions suggest that it should be abundant?

3. What are some differences between photosynthesis and metabolism?

4. What are the parts of a lake? What are the parts of a stream? How are they different?

5. What is a microcosm? How does the concept apply to a lake or a stream?

6. What are the typical trophic levels?

7. How were Verndasky and Hutchinson similar in their outlooks on nature?

8. How did Lindeman modify the concept of trophic levels? How did this modification lead to the Ecosystem principle?

9. The Odums defined the concept of the ecosystem. How is the ecosystem different from the energy pyramid of Lindeman?

10. In what way is Galich Lake similat to the Great Salt Plains reservoir?

WETLANDS: GIVING AND TAKING

MUSKEG

Oh, the tundra sponge was golden brown, and some was bright blood-red;
And the reindeer moss gleamed here and there like the tombstones of the dead.
-Robert Service (Ballad of the Northern Lights)

I went to Alaska with my aunt and uncle during the summer of 1972, while I was still an undergraduate. We were there during mid-summer, and it was the first time that I had ever experienced the "white nights" of the high latitudes. This happened to be a particularly warm summer, and the temperature exceeded 100F several times in Fairbanks. We found that we had to balance the need to draw the curtains with the need for fresh, coolish air. On one of the late evenings, I decided that I would go for a walk into the nearby forest. As I left the gravel path, I was surprised to see how wet the ground was. Then, the moss-covered earth became springy, almost like a trampoline. Soon, I came upon a pool that clearly had formed by something large breaking through the surface of woven *Sphagnum* (see Figure 6-34), plant roots, and organic matter. Then, I realized that the water table was just inches beneath the soles of my boot.

Although I was consumed with curiosity, I was being consumed by legions of mosquitoes that sensed me as an easy meal. I stayed as long as I could stand it and retreated to the relative safety of my cousin's apartment. There, I began to describe my discovery, and my cousin laughed. He explained that the spongy forest floor that I described was called muskeg, and no one wants to go there.

The mosquitoes had pretty much convinced me of that anyway.

Years later, I learned that the kind of wetland called muskeg extended across Alaska and much of Canada. Although called something else, the same type of wetland extends across Siberia and Scandinavia. It is an enormous area dominated by mosses (particularly *Sphagnum*) and lichens that sit atop permafrost. The depth of the frozen soil depended on the latitude and local conditions of the site. If the frost-free layer were deep enough during the growing season, then trees, like those I had seen in the forest around my cousin's apartment could grow.

The muskeg itself is made of decayed, and partly decayed plant material called peat, a characteristic of many different wetlands with the generic name of bog or peatland. Other bogs (the non-tundra types) receive most of their water from rain, which is notoriously low in nutrients. Plants remain partly decayed because bogs tend to be deficient in nitrogen, an essential nutrient for all living things including cellulose-decomposing bacteria. The build-up of plant decay products also tends to keep the environment acidic. Plants and bacteria that inhabit bogs either fix nitrogen from the atmosphere or have adapted to capturing animals, usually insects, as particularly rich sources of nitrogen. Carnivorous plants, therefore, are characteristic of bog systems.

Bogs are not the only types of freshwater wetlands; however, categories and terms vary across the globe. In the US, wetlands with more mineral soils generally are called marshes (see Figure 6-35). These are inclined to be nutrient-rich and very productive. Usually, marsh plants are grasses, sedges, cattails, etc. Swamps are wetlands that are dominated by woody plants.

FIGURE 6-34. Sphagnum growing in a "bog" garden at my home.

FIGURE 6-35. The marsh on Assateague Island.

HISTORY OF STUDY

Research means going into the unknown with the hope of finding something new to bring home. If you know in advance what you are going to do, or even to find there, then it is not research at all: then it is only a kind of honorable occupation.
-Albert Szent-Gyorgyi (1971)

The study of wetlands as ecological entities evolved from scattered floristic studies of unusual plants, particularly *Sphagnum* in the peatlands. *Sphagnum* is a moss that has many species, but all have the ability to absorb and hold wa-

ter, up to many times their particular mass. In addition, they glean nitrogen from the immediate aqueous environment by exchanging hydrogen ions, thus making the water even more acidic.[39] Thus, *Sphagnum* controls its immediate environment with the result of a buildup of peat made mainly of dead *Sphagnum* whose common name is peat moss.

The study of peatlands as interesting botanical environments began around the turn of the 20th Century in Europe and the United States. One of the earliest studies was by Carl Albert Weber (1856-1931; Germany), who studied the plant ecology of the raised bog of Augustmal. A raised bog comes about as a consequence of the water-holding property of *Sphagnum*. If *Sphagnum* successfully establishes itself on flat ground or a slight depression, the growth of the moss and peat deposition will actually cause the growing bog to be mounded up or raised relative to its surroundings. Weber found this phenomenon to be interesting and produced a monograph in 1902, the first that considered the ecology of a wetland. Furthermore, he attempted to relate the Augustmal bog to other raised bogs in the world.

Other peatland studies followed, but they were sparse. Herman Kurz (1886-1996; USA) published on trees associated with rivers and wetlands in Florida. A. P. Dachnowski-Stokes (dates? USA) also studied peatlands through Florida and elsewhere. Unfortunately, wetlands suffered from public opinion that ranged from indifference to scorn. Even Carolus Linnaeus compared the Lapp wetlands of northern Scandinavia to the gates of hell. By most Americans and Europeans, wetlands were seen as waste areas, neither arable nor suitable for de-

---

[39] pH decreases (= acidity increases) as the concentration of hydrogen ions increases.

velopment. Also, wetlands occupied a position that was neither aquatic nor terrestrial.

With the development of the ecosystem concept and the holistic environmental view that it fostered, wetlands became appropriate and desired objects of study. Indeed, one of the founders of ecosystem theory, Howard Thomas Odum[40] (1924-2002; USA), created the Center for Wetlands at the University of Florida in 1973. By then, wetlands had entered the scientific mainstream.

Those who used the ecosystem approach to study environments like wetlands required much more that a catalog of species. They needed to know the climate, geology, geography, type of soil, and hydrology[41]. Much of the environmental work, particularly the hydrology and soil science had been done by Russian scientists. Furthermore, Russia produced Sergei Nikolaevich Winogradsky (1856-1953, Ukraine), the founder of soil microbiology. Winogradsky was trained in St. Petersburg as a botanist, but, after the spectacular revelations of Pasteur and Koch, he settled on microbes of the soil as his focus. The Bolshevik revolution forced him and his family to leave Russia and settle in Belgrade, and then finally to the Pasteur Institute in Paris where he lived and worked from 1922 until the Nazi occupation caused him to "retire".

Winogradsky came to understand that nutrient limitation in the soil governed microbial activity. He also recognized that microbes were mostly in a dormant state. He rejected the standard use of sterile laboratory methods to study microbial physiology because he wanted to understand how they behaved in the soil. By growing them in columns of soil, he studied how they caused the decomposition of cellulose (wood), the fixation of nitrogen from the atmospheric molecular form to a form that living things could use to make food. Much of what he did emulated the ways that wetland soils work.

FUNCTIONS OF WETLANDS

Wetlands have a poor public image.... Yet they are among the earth's greatest natural assets... mankind's waterlogged wealth.

- Edward Maltby, Waterlogged Wealth, 1986

Wetland soils are saturated with water, and, therefore, nearly devoid of oxygen. This favors the development of anaerobic bacteria. Also, water is plentiful; so, their growth is limited only by the presence of food and the necessary nutrients. Because wetlands, especially marshes, tend to be so productive[42], food is not a problem. Thus, the microbial communities grow rapidly until they run out of nutrients. So, nutrients in water flowing into a marsh is trapped in the microbial biomass, and in the case of nitrogen, often exported to the atmosphere in the form of molecular nitrogen. In this way wetlands function as nutrient filters. In a less complex way they trap suspended silt and clay particles by slowing the water as it moves overland. Thus, wetlands are among the most important environments for cleaning water before it enters our streams and lakes.

Wetlands serve to clean the surface water before it enters the groundwater, also. By definition, wetlands are places where groundwater is very close to or

---

[40] See *Ecosystems: Form, Function, and Wonder.*
[41] The way in which water flows on and under ground.

---

[42] By this, I mean that wetlands are efficient at producing food. Their rate of food manufacture is equivalent to that of a productive corn field.

just above the surface. So, they can function as sites for the recharge of groundwater, or of discharge of groundwater when the water table is high.

At times of high runoff, wetlands tend to slow down the water, hold it and release it slowly. In a sense, they behave as sponges. Because they release water more slowly than do streams, they have the potential to reduce the impacts of flooding.

SCIENCE AND PUBLIC POLICY

Wetlands are areas where water covers the soil, or is present either at or near the surface of the soil all year or for varying periods of time during the year, including during the growing season. Water saturation largely determines how the soil develops and the types of plant and animal communities living in and on the soil. Wetlands may support both aquatic and terrestrial species. The prolonged presence of water creates conditions that favor the growth of specially adapted plants and promote the development of characteristic wetlands soils.

- EPA, America's Wetlands: Our Vital Link Between Land and Water

With such important functions for the maintenance of clean water and mitigation of flooding, how might wetlands be recognized? The definition by the EPA indicates two ways: look at the soils and look at the plants. Microbial action within the anaerobic saturated soil produces characteristic mottling. Most obvious is the gray clay (called gleying). Plants that inhabit saturated soils have specializations that allow them to deliver oxygen to their roots and rhizomes.

Armed with scientific knowledge and means to recognize and delineate wetland sites, congress added wetland protection to the Clean Water Act of 1972. Although this curbed the loss of wetlands in the US, it did not eliminate their loss. Some wetlands are lost due to road construction, agriculture, etc. In such cases, an equal area of wetlands is supposed to be constructed to mitigate their loss. In truth, though, mitigation sites rarely work as well as the original wetlands did.

The US could strengthen the wetland regulations as proposed by a 2001 report by the EPA. However, at issue is the problem of what is called regulative takings. For example, a farmer who has 2,000 acres, but 200 acres are classified as wetlands, has lost 10% of his land, usually without compensation. From the point of view of the farmer, the government has taken 10% of the land.

These issues are not simple and will not go away with other regulations. The protection of wetlands will, in the end, be determined by how they are valued. Until around 1970 wetlands were waste places, even the mighty Everglades was shrinking at an alarming rate due to government policies. Now, they are being restored.

In the long run, though, we have to stop trying to put values on such environments for what they can do for us. Such thinking presupposes that we already know all that wetlands do for us. We have to just value them and come to understand that wetlands are not ours to keep or to destroy, but they are precious, diverse, and complex systems that carry out a variety of important functions. More importantly, though, wetlands are ecosystems that we have borrowed from the future of our children.

-2005

References:

Bowler, Peter J. 1992. The Fontana History of the Environmental Sciences. In: Porter, R., ed. Fontana History of Science Series. Fontana Press. HarperCollins Publishers. London.

Chung, K-T. and C.L. Case. 2001. Sergei Winogradsky: Founder of Soil Microbiology. SIM News. 51(3):133-135.

Crum, H. 1998. A Focus on Peatlands and Peat Mosses. In: Wagner, W.H., ed. Great Lakes Environment. The University of Michigan Press. Ann Arbor.

Johnson, C.W. 1985. Bogs of the Northeast. University Press of New England. Hanover.

Miller, G.T. 2004. Living in the Environment. 13th edition. Thompson, Brooks/Cole.

Mitsch, W. J. and J.G. Gosselink. 2000. Wetlands. 3rd edition. John Wiley and Sons, Inc. New York.

> *I enter the swamp as a sacred place--a sanctum sanctorum. There is the strength, the marrow of Nature.*
> -Henry David Thoreau

Questions to Think About

1. What is a peatland?

2. Distinguish between marshes, bogs, and swamps.

3. What is *Sphagnum*, and why is its biology important to the understanding of some wetlands?

4. Why are marshes so productive?

5. What did H.T. Odum do for wetland studies?

6. What are some characteristics of wetland soils?

7. What law serves to protect wetlands from further loss?

8. What is the issue of takings?

9. George H. W. Bush promised that wetlands would not experience a net loss. What did he mean by that?

10. What are some functions that wetlands carry out for us?

SUCCESSION IN A SKEPTIC'S GARDEN

BIOENERGY

Vernadsky called the biosphere controlled by the mind of man the noosphere.

        - Andrey Lapo

On the fourth of July in 2002 I had just arrived in Yaroslavl, Russia and settled in to my apartment. Right off, I had an appointment with a chiropractor and went there in the afternoon. Before he put me on the table, he asked that I submit to a "reading" of my bioenergy. For this procedure, he had me put my finger at the vortex of a set of diverging rays on a piece of paper. Then, he suspended a cone of copper or brass by a string over my finger and recorded the path of the swinging cone over my finger. He did this for several sets of similar figures. For each one he called out readings as parameters to be recorded as data (The "data sheet" can be found in Figure 6-36). He discovered several problems that I had with my feet, my pelvis and lower back, and my neck. He found these by touching and pressing and showed me some simple exercises to follow in helping to mitigate the problems. I was impressed by his ability to discern the problems so quickly and precisely. He then asked that I return in the evening, around 7, and I agreed.

On my return I expected to be subjected to some more massage, tapping, and pulling. Instead, the chiropractor asked me to sit down and put my finger on a piece of paper as before. This time, however, he asked me to do this with a succession of about five different pieces of paper, each with a different design on it. As he allowed the copper cone to swing over my finger, I repeated, "energize me", over and over. When he finished, the chiropractor asked me to sit silently for seven minutes with the pieces of paper tucked into my belt. Then, at the appointed time, he came in, took the paper from me, and ignited it.

After all that was over, he sat me down and told me that my bioenergy was very low and that this procedure will help me to recover it. Also, he said that his readings suggested that I had near-death crises when I was 33 and 37. (I could not remember such crises, but maybe I just didn't notice). I know that he said other things, but what overshadowed everything for me and caught my complete attention was when he told me that this exercise was done according to the science of Vladimir Vernadsky (1863-1945), a Russian geochemist who began to view life as higher order of geological process. Indeed, he saw life as the controlling part of geological cycles. Thus, he saw the whole skin of the earth as alive and coined the term, Biosphere. He then said that the biosphere will continue to develop into a higher level of organization through the collective intelligence of humanity. This new plane he called the Noosphere. The chiropractor claimed that he was reading my bioenergy field within the nascent Noosphere through the use of his metal cone.

HOLISM & MATERIALISM

The ecosystem was ... an invention of botanists.   -Paul Colinvaux (1978)

Vernadsky saw the geology, environment, and life on planet Earth as a continuum and not as discrete entities. As I indicated before[43], the holistic approach of Vernadsky and others was instrumental in the creation of the Ecosystem concept, a powerfully illuminating theory in the science of Ecology. In part, this was a system in which

---

[43] See *Ecosystem: Form, Function, and Wonder.*

the flow of energy from the sun through the biota determines the biotic structure and its stability.

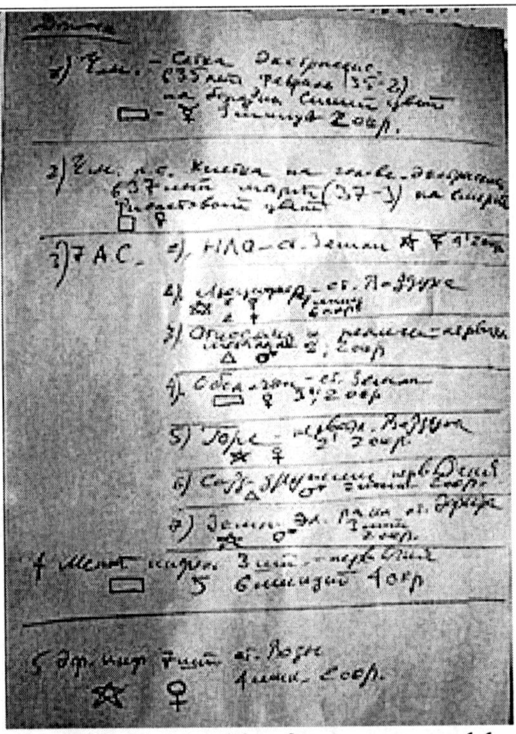

FIGURE 6-36. The form generated by the reading of my bioenergy field within the Noosphere.

The ecosystem evolved as a concept by those who studied freshwater environments, particularly lakes. It also came from the pioneering work of a collection of botanists who studied plant communities in Europe and the United States during the first half of the 20th Century. The work of the botanists began in Europe as a way to convert the descriptive discipline of plant natural history to a more rigorous form. There, they applied statistical techniques to plant groups or associations to try to determine the underlying laws that determined the occurrences of particular plant associations.

I will try to explain what they were doing in Europe by a more local example. In parts of northern Pennsylvania,

the American Beech-Sugar Maple forest is a typical mature forest type. This association or plant society is an obvious discrete unit. Many other plant species occupy the Beech-Maple forests, though. Statistical methods and extensive surveys can be used to distinguish subtle differences between different types of Beech-Maple forests.

In the view of phytosociology the plant society or association was more important than the particular plant species in the association. Europeans such as Josias Braun-Blanquet (1884-1980) studied whole forests as units, but their holistic approach was unable to show that plant groups existed in anything but continuums of association relative to their environments.

The Dane, Eugenius Warming (1841-1924), used plant physiology as the basis for explaining why certain plants occurred where they did. As such, his was a reductionist or materialist approach. He identified a uniform group of plants in a particular area as a community, usually designated by the dominant plants in the assemblage. Warming set out this theory in an influential textbook on plant ecology (*Oecology of Plants*) in 1895. His work, and particularly his book, became the basis for the research on plant groups that blossomed into two different schools within the United States.

Henry Chandler Cowles (1860-1939) of the University of Chicago embraced the materialistic approach of Warming and adapted it to his ecological studies of plant communities around the shore of Lake Michigan. He became interested in the dynamic nature of disturbed plant communities. That is, when a mature community was damaged by cutting or some natural disaster, the area goes through a series of successional stages that culminate in a stable or climax community.

The concept of succession was not a new one. Even the ancients had commented on how plants change over time in response to disturbance. When a mature plant community, one that Cowles called the climax community, is cut to bare ground, the first plants to appear are the weedy pioneers. These are plants that shed lots of seeds or other types of propagation structures called propagules. Their seeds are numerous but usually contain little stored food, so they require sunlight for germination and early growth. Also, they germinate quickly and generally grow quickly thus devoting much of their total biomass to making more propagules. Usually such plants are annuals and can tolerate more extreme conditions such as exposure, soil moisture, wind, temperature, etc. A community that is perennial, and less tolerant to environmental extremes replaces these plants. Succeeding communities have their particular characteristics, but they do not replace themselves until the climax community is arises. The steps leading to the climax can take hundreds of years in the case of a mature forest land. This type of change in plant community over time was called secondary succession.

Cowles' major contribution was in the recognition and detailed study of natural succession or primary succession. He considered what kind of changes in vegetation might occur as a pond fills in with organic material as it changes to a marsh and then to a forest. In the case of natural environments around Lake Michigan in the Chicago area, the successional stages went from beach to dune to bogs to woods. The climax forest type also was Beech-Maple. This type of succession could take thousands of years. More importantly, he found various stages of succession around Lake Michigan relative to a longitudinal gradient from the lake itself. Thus, succession could be ar-

rested at any particular stage relative to local environmental conditions. Cowles interpreted this to mean that succession was not only the expression of the dynamism or fluctuation of plant communities relative to each other but also to fluctuations in the environment.

Further south in Kansas, Charles Edwin Bessey (1845-1915), trained in physiology, began to be interested in what remained of the original prairie communities before agriculture destroyed all remnants of them. His most influential student was Frederic E. Clements (1874-1926). They and others studied the occurrences of particular prairie grasses and secondary succession from abandoned farmland to prairie. They took the holistic approach of the European Phytosociologists. However, they were dissatisfied with their methods and assumed that they did not find the organizing principles for community structure because their methods were not rigorous enough. Clements and his colleague Roscoe Pound (1870-1964) marked off quadrats of many square meters, but mostly small areas (to one square meter) and counted every plant in the particular area. Clements and Pound set up such quadrats all over the prairie to identify the diversity of grass communities. Then, they cleared some of the quadrats of all plants and monitored succession back to the climax community.

Clements began to regard the plant community as a super-organism and the successional stages as stages in the development of that organism. He believed that any particular area would always give rise to the same climax community. Thus, any area would return to its determined climax as a wound would heal over. He advised farmers to learn what the climax of the area should be so that they would be able to control the beast that they were holding at bay by the plow. Clements was a persuasive writer and his views had great influence on the science of Botany and on methods of agriculture and land management. Like Vernadsky, Clements' views were holistic and implied a kind of vitalistic[44] life force that transcended individual organisms. Curiously, the holistic views of both men also promoted science as a means of controlling the economy.

GARDENS AND WEEDS
We must cultivate our garden.
  -Voltaire (1694-1778) from Candide

Knowledge about succession and plant communities is not limited to plant ecologists. Succession and plant communities are the great beasts that all gardeners wrestle with every summer. Like clockwork in my garden redroot pigweed, dandelions, gill-on-the-ground, Canadian thistle, garlic mustard, wild onions, grass, sourgrass, bishop's miter, purselane, spurge, etc. all appear at their appointed times and cover the garden beds. We typically call such plants weeds. Although a strict definition of weed is elusive, an unwanted plant is about the best one that I know of. From a plant community perspective, these particular plants are pioneers in the first stages of secondary succession.

Where do weeds come from? Well, most germinate from a large seed bank in the soil. The concept of a seed bank is very apparent in the garden. To illustrate that, I weeded and cultivated a section of garden about 0.3X4 meters. After two weeks the bare plot looked as it does in Figure 6-36. During that time (June 17-July 1, 2002), the ground was covered by a carpet of weeds. By August 8, 2002, that same plot became overpowered by redroot pigweed, some of which grew to 3 meters tall! Clearly, if left alone, any simple community (in this case a path that should have no plant species on it at all) becomes more complex, particularly through the addition of opportunistic species (see Figure 6-37).

Such early successional plants are well adapted to the extremes in soil moisture that bare soil presents. Also, they require sun for germination and successful growth. The bare patches in the path had a thin veneer of grass clippings. Just the shade from that much mulch was enough to prevent spurge, purselane, and redroot pigweed from growing, even after 7 weeks.

My garden is only about 400 square meters if I do not count the space set aside for fruit trees and shrubs, and grape vines. The problem of weeding that small area usually occupies much of my time when I am home during the growing season. Now consider the problems of operating a farm that is much more than just a larger version of a garden. It operates by removing the native plant community and replacing it with a single species, a monoculture. Thus, a farm has to combat the tendency of the bare soil to return to a climax community through stages of succession (see Figure 6-38).

The textbook version of the stages of secondary succession goes like this. The weedy species that appear as pioneers grow quickly, mostly are annuals, and much of the energy of the plants is devoted to the production of seeds [Note that most crop plants fit this same profile]. Later stages of succession are characterized by plants that store much of their food in the form of stems, roots, etc. and tend to last more than one year. Thus, the relative amount of energy put into seeds diminishes with the stages of succession. In a climax forest dominated by oaks, most of the living mass of the plants is tied up into large structures that can survive hundreds of years and the relative contribution to seeds is quite low. However, because oaks can be very large, the total number of acorns that they produce still exceeds the

---

[44] See *A Vital Science* for the concept of vitalism.

number of trees that could grow there by thousands of times. As dominant climax species, oaks replace themselves. Thus, the seeds store a large amount of food in them that allows the seedlings to gain a foothold and begin to grow even under very low light conditions. If a break in the forest canopy appears, the young sapling will be there to take advantage of the situation. This is the view according to Clements, the community as a super-organism with predictable stages in succession leading to a determined climax

A. growth after 2 weeks   **B. growth after 7 weeks**

FIGURE 6-37. An experiment on a path in my garden between beds of onions and potatoes. The weeds, include purselane, spurge, sourgrass, redroot pigweed, dandilion, grass, and Canadian thistle. Note that by seven weeks the redroot pigweed (the tall plant) over-tops everything else and the mulched area in the foreground still remains weed-free.

FIGURE 6-38. Successional stages on a farm near Susquehanna University. Freshly tilled field in the foreground, an old field of alfalfa and other plants, and then the hedgerow of mature trees.

Plant Ecologists began to challenge the persuasive view of Clements almost right away. Arthur G. Tansley (1871-1955) of Britain and Henry Allen Gleason (1882-1975) of the United States pushed the materialistic view of plant community ecology. By the 1920's both had argued that plants occurred in communities because they had similar requirements (climate, soil-type, etc.). Also, their associations were a consequence of considerable chance. Gleason, in particular, took the materialistic view and defined it to say that succession and climax were illusions of the collective of individual species that live in a particular area. Thus, they argued that stable communities in any particular area are highly predictable but not as absolute or as deterministic as the super-organism would imply. This was due to the nature of natural disturbance as both highly unpredictable in its occurrence and quite variable in its severity. Also, individual species in one community might also occur in another stable community.

Gleason argued that only his individualistic theory of plant succession could explain how some environments could degrade in a reverse or retrograde succession. For example, overgrazing by cattle caused a simplification of rangeland, and the chestnut blight caused the elimination of the American Chestnut as a dominant in the Eastern Deciduous forest. The greatest blow to the super-organism theory was the Dust Bowl of the 1930's in which whole regions of farmed prairie turned to desert. Clearly, the "super-organism" did not always recover. Despite that, both the holistic

556

theory of Clements and the materialistic theory of Cowles-Tansley-Gleason continued throughout the first half of the 20th century embraced by different schools and used by different research programs. Together, the philosophies of holism and materialism both supported rigorous research programs and generated much knowledge about nature.

DAVID HUME IN THE GARDEN

Professional training in philosophy does provide a set of tools, modes and approaches, not to mention a feeling for common dangers and fallacies, that few scientists (or few "smart folks" of any untrained persuasion) are likely to possess by the simple good fortune of superior raw brainpower.

-Stephen Jay Gould (2002)

That is what science does. It generates knowledge and understanding about nature. However, as a philosophy (yes, science is a philosophy) the struggle of science is to take observations and use those to construct explanations about how nature works. Those explanations, also known as theories) then become modified as new data and observations mount. That is how science has worked since its modern period began in the 18th century. The only corollary that has been added during the past 100 years is that all theories must be consistent with the laws of chemistry and physics. These rules are accepted by scientists as a standard way of doing business, though few scientists actually study the philosophy of what they are doing.

Philosophers, however, seem to be fascinated by science and how it generates knowledge. They have struggled with a variety of issues that the process of science generates. Some of the important issues include:

- how we can trust our senses to give us an accurate picture of an external reality.
- how we can make a general statement based on a few observations (the type of reasoning called induction).
- how we can say that one event caused another one to happen (the problem of cause and effect).

Consider the question of cause and effect. How can we observe an effect and assign a cause to it? Early philosophers of the Enlightenment claimed that the cause was already part of the effect. Others said that cause and effect were separate events that we just put together in our minds. For example, what is the cause of the weedy path in my garden (Figure 6-37)? I gave several of them: a seed bank, rapid germination and growth of weeds. Later, I gave some auxiliary causes as characteristics of weeds and plants that emerge from bare ground. I might apply a Clements-style cause of the early growth and development of the super-organism of the climax community. I could also apply a Gleason-style cause that all of the plants that emerged there had similar environmental requirements and tolerances, and their seeds just happened to be there.

David Hume (1711-1776) was a Scottish historian and philosopher who dealt with these issues in science. Fundamentally, he wrestled with the philosophy of Skepticism. In the extreme form of this philosophy, a philosophy that was as old as that of science, the practitioner doubts everything. That is, the person would even doubt the information of the senses. Although appearing erudite, Hume recognized that followers of such a philosophy were intellectually barren and could make no contributions to humankind. He rejected the Neoskepticism that had become fashionable during the Enlightenment and finally said that scientists must be skeptical, but their skepticism has to be mitigated by the custom of accepting that our senses provide us with an accurate picture of the external reality of nature and that the future will resemble the past. This, Hume derived from the "Academical Philosophy" of Plato's school in which extreme skepticism was corrected by "common sense and reflection". He declared that there was no logical reason to assume such a thing but that the alternative was "sophistry and illusion". In a phrase, David Hume had identified what scientists have become, "mitigated skeptics". Today, philosophers of science have labeled us as "naïve realists".

Now, let us evaluate the concepts of Vernadsky's Noosphere, Clements' Super-organism, and Gleason's Individualistic Ecology from the standpoint of a Hume's skeptic. All three are dynamic. That is, they assume that a change will occur and attempt to predict and explain those changes. The super-organism concept was based on careful and meticulous methods that were repeated in many different areas and habitats. Clements observed succession and constructed his theory to explain his observations. Today, we reject his explanation for the causes of successions and the formation of a climax community and lean more toward the explanations of Cowles, Tansley, and Gleason. Still, both represented good science in that they followed methods based on observation and developed theories that were consistent with the fundamental laws of science. Certainly, in the case of theories of succession, the future must resemble the past.

This is not true in the case of the current concepts of the Noosphere, the Biosphere controlled by the minds of humanity. Vernadsky was on solid scientific footing when he proposed the concept of the Biosphere. Though holistic, the Biosphere was also mechanistic and present to be observed. The Noosphere, however, is in its developing stages and can be accessed only by certain parapsychologists who are trained and tuned to it. Therefore, it is not objective, and it has not yet come to pass, so, in this case, the future cannot resemble the past. Any number of possible futures await humanity and the biosphere. There is no reason that a skeptic or scientist should accept Vernadsky's deterministic future (the Noosphere) as the particular path that the Biosphere will take. As such the concept of the Noosphere is not based on methods of observation. As a skeptic (in the Humean sense) and a naïve realist, therefore, I am forced to reject the concept of the Noosphere as a science. My position goes beyond the very real problem that the concept of the Noosphere is not consistent with the laws of chemistry and physics.

The Noosphere (the Biosphere controlled by the mind of humanity) in a strict objective sense might be with us and around us. Here, I interpret the mind to include the physical extensions of the human mind: the hand and tools of humankind. Thus, humanity has been exerting control over the Biosphere for millennia.

I see almost no plant communities that are not controlled or managed in one way or another. The garden and the farm are extreme forms of management, but even such "natural" environments as state forests and national parks are subject to methods of control and management. This revision of the mystical conception of the Noosphere is one that I, a mitigated skeptic and naïve realist, can accept.

-2002

References:

American Environmental Photographs. (Date accessed: Jume 27, 2002). http://memory.loc.gov/ammem/award97/icuhtml/

Bowler, Peter J. 1992. *The Fontana History of the Environmental Sciences.* Fontana Press. London.

Colinvaux, Paul. 1973. *Introduction to Ecology.* John Wiley and Sons, Inc. New York.

Colinvaux, Paul. 1979. *Why Big Fierce Animals Are Rare.* Princeton University Press. Princeton.

Hume, David. 2000 (first published 1739-40). A *Treatise of Human Nature.* Norton, David Fate and Mary J., eds. Oxford Philosophical Texts. Oxford University Press. Oxford.

Hume, David. 1999 (first published 1748). *An Inquiry Concerning Human Understanding.* Beauchamp, Tom L., ed. Oxford University Press. Oxford.

Mossner, Ernest Campbell. 1980. *The Life of David Hume.* Second ed. Clarendon Press. Oxford.

Pearl, Judea. 2001. *Causality, Models, Reasoning, and Inference.* Cambridge University Press. Cambridge, UK.

Pidwirny, Michael J. 2000. *Fundamentals of Physical Geography. 9 Introduction to Biogeography and Ecology.* http://www.geog.ouc.bc.ca/physgeog/contents/9i.html

Townsend, Colin R. 2000. *Essentials of Ecology.* Blackwell Science, Inc. Malden, Mass.

United States Department of Agriculture. 1970. *Selected Weeds of the United States.* Government Printing Office. Washington.

Questions to Think About

1. Who was Vernadsky, and what was the noosphere?

2. Why did Paul Colinvaux write, "The ecosystem was…an invention of botanists?"

3. What are the attributes of an ecosystem?

4. What two schools of plant ecology arose in the US during the early years of the 20th Century?

5. What is succession? How do primary and secondary succession differ?

6. What were the contributions of Cowles, Bessey, Clements, and Gleason? How did the Dust Bowl signal the death of the Superorganism Theory?

7. David Hume is best known for his philosophy of skepticism; however, he found skepticism to be empty when carried to the extreme. How did he describe himself?

8. What is the problem of cause and effect?

9. What is the importance of the phrase: the future will resemble the past?

10. I rejected the noosphere in a general sense, but accepted it in a strict sense. What do you think of that interpretation?

STUDENTS OF NATURE

AN UNCOMMON STUDENT

I am moved by strange sympathies; I say continually "I will be a naturalist."
-Ralph Waldo Emerson

I had been teaching college for just a few years when John Clark (Figure 6-39), a lanky, grizzled man with a large black mustache, plopped down in a seat at the front of the room on the first day of Plant Diversity. John was uncommon in many ways. For one, he was older than the other students. In fact he was around eight years older than I was. His dress was more like that of a carpenter than that of a college student. Right off the bat, he exhibited an unabashed curiosity and interest that made some of the other students in the class somewhat uncomfortable. I found it refreshing to see that John didn't care one bit.

He always sat in the front of the room and took notes on a 3X5 inch card (front and back). If I covered more information than he could fit on the card, he just sat politely, interestedly, but took no more notes. I asked him about that later in the semester and John replied that besides the reading assignments, he could not absorb more than he put on an index card each class period. Results of exams at that time suggested that John was not the only one in that situation.

Through his matriculation at Susquehanna University, he became interested in plants more and more. First, he made an effort to understand and recognize most common plants. Then, he attacked ferns and mosses. Upon graduation, John was an accomplished field biologist, and it was not long before my former student became my teacher.

FIGURE 6-39. John Clark on Assateague Island.

ANOTHER BOTANIST

John Bartram...is the greatest natural botanist in the world. -Carolus Linnaeus

John and I attempted many joint projects, some more successful than others. Several summers running, we taught an Elderhostel course in which we presented general field botany in the context of foraging and wild foods. In that course, John suggested that we try to find the local places mentioned in a

561

journal by an 18th century botanist named John Bartram.

John Bartram (1699-1777) was born in Darby, Pennsylvania and grew up with a standard Quaker education. Around 1711 his family moved to a new homestead in the Carolinas. Soon, however, the native inhabitants rose up against the encroachment of the settlers and in a raid, killed John Bartram's father and took his family captive. Surviving that, John, his stepmother and siblings returned to Philadelphia where the property settlement and disposition of his father's will became entangled in a morass of claims. Finally, when he was 21, John Bartram inherited a small amount from the liquidation of his father's Pennnsylvania property. After the death of his grandmother, John Bartram inherited a 200-acre farm on the banks of the Schuylkill River in 1722/23. He purchased some additional land, lived there, and farmed it for the rest of his life. In 1730 he designed and built a somewhat eclectic house that he added to over the years.

Bartram quickly developed into an enthusiastic farmer and made quite a name for himself as an amateur naturalist. At this time, Peter Collison, a London weaver, avid gardener, and fellow Quaker, had been looking for sources of exotic plants. Disappointed by others whom he had engaged to send back plants and seeds, Collison learned of Bartram and thus began a successful partnership. Collison provided Bartram with other patrons, books, and scientific contacts, including Linnaeus.

John Bartram just as enthusiastically began to collect all types of specimens. As expected, he collected seeds and plants of many North American plants a well as bird skins, butterflies turtles, etc. All of these found ready buyers in England and other parts of Europe. He began to go on extended collecting trips through the northeast and into the south. Bartram brought back plants and seeds and experimented with their cultivation and germination to which he devoted much time and land.

A FERN GARDEN

The works of a person that builds begin immediately to decay; while those of him who plants begin directly to improve. In this planting promises a more lasting pleasure than building.

-William Bartram

John Clark had become interested in local native ferns and attempted many experiments with germinating spores and propagating plants. He and I advised a student project called the campus arboretum project. Among other things, we tried to create an area in the middle of the Susquehanna campus that would house most of the native ferns and fernallies in Pennsylvania. He spent an enormous amount of time making pockets of earth and rock outcrops that corresponded to the requirements of particular fern species. In the mean time, he filled his rooms with small terraria and pots with different soil mixtures, humidity variations, and light exposures. Within a year, he began to supply a trickle of plants. Then more and more until he had created an island of native plants in the middle of the campus (Figures 6-40 and 6-41).

John Bartram, too, created a working garden of native plants. To many, however, it seemed messy. Indeed, George Washington wrote that Bartram's garden was little more than a weed patch. Today, Bartram's Garden is a garden spot in Philadelphia (Figure 6-42).

FIGURE 6-40. Northern Maidenhair Fern in the Fern Garden.

FIGURE 6-41. In the *Fern Garden.* at Susquehanna University.

FIGURE 6-42. In Bartram's Garden.

John Bartram was a farmer, a collector, a horticultualist, and botanist. Also, he had a very good business sense and remained prosperous through his life. Unfortunately, John's third son, William (called Billy by his father), shared his father's love of nature, but failed at almost everything else. John bailed out his son from one failed venture to another until William stopped trying.

John Clark made a stab at business after he graduated. He created a corporation called The Wetlands Advisory Group, a venture that cost him much time and was only marginally successful as a moneymaker. Still, it was clear to me that John had other measures of success and his monetary needs were quite modest.

THE BOTANISTS' EDUCATIONS
One cannot abstain when in the sight of the rich treasures scattered so freely over this fertile land, from a feeling of pity for those gloomy indoor theorizers who pass their lives in hammering out vain systematics. -Phillip Commerson

Both John Clark and John Bartram studied plants incessantly. Their studies took them to the field and to the books. Indeed, both of them learned their botany by doing it. Peter Collison sent books and suggestions to Bartram about how to study and how to check his identifications. Bartram struggled with the Latin descriptions and learned the Latin names.

John Bartram together with his son William discovered and delivered about 200 new plant species to Europe by way of Peter Collison. Unfortunately, Bartram did not take the time to describe and name the new plants and left that chore to others.

John Clark too, struggled to learn academic botany often staying up all night to key out and confirm identifications of sedges and other troublesome plants. Through this kind of self-teaching, John quickly became one of the most competent field biologists in Pennsylvania. He then began to work with the local universities on a variety of research projects and with environmental groups as a professional volunteer.

John Clark often queried local landowners and other amateur naturalists about plants, their habits and locations. His disarming way and easy conversation quickly put others at ease. Often disappointed, he occasionally ferreted out information locked away from the more academic types. More importantly, he used this method gently and firmly to teach the common person about the intricacies of nature.

TRAVELS IN PENNSYLVANIA

It is a misfortune to the publick, that this ingenious person had not a literal education, it is no wonder therefore, that his stile is not so clear as we could wish, however, in every piece of his, there are evident marks of such good sense, penetration and sincerity, join'd to a commendable curiosity.

-J. Whiston & B. White, Fleet Street Publishers

John Clark had read and studied Bartram's *Travels in Pensilvania* (sic) *and Canada* as another source about the primal nature of central Pennsylvania. He and I had often talked about following the journal left by John Bartram and trying to find some of the sites described therein. The book was Bartram's personal journal of a trip from his farm up through the Susquehanna Valley and on to Lake Ontario in 1743, and it was never intended for publication. Peter Kalm, a student of Linnaeus, visited Bartram and asked to take the journal to show to some scientists in Europe. Once there, a copy found its way to Fleet Street Publishers J. Whiston and B. White who printed the journal without Bartram's permission and then gently chided the author in a preface for his rough style. Still, the action of Kalm (after whom Linnaeus named Mountain Laurel, *Kalmia*) has given us a very early description of Pennsylvania, as well as people of the Iroquois and Delaware nations.

Bartram left his farm on July 3, 1743 with Lewis Evans who would later produce a map of the northeastern region (Figure 6-43). They went to the home of Conrad Weiser who joined them and traveled to the north to meet with the Five Nations of the Iroquois. Bartram and his companions were plagued with mosquitoes and rain. At first, the insects and weather kept Bartram from sleeping for several days. Finally, he gave up and described sleeping in the rain without shelter. He wrote about most hardships without grumbling in his journal. He described coming into Shamokin (present-day Sunbury), a Delaware town. The description is brief but almost certainly refers to a path that exists today on the southeast part of the city of Sunbury (Figure 6-44). The path lies on a steep hill with an almost unique collection of understory plants, the diversity of which suggests that the area, if logged, was cut very long ago.

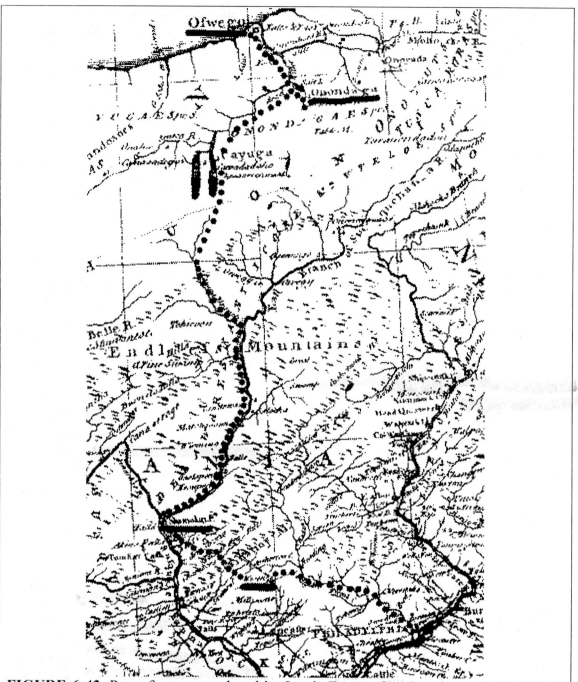

FIGURE 6-43. Part of a map produced by Lewis Evans after the trip to Lake Ontario. The dotted line represents the approximate route that the Bartram-Weiser party took to Lake Ontario. The heavy underscore lines are (in order from the south) Conrad Weiser's home, Shamokin (now Sunbury), Onondoga, Oswego.

FIGURE 6-44. *The bottom of this descent is washed by Shamokin Creek three rods wide, this we forded to a fruitful bottom half a mile wide, beyond which, two miles of good oak land brought us to the town of Shamokin.* The path as described by John Bartram outside of Sunbury:

There, the group met Shickellamy, a chief and liaison with the five nations, and prepared for the journey northward. From there on, Bartram occupies most of his journal with habits and characteristics of the Iroquois and Delaware who guided them to their destination. He seems to have found almost no plants worth collecting and his descriptions are almost cursory.

Twice on the trip he writes about encounters with rattlesnakes (see Figure 6-45 for an example of an Eastern Timber Rattlesnake), both of which were killed. Bartram does observe that the scales, so iridescent in the living snake became dull after the animal died. Such accounts of snakes and native Americans thrilled European audiences. This book, although not sanctioned by the author, sold fairly well and helped to establish John Bartram's reputation.

FIGURE 6-45. A Pennsylvania rattlesnake that I encountered while on a hike with a descendant of Conrad Weiser.

EXTINCTION
For people who hate to learn the names of things, the earth is getting better every day. -Charles Bowden

John Bartram stood at the beginning of the great Linnaean revolution. Then, the continent was a new place with many new species. Now, almost all of the plants in the U.S. and Canada have been identified, described and catalogued. On a foray through the southern colonies in 1765, John Bartram and his son William came across a small stand of "very curious plants" that grew along the Altamaha River in Georgia. They collected small plants and seeds of the camellia-like plant and returned to Philadelphia. There, Bartram suggested that the new plant be named after his friend Benjamin Franklin. He left it to his cousin, another nurseryman named Humphrey Marshall, to provide the Latin description of *Franklinia* (Figure 6-46).

King George III named John Bartram "The King's Botanist" upon his return from the southern trip. This was more than an honorary title, as King's Botanist, he received a stipend of £50 for the rest of his life.

FIGURE 6-46. *Franklinia* in flower on the Susquehanna University campus.

Franklinia grew well in Bartram's garden and the Philadelphia area. However, when William Bartram returned to the Altamaha River in 1773, he could find no living *Franklinia*. The plant had become extinct in the wild during those few intervening years. Today, all of the *Franklinia* plants in the world are descended from the plants collected by the Bartrams.

The story of rescue from the brink of extinction is a rare one for the 18th century. It has become an all too common

one for our century. Many who study biological diversity now work to maintain the biological diversity that exists in areas that continue to shrink in size.

FIGURE 6-47. The native shooting star.

John Clark became interested in the rare plants of Pennsylvania and spent much of his time looking for them. He documented locations for the native shooting stars (Figure 6-47) and lupines. He spent much of his time teaching those with rare plants and wetland areas about their special natures. He was especially successful in working with progressive landowners in central Pennsylvania where he managed to create sites for long-term ecological study.

DIVERSITY

To disregard the diversity of life is to risk catapulting ourselves into an alien environment.   -E. O. Wilson

Currently, those who study species diversity concern themselves with long-term studies in which patterns can be discerned. The Species-Area curve of MacArthur and Wilson was the first such global pattern that ecologists could model[45]. Briefly, this theory says that the larger the area, the more species can be found in that area. This is true of

---

[45] I described the Species-Area curve in *Islands and their Lessons in Biogeography.*

nested or contiguous regions. For example, Pennsylvania has 3319 species of vascular plants. The northeastern quarter of the U.S. has 4,666 species. The explanation for this seems to be obvious: the larger the area, the more different individuals and habitats should be contained in that area. Thus, there should be more species.

Other relationships seem to be much more tentative. Why is species diversity so high near the equator and why does it decline as one goes from the tropical to the temperate to the subarctic? The pattern has been well established, but explanations for the pattern are inadequate.

The fossil record seems to indicate that the biosphere has increased its diversity gradually over the past 600 million years. Is this a real change or is it an artifact of the irregular and patchy nature of the fossil record? Also, we still have no idea how many different species live on this planet. Currently, less than two million species have been described and named; however, estimates of real species numbers range from 10 to 100 million. We only know that 2 million is a very low count.

GOOD-BYE

Is it possible that humanity will love life enough to save it?   -E. O. Wilson

John Clark was interested in the long-term questions, their patterns and their explanations. He recognized that the solution to ecological degradation lay in education. To John, education meant sparking interest not sterile speculation. In his view, a student could learn botany only by getting hands dirty and knees stained. That is why he worked in the field with students of all types, backgrounds, and ages whenever he could.

I never got to go with John on the Bartram trail though we planned it several times. We talked about Bartram, Shamokin, as well as the past and future of the Susquehanna Valley as he lay dying of lung cancer last May. Then, he implored me to make sure that his plant collections, his books, and his notes would be put to good and fruitful use.

Both men, John Bartram (1699-1777) and John Clark (1943-1999) touched many lives. More than that, I can say that both men loved humanity and the nature that sustained it. Certainly, the earth is a better place for their having been here. I can think of no better epitaph for a naturalist.

-1999, revised 2005

References:

Bartram, John. 1751. *Travels in Pensilvania and Canada.* Reprinted by Readex Microprint Corporation 1966.

Bartram, William. 1791. *Travels of William Bartram.* Edited by Mark Van Doren. Reprinted by Dover Publications, Inc., New York.

Berkeley, Edmund and Dorothy Smith Berkeley. 1982. *The Life and Travels of John Bartram From Lake Ontario to the River St. John.* Florida State University Press. Tallahassee.

Evans, Howard Ensign. 1993. *Pioneer Naturalists, The Discovery and Naming of North American Plants and Animals.* Henry Holt and Co., New York.

Gleason, Henry A. 1963. *The New Britton and Brown Illustrated Flora of the Northeastern United States and Adjacent Canada.* Vol 1-3. For The New York Botanical Garden by Hafner Publishing Co. New York.

MacArthur, Robert H. and Edward O. Wilson. 1967. *The Theory of Island Biogeography.* Princeton University Press. Princeton.

Paullin, Charles. 1932. *Atlas of the Historical Geography of the United States.* Carnagie Institution of Washington. Plate 26. A. Hoen & Co., Inc. Baltimore.

Rhoads, Ann Fowler and William McKinley Klein, Jr. 1993. *The Vascular Flora of Pennsylvania, Annotated Checklist and Atlas.* American Philosophical Society. Philadelphia.

Rosenzweig, Michael L. 1995. *Species Diversity in Space and Time.* Cambridge University Press. Cambridge, UK.

Slaughter, Thomas P. 1996. *The Natures of John and William Bartram.* Alfred A. Knopf. New York.

Wilson, Edward O. 1984. *Biophilia, The Human Bond With Other Species.* Harvard University Press. Cambridge, Mass.

Wilson, Edward O. 1992. *The Diversity of Life.* W.W. Norton & Co. New York.

Wilson, Edward O. 2002. *The Future of Life.* Alfred A. Knopf. New York.

From a scrap of paper in John Clark's weathered copy of Gleason & Cronquist, Manual of Vascular Plants.

The rarity and value of scientific knowledge
Is too little understood - even as people
Who are not botanists find it hard to believe
Special knowledge of the subject can add
Enormously to the esthetic appreciation of flowers!
Partly because in order to identify a plant
You must study it very much more closely
Than you would otherwise have done, and in the process
Exquisite colours, proportions, and minute shapes spring to light
Too small to be ordinarily noted,
And more than this - it seems the botanist's knowledge
Of the complete structure of the plant
(Like a sculptor's of bone and muscle)
- Of the configuration of its roots stretching under the earth,
The branching of stems,
Enfolding of buds by bracts, Spreading of veins on a leaf
Encircles and snakes three dimensional
His awareness of its complex beauty.

-Hugh McDrumond

Questions to Think About

1. Who were John Clark and John Bartram?

2. In what ways were their lives similar?

3. What is meant by the term, Botany?

4. What is the significance of Collison having introduced Linnaeus to John Bartram?

5. Where is Bartram's Garden?

6. How many species are known? How many more species might there be on Earth?

7. Why did John Bartram travel through Pennsylvania and New York in 1743?

8. How did that trip help to secure Bartram's reputation as a naturalist?

9. What plant did the Bartrams save from extinction?

10. Fundamentally, what is the species – area relationship?

ISLANDS AND THEIR LESSONS IN BIODIVERSITY

ISLAND OF THE DODO

The extinction of the dodo is representative of modernity in several ways, not the least of which is that the event occurred on a small island.

-David Quammen (1996)

When I was in London five years ago I had one day to stay in the city before our plane left for New York. With all of London to choose from, what does one do in one day? Well, for me there was no question. I had to go to the British Museum of Natural History. The main attraction was its collection of dinosaurs.

I walked throughout the museum, and then paused at a display of animals that had become extinct during historic times. There was a stuffed Passenger Pigeon, birds once so numerous in North America that their flocks blackened the sky as they flew over. Nearby, there was a Dodo, another pigeon. This animal was large. In fact everything about this bird was large except its wings. Its skeleton indicated that the Dodo was flightless. Not only were its wings short, but its breast bone was too small to support flight muscles. Clearly, it could not fly, and its reconstruction made it look even more comical with a bald face and a body covered with fluffy down-like feathers (see Figure 6-48).

Portuguese sailors discovered the Dodo's Island in 1510. The island, a small point of land in the Indian Ocean east of Madagascar, became known as Mauritius. The earliest record of the Dodo was in 1598. By 1681, the last Dodo had been killed. Isolated island habitats seem to favor the evolution of flightless birds (as well as miniature mammals and giant rep-

tiles). Birds probably become flightless because birds that lose their ability to fly are not selected against in habitats with plenty of food and no predators.

Thus, on its little island in the Indian Ocean, the Dodo was a successful species. However, when Portuguese sailors began to kill them for food, they brought their associates like pigs and rats. Together with the wholesale slaughter, destruction of forests and nests, the last Dodo died in 1681, only 83 years after it was first sighted.

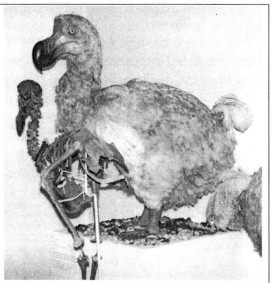

FIGURE 6-48. A reconstruction of a Dodo that emphasizes its stubby wings and stocky body. I photographed this exhibit at the British Museum of Natural History.

Mauritius and similar isolated islands are volcanic and therefore can be made very far from continental land masses (and their biota). The island also is surrounded by a large fringing coral reef. Although volcanic activity seems to have been quiet for the past million years, the island continues to grow through the accretion of limestone by the growth of coral.

ARCHIPELAGOS AND BARRIERS

Islands have had two distinct modes of origin – they have either been separated from continents of which they are but detached fragments, or they have originated in the ocean and have never formed part of a continent or any large mass of land. -Alfred R. Wallace (1880)

Unlike Mauritius, Puerto Rico is part of a chain of islands (archipelago) called the Greater Antilles and forms a boundary between the Atlantic and the Caribbean. Like Mauritius, Puerto Rico was formed by volcanic activity and is surrounded by a fringing coral reef. However, its geology is older and much more complex. Puerto Rico seems to have been formed from the floor of the Atlantic Ocean around 190 million years ago. Originally, It was an arc of volcanic islands that coalesced. Around it in the shallow sea, reef builders made thick deposits of limestone.

This history can still be seen in the landforms of the island. The ancient island arc is now a mountain chain that runs east to west across Puerto Rico. On the north and south are areas of limestone from the reef-builders. This geological mosaic creates a large number of habitats in a small area. In fact, the island is only about 100 miles long (E-W) and 40-50 miles wide (N-S). In that relatively small area (3,515 mi^2), Puerto Rico has rain forests, dry forests, mangrove swamps, coral reefs, etc (see Figure 6-49).

Consider the number of bird species in Puerto Rico. The island has about 280 species of living birds (both residents and migrants). All the rest of the United States has about 650 species of birds. Thus, the number of birds in Puerto Rico may be less than half that of the rest of the US, but the surface area of Puerto Rico is less than one-tenth that of Pennsylvania (46,058mi^2). Since the surface area of the United States is about 3,787,425 mi^2, Puerto Rico has 469 times more bird species per square mile than does the rest of the US!

Consider what that means in the context of bidiversity. The numbers indicate that the destruction of a square mile in Puerto Rico has a much greater impact on bird species than the loss of a square mile in central Pennsylvania.

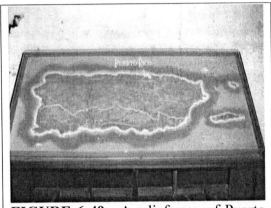

FIGURE 6-49. A relief map of Puerto Rico.

Assateague Island is quite different from Puerto Rico. It is part of the North American continent and formed by the outwash of sediments from the eastern seaboard and their reallocation by ocean currents. Barrier islands are long and narrow bits of land with narrow strips of different environments. Most of the wave action occurs on the ocean side. The mainland side of the barrier island is marsh and bay (see Figure 6-50).

A walk across the island will take you through several distinct environments (see Figure 6-51). The leading edge of the island is a sandy beach that is delimited by a main dune. Other smaller dunes occur in the area immediately behind the main dune. This area looks almost like a desert with some cactus and scrubby plants.

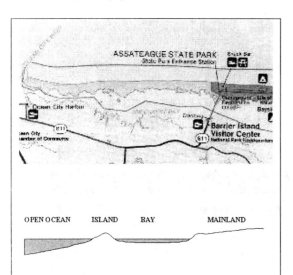

FIGURE 6-50. Top: Map of Assateague Island. Note the long, thin aspect of the island. North is to the left. Bottom: Diagram of a barrier island that illustrates the open ocean, island, bay and mainland. Barrier islands also serve to dampen wave action thereby changing the character of the marsh than fringes the bay.

By and large, barrier islands like Assateague are dynamic; that is, they are constantly changing. Consequently, permanent construction on them often is a lesson in futility. The dynamic nature of the island can be seen on the beach where black peat and blackened clamshells from an ancient marsh continually erode in the surf. That is because the island is slowly rolling over itself toward the mainland as it has done since its formation at the end of the last ice age.

As you walk from the beach and dunes toward the bay, you encounter a forest dominated by long-leaf pine. The forest, in turn abruptly changes to marsh. Pine trees grow on higher ground with less chance of salt-water intrusion.

The beach and main dune.

Scrub behind main dune.

Long-leaf pines with marsh in the foreground. Note how the height of the trees rises the farther they are from the bay (to the right).

Salt marsh, one of the most productive ecosystems on earth.

FIGURE 6-51. Illustrations of the beach, dunes, scrub, pine forest, and salt marsh in a straight line across the barrier island.

All of these different zones occur in an area that is sometimes less than a mile across. The diversity of habitat allows nearly 300 species of birds to occur there. Although the island has a high diversity of plants and animals, a barrier island like Assateague is too close to the mainland to have unique species (This includes the ponies and Sitka Deer, animals that are artificially maintained and controlled). Unique or endemic island species occur on isolated islands like Mauritius.

AMONG THE FIRST TO STUDY ISLANDS

Mr. Darwin appears to have been the first writer who called attention to the number and importance, both from a geological and a biological point of view, of oceanic islands.

                -Alfred R. Wallace (1880)

The Galapagos Islands (Figure 6-52) are much like Mauritius in that they are volcanic and rise from a very deep ocean bottom. Unlike Mauritius, though, the Galapagos is an archipelago and relatively close to South America. Although the islands lie on the equator, they are bathed by a cold water current so that coral does not grow on them. This island chain is relatively young and many of the organisms that inhabit it show clear affinities with those of the South American continent. These characteristics helped to give Charles Darwin[46] some of the important clues about the operation of evolution.

The Galapagos Islands are true desert islands. The surrounding cold current causes the air to dry out so rains

[46] You may find much more background information about Charles Darwin in *Parasites and Darwin's Intellectual Triumph, The Mentor and the Heretic,* and *A Tale of Two Stones.*

rarely fall. In this harsh environment relatively few species live on the island surface, but the surrounding waters are teeming with life. Thus, a species of *Iguana* has taken to the sea and feeds on algae. Another amphibious oddity is the Galapagos penguin, an animal whose ancestors must have traveled northward on the Antarctic current.

The Beagle circumnavigated the globe during Darwin's five-year voyage. After the ship left the Galapagos, it headed across the Pacific toward Australia. On the way, Darwin visited many other oceanic islands, many of which had coral reefs, most of which were atolls. One of the first books that Darwin wrote after his return to England was *The Structure and Distribution of Coral Reefs* in 1842. In it he described the distribution of coral islands and differentiated between islands with fringing reefs and islands with atoll lagoons. He speculated that atolls came from fringing reefs that grew on a subsiding volcano (see Figure 6-53). As the water level rose relative to the volcano, the coral grew higher on the mountain until all that could be seen was a ring of coral islands surrounding a lagoon.

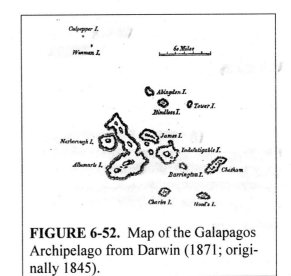

FIGURE 6-52. Map of the Galapagos Archipelago from Darwin (1871; originally 1845).

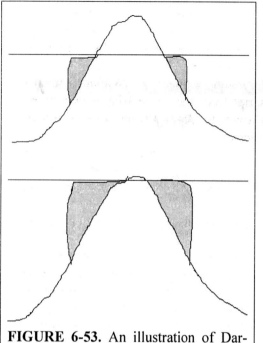

FIGURE 6-53. An illustration of Darwin's theory of the formation of coral atolls. During a period of growth, a volcano has a fringing reef, which as the volcano sinks (or the ocean rises), the coral continues to grow up along the sides of the mountain. If the mountaintop is under water, all that is left is the ring of coral islands surrounding a lagoon.

While Darwin speculated about the origins of islands and ruminated on the island biota, Alfred Russel Wallace[47] lived for years in the islands of the Malay Archipelago and studied its island life first hand. Wallace traveled all over the region collecting, observing, and writing. His most striking and enduring observation was that islands that shared the continental margin with Asia were dominated by Asian species. Those islands that occurred on the continental margin of Australia were dominated by Australian species. He explained that these ar-

---

[47] Find more information about Wallace in *The Mentor and the Heretic.*

eas must have been connected to their respective continents when ocean water levels were lower as they must have been during the great ice ages.

He divided the region according to the distribution of animals on the islands. Wallace drew an imaginary line (now called Wallace's Line; see Figure 6-54). An Asian fauna dominated the area to the west of the line while an Australian fauna dominated to the east.

In Wallace's words:

In this archipelago there are two distinct faunas rigidly circumscribed which differ as much as do those of Africa and South America and more than those of Europe and North America; yet there is nothing on the map or on the face of the islands to mark their limits. The boundary line passes between islands closer together than others belonging to the same group. I believe the western part to be a separated portion of continental Asia while the eastern part is a fragmentary prolongation of a former west Pacific continent. In mammalia and birds, the distinction is marked by genera, families, and even orders confined to one region; insects by a number of genera and little groups of peculiar species, the families of insects having generally a very wide or universal distribution.

Also from *The Malay Archipelago, Volume 1.*

He saw the most striking aspect of the relationship when he traveled from Bali, an island off the tip of Java. Its birds and mammals were clearly Asian. However, Lombok, only 25 miles away by sea, had cockatoos and marsupials typical of Australia.

East of the Wallace Line, he sought the ultimate prize, the Bird of Paradise. Species had been described from skins of birds that had been collected by native bird hunters. Their preparations were fairly good and preserved the delicate plumage. However, they considered the feet to be useless, and threw them away. They were so skillful at sewing the skin that western taxonomists thought that the birds had no feet. In fact one was named *Paridisaea apoda* (the footless paradise bird).

FIGURE 6-54. Wallace's map of the islands around Celebes from Wallace (1892). I added the dotted line to indicate Wallace's line separating the Asian and Australian faunas.

Footless or not, the delicate plumage was almost of another world. He succeeded in catching many of the birds and even discovered a new Bird of Paradise that was named for him, *Semioptera Wallacei.*

During the eight years that Wallace spent as an explorer in the Maluccas, he collected 125,600 specimens and traveled 14,000 miles. In the mean time, the idea of Natural Selection (the key to modern evolutionary thought) came to him as it had come to Charles Darwin 20 years earlier. Still, Darwin had not published the concept and Wallace's manuscript from the Spice Islands convinced Darwin to begin writing *The Origin of Species.*

Upon his return to England, Wallace settled down to a life of cataloging his enormous collection and writing. His most influential book in his day was *The Malay Archipelago*, published in 1869. However, his most enduring work might have been *Island Life,* published in 1880. This book helped to establish Biogeography as a discipline in the developing science of ecology. He did no more exploring after this and lived as an eccentric, but fruitful scientist until his death on November 7, 1913.

Thus, the study of islands, a study that produced the foundation for the fact of evolution and the theory of natural selection languished for more than 50 years. Island studies did continue to support evolutionary biology by studying their endemic species. However, the direction of island studies changed and gained momentum when two American ecologists, Edward O. Wilson and Robert H. MacArthur, adopted it.

ISLAND BIOGEOGRAPHY
Many of the principles graphically displayed in the Galapagos and other remote archipelagos apply in lesser or greater degree to all natural habitats. - R.H. MacArthur and E.O. Wilson (1967)

In 1954 E.O. Wilson was given the opportunity to go to New Guinea and study the diversity of tropical ants there. Wilson had begun as a budding naturalist when he was a young man in Alabama. However, a childhood accident had left him blind in one eye, so he had trouble using a microscope.

Wilson claimed that he was inspired to study ants in the tropics when, as a 10-year old boy, he read the following passage from National Geographic in 1934:

I remember one Christmas day at the Mina Carlota, in the Sierra de Trinidad of Cuba. When I attempted to turn over a large rock to see what was living underneath, the rock split in the middle, and there, in the very center, was a half teaspoonful of brilliant green metallic ants glistening in the sunshine. They proved to be an unknown species.

He enjoyed insects, but during World War II and its aftermath, insect pins were hard to get. Although pinning preserves most insects, some, like ants, are usually preserved in alcohol. Thus, E.O. Wilson began to study ants in an academic setting. He stuck with them and studied under some of the most important names in insect biology and evolutionary theory. As a graduate student, Wilson collected ants across the U.S., and was then was funded to go to Cuba.

New Guinea was even more exciting. Finally, he was going to a place where very little collecting had been done. He described the excitement and intensity with which he collected in the tropical forests. Then, a remarkable insight came to him. He noticed that in any area of the New Guinea forest, he would encounter about 50 species of ants in any hectare (about 2.5 acres). The amazing thing is that in hectares very close together, each with about 50 species of ants, there would be only about 30-40 species in common. Thus, the number of species seemed to be as important as the particular species present.

Back in 1943 Philip J. Darlington, a mentor of Wilson at Harvard, had noticed a relationship between the size of islands and the number of reptiles that occurred there. Cuba, about 40,000 square miles supported 76-84 species of reptiles and amphibians. Whereas, Puerto Rico (4,000 square miles) had about 39-40 reptiles and amphibians. It appeared that as the land area dropped by a factor of 10, the number of species that the area could support was cut in half. Darlington's study produced the data in Table 1.

Wilson had known of Darlington's work. However, his own work on ants seemed to indicate that the number of species in a given area was the important characteristic. Thus, it could be tested. Wilson, a taxonomist and population biologist, teamed up with a brilliant ecologist, Robert H. MacArthur (1930-1972), to explore that question.

TABLE 6-4. Data generated by Darlington that suggests a relationship between the size of an island and the number of reptile species on that island.

Area (square miles)	Number of species
40,000	76-84
4,000	39-40
400	[20 estimated]
40	9
4	5

MacArthur completed his doctoral work under the direction of the legendary G. Evelyn Hutchinson at Yale University. He worked on the evolutionary ecology of closely related flycatchers (birds) in the forests of New England. He employed careful observations and united them with sophisticated mathematics in the style of Hutchinson.

One of the first tests of the species-area concept involved a careful inventory of living things on the island of Krakatoa. This was a small island in Indonesia (in the Sunda Straits between Sumatra and Java, also part of the Malay Archipelago) whose volcano exploded in 1883 with such force that it erased all life from what was left of the island. Fortunately for science the Dutch began to do periodic inventories of plants and animals on the island. Given its size, MacArthur and Wilson estimated that it should have about 30 species of birds.

Their island studies convinced them that extrinsic factors also came into play in determining the number of species. For example, the distance from a mainland source could profoundly affect the number of species that can get to the island. They realized that the number of species on the island had to be the consequence of an equilibrium between the loss of species due to extinction and the gain in species from colonization (and evolution over a very long time). Also, they realized that the number of species depended upon the group in question. That is, an island of a particular size and distance from a mainland would have different stable numbers of insects, reptiles, birds and trees.

Also, a definite species gradient exists from the equator to the poles. The number of species drops precipitously even from the sub tropics to the temperate zone. This is one of the explanations for the differences in bird species numbers between Pennsylvania and Puerto Rico. Why this happens still is a mystery, but, clearly, only islands in the same latitude can be compared.

Why are areas correlated so well with specific numbers of species? Perhaps because larger areas have more habitats in which to house more species. This answer, while simple, is quite powerful as an explanatory tool and as a heuristic, a theory that generates more questions.

They began to realize, as had Wallace, that many different types of environments behave as islands. For example, a pond is an "aquatic island" within a terrestrial environment. The same holds true for plots of prairies and strips of state forests. MacArthur and Wilson understood that large islands of prairies or rainforest in Amazonia were necessary to maintain their rich biological diversity. Put another way, a one or two-acre prairie would have only the shadow of the diversity that a ten thousand-acre prairie would have. Thus, to save biological diversity in stable environments, we need to set aside large island tracts. In 1967 Wilson and MacArthur published *The Theory of Island Biogeography* and changed the way that we view landscape and the preservation of isolated environments.

To illustrate the power of this theory, I graphed Darlington's data from Table 6-4 in Figure 6-55. This time I transformed the data with the log function. The line flattened into a straight line. Thus, it would be possible to predict the number of expected reptile species on any sized island in the Caribbean. The relationships seem to be constant when considering the same type of living thing (lizard, bird, tree, etc.) at the same latitude. However the slopes of the line change from one kind of organism to the next. What does that mean? Ecologists really don't know. Nevertheless, the relationship is a powerful tool in determining questions like what sized plot is necessary to maintain 90% of the tree species in a particular type of forest.

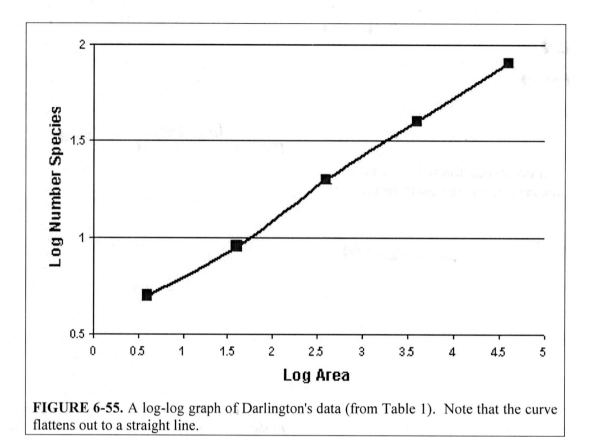

FIGURE 6-55. A log-log graph of Darlington's data (from Table 1). Note that the curve flattens out to a straight line.

ISLANDS AND ANSWERS

Unlike experimental biologists, evolutionary biologists well versed in natural history have an abundance of answers from which to pick and choose. What they most need are the right questions. They look for the best stories nature has to tell us, because they are above all, storytellers. -Edward O. Wilson 1994

Darwin, Wallace, Darlington, Wilson, MacArthur and many other naturalists were brought to truths of evolution and ecology through their studies of island life. Most of all they asked good questions because they sought out nature's stories. Most of these naturalists came to ecology through a love of collection, but collection alone is empty because it is all question and no story. The story comes when the collection begins to make sense. That happens through careful observation and meticulous notes. Then, grand discoveries like the mechanisms of evolution and island biogeography can happen.

Of the founders of Island Biogeography, MacArthur died too young from renal cancer but continues to have an impact on ecology through his students. Wilson remains a premier naturalist and has championed controversial theories in evolution and ecology. He has become one of the strongest voices today for the preservation of biological diversity because he is such a good storyteller.

For us today, some of the most important stories are those of the Dodo, Bird of Paradise, and similar island creatures. Odd birds such as the those can evolve and exist on islands because, although diversity may be high, the total number of species that an island can support is lower simply because the land area of an island is smaller than that of a continent. So, on very small islands like

Mauritius and Lombok, species have a very limited range and are usually small in number. Therefore, it is not surprising that of all the birds that have become extinct since the demise of the Dodo, 90% have been island birds.

This lesson is a very important one as we carve up forests and other natural habitats on continents. In effect, the eastern deciduous forest has become an archipelago across the northeastern U.S. As those island habitats become isolated and smaller, they can no longer support the number of species that the whole eastern deciduous forest once could. Thereby, the whole ecosystem becomes simplified and degraded.

In considering the biodiversity situation in the Malay Archipelago (now Indonesia), Penny van Oosterzee in a book about the Wallace Line concluded:

"This book has been a great joy and a great sadness to write. If Wallace were to retrace his journey today, in truth he would have found little to inspire him. And without inspiration it is doubtful he would have developed the theory of evolution and the intellectual mystery of The Wallace Line. We lose more than wildlife in destroying nature, we lose our humanity.

Indeed, we are affected spiritually, as she concludes. However, we are also affected materially because we are among the living things on this planet.

I stumbled onto some NASA images of the earth several days ago. I was reminded of the Apollo 8 mission and the first time that I had seen the entire disk of our planet. Launched December 21, 1968. Apollo 8 was the first flight of the giant Saturn V with a crew. Frank Borman, James A. Lovell Jr., and William A. Anders circled the moon 10 times on Christmas Eve and Christmas Day. I was a senior in high school and this was my last Holiday season while I still lived at home. The moon's surface was gray and dull, but the earth looked like a tiny blue island in the great black sea of space.

What will we do with this precious island? Will we continue to splinter, simplify, and degrade its ecosystems? Will we learn the lesson of the Dodo?

FIGURE 6-56. Island earth. The arrow indicates the location of the island of Mauritius. The image is taken from: http://images.jsc.nasa.gov/iams/html/pao/

References:

Beddall, Barbara G., ed. 1969. *Wallace and Bates in the Tropics, an Introduction to the Theory of Natural Selection.* Collier-Macmillan Ltd. London.

Bowler, Peter J. 1992. *The Fontana History of the Environmental Sciences.* Fontana Press. London.

Darlington, Philip J. 1957. *Zoogeography, The Geographical Distribution of Animals.* John Wiley and Sons, Inc. New York.

Darwin, Charles R. 1897 (originally 1842. *The Structure and Distribution of Coral Reefs.* 3rd edition. D. Appleton & Co. New York.

Darwin, Charles R. 1871 (originally, 1845). *Journal of Researches into the Natural History and Geology of the Countries Visited During the Voyage of the H.M.S. Beagle Under the Command of Cpat. Fitz Roy, R.N. New Edition. D. Appelton & Co. New York.*[48]

Darwin, Charles R. 1859. *The Origin of Species by Means of Natural Selection.* The corrected copyright edition (1902). John Murray. London.

Darwin, Charles R. 1958 (first published in 1892 as edited by Francis Darwin). *The Autobiography of Charles Darwin and Selected Letters.* Dover Publications, Inc. New York.

Darwin, Francis, ed. 1896. *The Life and Letters of Charles Darwin, Including an Autobiographical Chapter.* Vol. 1&2. D. Appleton & Co. New York.

Holt, Jack R. and Patricia Nelson. 2001. *Paths of Science, Explorations for Science Students and Educators.* Kendall/Hunt Publishing Co. Dubuque, Iowa.

Loewenberg, Bert J., ed. 1959. *Charles Darwin: Evolution and Natural Selection, an Anthology of the Writings of Charles Darwin.* Beacon Press. Boston.

MacArthur, Robert H. and Edward O. Wilson. 1967. *The Theory of Island Biogeography.* IN: Levin, Simon A. and Henry S. Horn, eds. *Monographs in Population Biology.* Princeton University Press. Princeton, NJ.

Mason, Stephen F. 1962. *A History of the Sciences.* Collier Books. New York.

Quammen, David. 1996. *The Song of the Dodo, Island Biogeography in an Age of Extinctions.* Scribner. New York.

Raby, Peter. 1996. *Bright Paradise, Victorian Scientific Travelers.* Princeton University Press. Princeton, NJ.

Raffaele, H.A. 1989. *A Guide to the Birds of Puerto Rico and the Virgin Islands,* revised edition. Princeton University Press. Princeton, NJ.

Rosenzweig, Michael L. 1997. *Species Diversity in Space and Time.* Cambridge University Press. Cambridge, UK.

Shepard, A. & D. Slayton. 1994. *Moon Shot, The Inside Story of America's Race to the Moon.* Turner Publishing Co. Atlanta.

Trefil, James and Robert Hazen. 1995. *The Sciences, An Integrated Approach.* John Wiley & Sons, Inc. New York.

Udvardy, Miklos D.F. 1969. *Dynamic Zoogeography.* Van Nostrand Reinhold Co. New York.

Van Oosterzee, Penny. 1997. *Where World Collide. The Wallace Line.* Cornell University Press. Ithaca, NY.

Wallace, Alfred R. 1874. *The Malay Archipelago, The Land of the Orang-Utan and the Bird of Paradise..*MacMillan and Co. London.

Wallace, Alfred R. 1892. *Island Life or the Phenomena and Causes of Insular Faunas and Floras.* Macmillan and Co. London.

Wallace, Alfred R. 1895. *A Narrative of Travels on the Amazon and Rio Negro.* 5th edition. Ward, Lock, & Bowden. London.

Wilson, Edward O. 1984. *Biophilia.* Harvard University Press. Cambridge, Mass.

Wilson, Edward O. 1992. *The Diversity of Life.* W.W. Norton and Co. New York.

Wilson, Edward O. 1994. *Naturalist.* Island Press/ Shearwater Books. Washington, D.C.

---

[48] This book is known also as *The Voyage of the Beagle* and *Journal of Researches.*

Questions to Think About

1. The Dodo was a successful species on the island of Mauritius. Why did it go extinct?

2. Why were the Galapagos Islands, although only briefly mentioned in the The Origin, so important to Darwin?

3. What were some of the striking observations that Wallace made as he traveled over the Moluccas?

4. What is a coral atoll? How is it made?

5. How do Mauritius, Puerto Rico, and Assateague Islands differ?

6. What inspired E.O. Wilson to want to study ants in the tropics?

7. How did the publication of the Theory of Island Biogeography change the way we view the preservation of isolated environments?

8. Why does the destruction of a square mile in Puerto Rico have a much greater impact on bird species than a similar loss of a square mile in Pennsylvania?

9. What is the species-area relationship?

10. Comment on the statement by Penny van Oosterzee :"We lose more than wildlife in destroying nature, we lose our humanity."

UNDER THE MICROSCOPE

MICROSCOPES

In the absence of any formal conception of biology [prior to 1750], the microscope taught the unity of nature.
-Catherine Wilson (1995)

One time I had a discussion with a group of biologists at Susquehanna University about the discipline and what we should teach in the introductory courses. The subject of instrumentation came up and an animated discussion ensued. I made the comment that the microscope was the quintessential instrument and therefore should be covered by all means. That was met with some disbelief, a brief period of debate that cooled and evolved to a different plane. Anyway, I thought about that discussion long ago and set out to test it. I walked the biology floor and stood at the door of each teaching-research laboratory. All 10 of them had at least one microscope although the other forms of instrumentation varied. That did not count the two specialty laboratories that were devoted solely to some form of microscopy. Why is the microscope so useful to laboratories that study various things like physiology, molecular biology, and ecology? I believe that the answer to this question is that although life exists at different scales, it is on a fundament level a cellular phenomenon. Microscopes did not always dominate biology (the study of life) in this way. Indeed, there was a time when most scientists mistrusted evidence from such devices. How did that happen, and how did the rise of the modern microscope mirror the advent of modern biology?

CRYSTAL BALLS & EYE GLASSES

Where the telescope ends, the microscope begins. Which of the two has the grander view? -Victor Hugo (1862)

The ancients recognized that certain crystals could make things appear larger. This was especially obvious when considering magnifying effect of water in a glass. Claudius Ptolemy[49] (85-168) of Alexandria defined why in his law of Refraction. He said that although a ray of light tends to move in a straight line within a uniform homogeneous medium, it bends as it enters a medium of different density. For example, light moving from air to water bends toward a line perpendicular to the water. This is called the law of refraction and the study of this property of light helped to explain how we see and, ultimately, how to make lenses.

Until the time of the Arab Empire, the study of light did not proceed much further than the explanations of Ptolemy. Ibn Al-Haitham (known in the West as Ibn Al-Hazen; 965-1043), a mathematician, philosopher, and scientist from Persia (modern-day Iraq) was intrigued by light, vision and rainbows, and he sought an explanation by using crystal balls. His crystal balls were not those of the soothsayers and mystics, though. He used them to explore the nature of refraction. In particular, he noticed that the image of an object reverses as it passes through the crystal (see Figure 6-57). His discoveries completely changed the old standard explanations for vision. Aristotle and others explained vision as a kind of sense of touch. That is, we saw

---

[49] Read more about Ptolemy in *Maps as Models* and *Principia Mathematica: The Foundation of Modern Physics*.

things because a touch-like sense emanated from our eyes and touched objects. Alhazen instead explained vision in a modern way. The eye sees light, he said, because light comes from an object and behaves strict geometrical laws. Thus, the eye has to focus the incoming light (see Figure 6-58).

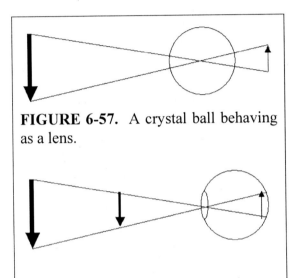

FIGURE 6-57. A crystal ball behaving as a lens.

FIGURE 6-58. The eye focusing an object. Note that the distant arrow and the closer arrow fall in the same cone and thus form the same image on the eye.

In this line of research he also explored the convex lens and the way in which the lens magnifies objects (see Figure 6-59). Little more happened in the realm of optics until an explosion of activity began in Western Europe hundreds of years later. There, lens makers sprang up to help aleve the aged of the "disease" of far-sightedness, a problem more desperately acute because the printing press had made the printed word so available (and small). Such craftsmen did not care much for the science or mathematics of optics, but they did perfect the art of glass making and grinding lenses.

Almost certainly it was spectacle makers of in Holland who made the first telescopes and microscopes (the fundamental design is the same, see Figure 6-60) after 1590 but before 1609. The names most often given are Zacharias and Hans Janssen of Middleburg. Galileo Galilei[50] (1564-1542) then got hold of these instruments and modified them. Sometime in 1609 Galileo made a more powerful telescope. It was that instrument with which he made observations of the moon, the Milky Way, and Jupiter's moons. He published his observations in the book, *Siderius Nuncius* in the next year (1610). He also ground lenses and used a two-lens microscope to describe and draw details of a honey bee. This likely did not magnify much more than 20X. Still, the bee appeared much more complex than seemed possible.

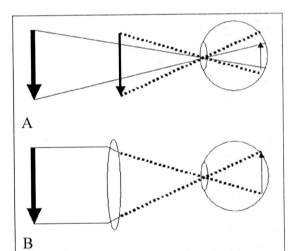

A

B

FIGURE 6-59. A.. This shows how two objects the same size but different distances create different images in the eye. The nearer object creates much larger image because it generates a larger cone. B. The biconvex lens makes a distant object create the same light cone as a much closer object. Thus the object has been magnified.

[50] Read more about Galileo and his telescope in *A Man With a Telescope.*

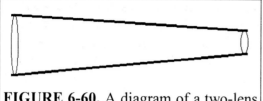

FIGURE 6-60. A diagram of a two-lens system, which could be either a microscope or a telescope.

During the ensuing period the microscope languished, but the popularity of the telescope prompted a new surge of interest in optics. Johannes Kepler (1571-1630) had produced an excellent treatise on lenses in 1604 and later expanded it to include the state of optics in 1611 (*Dioptrice*). Later Rene Descartes sought to relieve the lens-maker's trade from the trial and error aspect. To that end, he attempted to provide the theory of optics in his book called *Dioptrique* (1637) in common language. This book not only described the theory of lenses, vision, and the nature of light, it also described and illustrated telescopes as well as microscopes, one of which was taller that a man. Still, science gained little from the microscope until 1665 when Robert Hooke (1635-1703) published one of the most popular books of the 18th Century, *Micrographica.*

MICROGRAPHICA

It is my hope as well as belief, that these labours will be no more comparable to the productions of many other Natural Philosophers, who are now there busie about greater things; then my little objects are to be compared to the greater and more beautiful works of nature, a Flea, a Mite, a Gnat, to a Horse, an Elephant, and a Lyon.

      -Robert Hooke (1665)

Micrographica went through a series of printings and copies sold out almost as soon as they were produced. At the time Hooke was the secretary of the Royal Society of London, the first scientific society. The members met periodically to discuss recent findings, to demonstrate techniques, and to observe demonstrations. Hooke had a particular genius for designing instruments and the experiments they were to support. Indeed, Hooke had been Robert Boyle's assistant and likely was the mastermind behind Boyle's achievements. The Royal Society commissioned Hooke to construct a microscope and make observations with the instrument. In particular, they wanted to know what the microscope might be good for as a scientific instrument.

Hooke's microscope had two lenses and used a separate lens (the condenser) that helped to gather more light to shine on the specimen. The condenser did not contribute to the overall magnification of the microscope. It was important because in the process of magnification, a microscope separates the light rays so that they must illuminate a larger area. In other words, Hooke's microscope magnified 50X, and therefore required 50X as much light on the specimen in order to see it.

What astonished the members of the Royal Society and his readers were his illustrations. Hooke was not only an astonishingly precise instrument maker, he was also a very precise observer and illustrator. Consider his drawings of the flea (Figure 6-61A) and the cells of cork (Figure 6-61B). Indeed, Hooke coined the term cell in *Micrographica* as he described the appearance of the cork at the microscopic level. Hooke went on to say that the microscopic analysis of the cork "hinted to me the true and intelligible reason for all the Phenomena of Cork".

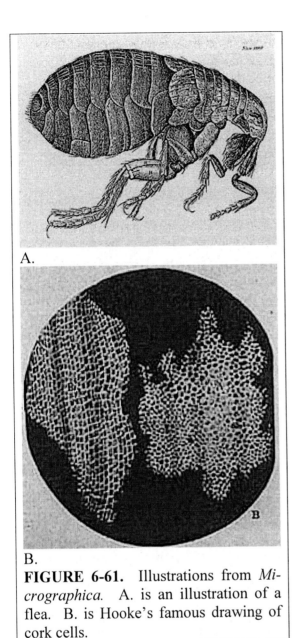

A.

B.

FIGURE 6-61. Illustrations from *Micrographica*. A. is an illustration of a flea. B. is Hooke's famous drawing of cork cells.

Excitement about the new instrument began to blossom. Nehemiah Grew (England, 1641-1712) used the instrument to study the microanatomy of plants, particularly their reproductive structures. Jan Swammerdam (Holland, 1637-1680) spent ten years (1663-1673) studying a multitude of biological subjects. Chiefly, he published on the microanatomy of insects and related that to their life histories. Also, he discov-

ered the cellular nature of blood. Swammerdam was set to conduct much more work but his father , under the influence of religious fanaticism, withdrew his support.

The Royal Society following the success of *Micrographica* began to consider other questions that required microscopy to answer them. Finding no takers in Britain to make a detailed microanatomical study of the silk moth, the society looked to the continent of Europe and found Marcello Malpighi (1628-1694), a professor of anatomy at Pisa, Messina and Bologna. He had already worked out the histological (=microanatomical) details of the lungs and many other vertebrate organs and published them through the Royal Society. He helped to confirm the existence of capillaries, microscopic vessels that connected the arteries and veins in the circulatory system. His treatise on the silkworm was remarkably thorough with the first detailed study of a particular insect from egg to adult. His studies were not limited to animals. He also examined plants with the microscope and published many discoveries of their microanatomy, including development of the plant embryo within the seed.

Although Hooke, Grew, Swammerdam, Malpighi and others were to make remarkable observations, their microscopes labored under the common problems that beset all lensing systems of the day: chromatic aberrations, spherical aberrations, and limited resolution. Chromatic aberrations were the features of lenses that even Newton thought could not be overcome because a lens separates light, all colors refract differently. Thus, a lens behaves as a prism. In the worst cases, all objects have rainbow rings of color around them. This problem was not restricted to microscopes; Galileo's telescope suffered the same obstacle.

Spherical aberrations are always with lenses. Because lenses have curved surfaces, the margins of the image produced by them are distorted when the image in the center is at its best. So, only a part of the field can provide useful information. Thus, Hooke's illustration of cork cells (Figure 6-61B) clearly is a composite rather than a faithful rendition of what he saw in a particular field.

Because their microscopes had two lenses, the spherical and chromatic aberrations were compounded. Thus the effective magnification of the double lens microscopes of the day could not have been much more than about 30-50X. Such problems seemed inescapable. Isaac Newton (1642-1727), who published *Optiks* in 1703, the year of Hooke's death, held little hope for instruments that magnified with the use of lenses. Thus, he invented the reflecting telescope[51] and ignored microscopes altogether. Perhaps the enmity that existed between Newton and Hooke played a role in that, too. Anyway, after Newton became president microscopical studies of the type published in *Micrographica* fell out of favor.

WEE BEASTIES

Now I can spend all my days, well, at least my nights studying the little things about me.   -Anton van Leeuwenhoek

In *Micrographica* Hooke wrote that a single lens microscope could avoid the worst aspects of chromatic aberration and give the clearest images. However, they were very difficult to use. As Hooke put it, "I have found them [single-lens microscopes] offensive to the eye, and to have much strained and weakened the sight, which was the reason why I omitted the use of them." The single lens microscope did not disappear, however. Soon after publication of *Micrographica* the Royal Society began to receive reports of detailed microscopic observations made by an amateur naturalist in Holland.

Anton van Leeuwenhoek (1632-1723), a cloth merchant from Delft, had both great skill at grinding lenses and very acute eyesight. He began his observations by holding his hand-ground biconvex lenses up to a cow's eye, sheep hair, wood and seeds. With a steady hand, he dissected the brain of a fly and mounted it on a needle. His curiosity, like the kitten's was boundless. Soon, he mounted the lens between two small brass plates (bout 1 x 1.5 inches) and held the specimen with a screw mechanism. Thus, he designed a different kind of microscope with an effective magnification of better than 100X.

Up to that point he had restricted his explorations magnifying things that he could see. Then, one day, he looked at a drop of rainwater that had been sitting for some days. What he saw astonished even him. He watched "wretched beasties" cavorting on "divers tiny legs" and looked for them in other sources of water. He saw them and hired a local artist to sketch them. His drawings are so clear that I have little difficulty in determining to which group or species that the organism belonged.

His observations astounded scientists of the day. Even though he had little schooling, the Royal Society of London made him a corresponding member. Leeuwenhoek sent many letters in which he described his neighbors, his health, Delft, and of course, his wee beasties. He continued his correspondence for

---

[51] Read more about Newton's reflecting telescope in *A Man With a Telescope.*

nearly 50 years and described everything from bee stingers to bacteria scraped from his (and others') teeth.

In one of his letters, he wrote, "In perfecting these researches, so many marvels of nature were spread before my eyes that I experienced an internal pleasure which my pen could not describe." This was the joy of the explorer; the discoverer. As remarkable as his observations were, the Royal Society was interested in replicating the instrument and repeating the observations. Leeuwenhoek interpreted this interest as an attempt to steal his invention and rob him of his discoverer's status. He was not entirely secretive, though. He made hundreds of microscopes, many of which ended up in the possession of the Royal Society and its members. However, he did not give out or divulge the plans for his highest quality instruments. He would not even leave visitors alone in the same room with them. Thus, the secret of his design effectively died with him.

Thus, the technical aspects of the microscope remained without change for about 150 years. The high magnification single lens microscope was too cumbersome to use. The two-lens microscope changed little from the instrument that Hooke designed. Some advances in lens design prepared the technicians for the next great advance in microscopy. This occurred in Germany during the latter part of the 19th Century.

19TH CENTURY MICROSCOPES

No amount of peering down a light microscope and no effort of attention could now avail; there was an intrinsic cognitive barrier. -*Peter Medawar (1984)*

There were two important barriers to the rapid advancement of the microscope after the spectacular achievements of the 16 and early 17th Centuries. One was the problem of the delicate instrument itself. The technology of lenses, fine gears, etc. required an industrial base to make such things. Either that or every microscopist would have to develop the gift that Hooke and Leeuwenhoek had for making instruments. That leads directly to the second requirement. Microscopes had become expensive precision instruments; so, scientists had to specialize in order to justify the expense in time or money that the microscope demanded. Science had begun to mature by the beginning of the 19th Century so that such specialists could appear.

The first major advance was the development of lenses that could reduce the chromatic aberrations. This was accomplished by making lenses from different layers of glass with different refractive properties. The instrument also assumed the shape that we are used to seeing. So in the first half of the 19th Century, the microscope had become generally useful in histology and other microscopic disciplines. At last enough living things had been observed so that the botanist Mathias Schlieden (1804-1881) and zoologist (1810-1882) Theodor Schwann proposed the cell theory around 1839. That is, all living things were constructed of cells. Next to evolution, this was one of the most important biological insights that came out of the 19th Century.

Carl Zeiss (Germany; 1816-1888) teamed up with a glass chemist (Otto Schott), and a brilliant physicist named Ernst Abbe (1840-1905). Together they formed Carl Zeiss, Inc, which became one of the most successful optical corporations in the world. The technical successes were due mainly to Abbe who had begun to make a series of detailed studies of lenses in order to create a theoretical framework for their improvement.

Abbe understood that the ability to magnify really was based on the ability of a lens to distinguish two points. This was called the resolving power or resolution of the lens. Abbe demonstrated that objects smaller than 0.5 times the wavelength of light could not be resolved. That meant visible light could magnify objects only 0.2-0.5μm (1μm is one-millionth of a meter). He derided the microscopist's practice of using very high power ocular lenses to achieve a magnification of greater than 2,000X. Because of the loss in resolution, much of the magnification was devoid of extra information, something that Abbe called "empty magnification" (see Figure 6-62). Thus, the microscopist's dream of visualizing the ultimate components of nature was physically impossible.

When Abbe began his work on lenses and the technology of microscopes, the resolving power was not close to the theoretical limit. He experimented with different types of glass and introduced many other elements besides silicon dioxide. He designed achromat lenses (lenses without chromatic distortions) that had as many as 10 different layers. He worked on perfecting the condenser lens and eliminating spherical aberration. By the time he had finished with the microscope, it had become a truly modern scientific instrument that approached the theoretic limits imposed by visible light.

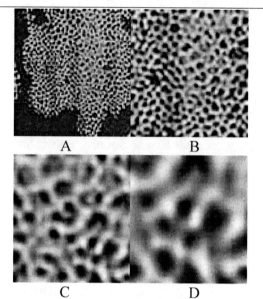

FIGURE 6-62. I used Hooke's illustration of cork (Figure 6-61B) and doubled the magnification in each succeeding drawing. Note that although the pictures are magnified, the information is not. This is empty magnification.

Upon the death of Zeiss in 1888, Abbe assumed control of the Zeiss Corporation. With this freedom he began other innovations such as the use of filters to allow only light of certain wavelengths to enter the lenses (another way to address the chromatic problem). This coupled with the 19th Century invention of using dyes to visualize cells, tissues, and organelles (subcellular components like the nucleus). He even pioneered the use of ultraviolet light as a light source. The shorter wavelength of UV effectively doubled the resolution of microscopy. Still, even with all of these innovations, many cellular details and all of the viruses remained effectively invisible.

ELECTRON MICROSCOPY

The electron microscope and its ancillary methods have now opened up this extraordinarily important area of biological structure for visual exploration.   -Don W. Fawcett (1966)

Other changes began to happen with the light microscope in the 20th Century. The ability to resolve or visualize smaller objects began to take advantage of the wave properties of light. As the light waves move up through the specimen, light waves change, and therefore can interfere with each other. If two waves interfere constructively, the light appears brighter than a wave would alone. The opposite is true of destructive interference. Thus, an apparent increase in resolution can result when the wave are reconstituted. Microscopes such as phase-contrast, differential interference contrast, and confocal microscopes all utilize this principle. Nevertheless, they increase the resolution only in small increments. They still run up against the ultimate barrier imposed by the nature of the light wave itself. What was needed was a "light" with a much smaller wavelength.

In 1920's after Louis de Broglie (1892-1987) theorized that electrons should be wave-like particles[52], the German physicist Hans Busch wrote a formula that equated electron waves and light waves. Thus, "electron optics" was born. The beauty of electron waves was that they were much shorter than those of light. Thus, the theoretical limitations on resolution of an electron microscope fall into the range of a diameter of an atom. Some problems had to be solved. First, electrons had to be focused by strong electromagnets that work as

lenses. Secondly, electrons are readily absorbed or deflected by all matter. Thus, the electron beam could propagate only in near total vacuum. These limits not withstanding, the first simple electron microscopes were made in the early 1930's.

The first transmission electron microscope (TEM) was made by a team of physicists in Toronto in 1938. After that RCA collected its own team under the leadership of Vladimir Zworykin, (1889-1982) a talented Russian-American physicist. He was an able and creative director of the project that culminated in the first commercial electron microscope.

The TEM uses electron beams like a light microscope uses light. An electron source, usually a glowing filament much like those in an incandescent light bulb, sends electrons down a column surrounded by electromagnets. The electromagnetic lenses then collect and focus the electrons, which pass through the specimen and then are magnified by another set of electromagnetic lenses (they form a cone just like visible light does when it is magnified). This "shines" onto electron-sensitive film that forms an image. In the case of TEM images, the electrons must pass through very thin sections of cells (on the order of 0.025μm (one-fortieth of a millionth of a meter!).

The images thus generated at 10,000X the resolution possible with a light microscope were stunning and ushered in a new period of published micrographs, not unlike Hooke's *Micrographica*. Thus, biologists began to understand that the cellular structure of living things was remarkably complex and ordered. The cell was much more than protoplasm and nucleus. The cells were filled with membranes and organelles

---

[52] Find more about the particle-wave duality in *Questioning Reality*.

that had more detailed structure than had been imagined. Whereas the light microscope introduced biologists to microbes, cell and tissue types, the TEM introduced them to very fine structure, or ultrastructure, of the cell.

Unfortunately, some limitations apply to the electron microscope and the images that it produces. Electron micrographs cannot provide color (a property of visible light). The objects can be observed only when they are dead, and in the case of the TEM, sliced very thin. Thus, details of behavior and the interactions of parts cannot be known by direct observation.

Later, Zworykin also got the idea of using a beam of electrons to scan an object to reveal fine structure of the surface. The beam would be directed in a rastor or back and forth pattern. He took out a patent on the idea and the scanning electron microscope (SEM) was born. A spin-off of that was the first television camera and television receiver.

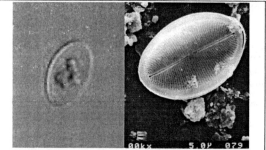

FIGURE 6-63. *Cocconeis placentula*, a common one-celled organism in the local creeks, with a light and an electron microscope.

LIMITATIONS, & DISCOVERY

There is no limit to the development of instruments and equipment that make it possible …to search for new answers to old and new perplexities.

Alma Smith Payne (1966)

Thus, the technology of the electron microscope fed the more commercial technology of the television. They both have contributed to the scientist's general understanding of nature. Thus, the interaction between science and technology strengthens both. Yet, it also leads to a general confusion between the two. Science is the enterprise of discovery in which the participants (scientists) seek to explain nature. The explanations must be consistent with observations and in agreement with physical law. The very first step in that enterprise requires exploration and careful descriptions of things discovered.

Technology, on the other hand is a means to solve particular problems. For example, I want meat so I fashion a spear from a long stick. I can improve on that by making a spear point of sharp stone, etc. Neither my ancestors nor I have to know about the science of sticks and stones in order to make a spear.

The same was true of van Leeuwenhoek's microscopes. He had seen lenses and developed his technique for grinding them over time. He also developed a lens and specimen holder. His design was not necessarily the best, but it worked. There is no evidence that van Leeuwenhoek applied any optical science or calculations to his microscopes. In his mind, too, there was a clear distinction between the microscope (instrument and machine) and the science of describing occupants of a microscopical world.

Ironically, van Leeuwenhoek's letters and specimens (he also mailed specimens to the Royal Society) have been the object of study. These have been reexamined with modern light microscopes and Scanning Electron Microscopes. With advances in technology, the same specimens may yield even more information.

When technology becomes coupled with science, both grow at a fantastic rate, each feeding on the other. As Alma Smith Payne indicates in her short biography of van Leeuwenhoek, we will continue to create instruments to extend the senses for discovery. In general, exploration seems to be tied to advances in technology. Van Leeuwenhoek could not explore things that are so small that they must be magnified for our eyes to resolve them without the technology of magnifying lenses. Now, the microscopic SEM and TEM push that limit to scales that are even more removed from our every day experience.

How important is the microscope (a technology) to the science of biology? I say that it is indispensable. Much of what we now regard as common biological knowledge has come to us only through the use of optical and electron microscopes. Other techniques have given us knowledge, yes. However, we are visual creatures. We even refer to the collection of data as *observation,* and microscopes allow us to expand our vision into the micro world "to search for new answers to old and new perplexities".

-2002

References:

Adams, Alexander. *Eternal Quest, The Story of the Great Naturalists.* G.P. Putnam's Sons. New York.

Azimov, Isaac. 1964. *A Short History of Biology.* The Natural History Press. Garden City.

De Kruif, Paul. 1926. *The Microbe Hunters.* Blue Ribbon Books. New York.

Drake, Ellen Tan. 1996. *Restless Genius, Robert Hooke and his Earthly Thoughts.* Oxford University Press. Oxford.

Eisley, Loren. 1961. *Darwin's Century.* Anchor Books. Garden City, New York.

Fawcett, Don W. 1966. *The Cell, An Atlas of Fine Structure.* W.B. Saunders Co. Philadelphia.

Ford, Brian J. 1985. *Single Lens, The Story of the Simple Microscope.* Harper & Row, Publishers. New York.

Hull, David L. 1988. *Science as a Process.* University of Chicago Press. Chicago.

Jacker, Corinne. 1966. *Window on the Unknown, A History of the Microscope.* Charles Scribner's & Sons. New York.

Kessel, R.G. and C.Y. Shih. 1974. *Scanning Electron Microscopy in Biology.* Springer Verlag. New York.

Mason, Stephen. 1962. *A History of the Sciences.* Collier Books. New York.

Mayr, Ernst. 1982. *The Growth of Biological Thought: Diversity, Evolution, and Inheritance.* The Belknap Press of the Harvard University Press. Cambridge, Mass.

Mayr, Ernst. 1997. *This is Biology, The Science of the Living World.* The Belknap Press of the Harvard University Press. Cambridge, Mass.

Medawar, Peter. 1984. *The Limits of Science.* Oxford University Press. Oxford.

Payne, Alma. 1970. *The Cleere Observer, A Biography of Antoni van Leeuwenhoek.* MacMillan & Co., Ltd. Glasgow.

Postek, Michael T., Karen S. Howard,, Arthur H. Johnson, and Kathlyn L. McMichael. 1980. *Scanning Electron Microscopy, A Student's Handbook.* Ladd Research Industries.

Singer, Charles. 1959. *A Short History of Scientific Ideas to 1900.* Oxford University Press. New York.

Wilson, Catherine. 1995. *The Invisible World, Early Modern Philosophy and the Invention of the Microscope.* Princeton University Press. Princeton.

Questions to Think About

1. How are crystal balls and human eyes alike?

2. How is light bent to magnify objects?

3. How were the microscopes of van Leeuwenhoek and Hooke different?

4. Why was *Micrographica* one of the most popular books of its day?

5. Why did Isaac Newton not even consider microscopes?

6. How did Carl Zeiss help to advance the microscope?

7. What were the improvements of Ernst Abbe?

8. What is resolution? What are the implications of resolution when considering light and electron microscopes?

9. What are the limitations of electron microscopes?

10. What is the relationship between technology of microscopy and the science of biology?

A VITAL SCIENCE

A DISCUSSION

Throw theory into the fire; it only spoils life.　　　-Mikhail Bakunin, 1842

Some years ago I was asked to lead a faculty discussion about a book dealing with a biological subject. Silly me. I thought that the exchange would be fairly cursory, and that I would end up answering questions about biology. Instead, after an initial discussion and explanation of terms, several who objected to the book and its message because it was reductionist assailed me. This response took me by surprise because I had heard about this view and studied it in a course on the *History of Science*. I was intrigued to hear such anachronisms. I would have assumed that the whole exchange was tongue-in-cheek, except that the vocal participants were so passionate. Then, one of them (who retired from the university not long afterwards) in a patronizing tone advised me that I would never understand the real mystery of life until I adopted a more holistic view and rejected the notion that biology could be reduced to chemistry and physics.

The theory that my antagonist defended was called *vitalism*. Since the time of Aristotle, it was believed that life and non-life were fundamentally different. They were so different that Georg Ernst Stahl (1660-1734) declared that living things were not governed by physical laws but by laws or principles that are unique to life and the products of life. Adding heat could destroy the vital force. For example, a living branch of a tree could have its vital force removed by burning and its products (carbon dioxide, water, etc.) rendered non-living.

This separation is still apparent in the division of Organic and Inorganic Chemistry. The concept of vitalism persisted in the science of biology and medicine well into the 19th century.

WHEN IS IT SCIENCE?

All this made me feel that, to everyone of the main problems, I had better answers – more coherent answers - than they had.　　　-Karl Popper

Philosopher of Science Sir Karl Popper (1902-1994) struggled with the question of science and what separates science from pseudoscience. He recognized that pseudoscience could sometimes be right and that science could be in error. What makes theory scientific? He cast about for a measure and found it in the way in which the theory was presented and explained phenomena. In particular, Popper rejected the idea that scientific theories could be proven or even verified. He said what makes a theory scientifically valid is that it can be shown false or falsified. This, he thought was the fundamental attribute of science and that which separated science from pseudoscience.

Consider the rival theories of vitalism and mechanism in the 18th century and evaluate them them with Popper's falsification requirement. The Mechanist theory was a view that there was no fundamental difference between life and non-life and that all of nature existed on a continuum from inorganic to organic. A prediction of the mechanists was that spontaneous generation of life should occur often. The microscope had been invented and very tiny things were ob-

594

served in drops of water and scrapings from teeth. Surely, things as simple as these could appear spontaneously. We all see this spontaneous generation as bread goes moldy and forgotten soup in the refrigerator turns cloudy and begins to stink as it teems with bacteria.

The Vitalist prediction was that the mold and microbes appeared only because they came from spores that fell from the air or were not killed by the boiling. That is, spontaneous generation was not possible. Experiments had been performed in which beef or mutton broth were boiled and then sealed. John Needham (1713-1781) performed the first such experiment or test of the Vitalist theory. He boiled meat broth, sealed it, and the sealed broth began to turn cloudy. He used this as a confirmation of spontaneous generation.

An Italian named Lazarro Spallanzani (1729-1799) objected and said that Needham did not boil the broth long enough. Spallanzani repeated the experiment but boiled the broth for nearly 2 hours before he sealed the flasks. This time, the broth did not become cloudy. Mechanists like Needham said that Spallanzani boiled the flask so long that he destroyed the vital principle in the air and so spontaneous generation could not occur. Needham's objection seemed almost vitalistic.

In Popper's view, the Mechanist theory could be scientific, but its proponents did not set clear boundaries to demonstrate that they were false. The theory seemed to be true regardless of the outcomes. So, it failed Popper's most important test. All scientific theories must be falsifiable.

NORMAL OR REVOLUTIONARY?

A scientific theory is usually felt to be better than its predecessors not only in the sense that it is a better instrument for discovering and solving puzzles but also because it is somehow a better representation of what nature is really like.

-Thomas S. Kuhn (1970)

In a mild rebuttal to this idea, another philosopher of science named Thomas Kuhn (1922-1996) said that scientists work to confirm their theories, not to disprove them. In fact it runs counter to human nature to expect otherwise. He describes normal science as an activity of puzzle-solving. In this, scientists accumulate data and information as it is important within the context of a major theory or paradigm. Vitalism is an example of such a paradigm.

Sometimes, in the period of normal science, rival paradigms will arise (as in our example of mechanism vs. vitalism). Scientists then choose the paradigm that helps to better explain the phenomena explored by the theory. Scientists like Einstein, Newton, Darwin, and Mendel were revolutionaries. The hundreds of contemporary scientists who worked in the normal science mode as puzzle-solvers are much less well known. Revolutionaries make a better story.

As in political revolutions, scientific revolutionaries sometimes end as intellectual martyrs. Such was the case of Ignaz Semmelweis (1818-1865), a Hungarian born physician who came to the hospital of Vienna as a trainee in the obstetrics ward from 1844-1848. The hospital had two different birthing wards. The First Maternity Ward was staffed by physicians and the Second Ward by midwives. That said, he was disturbed by the disparity in death rate between the two wards. Women in The First Ward suffered a death rate of 6.8-11.2% due to an infection called Childbed Fever. The Second Ward had a death rate of only 2-2.5% in the same period.

It seemed to Semmelweis that the cause for this could be found and treated. Also, he was certain that the problem represented a difference in the two wards. So, he set about trying a long list of tests. He tried having women deliver on their sides. He changed the route that the priest walked as he went to give last rites to a dying patient (in case the presence of the priest scared the women to death).

He was nearly ready to give up when he went to Venice for a vacation to clear his head and attempt to think through the problem. Upon his return to Venice, he learned that the head of Forensic Surgery named Kolletschka had died of all the symptoms of Childbed Fever. This had come on him after he cut himself with a knife during an autopsy.

Semmelweis reasoned that Kolletschka had introduced cadaverous (dead) tissue into his bloodstream thereby transmitting the disease to him. Similarly, women in the First Ward were attended to by medical interns who had spent the morning dissecting cadavers. If they carried any "cadaverous" material on their hands or under fingernails, they could transmit the disease to women who had given birth. In 1847, Ignaz Semmelweis instituted a policy of thoroughly washing hands before seeing patients in the First Ward. Quickly, the death rate dropped from more than 12% to less than 2% in the same year.

Semmelweis had pursued a puzzle and solved it. Indeed, he seemed almost revolutionary. However, the physicians were not impressed. By 1848 he was expelled from the hospital, and he finally ended his days in an Insane Assylum where he died. The cause of his death was somewhat mysterious and he may have been the victim of murder.

Why didn't medicine follow his lead? Mainly because the "theory" of Semmelweis did not explain anything. He made certain changes and the death rate dropped. What was the connection? How could the transmission of cadaverous material cause disease?

GERM THEORY

An investigator with the standard medical view in mind, let alone one with a brain swept clean of all pre-hypotheses, could never have developed the whole concept of infecting microbes from the small evidence with which Pasteur began. -David Bodanis (1988)

Louis Pasteur (1822-1895) had an undistinguished career as a student and received his Ph.D. in Chemistry in 1847, the same year as Semmelweis' discovery. He had a short temper with a somewhat arrogant air about him. Still, he was a genius at cranking out ideas.

Through the 1850's he began to work on fermentation. Also, during this time he finally laid to rest the concept of spontaneous generation by a set of brilliantly conceived demonstrations that built on the work of Spallanzani. Rather than seal the flasks, Pasteur drew out the neck into a graceful s-shaped neck. This allowed air to enter the flask (countering Needham's objection) and still trapped air-borne microbes. Some of Pasteur's flasks from these experiments can be seen to this day at the Pasteur Institute in Paris.

He began to work on wine and its fermentation by yeast. He watched the yeasts through the microscope until he was convinced that they were alive and therefore, the agents that caused grape juice to ferment to wine. While studying wine, he noticed that bad wine contained yeasts and smaller microbes called bacteria. He reasoned that the bacteria were ruining the wine and devised a method to kill the unwanted microbes. He advised the wineries to heat the wine gently. (Today, this process is called Pasteurization). He began to work on diseases of silkworms and then tackled the beer industry (mainly because he hated the Germans and wanted French beer to be better than that of the Germans).

In 1868 he suffered a stroke that left his right leg partially paralyzed. Still, he did not stop or slow down for that matter. He began to work on disease and ways of curing it. His work with fermentation and the silkworms caused him to consider that disease might be the result of microbial fermentation in a living body. This was the beginning of the idea that we now call the Germ Theory of Disease. That is, living microbial agents cause particular diseases; they are not simply symptoms of disease.

During this time, Pasteur began to work on Chicken Cholera and then on Anthrax. He followed the research of Edward Jenner (1749-1843) who had pioneered the use of inoculation to immunize against small pox. Pasteur grew a weakened form of the chicken cholera and gave it to his chickens. He followed that with murderous doses of lethal bacteria and the chickens survived.

Pasteur applied his same method to immunizing sheep and cows against anthrax, a disease that caused large losses of livestock in France and could be transmitted to humans. He announced that he would make a vaccine that would protect livestock against the disease. Although his accomplishments were great, this boast brought the ridicule of the medical and veterinary communities. In a fit of anger, Pasteur challenged his detractors. He said that he would immunize 24 sheep with his anthrax vaccine and then inoculate 48 sheep with anthrax.

With great fanfare and showmanship, Pasteur inoculated the sheep and then on May 31, 1881, he inoculated all of the animals with the deadly form of anthrax. On the afternoon of June 2, all of the protected sheep were healthy while all of the unprotected sheep were dead or dying. Those who reported that day said that it was like a conversion experience. Some of those who scoffed the loudest before the demonstration asked Pasteur to immunize them against anthrax.

A RELUCTANT PHYSICIAN

Koch's genius in these experiments [with anthrax] *lay in the simple and yet extremely effective technique that he worked out; indeed, it was in this sphere that he afterwards won his greatest successes.* -Erik Nordenskiold (1928)

Robert Koch (1843-1910) was a German physician who had become interested in anthrax. He worked carefully and persistently through the 1870's on a particularly vexing problem with the disease. Why did certain fields seem to have the specter of anthrax about them? The aspect that seemed so puzzling was that the anthrax organisms, although deadly, were quite delicate and easily killed outside the bodies of animals. How could such delicate microbes live in a field until livestock are introduced?

Koch was extraordinarily patient and careful in his research (although he tended to neglect his medical practice). He devised a method to grow the microbes in a drop of fluid from a cow's eye with a tiny piece of infected spleen. Then, he set about to carefully prove that the anthrax bacillus caused the disease.

For this proof, Koch applied four postulates:

1. Find the microbe in an organism that shows symptoms of the disease.
2. Isolate and grow the microbe outside of the organism.
3. Infect another organism with the isolated microbe. The microbe should elicit the same disease symptoms.
4. Isolate the microbe from the organism and check to see that it is the same one.

By application of these postulates, Koch sought to provide a general method by which anthrax or any other agent of disease could be examined. He was concerned that others like Pasteur were too sloppy in their methods and thinking and needed to adopt more rigorous

He made careful microscopic observations of the *Bacillus* that caused anthrax (see Figure 6-64 for a photomicrograph of the anthrax bacillus). Finally, one day he observed dots appearing in anthrax microbes as the culture aged. He reckoned that these were spores and infected another culture with healthy spleen with them. The anthrax bacilli developed.

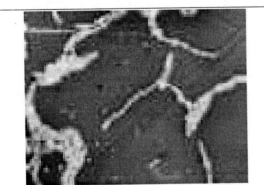

FIGURE 6-64. Light micrograph of a *Bacillus* culture. Note the endospores within the rod-shaped cells.

Koch and his assistants devised other methods of bacterial culture (the familiar agar plate was invented by his assistant R. Petri). He also pioneered the use of stains and microscopic photography. He also found that steam heat was most effective in killing bacteria and rendering items sterile.

With his experience and methods that he developed, Koch set out to discover the causative agent of tuberculosis. It was difficult work because the microbe grows very slowly. In 1882 Koch presented his results to a very skeptical group of scientists at a meeting of the Physiological Society. He was a soft-spoken and poor speaker, so he spent three days with microscopes and photographs showing them the microbe and the method by which he proved that it infected animals. He was to win the Nobel Prize in 1905 for his work on Tuberculosis.

Koch went on to tackle cholera, bubonic plague, sleeping sickness, malaria, and other diseases. Pasteur conquered rabies and produced a treatment. It seemed as though vitalism had triumphed and brought the dreaded specter of disease to its knees.

A FALL OF VITALISM

Even a confirmed vitalist who rejects the notion that living organisms are "nothing but" machines, will admit that progress in biological science has always depended on hypotheses formulated "as if" organisms were indeed machines.

-M. Gabriel and S. Fogel (1955)

Curiously, vitalism is no longer accepted in Biology. What led to its fall? Well, toward the end of the 19th century a crucial set of experiments began to show that life was much more complex than originally assumed.

Pasteur had written that fermentation could be caused only by microbial action. However, when yeasts were killed and carefully ground up, their broken cells caused fermentation to occur in a sugar-water solution. It didn't even require living cells. Also, the chemical components had been identified as compounds of carbon, many of which could be synthesized from inorganic substances. Where was the boundary?

The past 100 years in biology has seen a complete change in direction. Now, most of the research in the biological sciences is devoted to understanding mysteries at the cellular and molecular level. Vitalism has been relegated to the history books and the quacks of science.

Why did Pasteur and Koch make such an impact while Semmelweis was rejected? All three provided means to protect against disease. All had conducted the risky experiments as required by Karl Popper. All were consummate puzzle-solvers of the type described by Thomas Kuhn. However, Koch and Pasteur had provided more than a process. They led a revolution in the study and understanding of disease because they provided a theoretical framework within which to explain infection and infectious disease.

So, a study that was born in vitalism is now at home within a mechanist paradigm. Disease is now explained in mechanistic terms of celluar metabolism biochemistry, and immunology. The explanations of theories within biology in general can be reduced to the laws of chemistry and physics. This has become a strength of biology and a source of vigor in the sciences.

Still, popular culture embraces vitalistic notions when it comes to health. Look at the number of ads that stress *natural* foods, vitamins, or methods of healing (I've always wondered what unnatural foods would be like). The underlying message is clearly outside of science and verges on the religious. Those who push such ideas as scientific claim that biology is stuck in the mechanist paradigm and

needs a paradigm shift. Well, biology did consider vitalism. Its tenets were useful more than 100 years ago. Now, the explanations and predictions of vitalism are no longer useful nor consistent with the data generated by biology in this century. There may be other paradigm shifts in biology, but vitalism is dead, and biology is more vital as a consequence.

-1998, revised 2003

References:

Azimov, Isaac. 1964. *A Short History of Biology*. Natural History Press. Garden City, New York.

De Kruif, Paul. 1926. *The Microbe Hunters*. Harcourt, Brace & Co. New York.

Edmonds, David and John Eidinow. 2001. *Wittgenstein's Poker*. Harper-Collins, Publishers. New York.

Gabriel, Mordechai L. and Seymour Fogel. 1955. *Great Experiments in Biology*. Prentice-Hall, Inc. Englewood Cliffs, NJ.

Hempel, Carl. 1966. *Philosophy of Natural Science*. Prentice-Hall, Inc. Englewood Cliffs, NJ.

Horwich, Paul, ed. 1993. *World Changes, Thomas Kuhn and the Nature of Science*. A Bradford Book, MIT Press. Cambridge, MA.

Kuhn, Thomas S. 1970. *The Structure of Scientific Revolutions*. 2nd ed. University of Chicago Press. Chicago.

Kuhn, Thomas S. 1970. *Logic of Discovery or Psychology of Research?* In: Lakatos, I. And A. Musgrave, eds. *Criticism and the Growth of Knowledge*. Cambridge University Press. Cambridge.

Nordenskiold, Erik. 1928. *The History of Biology, A Survey*. Trans by L.B. Eyre. Tudor Publishing Co. New York.

Popper, Karl. 1957. *Philosophy of Science: A Personal Report.* In: Mace, C.A., ed. *British Philosophy in Mid-Century.* Allen and Unwin. London.

Popper, Karl. 1959. *The Logic of Scientific Discovery.* Hutchinson. London.

Popper, Karl. 1963. *Conjectures and Refutations.* Routledge & Kegan Paul, Ltd. London.

Thagard, Paul. 1997. *The Concept of Disease: Structure and Change.* http://cogsci.uwaterloo.ca/Articles/Pages/Concept.html

Vallery-Radot, Rene. 1931? *The Life of Pasteur.* Trans by R.L. Devonshire. Garden City Publishing Co., Inc. Garden City, NY.

Questions to Think About

1. What does Karl Popper use as a way to determine whether or not an idea or a theory is scientific?

   Falsifiability

2. What is Vitalism?

   Life and nonlife are fundamentally different
   — living things are governed by laws that are unique like ħ○

3. What is Mechanism?

   —No difference btwn life and non life rather existed on a continuum from inorganic to organic

4. Why did the theories of Vitalism and Mechanism have different predictions as to the origin of life in the 19th Century? Is that true today? Why is Vitalsim no longer accepted by practicing Biologists?

5. How do Kuhn's and Popper's views differ as to the way science is practiced?

6. Who was Ignaz Semmelweis? How did he approach the problem at his hospital? What was his solution? How did the medical community react to his solution?

7. Who was Pasteur? What were some of the motivations for his different research programs? Pasteur said, "Chance benefits only the prepared mind." What did he mean by that? Can you think of an example when Pasteur was prepared to benefit from a chance observation?

600

A HORSE AND MOLECULAR BIOLOGY

A HORSE OF VINES

The play's the thing...

-Shakespeare (Hamlet line 641)

I once attended a play in which one of the leading characters was a horse. Well, it wasn't really a horse, but it was a puppet of a horse. As such, it was controlled by a human being giving it directed movements and the ability to interact. However, it moved on stage with the grace and subtlety of a living creature. The designer had created a minimalist or essential horse. Indeed, it looked almost like a walking equine outline sketch. The genius of the design was in the use of grapevines to make the puppet. The supple nature of fresh grapevines provided an almost life-like motion to the horse. Indeed, the horse was so convincing that what appeared as a puppet transformed into a horse on stage.

FIGURE 6-65 The horse puppet.

How did a horse emerge from a design made of grapevines? In part, it was due to the acting ability of the person who controlled the puppet. However, most of it was due to the selection of grapevines as the basis and the creativity of its assembly. This order appeared to come from disorder. That is, the vines have a somewhat disordered growth that certainly does not resemble a horse (see Figure 6-66). The apparent lack of structural order is deceiving, and quite literally is only skin deep (see Figure 6-67).

FIGURE 6-66. The disorder of grapevines as they grow on a fence in my yard.

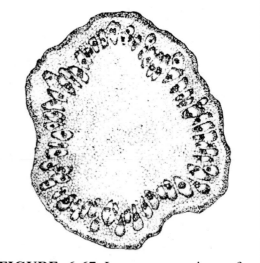

FIGURE 6-67 Low power view of a stem like that of grapes. Note the target-like arrangement of cells and tissues.

HEREDITY IS MECHANISTIC

It requires indeed some courage to undertake a labor of such far-reaching extent. -Gregor Mendel (1865)

Certainly, a horse puppet is less complex and ordered than a living horse or any other living thing for that matter. The complexity and order of the life process gave rise to the Vitalist paradigm[53]. However, as life was examined, it became clear that there were many common attributes. Life had a cellular organization and common structures such as chromosomes, membranes, etc. By the end of the 19th century, biologists had abandoned the vitalist view and embraced the mechanist view of life.

The mechanist view was confirmed when Hugo deVries and others discovered the work of an Austrian monk named Gregor Mendel (1822-1884) that had been published more than 30 years earlier. Mendel demonstrated that traits such as flower color, fruit type, etc. could be explained simply if pairs of genes (Mendel referred to them as particles. The term gene came much later.) provided the information or code for a specific trait.

Mendel's work showed by empirical, statistical means that the underlying basis of heredity was relatively simple and obeyed particular laws. This discovery brought about a true paradigm shift in the study of genetics. The explosion in work that followed was truly remarkable and very productive as the Mendelian paradigm provided a basis for experimentation and explanation. Quickly, researchers recognized the importance the importance of the chromosome in carrying the genetic information. Its structure, maps of genes, behavior during replication and division all became intense areas of study.

Another area of interest was mutation of the gene itself. Because changes in the gene could give rise to major changes in the organism, biologists began to question the need for Darwin's natural selection in evolution. Dobzhansky, Mayr and others created the "New Synthesis" in the 1930's in which mutation explained the origin of variation on which natural selection operated[54].

Attracted by the ferment brought about by "modern genetics" and cell biology in came others from other disciplines. Chemists were attracted to the study of the bewildering array of compounds produced by life and with particular functions in the life process. These Biochemists became interested in the chemical machinery, pathways, products and structures produced by cells. Foremost among these were the proteins.

Made of strings of amino acids, proteins serve many functions in the living process. Some, like collagen are structural, but most seem to be involved in controlling the steps of chemical pathways, themselves. The latter class of proteins, called enzymes, is integral in the chemical machine of metabolism. These are quite complex and sensitive to changes in temperature, salt concentration, pH, etc.

A third class of proteins, the carrier molecules, includes compounds such as hemoglobin and hormones. Chemists began to look at the structures of proteins and determine the orders of

---

[53] I explain the Vitalist Principle in *A Vital Science* and *Chance and the Prepared Mind.*

[54] I present the New Synthesis in *Parasites and Darwin's Intellectual Triumph.*

amino acids as well as the three dimensional structures.

ORDER FROM ORDER

The obvious inability of present-day physics and chemistry to account (for the events which take place in a living organism) is no reason at all for doubting that they can be accounted for by those sciences.

-Erwin Schrödinger (1944)

Physicists also began to be attracted to questions in biology. Niehls Bohr (1885-1962), Danish physicist and one of the founders of Quantum Theory, speculated that a new type of physics might be discovered if physicists would begin to study life (just as Quantum Mechanics came out of the physical description of atoms and atomic structure). Intellectual offspring of Bohr such as Max Delbrück (1906-1981) began to apply physics to the cell with particular emphasis on the mechanism of heredity.

Erwin Schrödinger, a founder of Quantum Mechanics[55], lost his university position in Vienna after the Nazi Anschluß in 1939. He moved to Dublin where he continued his work. In 1943, he began a series of public lectures called "What is Life?" The lectures were well attended not only because he was a captivating speaker, but also because there just wasn't much other entertainment during the war years.

Schrödinger's topic centered on the nature of heredity and the thermo-dynamics of living systems. He acknowledged that he knew little about chemistry and even less about biology. Nevertheless, life must have several properties to obey the laws of chemistry and physics. In particular, there must be some structural mechanism to provide for the storage and transmission of information from generation to generation. Thus, order in the structural nature of the gene stores coded information that is manifest in the ordered production of the cellular machinery (He got this idea from the earlier writings of Max Delbrück). Schrödinger supposed that the gene was an "aperiodic crystal that stored information in its structure." He published the lectures in a small 90-page book before the end of the war.

After the close of World War II, many physicists who had been involved in weapons research became interested in questions posed by biology and the biophysics of the molecular interactions. Many of them later claimed that they were influenced, in part, by Schrödinger's book. Mostly, physicists like Leo Szillard (1898-1964; the man who held the patent on the atomic bomb) and others began to consider the questions of structure and function of biomolecules, particularly of proteins.

The Cavendish Laboratory at Cambridge University assembled a team of chemists and physicists that focused on the nature and structure of molecules such as hemoglobin. Other laboratories such as Linus Pauling's (1901-1994) at CalTech tackled similar problems.

Max Delbrück helped to found a group that examined a group of viruses called bacteria phages (bacteria eaters). These were particularly important because they were made of protein and deoxyribonucleic acid (DNA), the two major components of the chromosome.

---

[55] See *Questioning Reality* and *Swords and Plowshares.*

THE DISCOVERY
It has not escaped our notice...
-James Watson and Francis Crick (1953)

DNA had been isolated in the last century and was studied by biochemists. They determined that the molecule, though large, was somewhat simple in its structure. It was made of phosphate, a five-carbon sugar (deoxyribose), and four nitrogen-containing bases called Cytosine, Guanine, Thymine, and Adenine. As complex as it sounds, DNA is still simpler than protein which is made of strings of 20+ different amino acids.

After the determination of the composition of chromosomes (DNA and protein), early assumptions were that the DNA formed the string to which proteins attached. Somehow, proteins served as templates for their replication The chain of proteins determined the sequence of genes on the chromosome.

A series of elegant experiments from the late 1920's through 1952 laid that idea to rest, however. They clearly demonstrated that the genetic material in bacteria and bacteria phages was the DNA, not protein. By the early 1950's the race was on to determine the structure of DNA.

Through questionable means, James Watson (b. 1928), fresh with a PhD from Delbrück's phage group, came to the Cavendish Laboratory at Cambridge. There, he met Francis Crick (1916-2004), a biophysicist who was working on the structure of hemoglobin by the use of X-ray crystal diffraction methods.

Maurice Wilkins (1916-2004), a physicist and former member of the Manhattan Project, was working on DNA at Kings College in London. He, too, was using X-ray diffraction methods to visualize the structure of the DNA molecule.

Rosalind Franklin (1920-1958), an associate of Wilkins at Kings, obtained superb X-ray diffraction photographs of crystalline DNA. Unfortunately, Wilkins and Franklin could not work together as collaborators. Watson and Crick used the results of Franklin and Wilkins along with insight as to how the bases must pair with each other to construct a model of the molecule.

FIGURE 6-68. The DNA model built by Watson and Crick. The model is part of the collection of the British Museum of Science and Industry. The ladder rungs represent paired bases and the backbones represent sugars and phosphates.

Watson and Crick published their model of the DNA molecule in Nature in 1953 (see Figure 6-68). The most important aspect of the molecule was that Adenine (A) always pairs with Thymine (T) while Cytosine (C) always pairs with Guanine (G). They end their short paper with one of the most famous understatements in the history of science:

> *It has not escaped our notice that the specific pairing we have postulated immediately suggests a possible copying mechanism for the genetic material.*

THE CENTRAL DOGMA

This [the Central Dogma] states that once "information" has passed into protein, it cannot get out again.

-Francis Crick (1957)

Quickly, those working on the gene problem saw that the structure not only bears clues as to its replication, but it suggests how the code is written. Still, DNA could not be the whole story. In organisms with nuclei, protein synthesis occurs out in the cell while DNA is always packaged in structures like nuclei. There must be an intermediate. Later, Crick and others realized that other nucleic acids called RNA (for Ribonucleic acid) occur primarily in the cytoplasm. This was different from DNA in that it had a different kind of sugar (ribose) and used the base Uracil rather than Thymine. More importantly, RNA was single-stranded.

By 1958, Crick published a possible sequence of events in the decoding of the genetic message. He proposed that DNA was rewritten to RNA that then served as the template for the construction of proteins. This he called the Central Dogma of Molecular Biology (see Figure 6-69).

Very soon Marshall Nirenberg, Crick and others through a series of simple and very informative experiments broke the code. That is, they demonstrated that linear sequences of nucleic acids code for linear sequences of amino acids that are assembled at sites in the cytoplasm called ribosomes. Messenger RNA that is transcribed from the DNA template moves into the cytoplasm and associates with ribosomes.

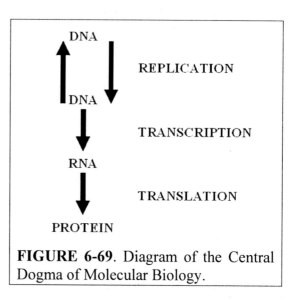

FIGURE 6-69. Diagram of the Central Dogma of Molecular Biology.

STRONG INFERENCE

It [Molecular Biology] is, rather, an intellectual transformation- indeed, a new conceptual dynasty – arisen within the realm.-Horace Freeland Judson (1979)

Units of three messenger RNA bases serve as code words or codons. Each codon triplet then pairs with a complementary "anticodon" on a special RNA (called transfer RNA) that carries a particular amino acid. The amino acids on adjacent transfer RNA molecules react and combine in the coded sequence. Thus, the code is translated from nucleic acid "words" to a sequence of amino acids in a protein.

Within 15 years of the determination of the structure of DNA, the details of the Central Dogma had been fleshed out. More importantly, the code was known and could be read.

Observing the enormous strides that were made in Molecular Biology (as this kind of study began to be called), John

Platt, a professor of biophysics at the University of Chicago, proposed that Molecular Biology employed another kind of scientific thinking. This he called "Strong Inference" and suggested that other more sluggish sciences should follow the example of Molecular Biology.

He defined the steps as:
1. Devising alternative hypotheses.
2. Devising a crucial experiment (or several of them) with alternative possible outcomes each of which will, as nearly as possible, exclude one or more of the hypotheses.
3. Carrying out the experiment carefully to get a clean (unambiguous result).

This sequence of steps defines the advance of Molecular Biology quite well up until around 1970. Judson in his superb history of Molecular Biology called *The Eighth Day of Creation*, suggests that at the discovery of the structure of DNA the questions were so large that large strides were inevitable as in the early days after the discovery of Mendel's work. The genius of Crick's Central Dogma provided guidance and focus to the questions. Judson said that the publications in the early years (1953-1970) read like chapters in a book on Molecular Biology. Later, the focus began to diminish and become more diffuse as Molecular Biology methods were applied to more and more different kinds of questions, from evolution to disease. This "slow down" is not a symptom of a sickness as Platt would put it, but a sign of maturity.

Now, the methods of Molecular Biology have insinuated themselves into nearly all aspects of the discipline. It has spawned an industry, and revolutionized biology and medicine.

With all of this knowledge and understanding, can we look at a strand of DNA and read it like a book? Not now. If you were to take all of the DNA in one of your cells and stretch it out, it would be about 2 meters long! Much of that is nonsense and is excised before messenger RNA leaves the nucleus. Still, there are thousands of genes that code for proteins. Even now, we could not guess the function of a protein by reading its amino acid sequence.

Molecular Biology provides us with a good mechanism for the explanation of biological phenomena, but prediction is still very difficult. In part, prediction is complex because enzymes operate together in the cell. This interaction causes the emergence of the property that we call life.

Emergence is an attribute of a complex system in which interesting high-level properties appear as a consequence of the interactions of lower level or simpler entities. In this case, genes and their products interact to produce something that is more than a bag of proteins. Cells and living things certainly emerge as more interesting than the sum of their parts (genes).

The puppet horse in a simpler sense displayed the property of emergence. The interactions of flexing grapevines attached at particular places as part of a design provided subtle, life-like motion that even she, the designer, had not predicted precisely.

Life is made of molecules and their interactions. Like a horse made of grapevines, it is the interactions that produce interesting properties. But, increasingly, to biologists it is the explanation of those properties that we find both interesting and rewarding.

-1998, revised 2003.

References:

Asimov, Isaac. 1964. *A Short History of Biology.* The Natural History Press. Garden City, New York.

Crick, F.H.C. 1962 *The Genetic Code.* In: Srb, A.M., R.D. Owen, and R.S. Edgar, eds. 1969. *Facets of Genetics.* W.H. Freeman and Co. San Francisco.

Emmeche, Claus, Simo Koppe, and Frederik Stjernfelt. 1997. *Explaining Emergence: Towards and Ontology of Levels.* Journal for General Philosophy of Science 28:83-119.

Heinig, Robin. 2000. *The Monk in the Garden, The Lost and Found Genius of Gregor Mendel, the Father of Genetics.* Houghton Mifflin Company. New York.

Iltis, Hugo. 1924. *Life of Mendel.* W.W. Norton & Co., Inc. New York.

Judson, Horace Freeland. 1996. *The Eighth Day of Creation, Makers of the Revolution in Biology.* Expanded edition. Cold Spring Harbor Laboratory Press. Plainview, New York.

Maddox, B. 2002. *Rosalind Franklin, The Dark Lady of DNA.* HarperCollins Publishers. New York.

Mayr, Ernst. 1982. *The Growth of Biological Thought: Diversity, Evolution and Inheritance.* Harvard University Press. Cambridge, Mass.

Mendel, Gregor. 1865. *Experiments in Plant Hypridization.* In: Peters, J.A., ed. 1962. *Clasic Papers in Genetics.* Prentice-Hall, Inc. Englewood Cliffs, NJ.

Murphy, Michael and Luke O'Neill, eds. 1995. *What is Life? The Next Fifty Years.* Cambridge University Press. New York.

Platt, John R. 1964. *Strong Inference.* Science. 146:347-353.

Schrödinger, Erwin. 1944. *What is Life?* Cambridge University Press. New York.

Stent, Gunther. 1971. *Molecular Genetics, An Introductory Narrative.* W.H. Freeman & Co. San Francisco.

Watson, James. 1968. *The Double Helix.* Anthenium Publishers. New York.

Watson, James. 1970. *Molecular Biology of the Gene.* 2nd edition. W.A. Benjamin, Inc. New York.

Watson, James and Francis Crick. 1953. *A Structure for Deoxyribose Nucleic Acid.* Science 171:737-738.

Wilson, Edward O. 1998. *Consilience, The Unity of Knowledge.* Alfred A. Knopf. New York.

Wolpert, Lewis and Alison Richards. 1988. *A Passion for Science.* Oxford University Press. New York.

Questions to Think About

1. How did the horse "emerge" from the woven grape vines?

2. Who was Gregor Mendel? Why was he important?

3. Erwin Schrodinger was not a biologist. In fact he knew hardly any biology. How, then, did he have an impact on the science of biology?

4. What did Watson and Crick discover?

5. Whose work made their discovery possible?

6. How do DNA and RNA differ? How are they similar?

7. What is the Central Dogma of Molecular Biology? Who first defined it?

8. How do Platt and Judson differ as to the explanation of why molecular biology made such great strides in their early days.

9. What is the concept of emergence?

10. Compare the emergence of the property that is called life with the emergence of other complex systems (go to the essay, *Butterflies*).

ORIGINS

IN MY BEGINNING

In the beginning there was simplicity.
                              –Richard Dawkins

In the beginning, I cannot say that I was confused. In fact, I had never really thought about the origin of life problem from a scientific perspective until I sat in a college classroom more than thirty years ago and listened to an instructor who tried to convince me that the "laws of probability" were against the mechanistic origin of life. I remember allowing that thought to swirl around in my head. The argument was compelling, and after all, he had written a book on it. He then assigned a critique of the current theories as to the origin of life as a paper topic. As I recall, I was at a loss. I did not know what to write about except the foundation of the argument for the mechanism of synthetic of organic compounds on the early earth. In particular, that assumption was that the early earth must have had a primal atmosphere very similar to that of the gas giants like Jupiter and Saturn. Their atmospheres likely represented that of the original accretion of the planets from the primordial disk.

That was the understanding of the first modern theorist on the origin of life. Alexandr Ivanovitch Oparin (1859-1927) was a Russian biochemist who supposed that the early earth had a reducing atmosphere dominated by hydrogen, ammonia, and methane. He supposed that this mixture, given appropriate energy input like solar radiation and lightning might bring about the synthesis of a range of organic molecules that would come together as colloidal aggregates or coascevates. These would allow organic molecules like amino acids, lipids, nucleic acids, carbohydrates, and other carbon-containing molecules to be close enough for the reactions that would make chains or polymers like most biological molecules. Oparin supposed that the coacervates would tend to capture other dissolved organics and allow for the enlargement of the coacervate structure, a kind of prebiotic growth. Then, as the coacervates took up more organics from the water, a shortage of raw materials for the formation of the coacervates gave rise to a prebiotic natural selection thereby favoring those aggregates that were efficient. This process would eventually give rise to eubiota or true cellular life.

Oparin wrote down his views in a book called *The Origin of Life on Earth* in 1924. He produced an expanded version of that work that was published posthumously in 1936, which was finally translated into English in 1938. Ironically, J.B.S. Haldane (1892-1964) British Biochemist and geneticist published his view of the origin of life in 1929 (before he heard of Oparin's ideas). Nevertheless, both men had remarkably similar views.

Like Oparin, Haldane supposed that the atmosphere of early earth had no oxygen. He further supposed that the oceans, also oxygen-free, were a mixture of dissolved CO_2, and ammonia, which could with the energy of ultraviolet light combine to form amino acids and chains of amino acids and other biopolymers. Thus, Haldane conceived of the oceans as a "hot, dilute soup" from which life sprang (This was the origin of the primordial soup concept). Then, the first cell emerged after acquiring a lipid membrane.

Norman Horowitz considered the prebiotic soup concept and concluded that as early membrane-bound packets of organic material absorbed and assimilated simple organic components and constructed their biopolymers like proteins, the environments would become even more dilute. Thus, the "cells" would have been subject to a very strong selective pressure to develop efficient and effective pathways. This would have rapidly given rise to rudimentary metabolism, the most fundamental characteristic of life.

Biophysicist John Desmond Bernal (1901-1971) in 1951 said that a dilute soup would not have been able to assemble the precells. The mechanisms for the abiotic production of organic materials could not have made a "soup" thick enough for the spontaneous assembly of coacervates or membrane-bound precells. Instead, he believed that a catalytic surface was needed. For such a ubiquitous catalyst, he suggested clay particles. Organic materials would have been adsorbed onto the clay minerals, which are charged. This would have concentrated the organic matter such that reactions could have taken place just through their proximity on the clay particle.

FROM THEORY TO EXPERIMENT
One good experiment is worth a thousand models; but one good model can make a thousand experiments unnecessary.

-David Lloyd and Evgenii I Volkov

Until 1950 the modern theories of the origin of life remained in a theoretical plane. Then, Melvin Calvin, the discoverer of the Calvin Cycle in oxygen-requiring cells, bombarded a mixture of hydrogen, water and carbon dioxide with alpha particles in a cyclotron. The operation produced small organic molecules like formic acid, acetic acid, and formaldehyde. However, this particular mechanism of organic matter formation did not seem to apply to the early Earth and, therefore, had little impact on science.

On the other hand, Harold Urey (1893-1981) and his graduate student Stanley Miller did make a great impact in 1953 with an experiment that did seem germane to the origin of organic molecules on the early Earth. They assumed the Oparin-Haldane atmosphere and made a mixture of such gasses (methane, ammonia, hydrogen, and water) in an experimental setup that introduced sparks (as a simulation of lightning). Shortly, the inside of the reaction chamber began to turn dark with a tar-like coating and the water began to fill with an array of substances. When they took the apparatus apart, they found numerous small organic molecules, many of which were amino acids, the building blocks of proteins. This experiment demonstrated that questions about the formation of organic molecules on a prebiotic earth could be explored and tested. Thus, Urey and Miller made prebiotic chemistry a legitimate study. Optimism seemed warranted with the prompt discovery of the structure of DNA and the rapid sequence of discoveries that founded molecular biology. The molecular level of life suggested that a prebiotic form of natural selection could have given rise to life through chemical evolution.

Just how the simple organics came together to form chains or polymers of larger molecules necessary for life became the subject of intense debate. In general, the theorists took a bottom-up approach. That is, like the Urey-Miller experiment, they assumed certain conditions and then saw what could be produced. Given the products, what further steps would need to be taken, etc? This seemed a more fruitful approach than to consider life as it is and then try to take it apart in backward steps.

The potential mechanisms for prebiotic chemistry included tidal action, the polymerization through the alternate wet and dry of a tidal pool. The aerosol surfaces at the interface between the ocean and the atmosphere might have served to concentrate organics in the meniscus or aerosol bubbles in which reactions could take place. The catalytic influence of clays and other minerals like iron pyrite also were considered. In the mean time, Sidney Fox made protenoid compounds out of simple chains of amino acids by simulating conditions in hot volcanic springs. The organics thus generated spontaneously formed spheres that selectively took up other dissolved organic matter and "grew". After they achieved a threshold size they "divided". Fox's protenoid spheres seemed to behave as though they were alive and such results seemed to fuel the enthusiasm

However, the search for a mechanism of prebiotic chemistry became bogged down and then stopped in its tracks as the very assumptions of the Oparin-Haldane early earth atmosphere came under fire. Studies of the other earth-like planets, Mars and Venus, suggested that the atmosphere that cooked out of the coalescing earth must have been similar and formed over a very short period of time, maybe 10-100 million years. The problem with the "new" atmosphere was that its composition was mainly CO_2, an almost inert gas. The other components, N_2 and water vapor were no better. Even with the energetic input of lightning and ultraviolet radiation, the yield of organic molecular building blocks would be woefully inadequate to the task of building prebiotic organic molecules like proteins.

At the same time more was being learned about the conditions of the early earth, the evidence for the appearance of life on earth kept being moved back and back again[56]. Finally, the discoveries of

microfossils had been found from rocks that dated almost to the earliest time at which life could be supported, the end of the great bombardment. That was the time, whose results are still frozen on the dead surface of the moon[57]. Some of those impacts imparted so much energy that they nearly boiled away the oceans. How could life have arisen in such a maelstrom? Where could the fragile incipient life have taken refuge?

DEEP OCEAN

These systems [hydrothermal vents] would have provided the combination of high temperatures and chemical environment (reducing conditions) necessary for converting carbon dioxide into organic material.

-Peter Ward and Donald Brownlee

The unusual chemistry necessary for the formation of small organics and the minerals that would serve as catalysts can be found at select locations on the ocean floor called hydrothermal vents. These are places in the deep ocean where the crust is thin and magma lies near the surface. Cracks in the rocks allow water to infiltrate and return super heated. Such water is chemically very active and is laden with chemicals that it gleans from the surrounding rocks on its way back. Such systems today support whole ecosystems of life that are driven solely by the chemical energy (and thermal energy) of the out flowing water.

---

[56] See *Red Planets and Microbes.*

[57] See *Moon Stories, Origins of the Earth-Moon System.*

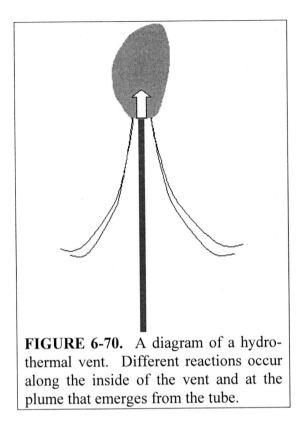

FIGURE 6-70. A diagram of a hydrothermal vent. Different reactions occur along the inside of the vent and at the plume that emerges from the tube.

The temperature and chemical gradients are quite extreme at the vents (see Figure 6-70). The ambient temperature at the ocean bottom hovers just above the freezing point whereas the water leaving the vents can be hundreds of degrees. In addition, the high pressures at such depths give water unusual properties (for example, it becomes less polar) that make water better suited as a medium for the production of small organics and their polymerization to form large biopolymers. The fine gradients and unusual chemistry produce narrow zones in which particular reactions can occur. These have been repeated experimentally and an array of small organics can be generated that rivals that of the Urey-Miller experimental design.

Advantages of the hydrothermal vent theory are not restricted to questions of the proper chemistry and products. The vents that occur today also produce layers of iron pyrite, fool's gold. This has

been suggested as a possible mineral on which organic matter would accumulate and polymerize. The theory is that the mineral accreted organic matter around it and was a necessary component of the earliest life. Then, the lineage that gave rise to most living things evolved to do without it.

Hydrothermal vents as islands of life on the sea floor exploded into science awareness when the crew of the deep submersible Alvin descended 2.6 kilometers to a site of ocean floor spreading near the Galapagos Islands. They were amazed to see highly diverse communities flourishing well below the depth at which photosynthesis could occur. These communities were fueled by the chemical energy of the plumes, a process called chemosynthesis. Later in 1985, John Baross and S. Hoffman suggested that the dominant chemosynthetic microbes (now called Archaea) adapted to high temperatures and pressures, also called thermal extremophiles hyperthermophiles, might represent the remnants of the earliest forms of living things. Curiously, many of the Archaea of thermal vents also have inclusions of iron pyrite. The decade following the proposal of Baross and Hoffman saw a surprising series of discoveries about the relationships of all living things. Particularly, it appeared as though living things fall into three distinct lineages: the Archaea, Eubacteria, and Eykaryota (see Figure 6-71). Figure 6-71 illustrates the difficulty of using the existing living groups to understand origin of life scenarios. Multiple lineages could have appeared during a time of chemical evolution, only one of which seems to have survived. This is the fundamental weakness of the top-down approach to the question of the origin of life. Thus, such evidence, tough interesting, is too circumstantial to be strong support for the "ventrists' point of view.

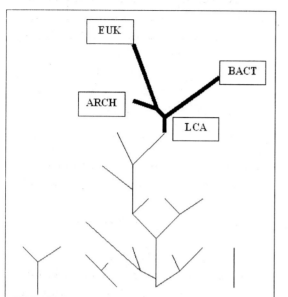

FIGURE 6-71. A diagram that shows hypothetical relationships between independent lines of protolife. One lineage culminates in the Last Common Ancestor (LCA) which gives rise to the Archaea (ARCH), the Eukaryota (EUK), and the Eubacteria (BACT). The Archaea has organisms, most of which are thermal extremophiles, that are closest to last common ancestor.

More compelling support from my perspective is the nature of the hydrothermal environment itself. It separates the delicate protolife structures from the vagaries of the surface environments. Particularly, deep hot environments that would be protected from ultraviolet radiation and buffered from the effects of ocean-boiling impacts are compelling as possible sites for incipient life to appear and take hold.

EXTRATERRESTRIAL CARBON

At a time when proposed solutions are still speculative, they are the driving force for the researches that will prove them right or wrong and will thereby put our thinking on a new and better track.
                                                     -Thomas Gold

In 1986 sensors trained on Halley's Comet returned the startling information that it was not just a dirty snowball, but that it had a high concentration of organic material. In fact it was nearly 20% organic matter. Consistent with that estimate, the nucleus of the comet has a reflectance (albedo) that is as low as coal. Given the volume of the comet, the total volume of organic matter translated to an equivalence of 10% of the total organic biomass on the Earth. Such an astounding observation suggested that all of the organic matter on the Earth (and a significant portion of its ocean) could be accounted for by the accretion of at least ten Halley's-sized comets. Given the accretion rate at the time of the great bombardment, that is very likely. The objection to this view is that comets, unless they have a somewhat "soft" impact, would vaporize any organic matter in them.

A rebuttal to that objection can be found in an ancient extraterrestrial rock (a chondrite) that landed in Murchison Australia. When the Murchison Meteorite was analyzed, the results indicated that it had an array of small organic molecules, including amino acids that rivaled those produced in the Urey-Miller Experiment. Thus, organic matter can survive the energies of impacts. These and similar finds indicate that sufficient organic matter for origin of life scenarios could be accounted for by the bombardment of comets and meteorites. Indeed, the environment of space could be ideal for the production of organic matter. So, the question of how carbon-containing molecules assembled themselves on the early Earth might have too many answers.

Suppose that the abundance of organic matter was just as high in the nebular cloud that gave rise to the solar system, the cloud from which the Earth accreted, then more than enough hydrocarbons should have been incorporated into the original mass of the Earth to account for all of its carbon, organic and inorganic. This was an old idea that was resurrected by Soviet scientists in the 1950's when they tried to make sense of the distribution of petroleum deposits on the Earth. In this view, vast reservoirs of hydrocarbons are found deep within the Earth and are "cooking" out of the mantle-crust region to move up through permeable rock layers. Although originally proposed to account for a variety of puzzling attributes of petroleum, natural gas, and coal deposits, this theory has important implications for origin of life scenarios. Thomas Gold (b 1920), an American astrophysicist who made important discoveries about the nature of pulsars, the magnetosphere, and the operation of the inner ear, popularized the abiogenic (non-living) source of petroleum. He countered the arguments that petroleum had cellular debris in it by proposing that the petroleum hydrocarbons served as a food source for deep-dwelling microbes, probably Archaea. If this view is correct, the realm of the Biosphere (living realm) goes very deep into the crust, a concept that Gold called the "deep, hot biosphere", could account for many times the total biomass of the surface biosphere that we know about. More importantly, the heat and pressure in deep crustal regions, assuming that sufficient water also is present, would serve to form biopolymers, the constituents of life[58].

The combination of extraterrestrial and earthly sources for organic compounds seems sufficient to account for the amount of organic matter on our planet. Although, hydrocarbons are nec-

essary, they alone are not sufficient to account for the appearance of life. Indeed, one of the most fundamental attributes of life is the transmission of information from one generation to the next. How did that develop? How could concentrations of biopolymers become alive?

RNA WORLD

To go from a bacterium to people is less of a step than to go from a mixture of amino acids to a bacterium.

-Lynn Margulis

Consider the complexity of the cell and how it operates (see A Vital Science, from the Saturday Scientist last month and A Horse and Molecular Biology, this issue). Cells have membranes of phospholipid bilayers. They use and incorporate carbohydrates of ranges of complexity. They are controlled and regulated by certain proteins (enzymes), and given structural support by other proteins. More than that, though, they store and transmit information from one generation to the next through nucleic acids. How could such a remarkably complex, balanced system originate even if a full array of organic materials were present? An answer must recognize that the steps to complexity are small and not at all inevitable. In the final analysis it is time, immense periods of time, that makes the improbable possible. So, any reasonable scenario must rely on many small steps in the construction of complex systems. Those steps also must be fueled by energy: heat, ultraviolet light, chemical energy, pressure, tidal action, etc.

I have given some solutions earlier, particularly those that rely on mineral scaffolds to provide the catalytic and information foundation from which proto life appeared. Some consider even more simple systems. For example Nobel Lau-

---

[58] Find more about Thomas Gold in *Pseudoscience, the Science of the Gullible.*

reate Manfred Eigen (b. 1927) of Germany believes that proteins alone are enough to constitute an organized protobiotic structure. Through competition with other protoliving structures for amino acids (the building blocks of proteins), efficiency and effectiveness would be selected for.

The problem arises when scenarios try to account for the association of nucleic acids and proteins in the way that we see them in the Central Dogma of molecular biology[59]. Usually, this produces a chicken and egg problem. That is, proteins require nucleic acids for their assembly, but DNA requires protein for its construction. Which came first? Freeman Dyson (b. 1923 England), an American physicist attempts to solve the chicken and egg paradox by proposing that metabolism (protein-mediated operation) and replication (nucleic acid) appeared independently and fused in a kind of symbiosis.

The resolution to this problem seemed hopelessly complex and unreachable. However, years earlier and spinning off of his success with guessing the Central Dogma, Francis Crick (b. 1917-2004, England) with Leslie Orgel (b. 1927, England) proposed that RNA, not DNA was the first information-bearing molecule. This theory languished in concept until 1986 when Thomas Cech published evidence of an RNA molecule that could splice itself. Thus it could act simultaneously as a catalyst and an information molecule. This was the first real evidence for the possibility of an RNA World (a term coined the same year by Walter Gilbert).

The RNA World scenario proposes that protolife first organized itself into packages (presumably membrane-bound) of RNA that carried out the func-

tions of metabolism and reproduction together. The function of metabolism then was co-opted by the more efficient and effective proteins (enzymes). The function of information storage then was transferred to the more stable DNA while RNA retained a role in reproduction and the translation of information through the steps of the Central Dogma.

The problem with the RNA World scenario is that RNA is capricious as a molecule. Because it has a single strand, it is less stable than DNA and very sensitive to high temperatures. Because almost all origin of life scenarios suppose ambient high temperatures, this is an important consideration. Most theorists who support the RNA World assume that the form of RNA must have been more durable and able to survive in high temperatures.

PANSPERMIA

Once started, the robustness of life as demonstrated in the recent articles ensures its essential immortality. It survives and is repeatedly regenerated in the warm watery interiors of comets. The space between stars is littered with cometary debris, some of which contains the seeds of life.

—Chandra Wickramasinghe

Other views of life consider that it is so improbable and yet once started so robust that its spread through the cosmos is inevitable. That is the fundamental position of astronomers Chandra Wickramasinghe (b. 1939, Sri Lanka) and his mentor Fred Hoyle (1915-2001, England). Though it was not a new idea, the theory of the spread of life through the cosmos, called Panspermia, is most commonly associated with them.

In the 1960's Hoyle and Wickramasinghe were analyzing interstellar dust through spectral analysis. The spec-

---

[59] See *A Horse and Molecular Biology*.

trum had an unusual and inexplicable dip in the graph, which they thought might be interstellar carbon (graphite). However, the agreement between the absorption of graphite and interstellar dust was not very good. They tried a number of different possibilities, but in 1979 they found that dried bacteria provided an almost exact match with the observed spectrum.

After their 1979 discovery, Hoyle and Wickramasinghe continued to search the heavens for signs of life. Their exploration produced evidence for very complex organic molecules in interstellar dust. These they took as confirmation of the existence of the "seeds of life" in the cosmos. This unorthodox view is accepted by very few in the scientific community. However unpopular their views, their explanations are grounded in science and based on unbroken natural law. The concept might have confirmation with evidence of Martian life from ALH-84001 (the Martian meteorite[60]). Sampling debris trails from comets, and capturing extraterrestrial microbial spores in the upper atmosphere might be an appropriate test of Panspermia. By and large, their theory is not accepted because alternate explanations can be offered without begging the question of how life began. In light of the available evidence, "somewhere else" is just not very satisfying as an answer.

INTELLIGENT DESIGN AND A SEARCH FOR ANSWERS

The origin of life ... is maintained to be an event that transcends the laws of chemistry and physics.-Donald England

Another point of view is that life arose as a creative act of an intelligent designer. This is the premise of "Creation Science", now called Intelligent Design, a religious viewpoint that is cloaked in the mantle of science[61]. The Creation Scientists, however, cannot propose theories that can be tested in such a way as to reject their fundamental theory. This is its essential flaw. "Creation Scientists" bring out problems with various mechanistic scenarios such as the complexity problem, the problem with the likelihood of spontaneous assembly of life, etc. These are legitimate questions when taken this far. However, to offer Intelligent Design as the only possible alternative is, at best, dishonest.

One objection that seems particularly compelling is the seeming violation of the second law of thermodynamics, an accepted law of physics. Surely, the violation of a law of physics would make mechanistic origin of life scenarios non-scientific. In fact, the second law, sometimes called entropy, says that disorder increases in closed systems. However, life is not a closed system. Indeed, the Earth is not a closed system. Energy flows through this system which provides the "force" to assemble macromolecules. That is why all origin of life scenarios are very careful about detailing the sources of energy and the types of energy gradients. Thus, to invoke the violation of the second law of thermodynamics as an explanation for why mechanistic origin of life scenarios could not happen is intellectually dishonest.

Why, although I received my college training in an atmosphere of "Creation Science", do I reject it? Mainly because of

---

[60] See *On a Performance of Durufle* and *Red Planets and Microbes.*

[61] Read more about Creation Science in its various guises in *A Rock, a Razor, and a Dinosaur: Models and the Appearance of Design in Nature, Pseudoscience, the Science of the Gullible*, and *Nature's Bounty.*

what Don England said at the beginning of this section. He said that the origin of life was an "event that transcends the laws of chemistry and physics." Science operates by attaching explanations to unbroken sequences of natural law, particularly the laws of chemistry and physics. That is the most fundamental tenet of science. By saying that his explanation somehow allowed the suspension of natural law, propels it into another intellectual dimension, that of religion. However, if he insists that it is science, then he forces it into the category of pseudoscience.

What could we gain by mechanistic speculation and experimentation? In part, we can and have learned more about RNA. Our speculations, experimentations and observations have led to surprising results as to the ubiquitous nature of hydrocarbons, both on and off the world. Our search has led to the realization that three fundamental forms of life inhabit this planet. We may not know the precise steps that led to the appearance of life. Indeed, we still would not know even if we were able to put together nonliving components to form living entities. It is the search that defines science and our reward is the cornucopia of unexpected answers.

-2003

References:

Bennett, J., S. Shostak, and B. Jakosky. 2003. *Life in the Universe.* Addison Wesley. New York.

Darling, D. 2001. *Life Everywhere, The Maverick Science of Astrobiology.* Basic Books. New York.

Davies, P. 1999. *The Fifth Miracle, The Search for the Origin and Meaning of Life.* Simon and Schuster. New York.

Delsemme, Armand. 1998. *Our Cosmic Origins, From the Big Bang to the Emergence of Life and Intelligence.* Cambridge University Press. Cambridge, UK.

England, D. 1972. *A Christian View of Origins.* Baker Book House. Grand Rapids, MI.

Fox, S. and K. Dose. 1972. *Molecular Evolution and the Origin of Life.* W.H. Freeman and Co. San Francisco.

Fry, Iris. 2000. *The Emergence of Life on Earth, A Historical and Scientific Overview.* Rutgers University Press. New Brunswick, NJ.

Gold, T. 1999. *The Deep Hot Biosphere.* Copernicus. Springer-Verlag. New York.

Keosian, J. 1964. *The Origin of Life.* Reinhold Publishing Corporation. Chapman and Hall Ltd., London.

Lahav, N. 1999. *Biogenesis, Theories of Life's Origin.* Oxford University Press. New York.

Ponnamperuma, C. 1972. *The Origins of Life.* Thames and Hudson. London.

Ward, P. and D. Brownlee. 2000. *Rare Earth, Why Complex Life is Uncommon in the Universe.* Copernicus, Springer-Verlag. New York.

Zubay, G. 1996. *Origins of Life on the Earth and in the Cosmos.* Wm. C. Brown Publishers. Dubuque, IA.

> **Jacques Monod (1971):** *Life was so unlikely that its a priori probability was virtually zero.*
>
> **Manfred Eigen (1971):** *The origin of life was inevitable based on appropriate conditions and laws of physics.*

Questions to Think About

1. What is the Oparin-Haldane Hypothesis?

2. Who produced the first experimental evidence to support the Oparin-Haldane Hypothesis?

3. What was the great bombardment? What implications might it have for an emergence of life scenarios?

4. What is meant by the last common ancestor?

5. Why are comets now considered sources of hydrocarbons for the early earth?

6. Who is Thomas Gold? What is his view of the earth's biosphere? How might this have implications for our search for life elsewhere?

7. What is the RNA World? Who first proposed such a thing?

8. What is meant by panspermia? What evidence exists for it?

9. What is wrong with the "Creation Science" fundamental assumption as expressed by Don England?

LANGUAGE, A NURTURE OF NATURE

EXPRESSIONS

The movements of expression in the face and body, whatever their origins may have been, are in themselves of much importance for our welfare.

-Charles R. Darwin (1872)

Last night I went home and just tried an experiment. I turned on the television but turned off the sound and tried to see how much I could understand in communication without words. The news reporters had fairly deadpan expressions as they attempted to inform their audience about floods, crimes, etc. Ahem. Others, like talk show hosts were very expressive, almost like caricatures of people speaking. Their eyes opened too wide, they grinned too wide. If they had been observed outside of that setting, they might have been considered deranged.

The subtle communication that we are capable of through our expressions is quite amazing. We can tell the general emotional state of someone just by observing all but the most poker-faced individuals. This is the kind of experiment that I do almost every day as a teacher. It is not hard to tell when students are interested and engaged with the topic. It is also very obvious when they are not (even when their heads don't fall onto their desktops). Their glassy eyes, distant stares, and great expressive yawns are dead giveaways that I have lost them.

I did that experiment as a consequence of reading a republication of Darwin's *The Expression of the Emotions in Man and Animals* (1872). [For perspective, Darwin published *The Origin* in 1859 and *The Descent of Man* in 1871. He died in 1882.] In this book,

Darwin attempted to show that human expression is a trait and further demonstrates our connection with the rest of life, particularly the other animals. The arguments begin by considering the expressions of emotions in animals such as dogs and cats. All I need to do is look at Figure 6-73, illustrations from Darwin's expressions book, and I know the emotional states of the dogs that are depicted. Darwin called expressions such as these, "the language of the emotions."

FIGURE 6-72. Expressions of interest, wonder, and caution (the bird).

Chimpanzees and other primates have an array of elaborate behaviors that include a battery of expressions of emotions. Darwin considered their expressions, especially their expressions of anger, in a chapter called "Special Expressions of Animals". Darwin described the response of the chimpanzee (illustrated in Figure 6-74) in this way:

The accompanying drawing represents a chimpanzee made sulky by an orange having been offered him, and then taken away. A similar protrusion or

pouting of the lips, though to a much slighter degree, may be seen in sulky children.

FIGURE 6-73. Illustrations from Darwin's Expressions book. It is quite easy to discern the emotional states of the dogs.

FIGURE 6-74. A chimpanzee disappointed and sulky (from Darwin's Expressions).

Darwin then devoted the rest of the book to human expressions. He described observations of expressions of suffering, hatred, disgust, surprise, etc. In all, he discussed the expression of nearly 40 emotional states and expressions (generally facial expressions) that accompany those states.

THE THIRD CHIMPANZEE

The chimpanzees, not the gorilla, are our closest relatives. Put another way, the chimpanzees' closest relative is not the gorilla but humans.

-Jared Diamond (1992)

Not only are chimpanzees expressive in ways that are similar to humans, but they appear to be our nearest living relatives. Molecular Biology has provided an array of powerful tools with which to study life. Evolutionary biology predicts that those species that are more closely related would share the greatest amount of DNA. That is indeed true of the human and the chimpanzee. In fact, Chimpanzees share 99% of their DNA with humans. That is the largest overlap in DNA that we have with any other species on earth. The interpretation is that Chimpanzees are a sibling species with whom we share a common ancestor. Without knowing of DNA and its importance, Darwin assumed as much because details of anatomy and physiology suggested the same things.

Faced with this evidence and an array of fossils, biologists, anthropologists, and psychologists have struggled with the question of what makes humans unique. Or, what are the characteristics that define our species. It seems that the torso of humans is quite similar to that of the apes. However, both ends (pelvis down and neck up) exhibit considerable change from the typical ape body plan.

Anatomically, the most obvious difference is that humans have a shallow pelvis and walk upright. Although the apes can do this for a short distance, they tire easily. Mostly, this is because the *Gluteus maximus* (the large muscles that form the curvature of our bottoms) are relatively small and attached to their elongate pelvis such that walking upright is mechanically difficult. Thus, much of their locomotion on the ground is by brachiation (knuckle walking).

An upright stride seems to be one of the first things that developed after the hominid line (our line) separated from the apes. An astonishing discovery by Mary Leaky at Laetoli in Kenya was three sets of footprints that had been made in volcanic ash after it had been wet by drizzle. Because volcanic material is relatively easy to date, she found that the tracks had been made about 3.6-3.8 million years ago. The astonishing part of the discovery is that the stride (though relatively small) was made by an upright, human-like gait. Fossils suggest the same thing. Very early, our line evolved a fairly human-like pelvis and legs. Therefore, the upright gait would appear to be the most fundamentally different characteristic that the hominid line possesses.

Obviously, there are other anatomical differences, but they seem to be there by degree. That is, we have less hair, a relatively larger head, smaller face, and smaller teeth (particularly canines) than the chimpanzees. However, as a fetus, a developing chimp looks just like us. This difference can be seen even in monkeys. Consider adult and baby baboons. The adult has an elongate, dog-like muzzle while the baby has a flattened, almost human face. These types of observations confirm the theory that in our lineage, development became arrested at more fetal stages. For example, the skulls of fetal chimps and humans are not very different. However, during growth and development, the face of the adult chimpanzee becomes much more elongate than the human face which deviates little from the fetal plan. In addition, humans became mature (stopped developing) before adult ape hair patterns, dentition, and elongate facial features appeared. We became a Peter Pan species, the chimpanzee that never grew up.

Still, most of the anatomical features seem to be characteristic of our whole line from the australopithecines to humans. The form of the body was ours, but the brain still remained like that of any other chimpanzee until a rapid increase in brain size began with the members of our own genus, *Homo*. What could have fostered that change? The opposable thumb? The upright stance? I suspect that they may have been part of the story, but only part of it. I suspect that our culture and technology followed another great set of changes that led to our increased ability to communicate. Those changes that involved facial expressions and the vocal apparatus in turn led to more sophisticated control by the brain.

BIOLOGY OF LANGUAGE

The language that each person acquires is a rich and complex construction hopelessly underdetermined by the fragmentary evidence available to the child. -Noam Chomsky

A large battery of facial muscles controls facial expressions, and they emerge through the interactions of the muscles. A human face has muscles that control the shape of the mouth and eyes as well as how the nostrils flare and the fore head wrinkles. Figure 6-75 shows an illustration of facial musculature that Darwin included in his book. Note the concentration of muscles around the eyes and mouth.

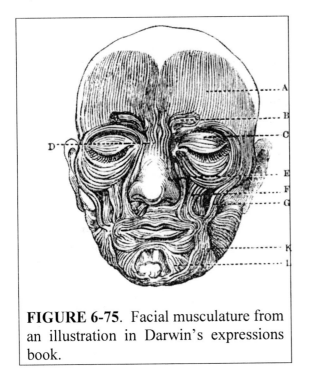

FIGURE 6-75. Facial musculature from an illustration in Darwin's expressions book.

Also, we are a noisy, communicating species. Although chimpanzees can make sounds, their range of sounds is limited. This is mainly due to the placement of the larynx, the organ that lies on top of the trachea (wind pipe) and contains the vocal cords. Humans have a trachea that lies well down in the throat. The resonating chamber in which the vibrating vocal cords can produce sound is, therefore, quite large. Chimpanzees, on the other hand, have their larynx at the back of the mouth, way up in their throats. So, their range of potential sound is quite limited.

The placement of our larynx does not come without its cost. Chimps and other apes can drink and breathe at the same time, something that I would not recommend anyone who is reading this

to try. It seems that vocalization is so important to our species that we evolved a mechanism that puts us at risk of choking every time we sit down to a meal. That and our puny teeth require that we soften most of our food by cooking it.

The tradeoff is well worth it. We can make a rich array of sound filled with subtleties and majesty when we sing (as I had the pleasure of doing recently when I sang R. V. Williams' *Dona Nobis Pacem*), or just rattle away in empty conversation. We are a communicating species.

Noam Chomsky and others in the study of language, see evidence that general linguistic rules are universal. That is, there are no mute groups of humans and all human languages seem to possess fundamental similarities.

Also, evidence suggests that children are born with the ability to learn a language, not a particular language. Infants begin by babbling and then acquire rules to the language that they hear such that they can construct novel sentences out of words that they have learned. The particular steps in the acquisition of language are objects of current study. Steven Pinker points out that children in their 3rd year who are acquiring English learn:

- Verbs end in –s in some sentences and are bare-ended in others.
- To search for grammatical causes of this situation.
- To make verbs agree in tense, aspect, number, and person.

They do this without being told or drilled or tested. Also, this applies to 3 year olds who are learning English regardless of whether their parents speak English, as a first or second language.

If fundamental rules of language acquisition are instinctive, then they must be controlled by particular parts of the brain. These areas would have to work in concert with portions of the brain that control the motor coordination of the tongue, larynx, and lips as well as regions in that store vocabulary and memory. Stroke victims show that areas such as Broca's area and the region where the parietal, occipital and temporal lobes come together are all important in language[62]. Damage to one or more of those areas leave the victim, who could once communicate quite well, impaired in speech or communicating ability. There is further evidence that certain speech/linguistic disorders occur in families and are inherited like any other genetic trait.

This view of language is not entirely comfortable for many who believe that language is cultural and is nurtured by the culture in which it is embedded. By culture, I mean the collection of traits or characteristics of a group of people. That is, in a cultural view, language is learned from others. In essence, this is the question about the differences between mind and body, sometimes called nature versus nurture.

The study of linguistics shows that the nature-nurture debate is an empty dichotomy. Genetics (nature) provides for the anatomy and physiology necessary for communication while culture provides for the particular linguistic rules and vocabulary. This is all built upon and supported by an impressive array of expressions.

Although humans have developed impressive abilities in communication, we are not entirely alone. Other apes, particularly chimpanzees, have been taught to communicate with humans. Although chimps and gorillas do not have the anatomy that allows them to vocalize human speech, they have learned sign languages or other symbolic languages. Some like the chimpanzee called Washoe can do much more than mimic sentences and can put words together in novel ways using the American Sign Language.

TIME MACHINE[63]

Man not only uses inarticulate cries, gestures and expressions, but has invented articulate language; if, indeed, the word invented can be applied to a process , completed by innumerable steps, half-consciously made.

-Charles Darwin (1872)

Does the ability of chimpanzees to communicate with us by a human language diminish us in any way? Of course not. Like most of our differences, we differ from the chimpanzees by degrees. We have converted our language to symbols that can be read and understood by others. This invention, written language, is without doubt the greatest achievement of our species. Written language allows me to speak to you now and forty years from now.

In a way, written language is a time machine. I can read the words of Darwin and discuss them with the words of Chomsky in my mind. In fact, in that way, I had a discussion with my father last week as I read a brief letter that he wrote before he died in1986.

We read and then write to contribute to and participate in the great discussion of humanity. That is why I stress writing so much in my courses. Of course, all writing is not good, most of it is trivial, some is downright evil. But as

---

[62] See *Evidence and Einstein's Brain* for more information about the major regions of the human brain.

[63] I expand on human evolution and human communication in *Our Great Leap Forward*.

a species, we have nurtured our nature to preserve some of the most moving and substantial thoughts created by humanity in the form of written language.

1998, revised 2003

References:

Cartmill, Matt. 1998. *The Gift of Gab.* Discover. 19(11): 56-64.

Darwin, Charles. 1998 (1872). *The Expression of the Emotions In man and Animals.* 3rd edition with an Introduction, Afterword and Commentaries by Paul Ekman. Oxford University Press. Oxford.

Diamond, Jared. 1992. *The Third Chimpanzee.* HarperCollins. New York.

Fouts, Roger. 1997. *Next of Kin, What Chimpanzees Have Taught Me About Who We Are.* William Morrow and Co., Inc. New York.

Johanson, Donald and Maitland Edy. 1981. *Lucy, The Beginnings of Humankind.* Warner Books. New York.

Johanson, Donald, Lenora Johanson, and Blake Edgar. 1994. *Ancestors, In Search of Human Origins.* Villard Books. New York.

Kurten, Bjorn. 1993. *Our Earliest Ancestors.* Trans. Erik J. Friis. Columbia University Press. New York.

Lumsden, Charles J. and Edward O. Wilson. 1983. *Promethean Fire, Reflections on the Origin of Mind.* Harvard University press.

Mayr, Ernst. 1997. *This is Biology, The Science of the Living World.* The Belknap Press of the Harvard University Press. Cambridge, Mass.

Pinker, Steven. 1994. *The Language Instinct, How the Mind Creates Language.* HarperPerennial. New York.

Questions to Think About

1. What was is the focus of Darwin's "Expressions" book?

2. Who is Washoe? Why is she of interest to scientists?

3. What allows the human face to be so expressive?

4. What evidences do evolutionary biologists use to conclude that chimpanzees are our nearest living relatives?

5. Why are humans able to stand upright?

6. What evidence suggests that the Hominid line has stood upright for at least 4 million years?

7. Why can a chimpanzee drink and breathe at the same time?

8. What evidence suggests that language is instinctive?

9. How does culture influence language?

10. How does written language function as a time machine?

OUR GREAT LEAP FORWARD

OUR CULTURE

I cannot imagine life without art, music, dance, speech, and books. These all are means of communication and what I consider to be the currency of culture. As I argued in *Language: A Nurture of Nature,* language in all of its forms has a genetic component as well as a learned component. On the genetic scaffold, fundamental rules of grammar are hung as we learn to talk and understand those who speak around us. Jared Diamond and others call the change to symbolic communication by our ancestors The Great Leap Forward. It appears unmistakably in the fossil record around 40,000 or more years ago and is a profound change in our lineage. The real problem in interpreting the leap and what caused it is that structurally modern humans appear thousands of years earlier than the cultural change. What really caused the changes and what led to the explosion in human culture?

OUR PREDECESSORS

Humans are not proud of their ancestors and never invite them round to dinner.
—Douglas Adams

The line that gave rise to humanity likely did possess rudimentary means of vocal communication. The chimpanzees, other apes, and monkeys all use vocalizations to varying degrees. These are useful in communicating information that is important for the safety and organization of the social group. There is no compelling reason to assume that our extinct ancestors were any different. Our line split from that of the chimpanzees about 7 million years ago (between 6 and 8 million years ago; see Figure 6-76).

Geological evidence suggests that about 6 million years ago, the time of the separation of the chimpanzee line and the hominid line, Africa experienced a sustained, drier climate. The period was dry enough that the Mediterranean basin, then completely land-locked, dried up. Similarly, the large expanses of African forest retreated to smaller relict patches. Savannah, a biome that has scattered trees in open grassland, replaced forests. In such an environment, a more upright stance and locomotion would have been favored. Studies of the energy expenditure of the knuckle-walking of chimps and other apes show that they are not as efficient when moving over open areas as the bipedal walking of our lineage. Also, the open grassland posed the problem of heat. An upright body presented a smaller cross-section to the tropical sun than the inclined body of a chimpanzee. Likewise, a body in the open sun would more likely be under heat stress. Thus, the loss of excess body hair allowed more efficient cooling. A behavioral advantage of bipedal locomotion allowed the transport of food back to a common location. This could have been important especially if the pairs bonded for life. The savannah then imposed selective pressures that were different that those experienced by the forest apes. There, the apes quickly evolved upright stance, bipedal gait, and loss of hair.

Following the split from the chimpanzees, our line was represented by two major genera, *Australopithicus* (literally means "southern ape") and *Homo* (the Latin word for man). The australopithecines stood upright and walked by a bipedal gait. However, they seem to have been partly arboreal which is seen in their relatively longer arms. Otherwise, they looked like smaller versions of us except that they had a larger face and a chimpanzee-sized brain with a brain volume of 450-550ml.

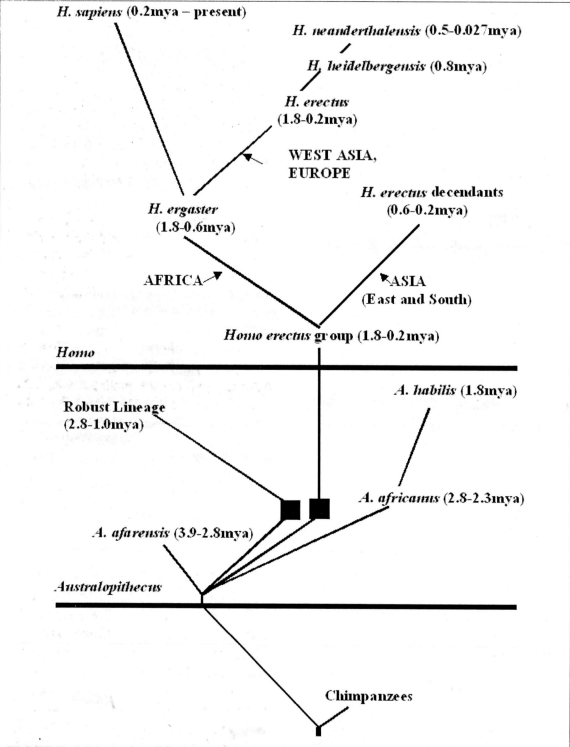

FIGURE 6-76. A simplified version of the hominid "family tree". The boxes represent member of an allospecies related to (and including) *Australopithecus africanus*. A second allospecies is the erectus group of species. Approximate time in the fossil record is given in parentheses.

The australopithicines remained in Africa and diversified into a number of different species. One line gave rise to a robust line of several species. These stood upright and had a very stocky build. Their skulls and teeth, however show the same kinds of adaptations that we see in gorillas today. They had large molars and a crest of bone on the top of the skull that allowed for the attachment of large jaw muscles. Like the gorilla they seem to have become adapted to eating large volumes of poor-quality food. One of these species, *Australopithecus boisei* (see Figure 6-77) persisted in the fossil record to within a million years of the present.

Almost certainly our line (as well as the robust australopithecines) came from a generalist, variable, and widespread "species" that ranged over much of Africa between about three to less than 2 million years ago. Technically, this group was an allospecies, or a widespread but separate set of closely related species that likely could interbreed. The most well-known member of this group was *Australopithecus africanus* (see Figure 6-77), a hominid that stood about 1-1.5 meters tall and had the head of a chimpanzee (400-500ml brain volume and somewhat elongate face.). They seem to have used and fashioned simple tools and lived in small social groups. In fact, this seems to be the case of all of our near relatives, extant and extinct.

About 2.4 million years ago, a near human appeared with the appearance of *A. africanus* but a head that was more human. It had a smaller face and a brain volume that was almost double that of its known predecessors. Its name is disputed and is placed in either *Australopithecus* or *Homo*. Figure 6-76 refers to it as was *A. habilis* because it seems to have been a different offshoot of the australopithecine generalist line, and, therefore, a dead-end. This new "human" seemed to have greater facility with fashioning stone tools, but remained restricted to eastern Africa.

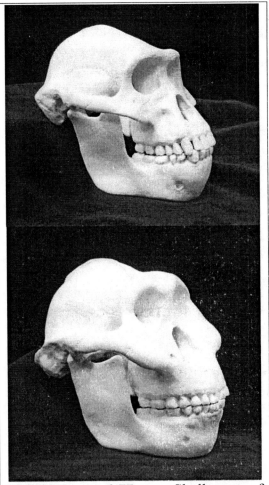

FIGURE 6-77. Skulls of *Australopithecus africanus* (top) and *A. boisei*[64] (bottom). Note the sagittal crest on the boisei skull[65].

Nearly 2 million years ago in Africa another allospecies appeared that was clearly related to us. The most well-known member was *Homo erectus*. Compared to its precursors, this group had species that were master toolmakers and had brain volumes that overlapped our own (750-1250ml). *Homo erectus* (see Figure 6-78) had a low forehead, and massive brow ridges. It was gracile

[64] The genus for the robust australopithecines has been changed to *Paranthropus*.
[65] All skulls shown in this essay are models.

628

in its appearance and ranged throughout Africa. Then, about 1.8 million years ago, it left Africa and ranged over much of warm Asia and the near east. Likely *Homo erectus* used fire and had a rudimentary form of language. Within the erectus allospecies sprang *Homo ergaster*, the species that likely gave rise to the Neanderthals and our own species.

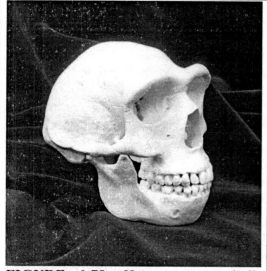

FIGURE 6-78. *Homo erectus* skull. Note the sloping forehead, heavy brow ridges, and receding chin.

Homo neanderthalensis (see Figure 6-79) and the related *Homo heidelbergensis* (both of which I will refer to as Neanderthals), first appeared in Europe and the near east around 800,000 years ago. Neanderthals likely appeared in Africa from a stock of the erectus group. They moved into the near east and on into Europe during a warm period between glaciations. Neanderthals were stocky in build and had long, low skulls that housed a brain with greater volume than most of ours. Like the erectus group, Neanderthals had pronounced brow ridges. They seem to have possessed unique structures in their large, bulbous noses which have been interpreted as adaptations to the extreme cold of ice age Europe. However, because Neanderthals seem to have evolved during a warm period, this interpretation seems very unlikely.

The occurrences of arthritic, wounded, and otherwise handicapped individualism among Neanderthal remains suggest that they possessed a culture that revered human life. Further, Neanderthal burials replete with artifacts and evidence of flowers hint at the belief of an afterlife. Clearly, they were not the brutish "caveman" beasts of popular belief. That they, a tropical species, were able to persist in Europe during one of its coldest periods, also points to their having developed a high enough level of technology to allow their survival and then to transmit that technology. However, what marked the Neanderthal technology was its persistence. Almost throughout their range, both in time and space, Neanderthal technology was almost unchanging. Neanderthals were not innovators.

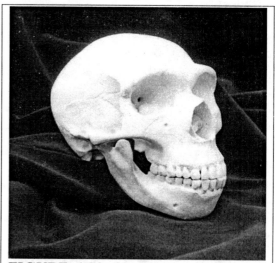

FIGURE 6-79. *Homo neanderthalensis* skull. Note the large nasal opening and sloping forehead. The brow ridges were not as pronounced as in *H. erectus*.

Neanderthals were not simply very conservative *Homo sapiens,* they were not human. That is, they were not members of our species. DNA taken from bones that had not petrified shows that they were more different from us than the diversity of all living humans today. The most cautious interpretation of those results would be that Neanderthals were a closely-related species. Were they reproductively isolated? That is, did Neanderthal genes find their way into our own species? Almost certainly they did. Several localities point to Neanderthals and our species occupying the same place at the same time. If they could have crossed, they would have left offspring. Either way, Neanderthals disappeared from the fossil record about 27,000 years ago.

An archaic form of our species seems to have appeared about 200,000 years ago (maybe up to 400,000 years ago) in Africa. By archaic, I mean that the adults had a mosaic of modern and "erectus" like features. Unfortunately, all non-Neanderthal remains from the last several hundred thousand years are lumped into the "archaic" human category. The diversity in form and the range of species, particularly through Africa suggests that we may be dealing with another allospecies. The African record certainly points to a good bit of evolutionary experimentation. The modern humans showed smaller brow ridges, higher brows, and a prominent chin.

OUT OF AFRICA AGAIN?

We may all be Africans under our skin, but we are all global villagers as well.
    —C. Stringer and R. McKie (1996).

Anatomically modern humans appeared in the Levant (Palestine) around 100,000 years ago and overlapped with the indigenous Neanderthals in that region. Surprisingly, they seem to have had the same style of stone-making technology until nearly 50,000 years ago. Then, the human stone technology diverged significantly. This marked the beginning of the displacement of Neanderthals in the Levant and ultimately through Europe. As we moved through Asia and into Australia, we likely came into contact with remnant populations of the erectus group, which, too, we displaced. By 30,000 years ago, we seem to have eliminated all other members of the hominids and for the first time since our line diverged from the chimpanzees, there was but a single species, *Homo sapiens* (see Figure 6-80).

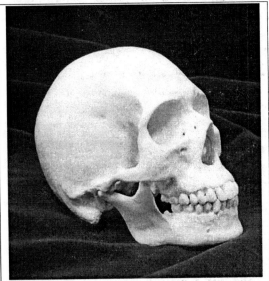

FIGURE 6-80. Skull of a modern human. Note the high forehead and that brow ridges are absent.

Where did the modern humans come from? In 1987, Rebecca Cann, Mark Stoneking, and Allan Wilson rocked the world when they reported the results of a study that compared DNA from 147 people from five different geographic populations. In particular, they compared the DNA sequences that occur in mitochondria, organelles that occur in all of our cells. What they found was that differences in the mitochondrial DNA (mtDNA) could best be explained if it originated in Africa and repeatedly invaded the outlying regions. Also, because mtDNA likely changes slowly and steadily (a concept called a molecular clock), the time of the "original" modern human mitochondrion should be about 200,000 years ago in Africa. Because the mitochondrion is inherited mother to child (the father contributes essentially no mitochondria to the child), the first modern human was dubbed "Mitochondrial Eve". In truth, Eve likely represented a small breeding population of 5,000 individuals that eked out a living in eastern Africa. The molecular clock also suggested ages of origin (presumably appearance) for individuals from the other geographic areas (see Table 1).

TABLE 6-5. Average age (in thousands) based on a molecular clock calibrated to a 2-4% divergence per million years. Note how these dates correlate with the movement indicated on Figure 6-81.

Geographic Region	Average Age
Africa	90-180
Asia	53-105
Australia	43-85
Europe	23-45
New Guinea	28-55

The concept of a late African exodus was met with a good bit of skepticism by some archeologists, namely Alan Thorne and Milford Wolpoff who claimed that the fossils and artifacts point to a much older origin. They claimed that evidence nearly 1 million years old suggests modern humans appeared separately in different regions after a much older (and much less frenetic) departure from Africa. Thus, in their view, modern humans appeared gradually in Asia, Australia, and Europe as well as in Africa. They called this the "Multiregional" origin hypothesis. In this theory, Neanderthals gradually changed to modern humans.

Then in 1998 Stephen Ambrose produced a synthesis of information that considered the influence of climate once again on our history. About 73,000 years ago, Mount Toba in Indonesia exploded with the greatest force of any eruption over the past several hundred thousand years. It coincided with one of the coldest periods of the past 100,000 years. Computer models suggest that the dust and aerosols flung aloft by such an explosion would have plunged the earth into an almost continuous winter for up to 6 years. The cooling effects might not have dissipated for another thousand years. Such a catastrophe likely eliminated the remnant erectus populations and reduced the Neanderthals. Also, it likely eliminated most of *Homo sapiens* and restricted the survivors to the tropics, Africa. Genetic studies imply that our species may have been reduced to as few as 3,000-10,000 individuals sometime before 60,000 years ago. If our species experienced such a "bottleneck", rapid changes in form could have occurred in the geological blink of an eye. Then the great human Diaspora began around 50,000 to 40,000 years ago. The "new human" not only had a new form, but a new way of thinking. We had experienced *The Great Leap Forward*.

THE GREAT LEAP

I've argued that we were fully modern in anatomy and behavior and language by forty thousand years ago, and that a Cro-Magnon could have been taught to fly a jet airplane. -Jared Diamond (1992)

That we changed physically, does not explain what happened around 40,000 to cause the great leap forward. Anatomically modern humans had been around for at least 200,000 years before the "awakening". What took them so long to develop modern behaviors?

Old ideas about the leap had to do with tool use. The litany went something like this. We developed bipedal locomotion, which freed up our

631

hands. The free hands then began to make tools. At first, those tools were primitive and then tool use began to allow for the selection of larger brains to make better tools, etc. It is an interesting story, and it is completely wrong. If bipedal locomotion gave rise to bigger brains, why did the brain size of the australopithecines remain about the same size as a chimpanzee? Why did the brain volume of the non-innovative Neanderthals exceed that of our own? Finally, why did the innovation so characteristic of our species appear after two-thirds of our current tenure on Earth? Tool usage may have played a part in the leap forward, but the answer must be far more subtle and wonderful than tool manufacture.

The awakening of humanity seems to be tied to innovations in culture, and since language is the currency of culture, I would consider the leap to be tied to our ability to communicate. Certainly, we did communicate before the leap. In fact, all primates communicate to a certain degree. However, what Diamond and others have argued is that some structural change, a change in soft tissue that would not necessarily show up in the fossil record appeared sometime before 40,000 years ago. Then, selective pressure provided by culture helped to project language to its modern complexity.

Let me back up and consider culture and its influence. Attributes that are considered good or beautiful would tend to persist in a group. Language allows us to transmit and implant those ideas from one mind to another. That is what Richard Dawkins referred to as thought viruses or memes when he said, *A meme is ... anything that infects itself from brain to brain* (Dawkins. 1998. *Unweaving the Rainbow*). We see the action of memes at work constantly. We infect each other with ideas and set phrases. For example, I remember when the phrase "yada, yada, yada", would have no meaning at all. Now, most of us steeped in western culture have a similar understanding of its meaning and the proper context for its use.

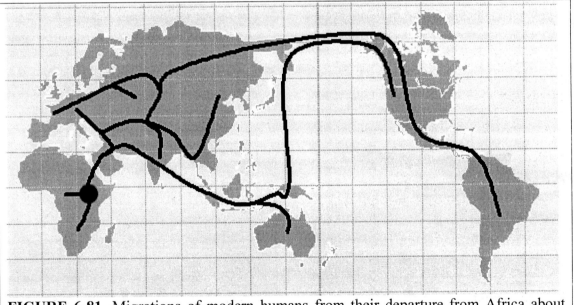

FIGURE 6-81. Migrations of modern humans from their departure from Africa about 50,000 years ago to their arrival in Eurasia, Australia, and the Americas. Adapted from National Geographic Magazine.

Proverbial language works the same way. If I were to use the phrase, "An apple a day", you would complete it with "keeps the doctor away" in your mind and apply the appropriate meaning to the situation according to the context. Nowhere is such culture-laden communication greater than in humor and what we think is amusing.

If concepts of beauty can be verbalized and then transmitted, its effects can be felt through the "infected" population like a wildfire. Then, if the concept of beauty also influences mating, the change in body form can be dramatic and rapid. That is exactly what Darwin meant when he used the phrase "sexual selection" in his *Descent of Man*. That mechanism was for him the driving force of human evolution. It still seems to be the most plausible explanation.

For example, if dark skin and wavy hair became codified and tramsmitted within a culture as a particular paragon of beauty, then they would be the most likely to mate and have children. Thus, in very few generations, a concept of beauty could become manifest in the appearance of the population at large. Curiously, such characteristics as skin color and hair texture serve to define the "races" today. That a small population about 60,000 years ago gave rise to the present diversity of human "races" is a testament to the power of memes.

The first clear signal that human behavior had changed was a modification in stone tool design in the Levant. Then, symbolic sculpture and cave art began to appear in Germany, Southern France, and Spain. This was the Cro-Magnon culture that produced amazing treasures of carvings in ivory and paintings on the walls of caves. The earliest art that we have dates back to 32,000 years as in the cave of Chauvet (more than 300 animal and abstract images). The more well-known cave images from Lascaux were produced 18,000 years ago.

The innovations in tool design and the appearance of art are likely the tip of the iceberg of what was actually produced. We have no clothing or items fashioned from more ephemeral materials like wood. Almost certainly major advances in spoken language (the most ephemeral of all possible art forms) preceded symbolic art.

New views of the appearance of language suggest that music and spoken language had the same origin and simply rest at opposite ends of a continuum of sonic communication. Steven Brown called the protolanguage musilanguage (see Figure 6-82). He suggested the relationship can be seen in similarities between music and language:

- Both employ phrasing.
- Both use a limited number of standardized sounds from an infinite number of potential elements.
- Both can generate higher order structures.

The musilanguage hypothesis implies that communication early in our line was ritualized and rhythmic as it seems to be in other apes today. The phrasing of spoken language and music both point to that. Also, given the unending number of possible sounds, we speak and sing relatively few of them. Even more compelling to me is the remarkable adaptation for singing that appears in our species. The range of sounds (a topic that I discussed in *Language, A Nurture of Nature*) that we make is enormous compared to all other primates and, as Darwin noted, is "more like bird song". The singing instinct also seems manifest in our response to rhythm. We can generate rhythmic sounds and vary the tempo, many other species do that though. We are the only animal that responds to external rhythm (rhythms made by devices other than the voice). Such response can be seen in dance, which is music made visible through motion. Music and dance, therefore are communicative, but they communicate in an emotive mode. As such, the communication might be powerful, but not precise.

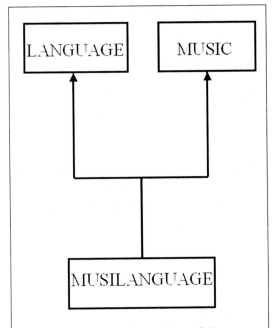

FIGURE 6-82. The origin of language and music from a more primitive "musilanguage". Adopted from Steven Brown (2001)

Consider the song, *My Country Tis of Thee.* If it is played here in the US, the listener might get patriotic feelings. If the same tune is played in the UK, the listener might feel the same degree of patriotism, but for a different reason. In Britain, that song is the English National Anthem, and it is called, *God Save the Queen.*

Spoken language, however, communicates with precision and allows the transmission of precise commands, instructions, and precise high level thought. Again, consider the example of the patriotic song. If words are used, they become part of the music, but convey a level of precise communication that identifies whether you mean *Of thee I sing* or *God save the Queen.*

Precision of meaning would have been very important in a social setting. It would have allowed much more than the transmission of ritualized commands. It would have allowed for versatility of communication and subtle differences in meaning that human language now has.

Poetry occupies a middle ground with emotive and precise components, almost in equal doses. Also, it often is spoken in cadence or rhythm. Contemplate Shakespeare's poetic rendering of the speech that Henry V gave to his men before the battle of Agincourt.

> *We few, we happy few, we band of brothers;*
> *For he to-day who shed his blood with me*
> *Shall be my brother; be he ne'er so vile,*
> *This day shall gentle his condition:*
> *And gentlemen in England now a-bed*
> *Shall think themselves accursed they were not here,*
> *And hold their manhoods cheap whiles any speaks*
> *That fought with us on Saint Crispin's day.*

-Shakespeare; Henry V; Act IV, iii

I cannot read those words and not be moved, even though I have heard them many times. I know that the historical accuracy of the play is minimal, but that does not matter. The sheer beauty of the language and the words used in the construction transcend that "problem".

In part, I am moved and see beauty because I have been acculturated to it.

As levels and layers of communication develop and the facility to communicate (music to language) is valued by a social group, Darwin's sexual selection will come to play. In this case, then, a witty speaker or an exquisite singer would have a better chance to find a mate and leave offspring. Thus, natural selection would quickly push the development of communication in all of its forms. It is this richness of transmitting ideas with emotion and precision that defines our humanity and permits me to contemplate my own origins at the same time that I listen to Mozart's Turkish Concerto.

Thus, each day is a celebration of our humanity as we interact with one another wearing bodies that were fashioned in Africa long before the last Ice Age and emotional structures that are suited to small bands as we wind our way through a global village of over 6 billion people. Our communication and the culture that it transmits refashion us and prepare us to meet challenges, understand nature and one another, and to express, and understand, and question goodness and beauty.

-December 2003

References:

Ambrose, Steven. 1998. *Late Pleistocene Human Population Bottlenecks, Volcanic Winter, and Differentiation of Modern Humans.* Journal of Human Evolution. 34(6):623-651.

Brown, Steven. 2001. *The "Musilanguage" Model of Music Evolution.* In: Nils Wallin, Bjorn Merker, and Steven Brown, eds. *The Origins of Music.* The MIT Press. Cambridge, Mass. Pp. 271-300.

Cann, Rebecca, Mark Stoneking, and Allan Wilson. 1987. *Mitochondrial DNA and Human Evolution.* Nature. 325:31-36.

Cavalli-Sforza, Luigi L. 2000. *Genes, Peoples, and Languages.* North Point Press. New York.

Dawkins, Richard. 1998. *Unweaving the Rainbow.* Houghton Mifflin Co. New York.

Darwin, Charles. 1873 (originally 1871). *The Descent of Man, and Selection in Relation to Sex.* D. Appleton and Co. New York.

Darwin, Charles. 1998 (1872). *The Expression of the Emotions in Man and Animals.* 3rd ed. With an introduction, afterward, and commentaries by Paul Ekman. Oxford University Press. Oxford.

Diamond, Jared. 1992. *The Third Chimpanzee.* HarperCollins. New York.

Diamond, Jared. 1997. *Guns, Germs, and Steel.* W.W. Norton and Co. New York.

Fouts, Roger. 1997. *Next of Kin, What Chimpanzees Have Taught Me About Who We Are.* William Morrow and Co., Inc. New York.

Hunt, Kevin. 1996. *The Postural Feeding Hypothesis: An Ecological Model for the Evolution of Bipedalism.* Sout African Journal of Science. 92:77-90.

Johanson, Donald, Lenora Johanson, and Blake Edgar. 1994. *Ancestors, In Search of Human Origins.* Villard Books. New York.

Kurten, Bjorn. 1993. *Our Earliest Ancestors.* Trans. Erik J. Friis. Columbia University Press. New York.

Lumsden, Charles J. and Edward O. Wilson. 1983. *Promethean Fire, Reflections on the Origin of Mind.* Harvard University Press.

Mayr, Ernst. 2001. *What Evolution Is.* Basic Books. New York.

Ovchinnikov, Igor, A. Gotherstrom, G.P. Romonaval, V.M. Kharitonov, K.

Liden, and W. Goodwin. 2000. *Molecular Analysis of Neanderthal DNA from the Northern Caucasus.* Nature. 404:490-493.

Pinker, Steven. 1994. *The Language Instinct, How the Mind Creates Language.* HarperPerennial. New York.

Rampino, Michael and Stanley Ambrose. 2000. *Volcanic Winter in the Garden of Eden: The Toba Supereruption and the Late Pleistocene Human Population Crash.* In: McCoy, F.W. and G. Heiken, eds. *Volcanic Hazards and Disasters in Human Antiquity.* Geological Society of America Special Paper 345: 71-82.

Stringer, Christopher. 1995. *The Evolution and Distribution of Later Pleistocene Human Populations.* In: Vrba, E., et al., eds. *Paleoclimate and Evolution, With Emphasis on Human Origins.* Yale University Press. New Haven.

Stringer, Christopher and Robin McKie. 1997. *African Exodus, The Origins of Modern Humanity.* Henry Holt and Co. New York.

Tattersall, Ian and Jeffrey Schwartz. 2000. *Extinct Humans.* Westview Press. Boulder, CO.

Thorne, Alan G. and Milford H. Wolpoff. 1992. *The Multiregional Evolution of Humans.* Scientific American. 266:76-83.

Vrba, Elisabeth. 1995. *On the Connections Between Paleoclimate and Evolution.* In: Vrba, E., et al., eds. *Paleoclimate and Evolution, With Emphasis on Human Origins.* Yale University Press. New Haven.

Wheeler, P.E. 1991. *The Thermoregulatory Advantages of Hominid Bipedalism in Open Equatorial Environments: The Contribution of Increased Convective Heat Loss and Cutaneous Evaporative Cooling.* Journal of Human Evolution. 21:107-115.

Questions to Think About

1. What is meant by the *Great Leap Forward*?

2. About how much time separates our line from the other apes?

3. What are some advantages to walking upright in a savannah?

4. What is an allospecies? Give an example of one in our line. What does an allospecies mean in terms of evolution?

5. What are some characters of *Homo erectus* that served it in its exodus from Africa?

6. Why can we now say that Neanderthals were not humans (at least not members of our species)?

7. What evidence suggests that our species originated in Africa?

8. Other than speech, what are the forms of language that our species employs?

9. What is the musilanguage hypothesis?

10. What does understanding of our origins have to say about our interactions in a global village?

KINGDOMS

AN EPIPHANY

Then all at once I see it and I know at once what it is: epiphany.

       -James Joyce (*Stephen Hero*)

One time while looking through a microscope at some amazing things, Lois Pfiester[66] watched a cell creep along the outside of an algal filament. Those of us in the lab watched it as it perched itself on the filament and then "sucked" the contents into itself, leaving an empty cell wall with a small round hole in it. After we had watched it for some time, the professor looked up from her microscope and said, almost as an epiphany that these things were not plants, but protists.

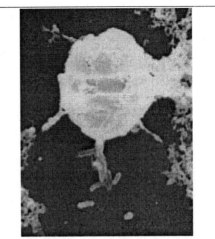

FIGURE 6-84. A dinoflagellate taken with a Scanning Electron Microscope. It has attached to a surface and is feeding on bacteria there (an animal-like characteristic)[67].

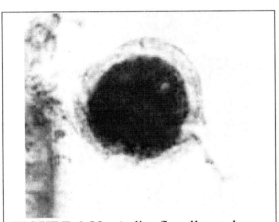

FIGURE 6-83. A dinoflagellate taken with a light microscope. The cell has a wall-like armor around it and is photosynthetic (both plant-like characteristics). The squiggly line that trails off to the lower right is a flagellum, a whip-like structure that allows the cell to move (an animal-like characteristic).

That is exactly the problem that I had been wrestling with since I had begun graduate school in 1973. I had studied a group of organisms called dinoflagellates in the Department of Zoology at the University of Oklahoma. There, they were called animals in a group of lower animals called the protozoa because they swim. By 1976 I had moved over to the Department of Botany and Microbiology at the same university where dinoflagellates were algae, a group of lower plants because they were photosynthetic and had a cell wall (see Figure 6-83). Later, I worked on a species that was photosynthetic and swam in the plankton during the day, but at night, it attached to a substrate and fed on bacteria (see Figure 6-84). Thus, dinoflagellates seemed to be neither plants nor animals but protists, a term that denoted things that generally were single-

---

[66] Consult my essays *Killer Algae* and *Night Lights* for more about Lois Pfiester and descriptions of dinoflagellates.

[67] Note the detail in the photomicrographs between Figures 6-82 and 6-83. Read *Under the Microscope* to find the reason for differences in resolution between light and electron microscopy.

celled and included a variety of organisms. Some were claimed by Botanists, some by Zoologists and some by Mycologists (those who study fungi). In the Protists, however, terms like higher and lower made no sense. Indeed, where did such terms come from?

CLIMBING THE LADDER

There is observed a continuous scale of ascent toward the animal.

-Aristotle of Stagira

Ask most people about the different kinds of living things and they will probably answer Plants and Animals. In many large institutions such as the University of Oklahoma where Lois Pfiester taught, Biology is divided into Botany (plants) and Zoology (animals). This "reasonable" differentiation is a reflection of an ages old dichotomy that was formalized by the philosopher Aristotle of Stagira (384-322 B.C.). He described a *Scala Naturae* (ladder of nature; see Figure 6-85) in which all things were ranked according to their *psyches* (roughly translated as "souls"). Rocks and other inanimate objects had no psyche, and all living things had one or more psyches. Thus, Aristotle believed in a fundamental dichotomy between life and nonlife[68]

Among living things, there was a clear hierarchy. Plants had a growing or vegetative psyche. Animals, too, had a growing psyche, but they also moved. Therefore, they had an additional or motive psyche. Humans could think, and had a rational psyche in addition to the other two. Categories within the ladder could be further subdivided so that some were higher and others lower. In such a scheme, designation of mosses as lower plants made sense, as did humans as

highest animals. In a broader sense, this way of thinking fostered the concept of separate plant and animal kingdoms. Further, it supported the notion that we, as human beings, were somehow not only higher than the animals but as different from them as plants were from animals.

MAN
monkey
QUADRAPEDS
flying squirrel
bat
ostrich
BIRDS
amphibious birds
aquatic birds
flying fish
FISH
eels and creeping fish
water serpents
REPTILES
slugs
SHELLFISH
pond mussel
lime-secreting worms
INSECTS
worms
polyp
sensitive plants
PLANTS
trees
shrubs
herbs
lichens
molds
mushrooms
truffles
STONES
stones with layers or fibers
unorganized stones
CRYSTALLINE SALTS
SEMIMETALS
MALLEABLE METALS
PURE EARTH
WATER
AIR
ETHEREAL MATTER

FIGURE 6-85. An example of a simplified *Scala Naturae* from Charles Bonnet (1764).

Aristotle characterized all groups within the *Scala Naturae* as essentially

---

[68] See *A Vital Science* for an expansion on the vitalist argument.

defined. That is, they could be defined in such a way that all members have a particular collection of characteristics. Such a collection of characteristics then defines or describes the essence of the group. Consider the following description:

> *Upright, bipedal primate; nearly hairless, with reduced dentition, opposable thumbs on forelimbs. Communicates by symbolic language.*

This definition, though cumbersome and jargony describes some characteristics that define the physical essence of our species.

Through the Medieval Period and into the Renaissance, essentialistic descriptions had degenerated into a system of seeking morals from nature. Consider the following paragraph from a 12th Century Latin Bestiary as a description of a human being:

> *Man (homo) is properly derived from Mud (humo). The Greeks called him Anthropos because, being raised from the dust, he alone among animals looks upward to the contemplation of his Maker[69].*

Such descriptions and definitions became cumbersome, unwieldy, and confusing.

Even today conveying information from one culture to another about a living thing can be very difficult. Consider how confusing it is now just to make sense of common names for creatures as familiar as the English Sparrow. In England, the same bird is called the House Sparrow. Elsewhere in Europe, the animal is called: Gorrion (Spain), Musch (Netherlands), Hussparf (Sweden) and Vorobei (Russia). This difficulty can be overcome by having rules for the unambiguous designation of a particular organism like the English Sparrow. Now, there are precise rules for taxonomy (classification) and taxonomic nomenclature (names used in classification). An International Zoological Congress has jurisdiction over names of animals like the English Sparrow which is called *Passer domesticus*, its unambiguous scientific name or Latin binomial.

A SWEDE'S KINGDOMS

To acquire knowledge of these things properly, individual specimens should be covered by a distinct idea and a distinct name, without which the copiousness of things would necessarily overwhelm us, and, in the absence of a common language, all communication will cease.

-C. Linnaeus

Carolus Linnaeus (1707-1778; originally called Karl Linne' and inventor of the Latin binomial designation) came from Sweden where the English Sparrow is called Hussparf. He had just returned from an expedition to Lapland, the largely unexplored northern region of Scandinavia, in 1732. He returned to Uppsala with the expectation that he would be greeted as a great explorer and scientist. Instead, he discovered that the Royal Society of Sweden and the University at Uppsala had little to offer him. Desperate, he set up a museum of the hundreds of specimens of plants and animals that he had collected and charged admission.

This was the first of a set of disappointments that encouraged Linnaeus to leave Sweden for a time. In the mean time, he sought to organize his collection for publication, but found that there were no useful classification systems in general use. This was when he decided to create a system that was hierarchical and unambiguous.

First, Linnaeus organized living things according to essential physical characteris-

---

[69] Translated by T.H. White (1960).

tics. For example, bats have hair and suckle their young, characteristics that make them Mammals. That they have wings and fly (live in the air) was of secondary importance. He organized flowering plants based on their floral parts as had Andreanus Cesalpino, regardless of their growth form (herb, shrub, tree).

He organized life within a hierarchical system. First, he recognized that all living things were in either the Plant or Animal kingdom. Each kingdom had many Phyla (Phylum is singular) which, in turn, had one or more Classes. There were one or more Orders within a Class and one or more Families within an Order. The Binomial (Genus and species) resides within a Family. Each level of the hierarchy had defining characteristics, and, therefore was essentialistic.

Consider the full hierarchical classification that includes our species:

Kingdom Animalia
  Phylum Chordata
    Class Mammalia
      Order Primates
        Family Hominidae
          Genus *Homo*
            species *sapiens*

The Binomial is a particularly important invention as I illustrated with the English Sparrow example. The first word of the binomial, the genus (genera is the plural), is capitalized and always is a noun. The second word, the species (species is both singular and plural), usually is in lower case and is a modifier of the Genus. The English Sparrow: *Passer domesticus*, the Human Being: *Homo sapiens*, the Red Oak: *Quercus rubra*, etc. for more than a million described species.

Linnaeus left for Holland where he took a degree in medicine and began to practice. He also took a manuscript that detailed the system that he had created. This he called *Systema Naturae* and found backers for its publication in 1735. It went through many more editions (see a page from the 10th edition in Figure 6-86). Although there was some initial opposition to Linnaeus' system, botanists found it to be quite useful and began to use it almost immediately. It was less useful for animals and met the greatest resistance from zoologists.

Systema Naturae (1735 et seq.), and *Species Plantarum* (1753) form the starting point for the modern taxonomic system. All scientific names, even binomials published before 1753 for plants and 1758 for animals are not recognized. Curiously, the innovation that led to the binomials in these books are found in the margins. Linnaeus provided sentence-long Latin names for the species. However, he annotated them with marginal *trivial names* for cataloging purposes. Those trivial names became our specific names and, coupled with the generic names, have become our useful binomials. It is the trivial names that have become so important and by which Linnaeus is known.

For Linnaeus, the whole nested system culminating in the Latin Binomial reflected an underlying order to nature. He was a very strong believer in the fixity of living things and, therefore, his system reflected order and stability in nature. He fully acknowledged that because he relied on a few structural characteristics, that his system should be artificial. That did not matter to Linnaeus. He sought to catalog life by simple and reliable characteristics. Relationships and "relatedness" had no meaning in a world in which species did not change.

934 PENTANDRIA. MONOGYNIA. Solanum.

224. SOLANUM. *Cor.* rotata. *Antheræ* fubcoalitæ, apice poro gemino dehifcentes. *Bacca* 2-locularis.

* *Inermia.*

verbafci- 1. S. caule inermi, fruticofo, fol. ovatis tomentofis inte-
folium. gerrimis, umbellis compofitis.

gvineenf. 2. S. caule inermi fruticofo, fol. ovatis integerrimis, pedunc. lateralibus filiformibus.

Pfeudo- 3. S. caule inermi fruticofo, fol. lanceolatis repandis,
Capficn. umbell. fellilibus.

diphylla. 4. S. caule inermi fruticofo, foliis geminis: altero mino-
ra, flor. cymofis.

Dulca- 5. S. caule inermi frutefcente flexuofo, fol. fuperioribus
mara. haftatis, racemis cymofis.

quercifol. 6. S. caule inermi frutefcente flexuofo, fol. oblongis late-
ribus finuatis, racemis cymofis.

bonarienf. 7. S. caule fubinermi frutefcente, fol. cuneiformibus fi-
nuato-repandis.

tuberofum. 8. S. caule inermi herbaceo, fol. pinnatis integerrimis,
pedunc. fubdivifis.

pimpinel- A. S. caule inermi herbaceo, fol. pinnatis integerrimis, ra-
lifol. cem. fimplicibus. *Cent.* 19.

Lycoper- 9. S. caule inermi herbaceo pilofo, fol. pinnatis incifis, ra-
ficum. cem. fimplicibus.

peruvia- 10. S. caule inermi herbaceo, fol. pinnatis incifis, racem.
num. bipartitis foliolofis, baccis pilofis.

montan. 11. S. caule inermi herbaceo, fol. fubcordatis repandis.

nigrum. 12. S. caule inermi herbaceo, fol. ovatis dentato-angulatis,
umbell. nutantibus.

æthiopi- B. S. caule inermi herbaceo, fol. ovatis dentato-angulatis,
cum. pedunc. fertilibus unifloris. *Cent.* 136.

* * *Spinofa.*

Melonge- 13. S. caule inermi herbaceo, fol. ovatis tomentofis inte-
na. gris, calyc. fpinofis, fructu pendulo.

campe- 14. S. caule aculeato herbaceo, fol. cordatis finuatis, calyc.
fbienfe. aculeatiffimis.

mamme- 15. S. caule aculeato herbaceo, fol. cordatis angulato-lo-
fum. batis: utrinque villofis fparfe aculeatis.

virginia- 16. S. caule aculeato herbaceo, fol. pinnatifidis undique
num. aculeatis: laciniis finuatis obtufis, calyc. aculeatis.

indi-

FIGURE 6-86. A page from *Systema Naturae*, 10th edition. The words in the left margins are the *trivial* names which became the specific names. In this case, they are species of the genus *Solanum*.

DARWIN'S INFLUENCE

Expressions such as that famous one by Linnaeus,...namely, that the characters do not make the genus, but that the genus gives the characters, seem to imply some deeper bond is included in our classifications than mere resemblance.

-Charles Darwin

Darwin grasped that the taxonomic hierarchy could be better understood in the context of descent with modification.

One of Darwin's only illustrations in *The Origin* (since straight lines were about all that he could draw) illustrated lines of descent dividing with some becoming extinct[70]. The result could be clustered organisms with various levels of relationships - just like the way that species are clustered in the taxonomic hierarchy. So, for Darwin and his successors, the

[70] You may see the illustration as Figure 6-7 in *Parasites and Darwin's Intellectual Triumph.*

way in which living things fit into the taxonomic hierarchy and system of Linnaeus was a confirmation that species were not fixed.

Considered another way, why were there so many beetles in a specially created world? Where was the static order? The exuberance of species argued for descent with modification. Some groups with a particularly successful and malleable form have more species. Some phyla (plural of phylum) like Ginkgophyta have only a single living species, *Ginkgo biloba*.

After the publication of The Origin, the relationship between evolutionary history and taxonomy became fixed. Such inferred lines of descent are called phylogenies, and the goal of taxonomy after Darwin was to produce a system that reflected evolutionary or phylogenetic relationships.

WHITTAKER'S FIVE KINGDOMS

No part of science is immune to reconsideration, and it may well be that the strength of the two-kingdom system is more in tradition than in inherent merit.

-R.H. Whittaker

The idea to separate the protists from plants and animals was an old one and originated with Ernst Haekel, the grand old German master of Darwinism in the latter part of the 19th century. He proposed a three-kingdom framework in which Plants and Animals were clearly defined. Then, he placed all of the groups like algae, protozoa and bacteria that did not clearly fit in either kingdom in a third group called the Protista. Later, proposals were made to separate the Bacteria from the Protista to make a four kingdom system. However, neither Haekel's nor any other system caught on and the two-kingdom concept persisted until an American, Robert H. Whittaker

(1924-1980) in 1959 promoted a five-kingdom system which included the fungi as a separate kingdom.

Textbooks and universities were slow to come over to this new system. Even as late as the late 1980's texts did lip service to the five-kingdom system while still teaching the Plant-Animal dichotomy. This usually was done by dismissing the "animal protists" in introductory Botany texts and vice versa in Introductory Zoology.

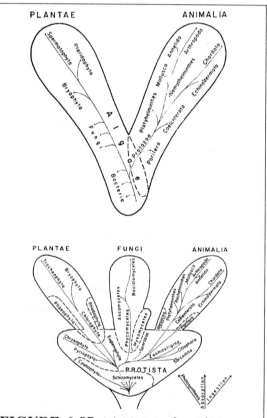

FIGURE 6-87. A comparison between the 2 Kingdom system (above) and Whittaker's 5 Kingdom system (below). From Whittaker's 1959 paper.

The Five Kingdoms of life were fairly easy to define. Bacteria had no nuclei and were fundamentally different from other things. For the multicellular kingdoms, Whittaker returned to Aristotelian-like functional definitions. In particular, he defined the three multicellular

643

kingdoms based on modes of nutrition. Animals were heterotrophic (ingested their food), Plants were photosynthetic (made their food by capturing light energy) and Fungi were saprobic (decomposers that release enzymes to break down large organic molecules externally and then pull the small molecules generated in this way across their membranes into their cells). Protists (like the bacteria) were defined structurally. That is, they were organisms with nuclei that generally were unicellular in form. Among them occurred organisms that exhibited all three modes of nutrition.

More recent descriptions such as *Five Kingdoms* by Lynn Margulis and Karlene Schwartz attempt to group organisms by structural details at all levels (molecules, cells, and bodies). This approach is the only way to return to the Darwinian call to classify organisms based on evolutionary lineages.

SYSTEMATICS
The essence of systematics is evolution.
-Lynn Margulis

The discipline that includes phylogenetic taxonomy is called Systematics[71]. Work in systematics is much more than the apparent drudgery of cataloguing species, it an exciting and lively discipline in which discovery and experimentation are necessary components. It is the science of Biodiversity.

The goals of Systematics according to Simpson and Cracraft (1995) are to answer the following questions:
- What are the Earth's species?
- What are their properties?
- Where do they occur?
- How are they related?

Certainly, this challenge is daunting. Indeed, right now Biologists have no

idea how many species might exist. The answer could lie anywhere between 2 and 100 million. So far, we have described about 1 million. Today, the five-kingdom system is challenged by other multiple kingdom views, some with more than 10 kingdoms. This is more than a trivial arrangement of taxonomic names. The way in which systematics organizes life represents a theory about life, its history and interrelationships between living things. In this sense, classification systems are deductive constructs that serve to explain living things as well as to organize them.

HIGHER? LOWER? OTHER?
The concepts of "lower" and "higher" organisms are subject to well-known ambiguities and various problems ...arise in this separation.
-Robert Whittaker

By the time that I left the University of Oklahoma in 1981, dinoflagellates were neither plants nor animals, but protists. The five kingdoms had come in to general acceptance by Biologists, and, by 1982, Margulis and Schwartz produced their first edition of *Five Kingdoms*. Still, the diagrams looked the same to me. The two kingdom diagram (Figure 6-87) was just a double-laddered *Scala Naturae*. Whittaker's 5-kingdom diagram was a three-pronged ladder. The concepts of "higher" and "lower" were implicit in the illustrations. Now the five-kingdom system is being abandoned for a system that embraces many more kingdoms[72].

About 1990 I had something of an epiphany, too. I recall reading some-

---

[71] See *The Systematics Wars* for a more detailed explanation of this biological discipline.

[72] The number of kingdoms has not been settled, but it is many more than 5. Paradoxically, recent systematic work suggests that Fungi may be allied with the Animal Kingdom. See *The Systematics Wars* for an explanation.

thing that stressed that all living things had been evolving as long as I had. Put another way, all other living species are at the ends of their own evolutionary histories. Of course, I knew that rationally, but at that moment, the understanding of the statement poured over me like warm water. In a flash, I had a new and deeper respect for other living things. This meant that there were no higher or lower organisms, just other organisms. For me, the *Scala Naturae* was gone.

-1999, revised 2006

References:

Adams, Alexander B. 1969. *Eternal Quest, The Story of the Great Naturalists.* G. P. Putnam's Sons. New York.

Aristotle (edited and translated by Philip Wheelwright). 1951. *Natural Science* and *Zoology.* Odyssey Press. New York.

Bowler, Peter. 1992. *The Environmental Sciences.* Fontana Press. London.

Darwin, Charles. 1882. *The Origin of Species.* 6th edition. D. Appleton and Company. New York.

Holt, Jack R., Jeffrey R. Merrell, David Seaborn, and Jeffrey Hartranft. 1994. *Population dynamics and substrate selection by three Peridinium species.* Journal of Freshwater Ecology 9(2):117-128.

Margulis, Lynn and Dorion. Sagan. 1986. *Microcosmos. Four Billion Years of Microbial Evolution.* A Touchstone Book. Simon and Schuster. New York.

Margulis, Lynn and Karlene Schwartz. 1982, 1992, 1998. *Five Kingdoms, An Illustrated Guide to the Phyla of Life on Earth.* Editions 1-3. W.H. Freeman and Co. New York.

Mayr, Ernst. 1982. *The Growth of Biological Thought, Diversity, Evolution, and Inheritance.* The Belknap Press of Harvard University Press. Cambridge, Mass.

Mayr, Ernst. 1997. *This is Biology, The Science of the Living World.* The Belknap Press of the Harvard University Press. Cambridge, Mass.

Peattie, Donald C. 1936. *Green Laurels, The Lives and Achievements of the Great Naturalists.* Simon and Schuster. New York.

Rosenberg, Alexander. 1986. *The Structure of Biological Science.* Cambridge University Press. New York.

Simpson, Beryl and Joel Cracraft. 1995. *Systematics: The Science of Biodiversity.* Bioscience 45(10): 670-672.

Singer, Charles. 1959. *A Short History of Scientific Ideas to 1900.* Oxford Universtiy Press. New York.

White, T. H., ed. 1960. *The Bestiary, A Book of Beasts.* Capricorn Books, G.P. Putnam's Sons. New York.

Whittaker, Robert H. 1957. *The Kingdoms of the Living World.* Ecology 38(3): 536-538.

Whittaker. Robert H. 1959. *On the Broad Classification of Organisms.* Quarterly Review of Biology 34: 210-226.

Questions to Think About

1. How is a dinoflagellate like a plant? An animal? A Protist?

2. What is the Scala Naturae? What are some vestiges of the Scala Naturae in use today?

3. What is the concept of essentialism?

4. What is the problem with common names?

5. How did Linnaeus resolve the chaos of classification in the 18th century?

6. Where did the Linnaean Latin binomials really come from?

7. The Linnaean system is hierarchical. How did that organization serve to confirm Darwin's concept of descent with modification?

8. How did Ernst Haekel and Robert Whittaker change the landscape of classification systems?

9. What is systematic biology?

10. Why do Biologists not use terms like higher and lower any more?

E PLURIBUS UNUM: SYMBIOSIS & EVOLUTION

THE LICHEN DILEMMA

If symbiosis is as prevalent and important in the history of life as it seems to be, we must rethink biology from the beginning. -L. Margulis and D. Sagan

The five-kingdom view of life supplanted the old plant-animal dichotomy and grew from a developing understanding of the complexity and diversity of life on earth[73]. Such an array of living things demanded at least five kingdoms to approximate a natural system of classification. By 1982 Lynn Margulis and Karlene Schwartz seemed to formalize the new system by the publication of a popular book called *Five Kingdoms.* In that year I embraced the five-kingdom concept and folded it into my courses because at the time it provided the best explanation for the organization and diversity of life.

Still, there are problems. For example, consider the lichen. This is a type of organism that often lives in fairly inhospitable situations like bare rocks and tree bark. In any case, they live where one is unlikely to find a fungus or an alga growing independently. However, the inside of a lichen is filled with fungal filaments and a particular layer that contains algal cells (see Figure 6-88). In this case, the fungus and the alga can be separated and grown. The algae appear to be unchanged but must live in water. The fungi become very different, sensitive to light and desiccation.

Most biologists consider the lichen to be a loose association of fungus and alga and usually classify it with the fungi. However, it takes on a form that is

unique and can be identified as a particular lichen. In addition, in the symbiotic association, the new entity becomes photosynthetic, a very unfunguslike mode of nutrition.

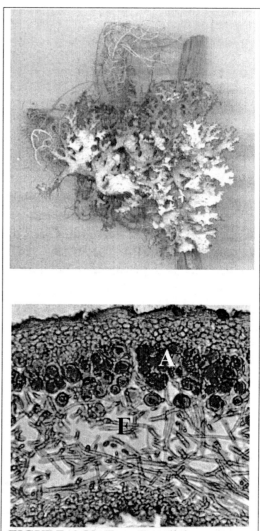

FIGURE 6-88. Top: Two lichens growing on a small stick. Bottom: A microscopic view of a lichen. F indicates fungal components. The round balls at the layer marked A are the algal cells.

---

[73] See the essay *Kingdoms* for a explanation of the development of the 5-kingdom system.

Where do lichens belong in the classification system of Whittaker? Both the fungus and the alga occupy different kingdoms in his system. Should they be treated as a fungus or as something completely different?

BUT ARE THEY DIFFERENT?

It is certainly more sensible to ask: how does a living system differ from one that is not alive?   -Manfred Eigen

Even though there are differences large enough to separate groups into kingdoms, Biologists recognize that all life has an array of features in common[74]. The most important commonality is that living things have a cellular organization. The cell packages the living stuff called cytoplasm, which is separated from the outer world by a membrane. It is important that cytoplasm would be so isolated because life is based on the specific interaction of molecules. Without the cellular package, specific interacting molecules would be too diluted to encounter each other except on a geological time scale.

The membrane is made of lipid (fat) with a phosphate attached to it. This is not very different from the composition of soap, so one might envision cellular components surrounded by soap films. In addition, living membranes contain proteins or chains of amino acids. Recall that proteins may be structural or active (enzymes). Simply put, enzymes mediate interactions of specific molecules and, thereby, collectively govern the living process. As components of the cell membrane, enzymes function to regulate and mediate the movements of nutrients and waste products into and out of the cell.

All living cells house DNA and other nucleic acids. Collectively, these operate as information storage (DNA) and retrieval (RNA). Specifically, a battery of RNA molecules such as messenger RNA, transfer RNA and ribosomal RNA serve to translate the nucleic acid code into specific proteins according to the Central Dogma of molecular biology. An important nucleic acid is Adenosine triphosphate or ATP. This molecule serves as a kind of energy currency within the cell. Many reactions that occur within cytoplasm would not normally occur without an addition of energy to the reacting molecules. ATP supplies that energy, and its generation is necessary for the process of life. To illustrate this, consider cyanide; a small amount can kill a human being. Specifically, cyanide blocks the production of ATP.

The fourth major class of organic molecules that make up the cell is the carbohydrate, which includes sugars and sugar polymers like starch and cellulose. These function in a variety of ways including energy storage (as do many lipids) and structural components, like the cellulose in the cell walls of plants. Collectively, these compounds function in living cells to convert and use chemical energy in metabolism. Because they use energy, all cells require an outside source of energy. Some take up organic molecules and use the energy stored in them. Others convert the energy of sunlight or inorganic compounds in the metabolic process to grow and reproduce.

---

[74] I explore this topic also in the essay, *Origins*.

TWO KINGDOMS AGAIN?

In giving the kingdom Monera the same taxonomic rank as the Animalia, Plantae, Fungi, and Protista, the five-kingdom formulation ignores the fact that the differences between Monera (prokaryotes) and the four other kingdoms are far more significant, and of a qualitatively different nature, than the difference among these four.

-C. Woese, O. Kandler, & M. Wheelis

With the same underlying cellular machinery, the five-kingdom system would make sense if all living things were constructed of the same kinds of cells. Unfortunately, there are two fundamental cell types that can be broadly defined as cells with nuclei (eukaryotic) and cells without nuclei (prokaryotic). An inability to acknowledge this fundamental difference is an important shortcoming of the five-kingdom system. More than the presence and absence of nuclei, eukaryotes and prokaryotes differ in very basic ways. Prokaryotes have a circular chromosome in each cell and lack organelles that are, themselves, separated from the cytoplasm by membranes. Further, cellular components like the membrane, chromosome, ribosome and the cytoplasm itself differ in important essential ways.

Eukaryotes have one or more long, linear strands of DNA together with certain proteins as chromosomes, which are packaged within membrane-bound nuclei. Protein synthesis requires that RNA move out of the nucleus to ribosomes that usually are associated with a cytoplasmic membrane system called endoplasmic reticulum.

Figure 6-89 illustrates some other membrane-bound organelles that commonly occur in eukaryotes. The double membrane of the mitochondrion functions in the generation of ATP. In addition to possessing unique enzymes and structures, the mitochondrion has its own circular chromosome of DNA. The organelle divides and grows independently of the division of the cell. The chloroplast is another double membrane bound organelle with many of the same characteristics as the mitochondrion, including a circular chromosome. It is filled with a membrane system to which is bound chlorophyll, other pigments, and the enzymatic machinery necessary to capture light energy and convert it to chemical energy as simple carbohydrates. Like the mitochondrion, it divides independently of the cell.

There are other membrane-bound organelles in eukaryotes such as golgi, peroxysomes, endoplasmic reticulum, among others. However, for this story, the flagellum is, perhaps, the most important. Both prokaryotes and eukaryotes propel themselves through water by whip-like organelles called flagella. The prokaryotic flagellum is a stiff corkscrew structure that turns to push or pull the cell through its environment. Although a little complex in design, the prokaryotic flagellum filament is made of a single proteinaceous filament.

Eukaryotic flagella superficially resemble those of bacteria. However, those of eukaryotes are much larger and have a complex inner construction of many proteinaceous microtubules. Curiously, basal bodies, structures from which the flagella emerge to the outside of the cell, can withdraw flagella during nuclear division and direct the growth of microtubules that serve to separate chromosomes. Thus, they seem to direct the development of external and internal microtubular systems.

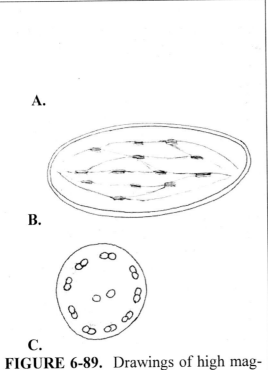

A.

B.

C.

FIGURE 6-89. Drawings of high magnification views of three organelles. Each appears as it would if sectioned and viewed with a transmission electron microscope at a magnification of 50,000X. A. A mitochondrion. The "fingers" are the infolded inner membrane. B. A chloroplast. The horizontal lines are produced by the internal membrane system on which the photosynthetic apparatus is attached. C. A flagellum. This cross section of a eukaryotic flagellum shows its characteristic inner microtubule structure (9+2).

It appeared that the Prokaryote-Eukaryote dichotomy was safe until Carl R. Woese, a microbiologist at the University of Illinois at Urbana-Champaign, began to work on an odd group of bacteria, the methanogenic bacteria. They live in conditions of anoxia and use carbon dioxide and hydrogen gas to generate methane and water. This generates enough energy to allow for the construction of food, growth, etc. Woese wanted to determine the relationship of these odd bacteria with other better-known bacterial taxa. He chose to compare them on the basis of their ribosomal RNA sequences, and what he found caused microbiologists to redraw the tree of life.

Woese and Fox reported in 1977 that the RNA sequences of the methanogenic bacteria were as different from the other bacteria as they were from the eukaryotes. Their analysis showed that the methanogens represented a third fundamentally different line. The dichotomy had become a trichotomy (see Figure 6-90): the Eukaryota, Euacteria[75] (true bacteria) and the Archaebacteria (methanogens and their relatives).

The Archaea (which means ancient ones), although prokaryotic in construction, are quite unique when compared with the Eubacteria on almost every count. They differ not only in the structure of their ribosomes but in their walls, aspects of genetic coding, metabolic pathways, etc. Most Archaea occupy extreme environments like hypersaline water and hot sulfur springs. Some characteristically occur in the acidic, sulfurous, hot conditions of smoldering coal mine tailings.

In recognition of these differences, Carl Woese proposed that a taxon higher than the kingdom be established, and he called this level the Domain. According to his view, there are three Domains, each with one or more kingdoms. He called the Domains Bacteria[76], Archaea, and Eukarya.

---

[75] I refer to this set of prokaryotes as the Eubacteria rather that bacteria, which has become a generic term for prokaryote. Thus, I use bacteria as an ecological term in the same way that I would use algae, tree, or shrub.

[76] Again, I argue that it is less confusing to call Woese's Bacteria the Eubacteria.

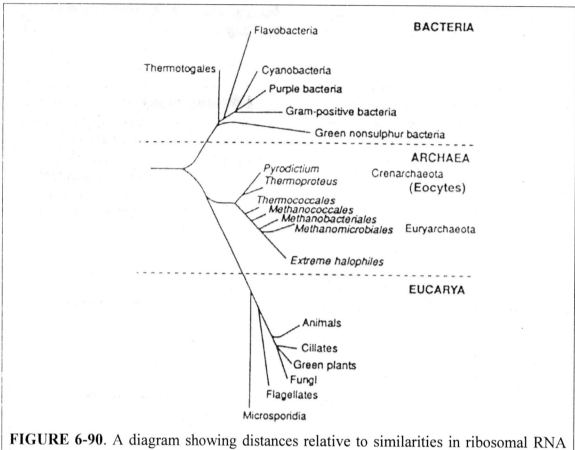

FIGURE 6-90. A diagram showing distances relative to similarities in ribosomal RNA from Woese and Fox (1977).

COMMUNITIES WITHIN

It is no good standing on dignity in a situation like this, and better not to try. It is a mystery. There they are, moving about in my cytoplasm, breathing for my own flesh, but strangers.

-Lewis Thomas

Still, the eukaryotes represent a very high level of complexity compared to the prokaryotes. How long must it have taken to evolve such cells with elaborate internal membrane systems, organelles, etc? Some Biologists who considered this question argued that the eukaryotic cell might have arisen when two or more bacteria entered into a symbiotic relationship. That is, the eukaryotic cell is made of cooperating bacterial cells.

Lynn Margulis championed the five-kingdom system of Whittaker very early. She recognized, particularly, that the fundamental differences between prokaryotes and eukaryotes could be explained in part by the strong similarities between mitochondria and chloroplasts with certain groups of bacteria. Indeed, the mitochondrion has a bacterial physiology, a bacterial chromosome, a bacterial membrane, and an array of other internal bacterial structures. She saw the acquisition of mitochondria by the earliest eukaryotes as the consequence of an invasion by pathogenic bacteria. So, initially they fed on the host cells but later developed a mutually beneficial relationship. The bacterial heritage of mitochondria is still evident in the way that they divide independently of the cell and its nucleus. Fortunately, there are so many mitochondria per cell that it is very unlikely that the daughter cells would not receive at least one.

Why would this have come about? Around 2 billion years ago, oxygenic photosynthesis had evolved. The atmospheric conditions in which life appeared were changing. A dangerous poison called oxygen was accumulating. Some bacteria, particularly those called the purple bacteria evolved a mechanism to take up oxygen and use it in their metabolic pathways to generate ATP. Such cells in a symbiosis with oxygen-sensitive cells could absorb excess oxygen and thereby protect the cell. In part, this is the Serial Endosymbiosis Theory[77] and serves to explain why eukaryotes seem to have evolved quickly after the atmosphere began to change.

Lynn Margulis and others suppose that the original host cell was an archaebacterium, one that lacked a cell wall and had stabilizing proteins associated with its chromosome. Such an organism exists today, and it is called *Thermoplasma*. Margulis believes that a *Thermoplasma*-like organism entered into a symbiosis with a spirochete, a eubacterium with many internal flagella. This organism then became the eukaryotic flagellum and provided the internal microtubular network called the cytoskeleton.

The new type of cell then became associated with a purple bacterium that retained part of its genome but gradually gave up most of its DNA to the host cell. The new organelle, the mitochondrion, used oxygen and efficiently generated ATP for the cell. The partnership or symbiosis became obligate so that nei-

ther of the original components could live alone.

The SET scenario is not universally accepted. Some believe that the eukaryotic flagellum emerged from the cell after it began to make its own internal cytoskeleton. Other more radical views suggest that the original nucleus was an endosymbiont like the group that gave rise to the mitochondria. Regardless of the scenario, most biologists accept that the mitochondrion formerly was a free-living eubacterium.

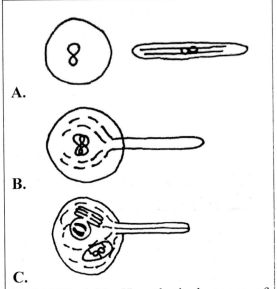

FIGURE 6-91. Hypothetical stages of the Margulis modification of SET. **A.** an archaea enters into association with a spirochete. **B.** The spirochete becomes intimately associated with the archaea and forms the flagellum and cytoskeleton. The DNA from the spirochete becomes associated with the DNA of the host cell. **C.** The mitochondrion becomes part of the new cell. The larger amount of DNA becomes surrounded by an internal membrane system.

A similar scenario exists for the chloroplast. This organelle came from the symbiosis of a photosynthetic bacterium (called a cyanobacterium, see Fig-

---

[77] SET was first defined by Max Taylor in 1974. Lynn Margulis modified the theory to include the incorporation of a spirochete

ure 6-92 for an example) and a host eukaryotic cell. These organisms used chlorophyll in their photosynthesis and generated oxygen as a waste product. They seem to have appeared more than two billion years ago, and their photosynthesis transformed the atmosphere[78].

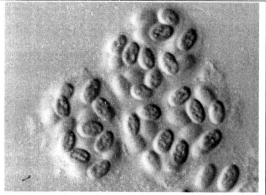

FIGURE 6-92. Living cyanobacteria from Snyder County, Pennsylvania.

Ribosomal RNA sequences of chloroplasts show that they are very closely related to cyanobacteria rather than to their host cells. Similarly, the ribosomes of mitochondria are closely related to purple bacteria. This is an important independent confirmation of the endosymbiosis theory.

LICHENS AND ME

The illusion of the independence of humans from Nature is dangerous ignorance.

-Lynn Margulis and Dorian Sagan

A consequence of endosymbiosis is that my cells are communities of bacteria, each with an independent lineage. I may be made of a fusion of three (and perhaps more) genomes per cell. In addition, my body is made of many cooperating cells. So, even without counting the array of bacteria in my gut, fungi and other bacteria on my skin, hitchhiking mites on my eyelashes, etc., I am a walking ecosystem at several levels.

This brings me back to the lichen conundrum. If eukaryotes are the products of symbioses between very different bacterial lineages, what does that say about current systems of classification? What does classification mean if eukaryotes are mix and match groups? First, it provides the warning that nature, particularly biology, laughs at categories[79]. For example, there may be eight or more unique eukaryotic lines. That means eight or more eukaryotic kingdoms! Secondly, it tells me to be cautious when attempting to determine relationships. It suggests that there are no privileged organelles or molecular components, so all must be considered rather than particular structures.

E Pluribus Unum, national motto of the United States, means one from many. This describes the eukaryote very well. It is made of many genomes, but is a single, different entity. That is much like the United States itself in that our culture is constructed of many cultural lineages. None of them is privileged to define alone the nature or character of this country.

- 1999, revised 2006

References:

Gray, Michael W., Gertrude Burger, B. Franz Lang. 1999. *Mitochondrial Evolution.* Science. 283: 1476-1481.

Margulis, Lynn. 1982. *Early Life.* Van Nostrand Reinhold Co. New York.

Margulis, Lynn. 1996. *Archaeal-eubacterial mergers in the origin of the Eukarya: Phylogenetic classification of life.* Proceedings of the Na-

---

[78] This is one of the central topics of *Red Planets and Microbes* and *Gaia: Science, Pseudoscience, or Fruitful Error.*

[79] A phrase that Harold C. Bold was supposed to use often.

tional Academy of Sciences, USA 93:1071-1076.

Margulis, Lynn and Dorion. Sagan. 1986. *Microcosmos. Four Billion Years of Microbial Evolution.* A Touchstone Book. Simon and Schuster. New York.

Margulis and Dorion Sagan. 1997. *Slanted Truths, Essays on Gaia, Symbiosis and Evolution.* Copernicus, Springer-Verlag. New York.

Margulis, Lynn and Karlene Schwartz. 1998. *Five Kingdoms, An Illustrated Guide to the Phyla of Life on Earth.* 3rd edition. W.H. Freeman and Co. New York.

Simpson, Beryl and Joel Cracraft. 1995. *Systematics: The Science of Biodiversity.* Bioscience 45(10): 670-672.

Taylor, F.J.R. 1974. *Implications and extensions of the Serial Endosymbiosis Theory of the origin of eukaryotes.* Taxon. 23: 229-258.

Whittaker, Robert H. 1957. *The Kingdoms of the Living World.* Ecology 38(3): 536-538.

Whittaker. Robert H. 1959. *On the Broad Classification of Organisms.* Quarterly Review of Biology 34: 210-226.

Woese, Carl R. 1994. *Microbiology in transition.* Proceedings of the National Academy of Sciences, USA 91:1601-1603.

Woese, Carl R. and George E. Fox. 1977. *Phylogenetic structure of the prokaryotic domain: The primary kingdoms.* Proceedings of the National Academy of Sciences, USA 74(11):5088-5090.

Woese, Carl R., Otto Kandler, and Mark L. Wheelis. 1990. *Towards a natural system of organisms: Proposal for the domains Archaea, Bacteria, and Eukarya.* Proceedings of the National Academy of Sciences, USA 87:4576-4579.

Questions to Think About

1. In what way(s) does a lichen defy categorization?

2. What are some of the underlying similarities of life?

3. How do they serve to confirm the interconnectedness of all life?

4. What are some of the fundamental differences between eukaryotes and prokaryotes?

5. How did Carl Woese and others shake up our understanding of life?

6. What was SET? What was the Margulis modification of the theory?

7. How are mitochondria and chloroplasts similar to each other?

8. What did Lewis Thomas mean when he said about mitochondria: *There they are, moving about in my cytoplasm, breathing for my own flesh, but strangers.*

9. How does SET make the systematics of eukaryotes more difficult?

10. What does SET do to *the illusion of the independence of humans from Nature?*

11. In what way did I use the motto of the United States to describe eukaryotes?